BENEVENTANUM TROPORUM CORPUS II

Part 3: Preface Chants and Sanctus

RECENT RESEARCHES IN THE MUSIC OF THE MIDDLE AGES AND EARLY RENAISSANCE

Charles M. Atkinson, general editor

A-R Editions, Inc., publishes seven series of musicological editions
that present music brought to light in the course of current research:

Recent Researches in the Music of the Middle Ages and Early Renaissance
Charles M. Atkinson, general editor

Recent Researches in the Music of the Renaissance
James Haar, general editor

Recent Researches in the Music of the Baroque Era
Christoph Wolff, general editor

Recent Researches in the Music of the Classical Era
Eugene K. Wolf, general editor

Recent Researches in the Music of the Nineteenth and Early Twentieth Centuries
Rufus Hallmark, general editor

Recent Researches in American Music
John M. Graziano, general editor

Recent Researches in the Oral Traditions of Music
Philip V. Bohlman, general editor

Each *Recent Researches* edition is devoted to works
by a single composer or to a single genre of composition.
The contents are chosen for their potential interest to scholars
and performers, then prepared for publication according to the
standards that govern the making of all reliable historical editions.

Subscribers to any of these series, as well as patrons of subscribing institutions,
are invited to apply for information about the "Copyright-Sharing Policy"
of A-R Editions, Inc., under which policy any part of an edition
may be reproduced free of charge for study or performance.

Address correspondence to

A-R EDITIONS, INC.
801 Deming Way
Madison, Wisconsin 53717

(608) 836-9000

RECENT RESEARCHES IN THE MUSIC OF THE MIDDLE AGES
AND EARLY RENAISSANCE · VOLUME XXV

BENEVENTANUM TROPORUM CORPUS II

Ordinary Chants and Tropes for the Mass
from Southern Italy, A.D. 1000–1250

Part 3: Preface Chants and Sanctus

Edited by John Boe

A-R EDITIONS, INC. · MADISON

BENEVENTANUM TROPORUM CORPUS

Edited by
Alejandro Enrique Planchart
and
John Boe

*Recent Researches in the Music
of the Middle Ages and Early Renaissance*

I. Tropes of the Proper of the Mass
from Southern Italy, A.D. 1000–1250
   Volumes XVI and XVII–XVIII

II. Ordinary Chants and Tropes for the Mass
from Southern Italy, A.D. 1000–1250

   Part 1: Kyrie eleison
   Volumes XIX and XX–XXI

   Part 2: Gloria in excelsis
   Volumes XXII and XXIII–XXIV

   Part 3: Preface Chants and Sanctus
   Volumes XXV and XXVI

   Part 4: Pater Noster Chants and Agnus Dei
   with Ite missa est
   Volume XXVII

III. Indexes, Inventories, and Analytical Studies
   Volume XXVIII

Publication of this book has been supported by generous grants from the
National Endowment for the Humanities, an independent federal agency.

© 1996 by A-R Editions, Inc.
All rights reserved
Printed in the United States of America

ISBN 0-89579-336-9
ISSN 0362-3572

∞ The paper used in this publication meets the minimum requirements of
the American National Standard for Information Sciences—Permanence of
Paper for Printed Library Materials, ANSI Z39.48-1984.

Contents

Introductory Essays and Commentary

Foreword — xi

Editorial Methods in Part 3 — xii
    Arrangement of Sanctus Chants, Tropes, and Pros(ul)as — xii
    Definition of Pros(ul)a in the Edition — xii
    Prosa and Prosula — xiii
    Enumeration of Pros(ul)a Elements — xiii
    Common and Proper Prefaces and Attached Sanctus Incipits — xiv
    Correlation with Corpus Troporum — xiv
    Notes — xv

The South Italian Preface Tradition — xvi
    Origins of Texts — xvi
    Sacramentaries and Missals — xvii
    Manuscript Collections and Printed Editions of Preface Texts — xx
    Commentaries for Texts of Prefaces Transcribed in Part 3 — xxii
    The Cursus — xxxiv
    Origins of Chants — xxxvii
    Preface Chant Formulas — xxxviii
    Cassinese Preface Chants — xl
    The Three Preface Chants from St. Peter's, Benevento — xlii
    The Francisca Version of Montecassino 127 and 339 — xliv
    Border-Area Preface Chants — xlv
    Sources of the Cassinese Double Preface-Chant Tradition — xlv
    Notes — lii

The South Italian Sanctus Repertory — lxiii
    Sanctus Repertories in the Manuscripts and Grouping of Sources — lxiii
    European Tropes for Sanctus — lxiii
    Italian Tropes for Sanctus — lxiv
    European Hosanna Prosas and Prosulas — lxv
    South Italian Hosanna Prosulas Imitating Northern Models — lxvi
    Local South Italian Sanctus Tropes — lxvii
    Summary and Comparison with Other Ordinary Trope Repertories — lxviii
    Ordering of the Sanctus Repertory in South Italian Collections — lxix
    Notes — lxxv

Plates — lxxvii

Manuscripts and Publications Cited — lxxx
    List of Manuscript Sigla — lxxx
    List of Cited Works with Abbreviations — lxxxiii

*

The Manuscript Sources of Preface Chants in Part 3 — 1
    Beneventan Sources — 1
    Cassinese Sources — 2
    Border-Area Sources in Roman Minuscule — 6
    Source from Apulia — 7
    Addenda — 8

Mass Preface Chants for the Celebrant from Southern Italy

Page numbers to the left of the commas, in small roman numerals, refer to commentaries for individual preface texts; arabic numbers, to the right, refer to complete prefaces notated in this volume.

I. Beneventan and Cassinese Common Prefaces		xxii,	11
Fixed Conclusions for Proper Prefaces		xxiii,	24
II. Proper Prefaces in the Missal Lo 3511 from St. Peter's *intra muros*, Benevento		xxiii,	26

In cotidianis diebus

CP 1322	Christmas, Purification, Annunciation	xxiii,	27
CP 863	Lent	xxiv,	27
CP 879	Holy Trinity	xxv,	28
CP 699	For the Dead	xxvii,	29

In festiuitatibus

CP 1294	Epiphany	xxviii,	30
CP 366	Assumption and Nativity of St. Mary	xxviii,	30
CP 1484	Apostles	xxix,	31

In sollemnitatibus

CP 1524	Easter	xxx,	32
CP 1165	Ascension	xxxi,	33
CP 813	Pentecost	xxxi,	33
CP 1200	Holy Cross	xxxii,	35
CP 203	Dedication of the Church	xxxiii,	35
CP 687	Lo 3511 Solemn Chant for the Common Preface Editorially Completed	xliii,	36

III. Common Prefaces of Mixed Traditions from Border Areas and the North		xlv,	38
Fixed Conclusions for Proper Prefaces		xxiii,	44
Pentecost Preface in Vallicelliana B 24		xxxi,	46
IV. Common Preface in the Canosa Missal, Baltimore W 6		xlvi,	47

*

Sanctus
Chants Having Tropes or Pros(ul)as in South Italian Sources

Smaller page numbers, to the left of the commas, refer to individual Sanctus commentaries in this volume; larger numbers, to the right, refer to complete Sanctus notated in the following main-text volume of the edition.

Thannabaur 74	*Admirabilis splendor*		
	Indefessas uoces	53,	3
Thannabaur 92	*Altissime Creator =*		
	Altissimeque rector		
	Conditor alme Domine	55,	12
Thannabaur 178	**Ante thronum Domini**	60,	20
Thannabaur 45	*Antra modicis deserti*	61,	22

Thannabaur 197	*Caelestia sidera* **Hosanna¹ Plasmatum populum** **Hosanna² Dulcis est cantica**	63,	24
Thannabaur 92	**Conditor alme Domine** (see *Altissime Creator =* *Altissimeque rector*, pp. 15, 12)		
Thannabaur 152 (=154, Vatican I)	*Corona iustitiae* **Gloria Christe omnes resurgamus**	65,	29
Thannabaur 63	*Cui pueri Hebraeorum* (see *Quem cherubim atque seraphim*, pp. 98, 93)		
Thannabaur 154 (152); Vatican I	*Deus fortis*, with cued **Qui uenisti ⟨carnem sumens⟩**	68,	32
Thannabaur 154 (=152); Vatican I	*Deus pater ingenitus* **Qui uenisti carnem sumens**	71,	38
Thannabaur 197 and BTC-Scs 3 (?=Thannabaur 111)	**Dulcis est cantica, Hosanna²** (see pp. 63, 24 and 123, 128)		
Thannabaur 152 (=154, Vatican I)	**Gloria Christe omnes resurgamus** (see *Corona iustitiae*, pp. 65, 29)		
Thannabaur 63	**Hebraeorum pueri ramos** (see *Quem cherubim atque seraphim*, pp. 98, 93)		
Thannabaur ?64 (cf. 60,66,67)	*Hodie Dominus Iesus Christus resurrexit a mortuis* (see pp. 77, 48 and 124, 131)		
Thannabaur ?64 (cf. 60,66,67)	**Hosanna cuncta procedens** (see *Inuisibiliter penetrauit rex*, pp. 77, 48)		
Thannabaur 197 and BTC-Scs 3	**Hosanna² Dulcis est cantica** (see pp. 63, 24, and 123, 128)		
Thannabaur 56; Vatican III	**[Hosanna] Omnes tua gratia** (see *Summe pater de quo*, pp. 110, 106)		
Thannabaur 197 and BTC-Scs 3	**Hosanna¹ Plasmatum populum** (see pp. 63, 24 and 123, 128)		
Thannabaur 226, Var.	**Hosanna Saluifica tuum plasma** (see pp. 104, 104)		
Thannabaur 46, var. 2	*Immortalis et uerus*	74,	46
Thannabaur 74	*Indefessas uoces* (see *Admirabilis splendor*, pp. 53, 3)		
Thannabaur ?64 (cf. 60,66,67)	*Inuisibiliter penetrauit rex* **Hosanna cuncta procedens**	77,	48
Thannabaur 60 (?=66,67)	*Laudatur trina maiestas* (see *Pax in caelo*, pp. 90, 76)		
Thannabaur 213, Var.	**Laudes Deo ore pio** (also see Thannabaur 223, pp. 82, 64)	79,	57
Thannabaur 223; Vatican XV	*Mundi fabricator* **Quem cherubim et seraphim non cessant** **Pie Christe descendisti**	82,	64
Thannabaur 56; Vatican III	**Omnes tua gratia, [Hosanna]** (see *Summe pater de quo*, 110, 106)		
Thannabaur 128	Pater Deus qui caret initio	87,	72
Thannabaur 60 (?=66,67)	*Pax in caelo* (=*Laudatur trina maiestas*)	90,	76

Thannabaur 49; Vatican IV	*(Perpetuo lumine)* = Perpetuo numine	93,	83
Thannabaur 223	**Pie Christe descendisti** (see pp. 82, 64)		
Thannabaur 197 and BTC-Scs 3	**Plasmatum populum, Hosanna¹** (see pp. 63, 24 and 123, 128)		
Thannabaur 62	*Quam pulchra est*	96,	90

Thannabaur 63	*Quem cherubim atque seraphim*
	    + *Cui pueri Hebraeorum*
	        Hebraeorum pueri ramos
		98,	93

Thannabaur 223; Vatican XV	*Quem cherubim et seraphim non cessant* **Pie Christe descendisti** (see pp. 82, 64)		
Thannabaur 86	*Quem cuncti angeli*	103,	102
	Qui uenisti carnem sumens (see *Deus pater ingenitus*, pp. 71, 38)		
Thannabaur 226, Var.	**Saluifica tuum plasma, Hosanna**	104,	104
Thannabaur 56; Vatican III	*Summe pater de quo* *[Hosanna] Omnes tua gratia*	110,	106

SANCTUS CHANTS LACKING TROPES OR PROS(UL)AS
IN SOUTH ITALIAN SOURCES

Chants followed by trope titles in parentheses appear in at least one source without trope or pros(ul)a but with them in other sources. Chants not so listed have Sanctus text only in the sources used. Chants with BTC-Scs numbers were not included in Thannabaur's index.

Thannabaur 32; Vatican XVII	114,	111
Thannabaur 41, Var.; Vatican XVIII	116,	114
Thannabaur 49; Vatican IV (see *Perpetuo numine*, pp. 93, 83)		

Thannabaur ?64 (cf. 60, 66, 67)
    (see *Inuisibiliter penetrauit rex*, pp. 77, 48;
    also see *Hodie Dominus Iesus Christus resurrexit a mortuis*, pp. 124, 131)		

Thannabaur 80	119,	117
Thannabaur 81	119,	118
Thannabaur 109	120,	120
Thannabaur 111, Var.	121,	121
Thannabaur 213, Var. (see **Laudes Deo ore pio**, pp. 79, 57)		
Thannabaur 216, Var.	121,	122
Thannabaur 223; Vatican XV (see *Mundi fabricator* and *Quem cherubim et seraphim non cessant*, pp. 82, 64)		
BTC-Scs 1	122,	124
BTC-Scs 2	122,	126
Appendix I: BTC-Scs 3 with the Benevento 40 version of **Hosanna¹** **Plasmatum populum** and **Hosanna² Dulcis est cantica**	123,	128
Appendix II: Easter Verses *Hodie Dominus Iesus Christus resurrexit a mortuis*	124,	131
Acknowledgments	128	
Index of Sanctus Chants by Thannabaur Numbers	129,	134

BENEVENTANUM TROPORUM CORPUS II

Part 3: Preface Chants and Sanctus

Introductory Essays
Preface Chants
Commentary

TERTIA PARS
BENEVENTANI TROPORUM CORPORIS II

Kenneth Levy

DICATA

Foreword

The multivolume edition *Beneventanum Troporum Corpus* (hereafter abbreviated as BTC) includes all tropes for the mass that survive in south Italian manuscripts in Beneventan script and notation from the late tenth through the early thirteenth centuries, along with those from Roman manuscripts written in ordinary minuscule script and central Italian notation from the later part of that period. The first volumes of the edition, BTC I, contain all tropes for the proper of the mass with their associated proper chants. The volumes comprised in BTC II contain all chants for the ordinary of the mass with their associated tropes and verses. The last volume, BTC III, supplies indexes, inventories, and analytical studies. Sequences and prosulas—except for prosulas imbedded within tropes, like those for Hosanna in excelsis and for the Regnum trope of Gloria in excelsis—are reserved for eventual publication in *Beneventanum Sequentiarum Corpus* and *Beneventanum Prosularum Corpus*. On occasion, versions of pieces in the south Italian repertory have been taken from manuscripts written in scriptoria bordering Beneventan territory, or from miscellaneous fragments surviving from within the region, when these versions usefully supplement the basic manuscripts. (Norman manuscripts, however, have been employed only in exceptional instances: hence the term "south Italian" as used in BTC excludes Norman manuscripts and Norman repertory.)

A General Introduction to the entire edition, found in the prefatory matter of BTC I, sketches the history of tropes in southern Italy, describes the manuscript sources in detail, and presents what is known or can be guessed about the way these pieces were performed in the liturgy. Repertory studies preface the proper tropes in BTC I and each group of ordinary chants and tropes in BTC II. Individual commentaries for the pieces in each repertory are grouped together at the end of the prefatory matter for each volume. Summary lists of manuscript sigla, with dates and provenance for each source used or referred to in the edition, are included before the commentaries in each volume. The main text of the edition consists of the music and words of each trope or verse together with its associated proper or ordinary chant, usually in multiple versions.

An alphabetical index of proper tropes is provided in BTC I. Ordinary tropes, verses, and chants are arranged for the most part alphabetically by first line, so as to be self-indexed. Complete indexes of trope elements will appear in BTC III.

Beneventanum Troporum Corpus is intended to meet the needs of various types of users. Students of Romance philology and of medieval Latin will wish to consult manuscript spelling and punctuation. Singers and directors will sometimes need the English translations supplied in the commentaries. Musicologists will employ melodic variants to trace the spread of a trope or chant; literary scholars, the reports of variants in the words. In satisfying these diverse needs by presenting texts that accurately reflect the content of the several manuscripts, the editors hope to illuminate the study of south Italian tropes and kindle interest in the performance of a neglected repertory of medieval chant.

John Boe
Alejandro Enrique Planchart

Editorial Methods in Part 3, Preface Chants and Sanctus

The Editorial Methods described in BTC II/1, pp. xviii–xxiii, for the arrangement of chants and tropes and the selection and presentation of versions and variants, for neumes and staff transcriptions, for the words of tropes, and for typical texts and translations remain valid in Part 3, Preface Chants and Sanctus. But additions to Sanctus chants often have a dual character, novel to the edition: roughly speaking, tropes are inserted in the first part of the base text and pros(ul)as at *Hosanna in excelsis*. The special principles used here for arranging and enumerating Hosanna pros(ul)a elements together with Sanctus tropes need to be explained.

Arrangement of Sanctus Chants Trope and Pros(ul)a Titles

Sanctus chants are arranged according to alphabetized standard titles derived from their first trope element. These trope titles appear in large italic type as the primary headings for the individual Sanctus chants in the main text with music and in the commentary. Titles of pros(ul)as associated with particular Sanctus melodies are printed in slightly smaller bold italic type just below the trope titles. The pros(ul)a titles are also interspersed alphabetically throughout the main text and commentaries as "see" references, directing the user to their associated troped Sanctus. Sanctus chants with pros(ul)a but no trope are alphabetized according to their pros(ul)a titles. Sanctus chants having neither trope nor pros(ul)a are entered last of all, according to their Thannabaur index numbers (see BTC II/1, p. xviii).[1]

Pros(ul)as are printed bold to distinguish them from tropes in the typical texts and translations that appear in the commentaries. But in the main text of the edition, the words with music are given without distinguishing type for different kinds of texts, just as they were copied without distinction of script in the sources. In typical texts and titles, the word *Hosanna* is printed bold or bold italic when it is an integral part of a pros(ul)a. The spelling *Hosanna* is used in standardized titles, general references, and English translations. But when a specific manuscript passage is referred to and in typical texts, the invariable spelling *Osanna* of the manuscripts is used.

Definition of Pros(ul)a in the Edition

What is a prosula? Now that Gautier's famous question, "Q'est-ce qu'un trope?"[2] can be answered, one can assert that a pros(ul)a is not a trope in the strict sense of the word—although certain cases make one wonder. What then is the difference between pros(ul)a and trope? How were the terms *prosa* and *prosula* used, if at all, in southern Italy, and how are they distinguished in BTC II/3? It is said that words of a prosula were underlaid to a preexisting melisma, one note per syllable. That is often true but not always. Some pros(ul)as included in this edition were copied without matching melismas into the sources, more or less one note per syllable. Even when a matching melisma was copied, one does not always know that it was preexistent. Sometimes pros(ul)a elements were broken up and distributed throughout Sanctus after the manner of a trope. Can such an addition still be considered a pros(ul)a, or must it be redefined as a trope according to its new function? Ordinarily at least one melodic phrase in a pros(ul)a is directly repeated with different words; but if there should be four or more such phrase repetitions, each to different words and to but one melody, it becomes difficult to distinguish the piece from a strophic hymn.

The term *prosa* and its diminutive *prosula* as used in this edition are collectively explained as follows. A pros(ul)a contains at least one melodic phrase that is immediately repeated with a different text or verset. The two versets for the one melody naturally have a similar number of syllables and often a similar scheme of accentuation. The presence of at least one set of two or more versets sung to a single melodic phrase is essential to the concept of pros(ul)a as understood in this edition. In longer pieces, there may be more than one melodic phrase and consequently two or more sets of paired versets, each pair having its own melody, syllable count, and accentuation. In longer pieces, an opening melodic phrase is sometimes not repeated, its single verset standing alone.

A pros(ul)a usually employs one note per syllable of text, but neumes of two or three notes may occur. A long melisma for one of the syllables of *Hosanna in excelsis*, usually in the second *Hosanna in excelsis* of the base text and often on the last vowel of *Hosanna*, may duplicate an entire pros(ul)a melody, repetitions included. Such a melisma often bears little or no relation to the Sanctus melody it follows. Sometimes two settings of the second *Hosanna in excelsis* were copied, presumably as alternatives—one setting having a melisma to match the pros(ul)a and the other integral to the Sanctus melody, for use when the pros(ul)a was not sung. Sometimes no independent setting of the second *Hosanna in excelsis* was copied at all but only the pros(ul)a words with their music, which in this case usually began *Hosanna* and led directly into the final *in excelsis*.

However, certain texts were underlaid more or less syllabically to the melismas of *Sanctus* acclamations, without paired versets. In BTC II/3, these are not regarded as pros(ul)as but as tropes using prosula technique.[3] Likewise, interpolated words that seem to have been underlaid to short melismas attached to the last syllable of preceding segments of base text are regarded as tropes.

Prosa and *Prosula*

Today musicologists tend to reserve the term *prosa* for the longish pieces that were entitled *sequentia* in east Frankish and Beneventan manuscripts. These pieces were usually sung at festal masses after the completion of the Alleluia verse and before the gospel. In Aquitanian manuscripts, a texted version of such a piece is labeled *prosa*, or its abbreviation: hence the modern use of the term *prosa*. The diminutive *prosula* is today applied to all the shorter pieces with paired versets or (sometimes) mere syllabic underlay of a melisma. These shorter pieces are found in a variety of contexts: within the Alleluia or its verse; within the tract, the offertory, the office respond, and within certain verses of Gloria in excelsis tropes; and at *Hosanna in excelsis* in the Sanctus. In Aquitanian manuscripts, such pieces were, I repeat, sometimes labeled *prosa* and sometimes *prosula*.

Originally it was intended that BTC II/3 should follow well-established contemporary usage and that all the Hosanna pieces should be called *prosulas*; but the restoration in *Corpus Troporum VII. Tropes du Sanctus*,[4] of the term *prosa* for some of them and Iversen's arguments in CT 7 have persuaded me that the modern demarcation between *prosa* and *prosula* purely according to liturgical destination imposes a consistency of nomenclature contradicted by the Aquitanian sources while at the same time obscuring an actual distinction of title according to liturgical destination that was strictly observed in southern Italy—a distinction differing, however, from the modern musicological one. The fact is that in southern Italy, a chant following the Alleluia verse and preceding the gospel was invariably called *sequentia* (abbreviated $\overline{sq}$ or $\overline{seq}$) even in the rare cases when it was short, whereas the shorter pieces modern usage calls prosulas were designated *Ps* or *ps*—which must usually stand for *prosa*. It is true that nowhere in the manuscripts written in Benevento or at Montecassino is the abbreviated term spelled out. It therefore cannot be asserted absolutely that it stood for *prosa*. In the Roman gradual Bod 74, however, the term is once abbreviated *P sa* (fol. 113ᵛ), which certainly should be read *Prosa* (*P* = Pro + sa); and once it is spelled out as the romance diminutive *prosunzola* (fol. 111ʳ). In both cases, the titles identify textual additions to Alleluia melismas. I know of no instance in a south Italian source where the diminutive form *prosula* is actually written out, although (as remarked earlier) the form is found in Aquitanian manuscripts, along with *prosa*, and might someday turn up in a south Italian source. The occurrence of the local diminutive *prosunzola* may serve as justification for retaining the standard diminutive *prosula* for some of these pieces. Yet the normal term for them in south Italy was clearly *prosa*. If *prosula* had been in standard use, the abbreviated Beneventan form would have been *psł* or *pslā*, with the stroke of abbreviation through the *l*. To my knowledge, this form never occurs.

The present editor, who shares the modern compulsion for consistency, has either adopted the title *prosula* or restored the normal south Italian term *prosa* on the following ad hoc basis: pieces having only one melodic phrase repeated for matching versets are entitled *prosula* in BTC II/3. Pieces having more than one melodic phrase (at least one of which is repeated) are entitled *prosa*. In the texts with music and the commentary typical texts, only abbreviations found in the manuscripts (unbracketed) or the standardized abbreviation [*Ps*] (within brackets since absent from the manuscript) introduce the piece.

Enumeration of Pros(ul)a Elements

Trope elements interpolated into Sanctus are enumerated by normal-size arabic numerals within brackets, as described in Editorial Methods, BTC II/1, pp. xxi–xxii. To facilitate comparison of the ubiquitous pros(ul)a versions in Part 3, another system of enumeration reflecting their structure was needed. (In Part 2, a few prosulas inserted in certain Gloria in excelsis tropes were printed without enumeration of their internal members, which usually consisted of but one set of double versets sung to a single melodic phrase.)[5] The superscript letters *a* and *b*, regularly employed in the literature on sequences to label versets sung to the same melody—as "2ᵃ" and "2ᵇ"—could not be used in this edition because superscript *b* is used to show a variant peculiar to Benevento. Instead, superscript roman numerals, either alone or placed after a dot centered mid-line, designate the first, second, and possibly third versets sung to a single repeated melodic phrase. Oversize arabic numerals designate melodic phrases. Very often, the oversize numerals are repeated: [2.I] and [2.II]. Sometimes a melodic phrase given a large arabic numeral contains smaller repeated musical elements within it. Thus in the twin prosas *Hosanna¹ Plasmatum populum* and *Hosanna² Dulcis est cantica*, elements [1.I] and [1.II] have internal repetition but [2] does not.[6] The longest prosas in BTC II/3 have only four distinct melodic phrases. In shorter prosulas, large arabic numerals are lacking in the enumeration of verbal elements all sung to a single melodic phrase. Superscript roman numerals enumerating their versets suffice.

Just as [5⁴] and [4⁵] indicate a reversal of two trope elements with respect to their position in the typical text,[7] the prosa enumeration [2.II'] shows that the *second* set of words sung to the second melodic phrase in the typical text of *Hosanna cuncta procedens* (here from Bod 74, BTC II/3, p. 78) is instead sung as the *first* set of words for the same second melodic phrase in the version from Ben 34 so enumerated (p. 55, main text).

In the special case of *Laudes Deo ore pio* as copied in Urb 602 (pp. 57–63), the words and melodies of the prosa have been inserted in the Sanctus text as tropes. Their new position and function is shown by superscript arabic numerals: [1.I]¹, [2.I]⁴, etc.

Common and Proper Prefaces and Attached Sanctus Incipits

No introductory tropes for Sanctus, to precede the first acclamation of the base text, are known from south Italian sources. Introductions were already provided by the ancient eucharistic dialogue *Sursum corda* and the solemnly chanted preface, the beginning of the celebrant's great prayer of thanksgiving, into which prayer the Sanctus text had early been imbedded.[8] Not even seasonal introductory tropes of the *Hodie* type were needed, because their function was supplied by the proper prefaces for feasts, fasts, and Sundays of the year. A preface always preceded Sanctus and ought therefore to precede Sanctus in any reconstructed performance of these Sanctus chants.

The complete repertory of chants for the preface from Benevento and Montecassino, along with a selection of chants from areas bordering the Beneventan zone, is transcribed from surviving eleventh and twelfth-century sources (pp. 11–49 below) along with commentaries, typical texts, and translations, to be found within the essay on The South Italian Preface Tradition, pp. xvi–lxi. The texts of several south Italian prefaces, with letter notation, are also included in certain individual Sanctus commentaries.

The standard conclusions of notated prefaces usually led into the unnotated incipit S̄cs S̄cs S̄cs; but notation was occasionally supplied for the incipit *in campo aperto*, just as for the preface. The incipits can usually be identified. They are transcribed in letter notation under Altar Book Incipits at the end of Sources for a particular Sanctus, as well as after the fully transcribed prefaces to which they are appended. More rarely, a complete Sanctus melody, not just an incipit, was notated after the conclusion of a preface, but in the altar books always without tropes. These complete Sanctus are listed with other sources in the commentaries and transcribed in the main text.

Correlation with *Corpus Troporum* Sigla and Abbreviations

References and concordances drawn from CT 7 have greatly enriched Part 3 of BTC II.[9] The Sanctus volume of the Corpus Troporum series presents a conspectus of European trope *texts*; its European point of view thus complements the provincial orientation of BTC II/3. Sources, readings, manuscript inventories, and manuscript facsimiles from CT 7 have been mentioned selectively in most BTC II commentaries. Moreover, the contrast between the two works mirrors the interaction between center and periphery, between European synthesis and a fiercely regional outlook. The user of BTC II/3 will therefore wish to have the Corpus Troporum volume, *Tropes du Sanctus*, available for ready consultation.

Sigla for manuscripts along with abbreviations and short titles for works frequently cited in essays and individual commentaries are expanded to their full forms in the List of Manuscript Sigla and List of Cited Works with Abbreviations, pp. lxxx and lxxxiii below.

Notes

1. Peter Josef Thannabaur, *Das einstimmige Sanctus der römischen Messe in der handschriftlichen Überlieferung des 11. bis 16. Jahrhunderts,* Erlanger Arbeiten zur Musikwissenschaft, vol. 1 (Munich, 1962). Hereafter, "Thannabaur."

2. Léon Gautier, *Histoire de la poésie liturgique au moyen âge: Les tropes* (Paris, 1886).

3. See for instance *Altissime creator = Altissimeque rector,* pp. 55 and 12 in BTC II/3.

4. Gunilla Iversen, ed., *Corpus Troporum VII. Tropes du Sanctus,* Studia Latina Stockholmiensia, 34 (Stockholm, 1990), especially pp. 31–35.

5. See BTC II/2, pp. 12–13, 26–29, and 30–31.

6. See BTC II/3, pp. 64 and 24–28.

7. See the fuller explanation in BTC II/1, pp. xxi–xxii.

8. See below, The South Italian Preface Tradition: Origins of Texts, p. xvi.

9. Gunilla Iversen kindly arranged for me to use a draft version of CT 7 before publication.

The South Italian Preface Tradition

Origins of Texts

From the sixth century at the latest, the word *praefatio* (from *praefor, praefari, praefatus sum*—in classical Latin, "to say beforehand, to recite a preliminary formula, to address as a preliminary prayer") was regularly applied to the beginning of the eucharistic *prex* or great prayer of thanksgiving in the Roman rite of the western church.[1] The opening dialogue and preface were in fact essential to the beginning of the "action"—*gratiarum actio*, the giving of thanks or eucharist. The dialogue from *Gratias agamus Domino Deo nostro*[2] and the blessing and thanking of God over the offered gifts of his creation that follow the dialogue probably had their roots in Jewish blessings at the winecup of thanksgiving during important meals and certainly derived from the Jewish concept of hallowing something by blessing God or giving God thanks for it—a concept evident throughout the Old Testament scriptures.[3] Hence the anaphora (or "the prayer of consecration," as it later came to be called) was originally regarded as beginning with the dialogue and preface, not with its western continuation *Te igitur*, where according to the later medieval view the "canon" began.[4]

Only from the later third century onwards were the scriptural acclamations *Sanctus, Sanctus, Sanctus, Dominus [Deus] sabaoth* . . . and the accompanying *Hosanna in excelsis* and *Benedictus qui uenit in nomine Domini* inserted into the great prayer. By the end of the fourth century they were used almost everywhere.[5] It is worth remembering that the opening dialogue with Sursum corda; the "preface" of the great prayer that gives thanks for creation and special acts of redemption; and the rest of the great prayer with its sections of recalling, invoking, offering, and interceding had anciently been continuous: Sanctus was the third-century interloper.[6] Once introduced, Sanctus came to be regarded as indispensable: no mass without Sanctus. Among the chant texts that were later regarded as forming the ordinary of the Roman mass, Sanctus was the least independent, the least susceptible to transfer elsewhere within the liturgy. Our habit of abstracting Sanctus from the liturgy as simply another "movement of the ordinary of the mass"—the equivalent of the western Kyrie eleison, Gloria in excelsis, and Agnus Dei—obscures its thorough integration within the anaphora of all the developed rites of Christendom. No Sanctus was ever sung in western Latin rites unless preceded by a chanted preface.[7]

The inclusion of Sanctus within the great prayer tended in the west to wedge apart the section of the prayer preceding Sanctus from the sections following it. The latter sections congealed into the single Latin "canon," invariable for all masses, saving only small changes *infra actionem* on the highest feasts, for the most part in the section beginning *Communicantes*.[8] (In the non-Latin rites of the Christian East, any given anaphora or great prayer remained unalterable, without variable elements: if change was desired, either an entirely different anaphora was substituted or a different liturgy was used—just as the liturgy of St. Basil is still used in the Byzantine rite on certain days in place of the liturgy of St. Chrysostom. No variable text corresponded to the western *praefatio*.)[9] Well before the eighth century, the section of the western canon following Sanctus had come to be recited in a low voice or silently; only the last words of the doxology concluding the entire prayer, *per omnia saecula saeculorum*, were sung aloud as an ecphonesis or cue for the Amen of the bystanding clerics and the congregation.[10]

The section of the great prayer preceding Sanctus came in the west to be regarded more as an introduction, a "preface" in the contemporary sense, to Sanctus. The preface was sung by the celebrant in a loud voice, audible to all, and it almost always ended with the word *dicentes* or, in non-Roman Latin rites, with some similar expression (*proclamantes* or *clamamus*). Moreover, this prefatory section had acquired a character proper to specific occasions or seasons, so that almost every set of prayers assigned to a given day in the early Latin collections had its own proper preface as well. Even as the number of proper prefaces increased, however, a contrary tendency set in to reduce their number, manifest first in papal mass books from the early seventh century.[11]

Most prefaces of Roman origin that can be traced to the fifth and sixth centuries employ the stylistic device now called *cursus* to regulate and mark the audible verbal rhythm of cadences. (Except for a few isolated clauses, the rest of the Roman canon, inaudible from *Te igitur* onwards, does *not* employ the cursus. See below, pp. xxxiv–xxxvii.)

Sacramentaries and Missals

I shall now briefly review the chief sorts of manuscripts having preface texts. I shall try to describe what they are called, how the collections came to be assembled, and how they grew and changed. Most prefaces are found in the western liturgical books that came to be called sacramentaries[12] or else in missals. The first sacramentaries, so it is thought, were assembled from *libelli*—that is, booklets and liturgical rolls containing individual masses or small groups of masses for a particular saint or occasion.[13] The masses in a sacramentary consisted solely of the prayers and other texts that were chanted or recited by the celebrant bishop or priest. In the Roman rite, the mass for each feast, Sunday, or weekday included at least three collects or brief prayers: the first to be chanted toward the beginning of the celebration; another, for silent recitation at the conclusion of the offertory (hence *oratio secreta*, the "secret"); and one to be chanted after communion. For some masses additional collects were supplied as alternatives, as commemorations of colliding feasts, or as extra prayers to be used at certain occasions and ceremonies—like the *super populum* prayer at the end of a Lenten weekday mass.[14]

All sacramentaries include proper prefaces for the highest feasts. Many sacramentaries provide them for lesser feasts and for some or most Sundays, and even for individual weekday masses of Lent and for masses of votive intention. The standard common preface (see p. xxii below) was always copied for use at celebrations not having proper prefaces. Early sacramentaries contain other texts belonging to the celebrant-bishop for such occasions as ordinations, the consecration of the holy oils, or the consecration of a church (in Gallican or Gallican-influenced books) —material that from the tenth century onwards was extracted and reedited in a book compiled especially for bishops, the "pontifical." The texts for administering baptism, penitence and absolution, the rites of burial, etc., in parishes or monasteries were transferred to priests' "rituals" or "manuals." From the late seventh century (if not before) sacramentaries were furnished with an *ordo missae* containing the fixed prayers of the mass and especially the dialogue, common preface, continuation of the canon, and Pater noster with its introduction and concluding embolism or expansion. But pure sacramentaries do not contain the lessons or the proper chants of schola and soloist.

Missals combined the prayers, prefaces, and other texts of the sacramentaries with the readings from scripture and the texts of the chants sung by the soloist and schola. These items were added from the reader's or the subdeacon's lectionary or epistolary; from the deacon's gospel book, the evangeliary; and from the mass antiphoners or graduals for the schola and the *cantatoria* for the soloist. The missal seems to have grown directly out of the *comes* or *liber comitis* of the seventh and eighth centuries—a "companion" book (companion to the sacramentary? or for the celebrant?) in which the passages of scripture from lectionary or evangeliary (or often both) were written out in liturgical order, instead of merely being indicated by rubrics in the margins of bibles or by incipits and explicits in separate "capitularies" that showed the beginning and ending of the liturgical lessons within specified books of the bible and chapters (hence the term "capitularies").[15] A *comes* might be bound together with a sacramentary in a single volume; but it was even more convenient for a priest celebrating alone to have the texts he needed integrated within each mass. Hence the missal.

South Italian missals of the late eleventh century had many rubrics, rubrics that usually presupposed a "solemn" mass with several ministers and the use of incense. These missals also included the new private prayers for the celebrant before, after, or during his own actions or the actions of others at mass. Certain votive missals, however, were clearly meant only for a single priest celebrating alone, whether in his parish or privately. Such votive missals usually select some important masses from the cycles of the temporal and sanctoral, while offering a large number of votive masses for all sorts of occasions and intentions, especially masses interceding for the repose of the souls of the departed. The need for such missals is obvious, but it is not so easy to see why the full missal mostly replaced the sacramentary for solemn celebrations in southern Italy.[16]

In south Italian missals, the items for the celebrant (excluding the new private prayers) were drawn almost entirely from the early Roman sacramentaries, whose mass formulas were written, assembled, copied, and revised during the period from the fifth to the early ninth centuries. Only to a much lesser extent did they draw upon the Gallican sacramentaries and missals of the Merovingian Franks and that mainly at second hand, through the later eighth and ninth-century sacramentaries that variously combined Roman and Gallican elements.

THE LEONINE SACRAMENTARY

The earliest surviving sacramentary appears to be the manuscript Verona, Bibl. Capit. lxxxv (80) from the beginning of the seventh century, generally known as the Leonine sacramentary from its misattribution to Leo I by an early editor.[17] It seems to have been derived from a collection of purely Roman and papal *libelli* in the Lateran archives. In its present mutilated state, it contains around 267 prefaces (depending on how the duplicates are counted), many of a personally papal, propagandistic, or tendentious nature, but some formulas for important feasts passed into general western use. (Other *libelli* having the masses for particular saints, usually martyrs, may have been kept at the various cemetery churches where the annual commemorations of these martyrs were held, with copies deposited at the Lateran. Only after the cults of particular martyrs spread to *all* Roman churches—after Gothic wars, Lombard sieges, and Saracen raids had devastated the cemeteries and their churches outside the walls and rendered access to them dangerous—was it felt that any single sacramentary ought to contain the masses of all or most of the saints and feasts celebrated within the diocese.)[18]

The Leonine sacramentary contains material that must have originated during the first half of the sixth century; other material in it is still earlier. Some items may go back to the time of Leo the Great (440–61). The manuscript itself, which for centuries has been kept in Verona, was written either there (Loew's view) or elsewhere in northern Italy or possibly at Rome—but in any case around the year 600. It may have been a private collection, the only one of its kind, made for study and reference rather than for liturgical use at the altar: the point is still being argued.

The Old Gelasian Sacramentary

The old Gelasian sacramentary survives only in the copy in the Vatican Library, Reginensis lat. 316, made around the middle of the eighth century by the nuns of Chelles Abbey, ninety miles east of Paris.[19] Its core seems to reproduce a Roman but non-papal mass book, edited during the last half of the seventh century for priests celebrating in titular and suburban churches. Many of its items are much older than the collection: some are also found in the Leonine sacramentary. Items for papal or episcopal functions were excluded when the core was compiled. No stations are mentioned. To this Roman, presbyteral core (presbyter = priest), a Frankish editor—working either when Reginensis 316 was copied, or earlier—added back certain episcopal ceremonies, including those for ordinations, the consecration of virgins, and the consecration of a church, drawing on Gallican texts. Nevertheless, the kalendar as well as the basic contents of the old Gelasian collection are Roman, though somewhat different from the contemporary Gregorian kalendar of the seventh century.[20] Other copies of the exemplar from which Reginensis 316 was made, along with similar Roman collections, must have been carried to Francia in the very late seventh and the eighth centuries and were there mingled with local Gallican and pre-Hadrianic Gregorian material so as to produce the so-called "Gelasians of the eighth century."[21]

The old Gelasian sacramentary has 54 proper prefaces, compared with 14 in the Hadrianic edition of the Gregorian sacramentary. The Gelasian sacramentaries of the eighth century among them assembled as many as 440 different prefaces but average around 200 prefaces per sacramentary. These numerous prefaces were in part drawn from non-Roman rites, which had many changeable formulas for certain parts of the great prayer.[22]

In titular and suburban churches of eighth and ninth-century Rome, collections of the old Gelasian type must have been gradually displaced by updated and expanded versions of the Gregorian sacramentary (see below). The ever more insistent ascription of this latter collection to Gregory I himself—for which there was some slight justification—and Gregory's rising reputation, especially in the monasteries, must have speeded the process.[23] Nevertheless, a great many prayers and prefaces of Gelasian origin survived in Francia in amalgamated editions having Gregorian format and chiefly Gregorian material.[24] Such additional material was however carefully segregated in the famous supplement to the *Hadrianum*, compiled between 800 and 815 by Benedict of Aniane, monastic reformer and ecclesiastical adviser to King Louis of Aquitaine (the later emperor, Louis the Pious), to augment the "authentic" edition of the Gregorian sacramentary, the *Hadrianum inmixtum*.[25] Through Benedict of Aniane's supplement and in other ways, the Gelasian collections profoundly affected the content and development of the later Gregorian sacramentaries and missals in northern Europe. As successive waves of reform spread from the north, beginning in the tenth century, the influence of the Gelasian collections again touched Rome itself.

The Gregorian Sacramentary

The Gregorian sacramentary served for the pope's own use, or for that of his vicar, at the Lateran and at stational masses celebrated in the different churches of Rome throughout the year. The Sundays after Pentecost and after Epiphany were not honored with papal stational masses and consequently were not included. Deshusses thinks the core of this collection—as it can be discerned beneath later developments—was assembled under Pope Honorius I (625–38) or one of his immediate successors. Deshusses writes:

> Cependant il faut souligner que les éléments qui le constituent sont plus anciens. En gros, il comportent deux sortes de pièces. Les unes sont des compositions

originales, sans parallèles antérieurs, et en général ne se répètent pas; les autres sont des passe-partout empruntés aux livres plus anciens et souvent répétées. . . . [U]n grand nombre d'oraisons de la première espèce (plus de quatre-vingt) utilisent des expressions qui se retrouvent nettement dans les écrits de S. Grégoire de sorte qu'on peut tenir qu'il en est l'auteur. . . . [O]n peut penser que S. Grégoire avait rédigé une collection d'oraisons et qu'elles ont été utilisées dans le sacramentaire qui est connu sous son nom, bien qu'il ait été constitué un peu plus tard que son pontificat.[26]

Successive Roman editions of the Gregorian sacramentary during the seventh and eighth centuries reflect the addition to the kalendar of the following feasts and fasts: in the first stage (660–70), the four Marian feasts—the Purification (originally *Hypapanti* or the "encounter" of our Lord with the aged Simeon), the Annunciation, the Assumption, and the Nativity—were added, along with St. Martin; in the second stage (682–83), St. George and St. Peter *ad uincula* were added; in the third (687–706), St. Gregory and St. Leo; and finally, under Gregory II (715–31), the addition of masses for the Thursdays in Lent rounded out the kalendar of the Gregorian sacramentary, as it was received in Francia just before A.D. 800.

TABLE I
Roman Sacramentary Types

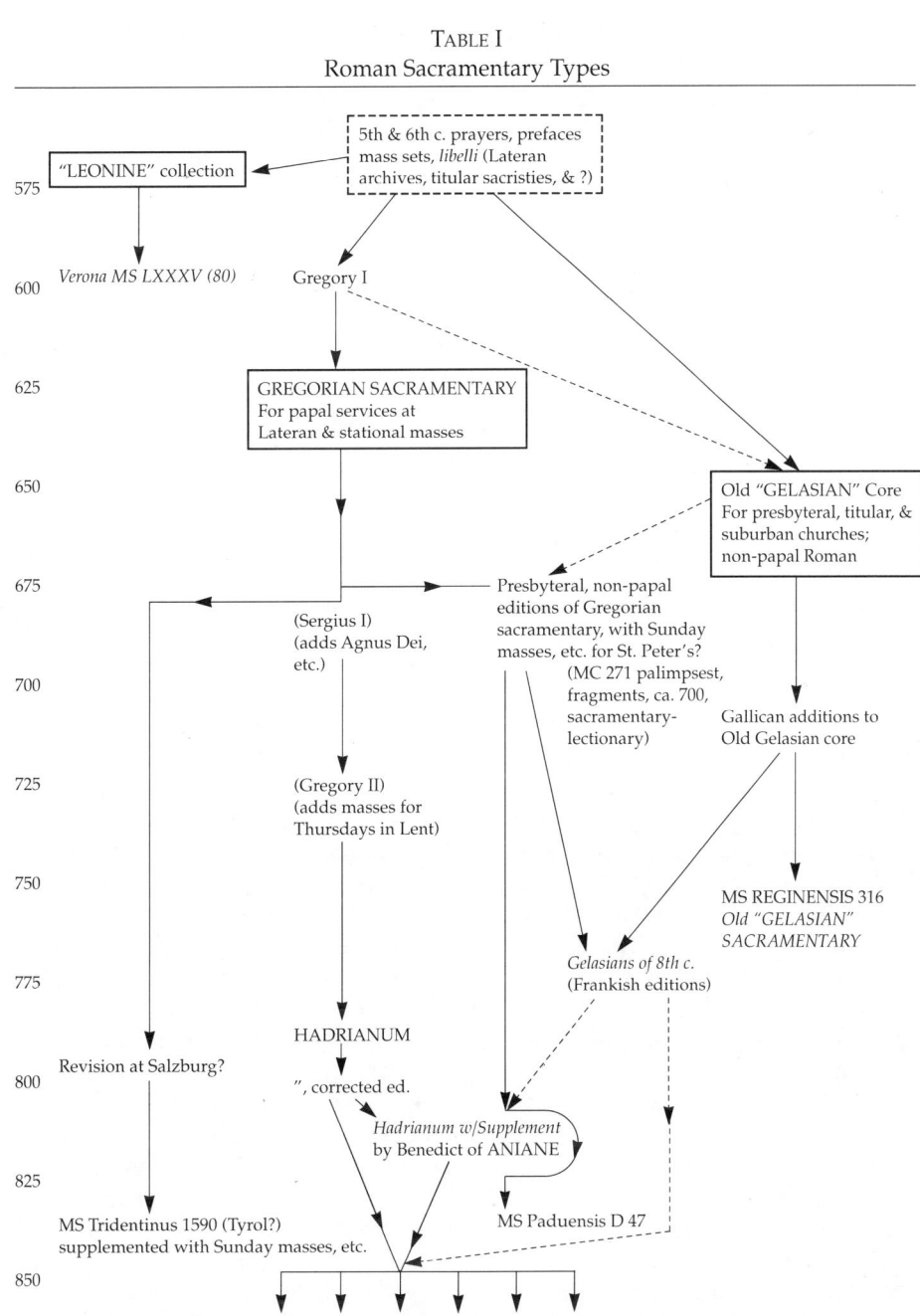

Charlemagne's ardent desire to conform the liturgies of his vast domains to the model of Rome insured the eventual prevalence of the Gregorian sacramentary. He requested and obtained a pure copy, *inmixtum*, of the "Roman sacramentary" from Pope Hadrian between 784 and 791. Copies of this book, called the *Hadrianum* or *authenticum*—namely, a post-732 edition of the Gregorian collection for papal use—were soon made: one of the copies survives, now Cambrai, Bibl. Municipale MS 164, the primary source Deshusses followed in his edition. As mentioned, this properly papal sacramentary contained no masses for most Sundays of the year. Besides, the Hadrianum had only fourteen prefaces, four of which were for special occasions like the anniversary of the pope's consecration. Additions had to be made if the book was to be used throughout Francia: the most influential was Benedict of Aniane's supplement (described on p. xviii above), and there were others.[27] In variously mixed and fused forms, supplemented largely with Gelasian and with some non-Roman material of Gallican or Visigothic origin, the Gregorian sacramentary by the tenth century had altogether supplanted its now superfluous competitors.

How and to what extent the several surviving missals of southern Italy (and the single complete sacramentary, Montecassino 339) drew upon Gregorian, Gelasian, and possibly older Campanian formularies that might have survived the Lombard invasion, has never been satisfactorily explained—certainly not in Rehle's editions of the missals Ben 33 and Baltimore W 6.[28] Scholarly attention has focused upon local old Beneventan items chiefly in the Holy Week liturgy, or upon aspects of chant and notation, or upon certain lections not found in the usual Roman rite. The main corpus of prayers and prefaces in these south Italian altar books has too often been grandly summarized as *romano-franque* or as "basically Gregorian with a Gelasian admixture."[29] One wants to know what the mixture was and where it came from. What was the Latin use at Naples? How much was imported from north Italy in the eighth century, after the conversion of the south Lombards to catholicism? The impact of successive Frankish penetrations has been acknowledged but not sorted out. Furthermore, the repeated impact of visits from the papal court and from papal synods held in Benevento, both before and especially after the city became a papal fief in 1051–52, has been neglected. Norman influence of a limited sort is evident at Montecassino but was hardly felt at Benevento except indirectly.[30]

To summarize the foregoing discussion of missals and sacramentaries, I reproduce a table of Deshusses' (table 1 above).[31] I have translated his terms and expanded his titles to conform with the BTC II text.

Manuscript Collections and Printed Editions of Preface Texts

Many of the prefaces whose texts were recorded in the sacramentaries and missals have been printed in two modern editions that require some discussion. The first is the formidable *Corpus Praefationum* (abbreviated CP) edited by Edmond (Eugène) Moeller. The last four volumes of the work (nos. 161A, 161B, 161C, and 161D) contain 1,674 entries of *praefationes, contestationes, immolationes,* and *illationes* taken from (1) scholarly printed editions of sacramentaries and missals or of surviving fragments, (2) the Pian Roman missal, and (3) the Roman missal of 1970.[32] Moeller by no means drew upon all manuscripts known to contain prefaces: "En principe, notre recueil se limite aux textes édités." But not even all the prefaces in printed editions appear: for instance, only the Purification preface from Baltimore W 6 (the Canosa votive missal) is included. Moeller apologizes, "Nous n'avons pu utiliser l'édition de S. Rehle [of Baltimore W 6]," without stating why he could not do so. He includes neither Desiderius' sacramentary (Montecassino 339) nor the Cassinese full missal (Montecassino 127) whose preface chants were modeled upon those in Desiderius' sacramentary. Thus the claim to completeness (even approximate completeness) implied by the title *Corpus Praefationum* is not justified, if indeed Moeller ever intended such a claim. Extensive as its contents are, the collection is in fact a *Florilegium Praefationum*.

Prefaces are arranged alphabetically in CP. The lack of either an index or a complete system of cross-referencing for variants makes it hard and sometimes impossible to find a given preface among the entries, if its incipit should differ from the form used in the CP entry. (Cross-references, when supplied at all, are buried in the small type of the Apparatus.) A separate volume of critical notes (the Apparatus) accompanies each volume of text, but its contents are arranged by number only, without title. Moreover, manuscripts are referred to in the Apparatus by means of sigla that rarely have any connection with their shelfmark. The key to these sigla is to be found only towards the end of the preliminary volume (numbered 161 in Corpus Christianorum, Series Latina, cited below as "CP 1" with page numbers following).[33] Moeller assumes that the reader of his important "Étude préliminaire" (in that same volume) has already been introduced to the history of western sacramentaries and to their chief sources. Moeller's comments are useful; his approach is disorganized. Nevertheless, CP supplies a concise means to identify preface texts and a way to trace their filiation and distribution, if in a limited and inconsistent manner. Preface texts entered in CP together with their respective commentaries in

Moeller's Apparatus are referred to below by a single number—as "CP 687" (the common preface) or "CP 1322" (the proper preface of the incarnation)—not by page number.

The second modern edition of preface texts, often referred to here, is found in Jean Deshusses' splendid work, Le Sacramentaire grégorien.[34] The fourteen preface texts in the Hadrianum and the more than two hundred in Benedict of Aniane's supplement are listed in a special section within the incipit-index of Deshusses' first volume, pp. 761–65.[35] Prefaces found in later editions of the Gregorian sacramentary but not in the Hadrianum or Benedict of Aniane's supplement are printed in Deshusses' second volume, pp. 335–55, #3669–3810, and are indexed alphabetically by incipit, pp. 454–61. (These include prefaces for supplementary votive masses, the common of saints, masses for local saints, etc.) An inclusive list of prefaces in all three volumes (that is, all the prefaces associated with any of the manuscripts used in Deshusses' edition of the Gregorian sacramentary) is given in the third volume, pp. 368–75.

Distribution of Preface Texts in South Italian Sources

The manuscripts used in BTC II/3 (see The Manuscript Sources of Preface Chants, pp. 1–7 below) divide into Beneventan sources, Cassinese sources, Border-Area sources (chiefly in Roman minuscule script instead of *littera Beneventana*), plus a source from Apulia.[36] Although these sources were chosen with regard to their preface chants, the chants are inseparable from their texts.[37] With respect to the distribution of prefaces in the manuscripts, two types of comprehensive sources are found. In the first and earlier type, we find twenty-five to thirty-five proper prefaces distributed among the individual mass propers without notation, just as they were in the Roman and Frankish sacramentaries of the seventh and eighth centuries. A single common preface appears within the *ordo missae* in its liturgical position after the secret prayer of the offertory, usually as part of the Easter vigil mass. For an example of this earlier type of source, the Canosa votive missal, Baltimore W 6 (copied in the late eleventh century from a very much earlier archaic provincial exemplar—see below, p. 7) will serve. Of its thirty-one proper prefaces, nine were scattered among the votive masses with which the missal begins; two were assigned to votive weekday masses and one to the votive mass of the Trinity; while nineteen prefaces enriched selected masses of the temporal and sanctoral. There are no proper prefaces in the common of saints nor in a small additional group of votive masses with which Baltimore W 6 now ends. Only the single common preface has notation, as is typical in such votive missals.

Nine of the nineteen prefaces in the temporal and sanctoral of Baltimore W 6 are also found in the early eleventh-century missal Ben 33 (which has a total of thirty-three proper prefaces); two of these, for Easter and for Pentecost, differ in at least half of their text. The other texts common to Baltimore W 6 and Ben 33 are those for All Saints' Day, the vigil of Christmas, the Assumption of the Virgin, the mass of the Trinity, the Apparition of St. Michael (in May), the Ascension, and SS. Peter and Paul. Rehle's statements notwithstanding, the sources used for these two early missals were not related, except in the most general way;[38] so much is clear from the striking variants within the Easter and Pentecost prefaces and from the completely different prefaces for St. John Baptist, St. John Evangelist, the masses of the Holy Cross, the third mass of Christmas, and the Purification. I wish I could trace the proximate derivation of the sets of proper prefaces and the other prayers of the mass formularies of Ben 33 and Baltimore W 6. Unica are rare among them: their *ultimate* source in the classic Roman sacramentaries is usually not in doubt. As remarked above, the prayers and prefaces of south Italian altar books have never been properly studied. It is beyond my competence and the scope of this essay to attempt such a study here. (See p. xx above.)

In the second, later type of preface source—especially in Cassinese and Cassinese-influenced manuscripts from the twelfth and early thirteenth centuries—a severely limited number of proper prefaces for the most important occasions were collected in one place, usually just before the common-preface chants. (They were sometimes accompanied by special proper wordings of the *Communicantes* section and a few other insertions *infra actionem* for some of these high feasts.) This type of preface source obediently followed Urban II's decree of 1095 at the Council of Piacenza adding the preface of the blessed Virgin to the mere nine prefaces allowed by the decretal attributed to Pope Pelagius II (579–90) by Burchard of Worms (965–1025) and taken thence into Gratian's influential collection of canon law (lxxi, De cons., dist I), though apparently forged by Burchard himself. (Burchard had already added the Trinity preface to the eight prefaces he selected from the fourteen in the Hadrianum.)[39] In at least one surviving source, Lo 3511, the collected proper prefaces were notated or at least ten of the twelve were; in ZaMR 166, they were not.[40] Within the individual mass propers of this second type of source, cues with the preface incipits directed the celebrant to the collection of proper prefaces. In full missals dependent on post-1071 Cassinese tradition, the common preface was written out not just once but at least twice, with different chants. (See the discussion of the Cassinese tradition that begins on p. xl below.)

The source types described above do not comprise fragments of missals or separate mass *ordines* inserted in collections other than missals. Sometimes a single notated common preface was joined to an ad hoc collection of votive masses, which sometimes also had proper prefaces, unnotated. One instance of a notated proper preface not part of a collection is known: the Pentecost preface in RoV B 24 (see p. 46 below).

Texts and Translations of Prefaces transcribed in BTC II/3 with Commentaries and References

The standard Roman text of the common preface is presented first below (as it appears in the south Italian manuscript Ben 33), together with two standardized proper-preface conclusions, shortly to be explained. Ordinarily, only the common preface text was notated. While some proper-preface conclusions (as from *Et ideo* onwards) were also notated, proper prefaces were notated only exceptionally—the proper prefaces collected together in Lo 3511 supplying the chief exceptional instance (see above). Texts and translations for proper prefaces in Lo 3511 are given in the same order in which the preface chants are transcribed (pp. 11–49 below), that is, grouped according to the chant versions *In cotidianis diebus, In festiuitatibus,* and *In sollemnitatibus.* (See the conspectus on p. 26.)

Manuscript sources for the preface texts are listed selectively below. For the common preface, only Ben 33 is cited, since the verbal text of the Roman common preface was essentially invariable. For the proper-preface texts, Lo 3511 (all of whose proper prefaces are transcribed) heads the Sources in the commentaries, followed by ZaMR 166, a later missal that groups together almost the same proper-preface texts as in Lo 3511 plus three more, but without notation. For these twelve proper prefaces, only two earlier south Italian sources are listed: Ben 33 and Baltimore W 6.

A necessarily technical discussion of *cursus*—the stylized verbal rhythms employed at the endings of phrases in Latin prose—is postponed until after the presentation of the texts (see pp. xxxiv–xxxvii below). Nevertheless, brief indications of the kinds of cursus present will be found in the commentaries just before each typical text. These indications will be fully intelligible only after the cursus discussion has been read. (The letters *p, t, u,* and *l* stand for the three standard types: *cursus planus, cursus tardus, cursus uelox,* and the less common *cursus laxus* or "trispondaic" ending, to be explained later.)

In the following commentaries, only texts are treated; the preface chants are discussed en bloc in the second part of this introductory essay and individually in the conspectus before each set of transcriptions below (pp. 11, 26, 38, and 47).

Common Preface and Dialogue 11
Corpus Praefationum 687
Vere dignum . . . Per quem maiestatem
with Proper-Preface Conclusions 24
Et ideo cum angelis & Quem (Quam) laudant

SOURCE OF TYPICAL TEXT

Benevento 33, fol. 80[r-v] (A description of the liturgical position of the preface in the MS is given under Beneventan Sources below, p. 1.)

NOTES AND REFERENCES

See CP 1: xxii–xxiii and CP 687. Also see Deshusses 1:#3, the common preface in the *ordo missae* and canon that begins the Hadrianum. For the probable Jewish roots of most of the opening dialogue, see above, p. xvi. For the erratic appearance of the cursus in the common preface, see below, p. xxxvi.

Per omnia sęcula sęculorum. ℞. Amen.
Dominus uobiscum. ℞. Et cum spiritu tuo ;
Sursum corda. ℞. Habemus ad dominum.
Gratias agamus
 domino deo nostro. ℞. Dignum et iustum est.

Vere dignum et iustum est. Ęquum et salutare.
Nos tibi semper et ubique gratias agere ;
Domine sanctę pater omnipotens ęternę deus ʏ
 per christum dominum nostrum ;
Per quem maiestatem tuam laudant angeli ʏ
adorant dominationes /
 tremunt potestates ;
Cęli cęlorumque uirtutes ʏ
hac [*recte*: ac] beata seraphim ʏ
 socia exultatione concelebrant ;
Cum quibus et nostras uoces ·
ut ammitti iubeas depręcamur ·
 supplici confessione dicentes ;
SANCTUS · SANCTUS · sanctus · Dominus deus sabaoth.
pleni sunt cęli et terra gloria tua. osanna in excelsis.
Benedictus qui uenit in nomine domini.
osanna in excelsis ;

 *

. . . now and forever. R. Amen.
The Lord be with you. R. And with your spirit.
Lift up your hearts. R. We lift them to the Lord.
Let us give thanks
 to the Lord our God. R. Meet and right it is!

Truly meet and right it is, salutary and just
 for us always and everywhere to give thanks to thee, O
Lord, holy Father, almighty, everlasting God,
 through Christ our Lord;
Through whom angels praise thy majesty,
 dominions worship, principalities tremble;
The heavens and heaven's powers, and the blessed
 seraphim together celebrate in kindred rejoicing;
With whom do thou command our voices also be heard,
we beg, humbly acknowledging thee and saying:

 HOLY, HOLY, HOLY
 Lord God of hosts . . .

The common preface is found in the old Gelasian sacramentary, as well as in the Hadrianum edition of the Gregorian sacramentary. The text must reach back to the fifth century at least and in part perhaps earlier still, to the time of the shift from Greek to Latin in the Roman church. (See below, pp. xxxvi–xxxvii.) It remained as the sole common preface of the Roman rite until it was ousted from the Roman missal of 1970.

When a proper preface was sung, the first line at least of the common preface served as a fixed introduction to the variable proper text. Thus the proper preface might begin after *salutare* (rarely), or after *agere, aeterne Deus* (very often), or after *per Christum Dominum nostrum*. The point of juncture was shown by a cue entered just before the beginning of the proper preface, thus: **VD** . . . *aeterne Deus. Qui* . . . (with the continuation of the proper preface). Furthermore, most proper prefaces ended with a standardized conclusion that differed from the conclusion of the common preface, namely:

> Et ideo cum angelis et archangelis
>   cum thronis et dominationibus ;·
> Cumque omni militia cęlestis exercitus
>   ymnum glorię tuę canimus
>   sine fine dicentes ;·
>   *
> And therefore, with angels and archangels,
>   with thrones and dominions,
> And with all the company of the heavenly host
>   we sing the hymn of thy glory,
>   ceaselessly saying:

The words *Et ideo* serve as the cue for this conclusion, used for most proper prefaces in south Italian altar books. (In the Hadrianum, the conclusion is written out at the end of nearly all the proper prefaces.)[41] In later Cassinese and Cassinese-influenced books, the entire ending is written out completely by itself and usually with chant, after or before the common preface chants—in addition to the cue words *Et ideo* after the proper prefaces themselves. (See pp. 24–25 below.) It may be helpful to show how the proper preface for Christmas (from Lo 3511) was expanded when sung. (See p. xxiv below for translation.)

> V[ere] D[ignum et iustum est ęquum et salutare ;·
> Nos tibi semper et ubique gratias agere ;·
> Domine sanctę pater omnipotens] ęternę deus.
>
> Quia per incarnati uerbi tui mysterium
>   noua mentis nostrę oculis
>   lux tuę claritatis infulsit ;·
> Vt dum uisibiliter deum cognoscimus ∕
>   per hunc in inuisibilium amorem rapiamur.
>
> Et ideo [cum angelis et archangelis
>   cum thronis et dominationibus ;·
> Cumque omni militia cęlestis exercitus
>   ymnum glorię tuę canimus
>   sine fine dicentes ;·]

One other proper-preface conclusion was sometimes copied by itself.

> Quam [*or* Quem] laudant angeli atque archangeli
>   cherubim quoque et seraphim ∕
>   non cessant clamare dicentes.

This conclusion is used to end the preface of the holy Trinity. (See p. xxv below for a translation.)

Still other proper-preface conclusions were formerly in use, of which the ancient Eastertide conclusion was the most important.

> Propterea [*or* Quapropter] profusis paschalibus gaudiis
>   totus in orbe terrarum mundus exultat.
> Sed et supernae uirtutes
>   atque angelicae concinunt potestates
>   hymnum gloriae tuae sine fine dicentes.

By the time of our manuscripts this conclusion had dropped out except at the vigil mass of Pentecost (which in a sense ends Eastertide), from which mass it passed in slightly edited form into the preface for the day of Pentecost. (See pp. xxxi–xxxii below, and consult CP 1: xxii–xxiv for other conclusions.)

Preface of the Incarnation 27
Corpus Praefationum 1322
Quia per incarnati uerbi tui mysterium

SOURCES

*London, B. L. Egerton MS 3511, *olim* Benevento 29, fol. 170ᵛ (first of twelve collected proper prefaces). Erroneously set to the chant version *In cotidianis diebus* of Lo 3511, except for the cues *eterne deus* for the juncture with the common preface and *Et ideo* of the conclusion, which have the chant *In festiuitatibus*. Rubric:

> *Prephatio de natale dn̄i. quę om̄ibus diebus usque in octauas
>   ad om̄s missas de natale dicenda est. Similit̄ quoque
>   et in purific et annuntiatio Sc̄e marie eadem dīc.*

Zagreb, MR 166, pp. 193–94 (first of fifteen collected proper prefaces, all without notation). Rubric: *Prepha̅ de nat̄le.*

Benevento 33, fol. 2ᵛ (in the Christmas mass *in nocte*; the folio is worn, broken off, and only partly legible but shows the complete proper preface conclusion beginning *Et ideo* written out). The rubric for the mass, on fol. 1ᵛ after the vigil mass of Christmas, reads: *Ite̅ mis̄ in nocte sc̄a.*

Baltimore, Walters Art Gallery, MS W.6, fols. 87ʳ–88ʳ (after the *sec̄ orati̅.Oblata domine munera ∕ . . . emunda ;· per* and before the *C̄o. Viderunt omnes* in the third mass for Christmas, which follows the vigil mass, the first and second masses of Christmas being omitted from this missal). The preface begins **VD** usque *ęterne deus. Cuius diuinę natiuitatis potentiam ∕ . . . predicamus ;·* [CP 115] and continues *Qui inuisibilis ex substantia tua ∕ . . . unicam credimus maiestatem;·* [in CP, found only in the Apparatus for CP 115], concluding with the text at hand, *Quia per incarnati uerbi tui mysterium ∕ . . . rapiamur ;· Et ideo cum angelis.* Rubric: *ppha̅.* and before the mass: *Mīs in nat̄ dn̄i.*

NOTES AND REFERENCES

Under CP 115 (the long form of the preface, beginning *Cuius diuinę natiuitatis potentiam* in the Canosa missal), Moeller cites a study by A. P. Lang and the review of that study by Antoine Chavasse, which suggest—through comparison with Leo's sermons—that the preface was based on works of Leo the Great and dates from 446. Jungmann however disagrees. Under CP 1322 (the short form of the text in the Hadrianum and the Pian missal, beginning *Quia per incarnati uerbi tui mysterium* as in Lo 3511), Moeller cites the same study by Lang and an article by B. Capelle attributing this form of the preface to Gregory the Great. Henry Ashworth also suggests it may be by Gregory and quotes passages from other writing of Gregory's having similar phrases; see Ashworth, "The Liturgical Prayers of St. Gregory," p. 121. Deshusses 1:#38 and Deshusses 1:#51 give the Hadrianum texts for the first and third masses of Christmas. The nearly identical prefaces both have the entire conclusion beginning *Et ideo*. Through the Gregorian tradition, the short form (CP 1322) passed into universal western use for Christmas, Christmastide, and other feasts of the incarnation.

Cursus:

tui mysterium	(t, accentual)
nostrę oculis	–
claritatis infulsit	p
deum cognoscimus	(t, accentual)
amorem rapiamur	ℓ

Source of text and translation below: Lo 3511

VD . . . eterne deus.

Quia per incarnati uerbi tui mysterium
 noua mentis nostrę oculis
 lux tuę claritatis infulsit ;
Vt dum uisibiliter deum cognoscimus /
 per hunc in inuisibilium amorem rapiamur.

Et ideo . . .

*

. . . everlasting God;

Because in the mystery of thy Word made flesh,
 a new light has shone out of thy radiance
 upon the eyes of our understanding:
 so that, perceiving God by seeing, we might through
 him be lifted up into love of things unseen:

And therefore . . .

Lenten Preface 27
Corpus Praefationum 863
Qui corporali ieiunio uitia comprimis

SOURCES

*London, B. L. Egerton MS 3511, *olim* Benevento 29, fol. 171ʳ (third of twelve collected proper prefaces). Set to the Lo 3511 version of the chant *In cotidianis diebus*. Rubric:

In quadrāg.

Zagreb, MR 166, p. 194 (third of fifteen collected proper prefaces, all without notation). Rubric:

In qādrag.

Benevento 33, fol. 80ᵛ (after the common preface and full Sanctus text—added in the original hand in the left-hand column beneath the illuminated arm of the T-cross for *Te igitur*, the continuation of the canon). Notation was never inserted. (This preface was omitted from the index at the head of the facsimile volume, PM 20, on p. 47*. The MS has another lengthy preface for the first Sunday in Lent.)

NOTES AND REFERENCES

See Deshusses 1:#1546, from the series of prefaces in Benedict of Aniane's supplement to the Hadrianum, where the text is assigned to *Feria iiii in capite ieiunii*, that is, Ash Wednesday; 1:#**161,** from Paduensis D 47, the pre-Hadrianic supplemented presbyteral edition of the Gregorian sacramentary, where it is assigned to the Friday after the first Sunday in Lent; and 2:#3762, from Trent 1590, yet another pre-Hadrianic edition of the Gregorian sacramentary, where it is assigned to Ember Saturday in Lent. The preface is found in various Gelasian sacramentaries of the eighth century. Other Lenten prefaces of broader scope are found in most of these books (including the Paduensis and Tridentinus) for other days in Lent and especially Lenten Sundays. It was this one, which stresses bodily fasting, which survived into the medieval missals and the Pian missal. It was not, however, included among Urban II's prescribed and permitted proper prefaces and is often therefore only found as an addition in the margins of later south Italian missals.

Cursus:

| uitia comprimis | (t, accentual and irregular) |
| largiris et pręmia | t |

Source of text and translation below: Lo 3511

VD . . . ęternę deus.

Qui corporali ieiunio uitia comprimis /
 mentem eleuas
 uirtutem largiris et pręmia.
  per christum dominum nostrum ;
[Per quem maiestatem tuam laudant angeli. . . .]

*

. . . everlasting God;

Who by bodily fasting dost curb [our] vices,
 dost lift up the mind
 and grant steadfastness and [its] rewards,
  through Christ our Lord;
[through whom angels praise thy majesty . . .]

Trinity Preface
Corpus Praefationum 879
Qui cum unigenito Filio tuo et Spiritu Sancto

28

Sources

*London, B. L. Egerton MS 3511, *olim* Benevento 29, fols. 172ᵛ–173ʳ (eighth of twelve collected prefaces). Inexplicably set to the Lo 3511 version of the chant *In cotidianis diebus,* including the juncture cue from the common preface, *ęterne deus,* and the entire written-out conclusion beginning *Quam laudant angeli.* If the preface had been intended only for votive masses of the Trinity, the choice of the everyday chant would have been fitting; but the preface was cued for use on the feast of the Transfiguration (6 August) along with other propers from the mass of the Trinity, as was customary in southern Italy. (See below.) Rubric:

> S̄c̄ę trinitatis.

Zagreb, MR 166, pp. 197–98 (tenth of fifteen collected proper prefaces, all without notation). Rubric:

> *De trinitate.*

Benevento 33, fol. 138ʳ (after the secret prayer of the offertory and before the cue for the communion *Benedicimus deum cęli* of the mass of the Trinity, placed at the *end* of the series of Sunday masses after Pentecost [here, after the third Sunday after St. Martin's Day]). In Ben 33, the mass of the Transfiguration has its own proper preface on fol. 117ʳ⁻ᵛ, *Qui tribus hodierna die assumptis,* CP 1265, although here the choir propers are those of the Trinity, to which propers those of the Trinity mass are cued. The rubric for the Trinity mass is partly illegible but probably read as transcribed in PM 20:

> M̄īs̄ in h̄ōn̄ [s̄c̄e et] indiuīā trinitatis.

The preface is rubricked *prephatio.* and ends with the cue *Quem laudant angeli.*

Baltimore, Walters Art Gallery, MS W.6, fols. 61ᵛ–62ʳ (after the ōr. s̄ēc. *Sanctifica quęsumus domine . . . munus ęternum, per* and before the c̄ō.*Benedicimus deum celi* of the votive mass of the Trinity, the rubric for which at the bottom of fol. 59ᵛ reads: M̄īs̄ *in honore* s̄c̄ē *trinitatis*). The preface is rubricked p̄p̄h̄ā. and ends with the cue *Quem laudant angeli.*

Notes and References

The preface appears in the old Gelasian sacramentary, Reginensis 316, in the mass formula for the octave day of Pentecost, *Orationes et preces in dominica octavorum Pentecosten,* as Chavasse quotes the rubric at the start of his extended discussion in *Le Sacramentaire gélasien,* pp. 253–62. (See the summary following the typical text, below.) It passed into the Gelasian sacramentaries of the eighth century and was included in Benedict of Aniane's supplement, as at Deshusses 1:#1621, but also assigned to Ember Saturday after Pentecost—in effect the vigil mass of the "vacant" Sunday after Pentecost and thus the octave of the Pentecost vigil, as at Deshusses 2:#3788. But it does not appear in either the Hadrianum or the pre-Hadrianic Paduense. It was included among Urban II's prescribed proper prefaces and passed into the Pian missal, where it was rubricked for use "on the Feast of the Blessed Trinity and on Sundays throughout the year." Its dogmatic formulations were ill suited to such frequent repetition, and the Roman missal of 1970 restricted it to masses of the Trinity.

Cursus:

spiritu sancto	(p, two-syllable final word)
unus es dominus	(t, accentual only)
singularitate personę	p
trinitate substantię	t
reuelante te credimus	t
spiritu sancto	(p, two-syllable final word)
discretionis sentimus	(p, irregular)
sempiternęque deitatis	ℓ
personis proprietas	(t, accentual)
essentia unitas	t
adoretur ęqualitas	t
atque archangeli	t
quoque et seraphim	(t, accentual only)
clamare dicentes	p

Source of text and translation below: Lo 3511

VD . . . ęternę deus.
Qui cum unigenito filio tuo et spiritu sancto
   unus es deus   unus es dominus ⁊

Non in unius singularitatę personę /
   sed in unius trinitatę substantię ⁊

Quid enim de tua gloria reuelante te credimus ./
   hoc de filio tuo   hoc de spiritu sancto
   sine differentia discretionis sentimus ⁊

Vt in confessionę uere sempiternęque deitatis ./
   et in personis proprietas /
   et in essentia unitas /
   et in maiestatę adoretur ęqualitas ⁊

Quam laudant angeli atque archangeli
   cherubim quoque et seraphim ./
   qui non cessant clamare dicentes.

*

. . . everlasting God;

Who, with thine only-begotten Son and the Holy Spirit
   art one God, one Lord,

not in singularity of one Person
   but in trinity of one substance.

For that which by revelation we believe of thy glory,
   the same we believe of thy Son,
   the same of the Holy Spirit,
   without [any] difference of inequality;

So that in acknowledging the truly eternal Godhead,
      individuality of Persons,
      unity of Being,
      equality of Majesty
   might be worshiped:

Whom angels and archangels praise,
   [whom] cherubim and seraphim
   never cease to acclaim, saying:[42]

The preface text is at least as old as the mid-seventh century and is very likely older still, although it is not found in the Hadrianum. It echoes concepts and phraseology used in Leo the Great's sermons for Pentecost. Accordingly, Chavasse and others have assigned the preface to Leo and to the years 441–47. Jungmann, however, thought that it must have been a sixth-century compiler, perhaps a Visigoth, who shaped the preface in its present form, though basing it on the sermons of Leo and other church fathers. In the Apparatus (CP 879), Moeller puts the arguments (freely translated below) as follows:

> Sur l'origine de cette préface, les avis diffèrent. A la suite de A. Chavasse (*Le Sacramentaire gélasien* ... p. 254–260), dont l'étude, malgré la date de parution, doit précéder celle de A. P. Lang, puisqu'il ne la cite pas, ce dernier analyse dans le détail trois sermons de Pentecôte de saint Léon-le-Grand (nos 75, 76 et 77), qui lui permettent d'attribuer la préface à ce pape, et qu'il date, respectivement de la Pentecôte 441 (11 mai) ou 442 (31 mai), 444 (11 juin) et 446 (19 mai) ou 447 (8 juin), à une époque d'hérésie pneumatologique, niant l'égalité divine de l'Esprit Saint (sémi-arianisme de l'évêque de Constantinople Macedonius: † 362), christologique, niant l'égalité du Père et du Fils (arianisme, nestorianisme, priscillianisme), et sabellianiste, minimisant la distinction des trois Personnes dans la Trinité.

> Opinions differ on the origins of this preface. A. P. Lang, following A. Chavasse . . . , analyses three sermons for Pentecost by St. Leo the Great (nos. 75, 76, and 77). Chavasse's essay must precede Lang's, since he does not cite it. On the basis of these sermons, Lang attributes the preface to this pope, dating the sermons, respectively, to 11 May 441 or 31 May 442, 11 June 444, and 19 May 446 or 8 June 447, during a time of heretical views concerning the third Person of the Trinity that denied the divine equality of the Holy Spirit (the semi-Arianism of Bishop Macedonius of Constantinople, † 362); of Christological heresy denying the equality of the Father and the Son (the Nestorian and Priscillian heresies); and the Sabellian heresy, which minimized the distinction between the three Persons of the Trinity.

Moeller then cites examples drawn from Leo's sermons (PL 54, sermons 75 and 76) and A. P. Lang, "Leo der Grosse und die Dreifaltigkeits-präfation," *Sacris Erudiri* 9 (1957): 116–62. Moeller continues:

> De son côté J. A. Jungmann rejette l'origine romaine de notre préface et sa date de composition (entre 441 et 447), pour la situer en pays gallicans, et plus particulièrement wisigothique, vers le milieu du VIe siècle, sans exclure l'utilisation de sermons de S. Léon, auxquels il ajoute celle de l'*Epistola* 7, no 12 (PL 67, 939) du diacre Ferrand de Carthage († ca. 546): «ut, cum bene intellecta fuerit, in essentia unitas, in personis proprietas, vera quoque in maiestate adoretur aequalitas», par le rédacteur («Um die Herkunft der Trinitatispräfation», dans *Zeitschr. f. Kathol. Theologie* 81, 1959, p. 461–65).

As regards the style of the Trinity preface: the many cadences having irregular or purely accentual cursus formations are hardly typical of Roman prefaces dating from the fifth and sixth centuries. Furthermore, the presence of rhyme of a sort (especially the endings *proprietas, unitas, ęqualitas*—borrowed from the deacon Ferrand though they be) is not at all characteristic of Roman products, although rhyme is found in Visigothic liturgical writing. On the other hand, most of the original layers of the old Gelasian sacramentary derive entirely from Roman material, as Chavasse has shown. Some of the collects in this very mass for the octave of Pentecost are also found in the so-called Leonine sacramentary; and it is exceedingly hard to imagine how a Visigothic preface could have found its way into this layer of the old Gelasian collection.

I doubt that the source of the Trinity preface will ever be determined. It seems to me that, as it stands, the Trinity preface was not composed by Leo the Great, though based in part on passages from his Pentecost sermons; that it was composed after the fifth century; but that by the seventh century it was in use in certain churches in Rome and was regarded as Roman when the core collection of the old Gelasian sacramentary was assembled.

Though its origin remains unsettled, the presence of a Trinity preface within the very Roman old-Gelasian mass for the octave day of Pentecost must have inspired the Franks to produce an entire mass in honor of the Trinity: Alcuin's votive mass is the best-known example. Alcuin's mass, which came to include the choir propers that begin *Benedicta sit sancta trinitas et indiuisa unitas,* was eventually accepted as a permanent part of the temporal cycle for "Trinity Sunday" on the old octave day of Pentecost. Conventional statements assign the feast of the Trinity to Stephen of Liège in the tenth century (whereas he should instead be credited with the rhymed *office* of the Trinity) and assign its adoption at Rome to the year 1264. But Cluny was already actively promoting the spread of Trinity Sunday on this date during the tenth century. However, Trinity Sunday is also sometimes found as a permanent part of the temporal cycle on the *last* Sunday of the post-Pentecost series, that is, as the Sunday before Advent, as in Ben 33.

Leo's Pentecost sermons and the Trinity preface derived in part from them and assigned to the octave day of Pentecost (the octave now being understood as Sunday—the Saturday evening ember-day vigil mass no longer being understood as the octave of the Pentecost vigil) must likewise have suggested to the Franks the octave day of Pentecost as the day especially suitable to honor the Trinity and must have facilitated the eventual reception of Trinity Sunday on that day by the western church, despite the firm opposition of Rome and southern Italy to the use of the Trinity mass on that day (up until the thirteenth century) and despite the consequent diversion in southern Italy of the Trinity mass to other occasions, particularly to the feast of the Transfiguration of Christ. The frequent assignment of some or all of the Trinity propers, including the preface, to the feast of the Transfiguration (6 August, or more rarely, 5 August) is a purely south Italian phenomenon that parallels the early introduction of this feast into south Italy—a feast originating in the fifth century in the East and only kept here and there in the West until Peter the Venerable, abbot of Cluny, added it to the Cluny kalendar in 1132 and composed an office of the Transfiguration (PL 169: cols. 266–68 and 953–72).

Preface for the Dead 29
Corpus Praefationum 699
Per quem salus mundi

Sources

*London, B. L. Egerton MS 3511, *olim* Benevento 29, fol. 173ᵛ (last of twelve collected proper prefaces). Without notation in the MS; the setting of the Lo 3511 *In cotidianis diebus* chant to this text is the editor's. Rubric:

Pro defunctis.

Zagreb, MR 166, pp. 201–2 (last of fifteen collected proper prefaces, all without notation, and the second of two prefaces for the dead). Without rubric.

Baltimore, Walters Art Gallery, MS W.6, fols. 38ᵛ–39ʳ (after the *or sec. Adesto domine supplicationibus nostris . . . assume ;· per* and before the *Com. Domine memorabor* of the second of four votive masses for the dead, all with proper prefaces). Only the introit, *Exurge quare obdormis domine,* is notated—the first notated passage in the missal. One more mass for the dead, without preface, was included in the additional votive masses toward the end of the MS, beginning on fol. 225ᵛ. The preface has the rubric *ppfa* and the mass, the rubric *Mis in depositi. iij. vij. xxx.*—that is, to be sung for the repose of the soul of the departed on the third, seventh, and thirtieth days after burial. The preface ends with the cue *per quem maiestatem* of the common preface, as in Lo 3511.

Notes and References

The text is indeed found in the old Gelasian sacramentary, Reginensis 316, but at the very end of the MS in an addition to the original core that was included in the copy made at the convent of Chelles around 750 or earlier. Chavasses says, "Ces . . . additions paraissent avoir été effectuées hors de Rome. La préface porte en effet le nom gallican de *contestatio*: ce titre est unique en son genre, dans le gélasien." The text was employed by Benedict of Aniane for the third of five prefaces for the dead in his supplement to the Hadrianum, Deshusses 1:#1735, and then in later supplemented or mixed editions of the Gregorian sacramentary, as at Deshusses 2:#2887, 2893, 2901, and 2966. The many variations found in the manuscripts adapt the text to particular funeral or commemorative occasions. The text was one of the most often used prefaces for the dead in the early middle ages. Although it dropped out of use along with the others, it was restored in the Roman missal of 1970 in edited form as one of five prefaces for the dead.

(The preface is not found in Ben 33 because the end of the MS, which contained almost all the common of saints and presumably a selection of votive masses as well, has disappeared.)

Cursus:

Per quem salus mundi	(p, irregular)
per quem uita hominum	(t, irregular)
resurrectio mortuorum	u
suppliciter deprecamur	u
digneris perpetuam	(t, accentual)
mortalitatis exutas	p
partem restituas	(t, accentual)

Source of text and translation below: Lo 3511

. . . Per christum dominum nostrum.

Per quem salus mundi ./ per quem uita hominum ./
  per quem resurrectio mortuorum.

Per ipsum te domine suppliciter deprecamur ./
  ut animabus famulorum famularumque tuarum
  (quorum memoriam agimus)
  indulgentiam largiri digneris perpetuam ./
  atque a contagiis mortalitatis exutas ./
  in eternę saluationis partem restituas ;·

Per quem. [maiestatem tuam laudant angeli . . .]

*

. . . Through Christ our Lord,

Through whom the world is saved,
  through whom mankind lives,
  through whom the dead arise;

Through this same [Christ] we humbly implore thee,
  O Lord, vouchsafe to grant
  the souls of thy servants and thy handmaids
  (whom we commemorate) eternal mercy;
  and grant them who are set free
  from mortal corruption
  a place of eternal salvation;

Through whom [angels praise thy majesty . . .]

There was no preface for the dead in the Pian missal until *In quo nobis spes beatae resurrectionis effulsit,* CP 505, was added in 1919. This text was retained in the 1970 Roman missal as the first of five alternative prefaces for the dead.

Epiphany Preface
Corpus Praefationum 1294   30
Quia cum unigenitus tuus

SOURCES

*London, B. L. Egerton MS 3511, *olim* Benevento 29, fol. 171ʳ (second of twelve collected proper prefaces). Set to the Lo 3511 version of the chant *In festiuitatibus*. Rubric:

In epyph usque in octauas.

Zagreb, MR 166, p. 194 (second of fifteen collected proper prefaces, all without notation). Rubric:

Preph In epypha.

NOTES AND REFERENCES

The text as given here was likewise assigned to the feast of the Epiphany in the Hadrianum (Deshusses 1:#89), whereas in the old Gelasian sacramentary it was assigned to the mass of the vigil, *In uigiliis de Theophania*. The Canosa missal, Baltimore W 6, has another preface for the Epiphany, *Nos te laudare omnipotens deus. qui notam fecisti in populis misericordiam tuam*. (*Nos te* . . . replaces *Nos tibi* . . . of the common preface: the preface was usually worded *Qui notam fecisti* or *Quia notam fecisti*, CP 605, like the preface *In Theophania* of Benedict of Aniane's supplement to the Hadrianum, Deshusses 1:#1525.) Which of the two prefaces appeared in Ben 33 is unknown: the Epiphany mass after the epistle is missing from the MS. Also see Deshusses 1:#60 (from the Paduense, a pre-Hadrianic version of the Gregorian sacramentary) and #30*. Both this preface and the one in the Canosa missal have been ascribed to Pope Leo the Great on the basis of similarities to passages in several of Leo's letters from the year 449. See A. P. Lang, "Leo der Grosse und die liturgischen Texte der Oktavtages von Epiphanie," *Sacris Erudiri* 11 (1960): 12–84 and especially 62–73. The preface in the present form was in the Pian missal but disappeared in the 1970 revision.

Cursus:

      mortalitatis apparuit   t
      luce reparauit   ℓ

Source of text and translation below: Lo 3511

VD . . . eterne deus.
Quia cum unigenitus tuus in substantia
    nostrę mortalitatis apparuit /
    in noua nos immortalitatis sue luce reparauit.
Et ideo . . . .
              *

. . . everlasting God;
For when thine only-begotten Son
    appeared in the substance of our mortal flesh,
    he restored us in the new light of his immortal nature;
And therefore . . .

Preface of St. Mary
Corpus Praefationum 366   30
Et te in assumptione (natiuitate) beatae Mariae

SOURCES

*London, B. L. Egerton MS 3511, *olim* Benevento 29, fol. 173ʳ (ninth of twelve collected proper prefaces). Set to the Lo 3511 version of the chant *In festiuitatibus*. The cue for the conclusion, *Quem laudant*. [*angeli atque archangeli*], was never notated: the setting given in the transcription below is the editor's. Rubric:

In assumptione / et natiuitate Scę Marię.

Benevento 33, fol. 119ᵛ (after the *sec*. *Intercessio quęsumus domine* . . . *reddat acceptos·; per*. and before the cue for the *Co*. *Diffusa est gratia* of the mass for the vigil of the Assumption of St. Mary). The variant wording is almost exactly that of the related Marian preface CP 602, found in several Gelasian sacramentaries of the eighth century and in Ambrosian books. In Ben 33, the variant wording begins *Nos te in tuis sacratissimis uirginibus exultantibus animis / laudare benedicere et prędicare·;* . . . The preface itself is rubricked *prephatio* and the mass (fol. 119ʳ) is rubricked *xviiii. k̄. uīḡ s̄ dī genitrīc marie*.

NOTES AND REFERENCES

In slightly longer form, the preface is found in Benedict of Aniane's supplement to the Hadrianum, Deshusses 1:#1652, beginning *Et te in ueneratione sacrarum uirginum exultantibus animis laudare* (= CP 366). Alcuin included it in his votive mass of St. Mary, Deshusses 2:#1846. The three versions—namely the form in Benedict of Aniane's supplement, the slightly shorter version of Lo 3511, and an earlier Marian preface (CP 602; see Ben 33 above)—all seem to have been modeled on a preface or prefaces taken from the common of virgins. (The Canosa missal, Baltimore W 6, fol. 177ʳ⁻ᵛ, has a preface for the Assumption beginning *Nos te in omnium sanctorum tuorum prouectu*, which seems to be even more directly derived from the common of virgins but which I cannot find in CP.) The text of CP 366 was shortened and altered almost to the form found in Lo 3511 by the early eleventh century, in such a way as to eliminate any reminders of its origin in the common of virgins. Retained by Urban II's decree of 1095 (see p. xxi above), in this shortened form it passed into general medieval use, into the Pian missal, and thence to the Roman missal of 1970.

Cursus: (Successive curtailments of the text may explain the absence of *cursus tardus* and the frequency of *cursus uelox*.)

       uirginis collaudare   u
       benedicere ⁀ et prędicare   u?
       obumbratione concepit   p
       gloria permanente   u
       mundo effudit   p

Source of text and translation below: Lo 3511

>VD . . . ęternę deus.
>
>Et te { in assumptione / in natiuitate } beatę marię semper uirginis
> collaudare ⸝
> benedicere et prędicare ⸵
>
>Quę et unigenitum tuum
> sancti spiritus obumbrationę concepit ⸝
> et uirginitatis gloria permanente ⸍
> lumen ęternum mundo effudit ʹ
> iesum christum dominum nostrum.
>
>Quem laudant. [angeli atque archangeli . . .]

  *

>Truly meet [and right it is, salutary and just,
> always and everywhere to give thanks to thee,
>O Lord, holy Father, almighty] everlasting God,
>
>and to praise, bless, and proclaim thee
> in the { Assumption / Nativity } of blessed Mary ever virgin;
>
>Who conceived thy only-begotten [Son]
> by the o'ershadowing of the Holy Spirit;
> and (the glory of virginity remaining)
> sent forth the eternal Light to the world,
> [even] Jesus Christ our Lord;
>
>Whom [angels and archangels] praise . . .

Preface of the Apostles   31
Corpus Praefationum 1484 = 1457
Te, Domine, suppliciter exorare

Sources

*London, B. L. Egerton MS 3511, *olim* Benevento 29, fol. 173ʳ (tenth of twelve collected proper prefaces). Without notation in the MS; the setting of the text to the Lo 3511 *In festiuitatibus* chant is the editor's. Rubric:

   In apostolis.

Zagreb, MR 166, pp. 198–99 (eleventh of fifteen collected proper prefaces, all without notation). Rubric:

   de ap̄l̄is.

Benevento 33, fols. 111ᵛ–112ʳ (after the s̄ēc *Hostias domine . . . et defendi , per.* and before the notated c̄o *Tu es petrus* of the mass *In nāt s̄ petri et p̄a.*). The text is the same as in Lo 3511, except for the spellings *set* and *hisdem* where Lo 3511 has *sed* and *isdem*.

Baltimore, Walters Art Gallery, MS W.6, fol. 165ʳ⁻ᵛ (after s̄ēc ōr *Hostias domine . . . et defendi , per.* and before the notated C̄o. *Tu es petrus* of the mass n̄āt ap̄l̄orum, immediately following the mass uīg ap̄l̄orum petri et p̄āu.). The text is exactly the same as in Ben 33. (See Rehle, *Missale von Canosa*, pp. 136–38 and #581.) Rubric:

   p̄p̄ha.

Notes and References

The version of Lo 3511, beginning *Te domine suppliciter exorare* immediately after the cued end of the first line of the common preface, *ęquum et salutare*, corresponds to the version at CP 1457. The similar version of CP 1484 begins *Suppliciter . . .* and omits the special link *Te domine.* The Leonine sacramentary and the old Gelasian sacramentary have the version CP 1484 in the mass *In natale apostolorum Petri et Pauli.*

The version CP 1457 appears in the Hadrianum for both the *Vigilia Sancti Petri* and the *Natale Sancti Petri*, Deshusses 1:#591 and #596, and in the Paduense for the *Vigilia Apostolorum Sancti Petri et Pauli* and the *Natalis Sancti Petri*, Deshusses 1:**540** and **544**. The text of Lo 3511 is exactly the same as the text of the Hadrianum, except for two differences in spelling. (The version CP 1484 is found in some later mixed editions of the Gregorian sacramentary, as shown in Deshusses 2:#1961, for the *Missa in Veneratione Plurimorum Apostolorum.*) Moeller cites J. Schmidt, "De Lectionibus Variantibus in Formulis Identicis Sacramentariorum Leoniani, Gelasiani et Gregoriani," where the prefaces are compared. The text of CP 1457 (namely that of Lo 3511) was included in the Pian missal but dropped from the Roman missal of 1970 as presumably not meeting the reformers' norms, namely, that a preface ought to express some element of thanksgiving or reason for giving thanks rather than consisting of pure petition.[43]

Cursus: (See the discussion of cursus below, p. xxxvi, where this preface serves as an example.)

Source of text and translation below: Lo 3511

>V[ere] D[ignum et iustum est] equum et salutare.
>
>Te domine suppliciter exorare ⸍
> ut gregem tuum pastor ęternę non deseras ⸍
> sed per beatos apostolos tuos ⸍
> continua protectionę custodias ⸵
>
>Vt isdem rectoribus gubernetur ⸍
> quos operis tui uicarios
> eidem contulisti pręesse pastores ⸵
>
>Et ideo . . .

  *

>Truly meet [and right it is,] salutary and just
>
>To entreat thee humbly, O Lord,
> that thou, eternal Shepherd,
> wouldst not forsake thy flock,
> but through thy blessed apostles
> wouldst guard it with never-ceasing care;
>
>So that it may be guided by those rulers,
> the successors in thy work
> thou hast charged as shepherds to lead the same;
>
>And therefore . . .

The preface of the Apostles was originally used only for the local martyrs and patrons of Rome, SS. Peter and Paul (29 and 30 June). It was firmly established at Rome by the early sixth century and must reach back to the fifth century, if not before. Its use was later extended to other feasts of apostles, although the feast of St. Andrew (a favorite saint of Gregory's, to whom a chapel was dedicated at the Vatican) already had its own proper preface, preserved among the fourteen in the Hadrianum (see Deshusses 1:#768 and #772).

Easter Preface   32
Corpus Praefationum 1527
Te quidem Domine omni tempore

SOURCES

*London, B. L. Egerton MS 3511, *olim* Benevento 29, fol. 171ᵛ (fourth of twelve collected proper prefaces). Set to the Lo 3511 version of the chant *In sollemnitatibus*. Rubric:

In pascha / usque in octauas / et o̅m̅ibus diebus d̅n̅icis. usque in ascensa.

Zagreb, MR 166, pp. 194–95 (fourth of fifteen collected proper prefaces, all without notation). Rubric:

In sab̅b̅o sc̅o̅. et do̅m̅.

Benevento 33, fol. 79ᵛ and fol. 83ʳ (after *sec̅ Suscipe domine plebis tue ⁏ . . . beatitudinem consequamur ⁏ per.* and before *Communicantes et noctem sacratissimam . . .* within the canon of the Easter vigil mass *In sab̅b̅. sc̅o̅.*, having the rubric *p̅p̅h̅a̅.* ; also after *sec̅ Suscipe qu̢sumus domine preces populi tui ⁏ . . . proficiant ⁏ per.* and before *Communicantes et diem sacratissimum celebrantes ⁏* of the mass for Easter Day, with the rubric *prephatio.*).

NOTES AND REFERENCES

With the special Easter conclusion *Propterea* (or *Quapropter*) *profusis paschalibus gaudiis totus in orbe terrarum mundus exultat. Sed et supernae uirtutes atque angelicae concinunt potestates, hymnum gloriae tuae sine fine dicentes*, the preface is found in the Leonine sacramentary and the old Gelasian sacramentary (for the vigil mass, *ad missam in nocte*). In the Hadrianum (as at Deshusses 1:#379, 385, 394, and 417—for the vigil, Easter Day, Easter Monday, and Easter Thursday respectively), the preface ends with the proper-preface conclusion beginning *Et ideo* as in Lo 3511, the Pian missal, and in many other collections. Also see the Pentecost preface below, CP 813 (Deshusses 1:#522 and #528), where the special Eastertide conclusion survives, shorn of the word *paschalibus*.

On the special Easter conclusion, cf. CP 1:xxiii and the extensive note at the end of the apparatus to CP 1527. Moeller mentions two letters of Paulinus of Nola (d. 431), which perhaps show that Paulinus knew this preface, at least according to Klaus Gamber. But the passages in the letters and in the preface might derive independently from well-known scriptural passages.

Cursus: (including the special conclusion—see above)

(equum et salutare)	u
omni tempore	–
gloriosius pr̨edicare	u
immolatus est christus	p
uerus est agnus	p
peccata mundi	–
moriendo destruxit	p
resurgendo reparauit	u
paschalibus gaudiis	t
mundus exultat	p
concinunt potestates	u
sine fine dicentes	p

Source of text and translation below: Lo 3511

VD . . . equum et salutare.

Te quidem domine omni tempore /
   sed in hac potissimum { nocte / die } gloriosius pr̨edicare /
   cum pascha nostrum immolatus est christ⟨us ⁏

Ipse enim⟩ uerus est agnus
   qui abstulit peccata mundi ⁏

Qui mortem nostram moriendo destruxit /
   et uitam resurgendo reparauit ⁏

Et ideo . . .

          *

Truly meet [and right it is,] salutary and just
to proclaim thee at all times, O Lord,
   yet more gloriously on this { night / day }
   as Most Mighty,
   because Christ our Passover is sacrificed [for us];

For he is the true Lamb who has taken away
   the sins of the world;

Who by his dying has destroyed our death,
   and by [his] rising again has restored life;

And therefore . . .[44]

The text quotes and paraphrases New Testament scripture: *Etenim Pascha nostrum immolatus est Christus* (I Cor. 5:7b); *Ecce agnus Dei qui tollit peccatum mundi* (John 1:29) combined with *lux uera* and *uitis uera* (John 1:19 and 15:1); and I Cor. 15: 12–49, especially *Nouissima autem inimica destruetur mors* (15:26).

The Canosa missal (Baltimore, W 6—which does not include the Easter vigil mass) employs a different preface for Easter Day, CP 1528, also beginning *Te quidem in omni tempore*. Although a few other phrases resemble CP 1527, most of this longer text varies. In the old Gelasian sacramentary (Reginensis 316), CP 1528 was assigned to Easter Day, *Dominicum Paschae*, as in several Gelasian sacramentaries of the eighth century. (In them, CP 1527 was assigned to the Easter vigil mass.) That is to say, the exemplar from which the Canosa missal must have been copied followed the Gelasian choice of preface for Easter Day, whereas the exemplar of Ben 33 followed the Gregorian choice. Such a divergence on such an occasion must imply different types of exemplars for the two south Italian missals.[45]

Ascension Preface 33
Corpus Praefationum 1165
Qui post resurrectionem suam

SOURCES

*London, B. L. Egerton MS 3511, *olim* Benevento 29, fol. 172^r (fifth of twelve collected proper prefaces). Set to the Lo 3511 version of the chant *In sollemnitatibus*. Rubric:

> In ascensa usque in oc̄t.

Zagreb, MR 166, p. 196 (seventh of fifteen collected proper prefaces, all without notation). Rubric:

> De ascensio̅.

Benevento 33, fol. 97^r (after sēc. *Suscipe domine munera . . . et ad uitam perueniamus ęternam ;· per.* and before *Communicantes et diem . . . quo dominus noster unigenitus tuus filius . . .* of the *Mīs in ascēns dn̄i.*). The text is the same as in Lo 3511, except for *tibi* for *hodie* in Lo 3511. Rubric:

> prephatio.

Baltimore, Walters Art Gallery, MS W.6, fol. 146^v (after the sēc ōr. *Suscipe domine munera . . . et ad uitam perueniamus eternam ;· per eundem.* and before the notated C̄o *Psallite domino* of the *Mīs in ascensio dn̄i*). The text is the same as in Lo 3511, except that the word *hodie* of Lo 3511 is omitted. Rubric: p̄ph̄a.

NOTES AND REFERENCES

Cf. CP 528 and CP 1163, two Ascension prefaces from the Leonine sacramentary. Moeller suggests that in the Hadrianum we see the shortened opening of CP 1163 combined with the ending of CP 528. See Deshusses 1:#499 for the version in the Hadrianum, identical with that of Lo 3511, except that the word *hodie* is omitted. (Also see Deshusses 1:#442 and 142*—that is, the same text found in other Gregorian collections.)

Cursus: manifestus apparuit   t
         eleuatus in cęlum   p
         esse participes   t

Source of text and translation below: Lo 3511

> VD . . . . Per christum dominum nostrum ;·
>
> Qui post resurrectionem suam omnibus discipulis suis manifestus apparuit ;·
>
> Et ipsis cernentibus hodie est eleuatus in cęlum / ut nos diuinitatis sue tribueret esse participes.
>
> Et ideo . . .
>   *
> Truly meet [and right it is . . . everlasting God,] Through Christ our Lord;
>
> Who after his resurrection manifestly appeared to all his disciples,
>
> And in their sight was lifted up into heaven, that he might grant us to share in his divinity;
>
> And therefore . . .[46]

Pentecost Preface 33
Corpus Praefationum 813
Qui ascendens super omnes caelos

SOURCES

*London, B. L. Egerton MS 3511, *olim* Benevento 29, fol. 172^{r-v} (sixth of twelve collected proper prefaces). Set to the Lo 3511 version of the chant *In sollemnitatibus*. Rubrics:

> In pēnt usque in octauas.   In uīg non dīc hodierna die

Zagreb, MR 166, pp. 195–96 (sixth of fifteen collected proper prefaces, all without notation). Rubric:

> de pentecos̄t.

*Rome, Bibl. Vallicelliana B 24, fol. 29^v (in the vigil mass of Pentecost). Beneventan notation *in campo aperto* of a preface chant *sui generis,* added in the early twelfth century to a sacramentary in roman minuscule script used at Subiaco, dating from the second half of the eleventh century. See Border-Area Sources, p. 6 below, and the conspectus of versions, p. 38, preceding the transcription, p. 46.

Benevento 33, fol. 99^v (after the sēc. *Virtute spiritus sancti . . . et intellegibilem nobis faciat et eternam ;· per. eiusdem spiritus sancti.* and before *Communicantes et diem sacratissimum pentecosten celebrantes* of the mass for the day, dōm scm̄ *pentecosten*). Almost the same wording as in Lo 3511, except *filiis* for *filios,* and *operaris* for *effudit*—the latter instance a scribal error.

Baltimore, Walters Art Gallery, MS W.6, fol. 152^v (after the sēc ōr. *Munera domine quęsumus oblata sanctifica !. . . emunda ;· qui tecum.* and before the notated C̄o. *Factus est repente* in the sole Pentecost mass in this missal, that of the day, *Mīs in pēn.*). The text begins like Ben 33 with the standard readings *filios* and *effudit* and then inserts the following passage, which I am unable to find elsewhere:

> Hodie enim sacratissimum pascha quinquagínta dierum misterio tegitur. et dispérsio linguarum que in confessióne facta fuerat./ per spiritum sanctum adunatur ;· Dum omnium linguarum tuas domine uirtutes atque angelice potestates./ ymnum glorię tue concinunt sine fine dicentes ;·

NOTES AND REFERENCES

The Hadrianum has the preface with the exact wording of Lo 3511 (CP 813) for both the vigil and Sunday of Pentecost (Deshusses 1:#522 and #528). The preface also appears in the Paduense, a pre-Hadrianic edition of the Gregorian sacramentary (see Deshusses 1:#462). The special conclusion is in fact the old Eastertide preface conclusion, where the first phrase read . . . *profusis paschalibus gaudiis.* (See above, p. xxx.)

The same preface, but with the beginning *Qui ascendit* and a different special conclusion (CP 814), was assigned in both the Leonine sacramentary and the old Gelasian sacramentary to the Pentecost vigil mass. It is also found in another pre-Hadrianic edition of the Gregorian sacramentary, the *Tridentinum,*

Trent MS 1590; see Deshusses 2:#3885, where the beginning reads as in the Hadrianum but with the ending of CP 814:

> Unde laetantes inter altaria tua domine uirtutum hostiasque tibi laudis offerentes [*Leoninum:* offerimus], cum angelis et archangelis . . .

Also see CP 1:xxiii, xxiv, and Bourque 1:113–14.

Cursus:

omnes cęlos	–
spiritum sanctum	(p, irregular)
adoptionis effudit	p
profusis gaudiis	–
mundus exultat	p
angelicę potestates	u
glorię tuę concinunt	(t, irregular)
sine fine dicentes	p

The slight rearrangement of word order from that of the old Easter conclusion (. . . *profusis paschalibus gaudiis; . . . angelicę concinunt potestates ymnum glorię tuę sine fine dicentes*) disturbs the cursus: cf. the cursus as given under the Easter preface above.

Source of text and translation below: Lo 3511

> VD . . . per christum dominum nostrum ;
>
> Qui ascendens super omnes cęlos /
>   sedensque ad dexteram tuam
>   promissum spiritum sanctum
>   hodierna die in filios adoptionis effudit ;
>
> Quapropter profusis gaudiis /
>   totus in orbe terrarum mundus exultat ;
> Sed et superne uirtutes atque angelicę potestates
>   ymnum glorię tuę concinunt
>   sine fine dicentes.
>   *
>
> Truly meet [and right it is . . . everlasting God,]
>   through Christ our Lord;
>
> Who, rising above all the heavens
>   and sitting at thy right hand,
>   today poured out the Holy Spirit
>   upon [his] adopted sons;
>
> Wherefore with joy unbounded
>   the whole world rejoices,
> while exalted powers and angelic principalities
>   sing the hymn of thy glory,
>   ceaselessly saying:[47]

Attempts have been made by Bourque and others to assign the Pentecost preface to Leo the Great himself—more precisely to the years 441–42, or else 455—on the basis of *other* prayers in the mass sets for Pentecost in the Leonine sacramentary, prayers that refer to a siege of Rome by hostile invaders (Goths or Vandals?). However, the preface itself might well be older than the Leonine mass sets that contain it. The notable emphasis on the ascension of Christ in the Pentecost preface suggests a time when the Ascension was not yet being commemorated as a separate feast at Rome but rather included in the great fifty-days of the Easter celebration—which would explain the use of the Easter conclusion. (Around the year 385, the pilgrim Etheria mentions that "a feast" was being kept at Jerusalem forty days after Easter. It is generally agreed that the separate feast of the Ascension originated at Jerusalem.) In the third century, Hippolytus at Rome had not heard of a feast of the Ascension. I do not know when the feast was adopted at Rome: certainly it was firmly established as a separate feast by the end of the fifth century. It received several mass sets in the Leonine collection.

The phrase *spiritum sanctum in filios adoptionis effudit* —which is similar to certain expressions in Leo's letters—compresses Gal. 4:4–8, especially verses 5 and 6: ". . . that we might receive the adoption of sons. And because you are his sons, God has sent forth the Spirit of his Son into your hearts, crying, Abba, Father . . . ." The likelihood that this famous scriptural passage might have been quoted directly and independently of Leo by another author tends to weaken the ascription of the preface to Leo, at least on the basis of this passage.

Preface of the Holy Cross   35
Corpus Praefationum 1200
Qui salutem humani generis

Sources

*London, B. L. Egerton MS 3511, *olim* Benevento 29, fol. 172ᵛ (seventh of twelve collected proper prefaces). Set mostly to the Lo 3511 version of the chant *In sollemnitatibus,* but the first two medial cadences use the Lo 3511 version *In cotidianis diebus.* Rubric: *In S̄ crucis.*

Zagreb, MR 166, p. 195 (fifth of fifteen collected proper prefaces, all without notation). Rubric: *De cruce.*

Benevento 33, fol. 122ᵛ (after the *sec̄* *Hęc oblatio domine* ỵ . . . *tulit offensa* ; *per.* and before the *postcō. Adesto domine deus noster* ỵ . . . *defende subsidiis* ; of the second mass, *Alia m̄s,* of the Exaltation of the Holy Cross, 14 September—*xviii k̄. [octobris]. exaltati s̄cē crucis. Can̄ req̄ in inuen̄ eiusdem*—the prayers and preface of this second mass being those of Alcuin's votive mass of the Holy Cross). The text is almost the same as in Lo 3511, except *humano generi* for Lo 3511's *humani generis* and *contulisti* for *constituisti*. Rubric: *ppha.*

Baltimore, Walters Art Gallery, MS W.6, fol. 63ᵛ (after the *sec̄ oratio. Hęc oblatio quęsumus domine . . . tulit offensa* ; *per.* and before the unrubricked and unnotated communion *Nos autem gloriari oportet* of the votive *M̄s in honore s̄ crucis*). The text has *humani generis* and *constituisti*, not the variants of Ben 33. The MS has both the Invention (3 May, fols. 133ᵛ–136ᵛ) and the Exaltation (14 September, fols. 181ᵛ–184ʳ) of the Holy Cross: the first has a different

xxxii

preface beginning *Precipue in die ista* (fol. 136ʳ), which consists of the opening lines of CP 731 (found in Gelasian sacramentaries of the eighth century and, altered, in the Ambrosian books, but not found in Ben 33). The second feast of the cross, the Exaltation, has no preface in the Canosa missal. Rubric: p̄phā.

NOTES AND REFERENCES

The preface CP 1200, which first appeared in Alcuin's votive mass of the Holy Cross for Fridays, was included in the sacramentary Alcuin compiled for St. Martin of Tours and eventually passed into the later supplemented editions of the Gregorian sacramentary. (It is not found in the supplement of Benedict of Aniane, which has another preface, CP 1151 and Deshusses 1:#1609 and #1667, for the Invention and Exaltation of the Cross. For CP 1200, see Deshusses 1:#133* and 2:#1837 = #3682 = #3717.) On Alcuin's masses, see Deshusses 2:25–26, 3:75–78, and Jean Deshusses, "Messes d'Alcuin," *Archiv für Liturgiewissenschaft* 14 (1972):7–41. It was included in the Pian missal for "Masses of the Passion or of the Holy Cross."

For the origin of the feasts of the Holy Cross and the complicated history of their introduction at Rome, see Chavasse, *Le Sacramentaire gélasien*, pp. 350–64.

Cursus: lacking, except for *ligno uincebat*, which forms an irregular *cursus planus*.

Source of text and translation below: Lo 3511

VD . . . ęternę deus ./

Qui salutem humani generis
 in ligno crucis constituisti ./

 ut unde mors oriebatur ./
 inde uita resurgeret ;

Et qui in ligno uincebat ./
 in ligno quoque uinceretur.

 per christum dominum nostrum.

*

Truly meet [and right it is] . . . everlasting God;

Who didst establish the salvation of mankind
 on the Tree of the Cross:

 that whence death sprang,
 thence life might arise:

And that the one who vanquished on the Tree
 on the Tree should also be vanquished,

 through Christ our Lord.

This text is the latest of the proper prefaces in Lo 3511 to have been composed. Alcuin, the English deacon from Northumbrian York who became Charlemagne's friend and court counsellor for religion and liturgy, wrote it around the year 800. Alcuin chose not to employ the cursus in this preface (see below, p. xxxvii), although he used it in some of the prayers he composed for his series of votive masses for the days of the week.

Dedication Preface 35
Corpus Praefationum 741 = 203
*Pro annua dedicatione tabernaculi
. . . Cuius uirtus magna est*

SOURCES

*London, B. L. Egerton MS 3511, *olim* Benevento 29, fol. 173ᵛ (eleventh of twelve collected proper prefaces). Set mostly to the Lo 3511 version of the chant *In sollemnitatibus,* but all medial cadences except those taken from the common preface use the Lo 3511 version *In cotidianis diebus.* Rubric on fol. 173ʳ: *In dedicatio ęcclę.*

Zagreb, MR 166, p. 199 (twelfth of fifteen collected proper prefaces, all without notation). The text begins *Cuius uirtus magna est,* exactly as in CP 203. Rubric:

De dedicationem.

NOTES AND REFERENCES

The Lo 3511 version begins as in the longer version (CP 741) of the Dedication preface but inserts *pro annua dedicationę . . . referre* after *salutare* within the common preface, instead of after *ęterne deus.* It ends after *ignoscas,* as in CP 203, omitting the rhetorical flourishes, each beginning *Hic,* that conclude the longer version, CP 741. Variants of, additions to, and subtractions from this preface abound. It is found in Gelasian sacramentaries of the eighth century and was included in certain mixed Gregorian books. See Deshusses 2:#3732 (= CP 203, as in Rheims, Bibl. Munic. MS 213 from Noyon but written at Saint-Amand—a sacramentary with a non-Gregorian supplement of mixed origin having an extended series of prefaces) and Deshusses 3:#4168 (= CP 741, in several Gelasian sacramentaries of the eighth century and the Bobbio missal). If the mass of the Dedication was originally included in Ben 33, it must have been among the now missing folios at the end of the manuscript. The Canosa missal, Baltimore W 6, has the mass as an addition to the manuscript on fol. 224ʳ, but without proper preface or lections.

The section beginning *Respice . . . de cęlo* condenses Solomon's prayer at the dedication of the temple, I Kings 8:22–53. On the Gallican sources of the rites for the dedication of a church as found in the old Gelasian sacramentary, see Chavasse, *Le Sacramentaire gélasien,* pp. 36–49. The Gregorian mass of the Dedication grew out of the dedication of the Pantheon as S. Maria ad Martyres in 609, but the present Dedication preface seems to have had no connection with this occasion. The preface can scarcely be Roman in origin. Roman usage until at least the eighth century had no special rites for the consecration of a church or altar; the celebration of mass in the new edifice, usually by the pope or his episcopal representative, sufficed.

Cursus:

tabernaculi huius	(p. irregular)
gratiasque referre	(p, irregular)
pietas copiosa	u
cęlo et uide	(p, irregular)
uisita domum istam	(u, irregular)
tuo supplicauerit	–
libenter exaudias	t
clementer ignoscas	p

Source of text and translation below: Lo 3511

VD . . . equum et salutare.
Nos tibi semper et ubique
   pro annua dedicationę tabernaculi huius
   honorem gratiasque referre.
Domine sanctę pater omnipotens eternę deus ./
   cuius uirtus magna est et pietas copiosa ;

Respice quesumus domine de cęlo et uide /
   et uisita domum istam ;

Vt si quis in ea nomini tuo supplicauerit
   libenter exaudias ./
   et satisfacientibus clementer [ignoscas ;

per christum] dominum nostrum.

*

Truly meet [and right it is,] salutary and just,
   that we should always and everywhere return honor
      and thanks to thee
   for the yearly dedication of this temple,
O holy Lord, Father almighty, everlasting God,
   whose power is great, whose kindness abundant;

Look down from heaven, we beseech thee,
   and behold and visit this house;
That if any shall call upon thy name in this place,
   thou mayst graciously hear and forgive
   those who make amends,
      through Christ our Lord.

The Cursus

The stylistic device called *cursus* governs the cadential rhythm of most of the preface texts examined above: that is, the cursus determines the number of syllables and their arrangement by accent and quantity in the *clausulae* of the texts. The cursus was widely studied from about 1880 to 1920; presently the topic is almost completely neglected.[48] The cursus is not even mentioned by Moeller in the several volumes of *Corpus Praefationum,* so far as I am aware, nor by Deshusses in *Le Sacramentaire grégorien.* A useful introductory definition is however found in D. M. Hope's *The Leonine Sacramentary.*

> The prayers [of the Leonine Sacramentary] are written in neither verse nor prose; rather are they written in what may be termed "rhythmic prose." The final clauses of the majority of these prayers appear not to have been written in a purely arbitrary way but in a combination of words specially designed beforehand and fixed according to particular rules. Similarly, the prayers of the other two ancient Roman sacramentaries, the Gelasian and Gregorian, have a large number of endings which suggest that they too have been influenced by the same literary principle. This combination of language and rhythm in a particular way, known as *cursus,* was a definite feature of Roman liturgical composition from sometime in the fourth century until the early part of the seventh.[49]

Moreover, the rhythms now called cursus were also employed in documents issuing from the papal *scrinarium* from around 390 until just after the papacy of Gregory I in the early seventh century. These rhythms took into account both accent and syllabic quantity or length, whereas the clausulae of Cicero's prose and of his imitators were purely quantitative.[50] The term *cursus* was invented (so far as I know) and applied to these rhythms in the twelfth century, when their use was revived in purely accentual form to authenticate documents proceeding from the Roman curia.

The three forms of cursus standardized in the twelfth century were *cursus planus* (abbreviated "p" in the preface texts above and in the following discussion), *cursus tardus* ("t"), and *cursus uelox* ("u"). Their accentual rhythms are set out below, using an example provided by Mocquereau and Leclercq: namely, the collect that used to be privately recited thrice daily at the ringing of the Angelus.[51] The cadences of this collect (a composition that probably dates from around the time of the introduction of certain Marian feasts at Rome just after the middle of the seventh century; see p. xix above) employ cursus forms that are regular when regarded accentually but highly irregular when measured against the simultaneously accentual and quantitative cadences of fifth and sixth-century Roman liturgical prose. They show the correct number of syllables in the final word of the cadence—it being understood that a "word" of four syllables, say, may consist of a three-syllable word preceded or followed by a closely connected monosyllable: *non deseras* or *conuersus sum*.

Cursus planus
Gratiam tuam, quaesumus Domine,
mentibus nostris | infunde,
　　 ´ ˘　　　 | ˘ ´ ˘
(paroxytone) | (paroxytone word of three syllables)

Cursus tardus
ut qui angelo annuntiante, Christi filii tui
incarnationem | cognouimus,
　　 ´ ˘　　 | ˘ ´ ˘ ˘
(paroxytone) | (proparoxytone word of four syllables)

Cursus uelox
per passionem eius et crucem ad resur-
rectionis gloriam | perducamur;
　 ´ ˘ ˘　　　　 | ˘ ˘ ´ ˘
(proparoxytone word of three syllables or more) | (paroxytone word of four syllables)

As stated, Roman collects and prefaces that can be dated to the fifth and sixth centuries characteristically combine quantitative patterns inherited from classical Latin prose clausulae and still in use in elevated prose of the late empire[52] with accentual patterns derived from the contemporary vernacular. The accentual patterns alone survive in liturgical pieces composed after A.D. 625 or thereabouts. The *cursus planus* and *cursus tardus* of the fifth and sixth centuries always have the same fixed quantitative patterns, respectively. The last accent in the *cursus planus* and the *cursus tardus* is preceded by a long syllable, a feature often missing in later purely accentual cursus forms. The *cursus uelox*, however, derives from several classical clausulae, and the distribution of quantities within it therefore varies.

To these three types catalogued in the twelfth century should be added a fourth type, called *trispondaïque* by Mocquereau and Leclercq. The term was confusingly applied by Mocquereau to cadences having *three* unaccented syllables intervening between the final two accents, the last word being a paroxytone (see below) without regard to the quantities implied by the term.[53]

　 ´ ˘　 | ˘ ˘ ´ ˘
(paroxytone) | (paroxytone word of four syllables)

I have chosen to replace the cumbersome and not always accurate designation "trispondaic" (or "dispondaic") by the term *cursus laxus* (abbreviated "ℓ"), because this formation lies between *cursus planus* and *tardus* having two intervening syllables, and *cursus uelox*, having four. (See below.)

When examining the preface chants, it is important to note how the final musical cadence (which usually coincided with a verbal cursus) was shaped. The accentual patterns of the clausulae—and these alone—are reflected in the musical formulas for the final cadences of prefaces (see below, pp. xxxix–xl). All cursus have two accents, with from two to four syllables intervening between them. The last accent may occur in either a paroxytone or proparoxytone word, depending on the type of cursus. Musical formulas for final cadences do not, however, reflect the quantitatively long syllable preceding the last accent, which long syllable regularly appears in the fifth and sixth-century *cursus planus* and *cursus tardus*. It would seem that the formula for final cadences—the most stable element in the various preface-chant traditions by far—evolved only after around 625. Prefaces known to have been written after this date have only *accentual* cursus, for the syllabic quantities were no longer recognized nor observed, not even (sometimes) in verse.[54] It is therefore fair to assume that after about 625, Roman celebrants when singing the preface no longer lengthened the syllable preceding the last accent in those clausulae later entitled *cursus planus* and *cursus tardus*.

In the examples to follow (mostly taken from Leclercq), the accentual aspect is given below the text and the syllabic quantities above. The length of the last syllable of the clausula—a syllable *anceps* (marked ⁼, either short or long)—does not matter, as it is followed by a breath and a slight pause.

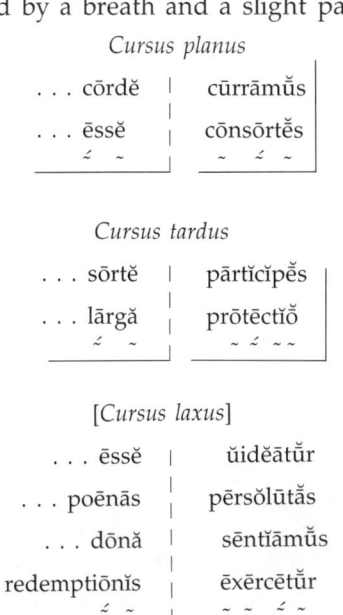

Cursus planus
. . . cōrdĕ | cūrrāmŭs
. . . ēssĕ | cōnsōrtĕ̄s

Cursus tardus
. . . sōrtĕ | pārtĭcĭpĕ̄s
. . . lārgă | prōtēctĭō

[*Cursus laxus*]
. . . ēssĕ | ŭĭdĕātŭr
. . . poēnās | pērsŏlūtăs
. . . dōnă | sēntĭāmŭs
redemptiōnĭs | ēxērcētŭr

Cursus uelox
. . . mūnĕrĕ | cōngrĕgēntŭr
. . . fīlĭŭs | uērĭtātĕm
. . . prĕcĭbŭs | ādĭŭēntĕr
. . . prĕcĭbūs | cōnsĕquāmŭr
. . . căpĕrĕ | uălĕāmŭs
. . . rēddĭtŭr | ēxōrāntĕ̄s

xxxv

Leclercq cites the preface of the Apostles (CP 1457; see p. xxix above) as using the three types of quantitative-accentual cursus: *planus, tardus,* and *uelox.* To this proper preface for the Apostles, the standard opening (from the common preface) and the standard proper-preface conclusion (beginning *Et ideo*) are added below.

> Vere dignum et iustum est, aēquŭm ēt sălūtārĕ,   u
>
> Te Domine supplĭcĭtĕr ēxōrārĕ,   u
>
>   ut gregem tuum pastor aetērnĕ nōn dēsĕrăs;   t
>
> sed per apostolos tuos
>   continua protectiōnĕ cūstōdĭăs;   t
>
>   ut isdem rectōrĭbŭs gŭbērnētŭr,   u
>
> quos operis tui uicarios
>   eidem contulisti praeēssĕ pāstōrĕs.   p
>
> Et ideo, cum angelis et archangelis,
>   cum thronis et dominationibus,
>
> Cumque omni militia coelēstĭs ēxērcĭtŭs,   t
>
> hymnum gloriae tuae canimus,
>   sine fīnĕ dīcēntĕs: p

The preface *In apostolis* was certainly written for the patron saints and local martyrs of Rome, Peter and Paul. In the form found in Gregorian sacramentaries (CP 1457), all but the first line of the common-preface introduction, *Vere dignum et iustum est, aequum et salutare* (which ends with the *cursus uelox*), is replaced with the special introductory line *Te Domine suppliciter exorare,* which also ends with the *cursus uelox.* The lines of the common-preface introduction that are replaced, namely,

> Nos tibi semper et ubique gratias agere,
> Domine sancte, pater omnipotens, aeterne deus;
>   (per Christum Dominum nostrum:)

have no regular cursus forms.

A similar substitution is found in the Roman Easter preface (CP 1527; see p. xxx above), where the special introductory line *Te quidem Domine omni tempore* replaces the same segment of the common-preface introduction. Originally, the conclusion *Et ideo* (now attached to the Easter preface) was also replaced by a special cursus-rich Easter conclusion:

> Propterea (*or* Quapropter) profusis paschalibus gaudiis,(t)
>   totus in orbe terrarum mundus exultat.   p
> Sed et supernae uirtutes
>   atque angelicae concinunt potestates,   u
>   hymnum gloriae tuae sine fine dicentes: p

This conclusion survives slightly altered, in the standard Pentecost preface (CP 813; see pp. xxxi–xxxii above).

The first half of the common preface (pp. xxii–xxiii above) hardly employs the cursus. Only the single cadence *aequum et salutare* (which was retained in the proper preface *In apostolis*) conforms to a cursus pattern. This line apart, the only phrases to employ the cursus occur toward the end of the common preface.

> Caeli caelorumque uirtutes   p
> socia exultatione concelebrant;   t
> ut admitti iubeas deprecamur,   u
> supplici confessione dicentes: p

The rest of the common preface proceeds without cursus but with a marked tendency to arrange syllables into sequential groups, each ruled by two accents—a sing-song effect studiously avoided in Ciceronian prose—as in the phrases *sēmpĕr ēt ūbīquĕ, grātīās ăgĕrĕ, Dŏmīnĕ sănctĕ, pătĕr ōmnĭpōtēns, aētĕrnĕ dĕūs, laŭdānt ăngĕlī, ădŏrānt dōmĭnātĭōnes,* and *trĕmūnt pŏtēstātĕs.* When compared to these phrases, the phrases towards the end that employ the cursus—especially *socia exultatione concelebrant* and *et nostras uoces ut admitti iubeas deprecamur*—seem to belong to another level of discourse. In the second instance, the main verb *deprecamur* governs a dependent *ut* clause with the subjunctive *iubeas,* which in turn governs the accusative *nostras uoces* with passive infinitive *admitti,* the inverted order delaying completion of sense until the last word.

It therefore seems likely that the simple wording of much of the traditional common preface—except for the phrases in its last half with cursus—may reach back into the fourth century, before rhetorical style had begun to influence the composition of Latin prayers and prefaces. Translated into Latin from the ancient Roman Greek liturgy, one imagines, and now written down (though still subject to alteration at least by the pope as celebrant), the old-fashioned common preface appears to have been retouched in the fifth and sixth centuries.[55] During Eastertide and the octave of the apostles Peter and Paul, it was almost completely replaced by more elegant texts. The aristocratic upbringing and Roman education in rhetoric enjoyed by the majority of popes and the Lateran administrators after the peace of the church naturally encouraged these changes and encouraged the abundant production of prayers and proper prefaces with traditional *clausulae,* defined by Latin quantity as well as by accent. By the mid-seventh century, the schools at Rome had disappeared, and a long series of non-Roman, mainly Greek popes had begun to rule the see of Peter. The quantitative aspect of the liturgical cursus disappeared.

The cursus forms of the proper prefaces in BTC II/3, drawn from Lo 3511, are listed below. Purely accentual or otherwise irregular forms are given in parentheses.

Christmas:	(t), p, (t), ℓ
Lent:	(t), t
Trinity:	(p), (t), p, t, t, (p), (p), ℓ (t), t, t
For the dead:	(p), (t), u, u, (t), p, (t)
Epiphany:	t, ℓ
B.V.M.:	u, (u), p, u, p
Apostles:	u, t, t, u, p (see above)
Easter:	u, p, p, p, u + t, p, u, p (see above)
Ascension:	t, p, t
Pentecost:	(p), p + Easter conclusion
Holy Cross:	(see below)
Dedication:	(p), (p), u, (p), (u), t, p

Of the twelve proper prefaces in Lo 3511, ten employ cursus having both accentual and quantitative features. The Trinity preface, though having accentual patterns belonging to *cursus planus* and *cursus tardus*, often has an "incorrect" number of syllables in the last word and often ignores quantity. Seven of its lines rhyme, or at least their last syllables do. For this reason (among others), a Visigothic origin has been proposed for the Trinity preface (see p. xxvi above). A striking exception to the general use of cursus proves the rule: namely, Alcuin's preface for the Holy Cross, which can be dated to around the year 800 (see above, pp. xxxii–xxxiii). In its six balanced and succinct lines, only one cadence, *ligno uincebat*, can be regarded as using any form of cursus, and in that line the long *o* would have to be shortened to conform to the quantitative norm for *cursus planus*. Alcuin's preface is not lacking in rhythm, but his rhythms in this piece are of a different sort.[56] Alcuin could write good quantitative hexameters; in this preface, he chose other means than the cursus to lend rhythm to his liturgical prose.

Clausulae regulated by both quantity and accent are characteristic, then, of Latin liturgical prose created for the Roman rite from the fifth until the early seventh century. The ubiquity of quantitative-accentual cursus within this period precludes the use of cursus to determine the particular author of a given text.[57] On the other hand, *absence* of this kind of quantitative-accentual cursus would seem to tell strongly against Roman origin within the period. Roman liturgical compositions that can be dated to the second half of the seventh or to the eighth centuries (like the Annunciation collect quoted above) usually show accentual cursus only, for the quantitative aspect of the clausulae had by then disappeared—or was fast disappearing. It is agreed on other grounds that the Roman canon of the mass—that is, the sections following Sanctus—had been tinkered into largely settled written form some time before Gregory, in part out of very much earlier Roman material (translated from the indigenous Greek?) and in part from disjointed importations of non-Roman Italian and even Gallican origin—or from their remnants. This long composite text, known as the Roman canon of the mass, is largely devoid of clausulae shaped by traditional quantitative formations.[58]

Origins of Chants

The preceding summary of how preface texts developed and functioned supplies the context for discussing preface chants. The term *anaphoral chant* is strictly appropriate for the preface and its introductory dialogue between the celebrant—who alone sang the preface—and the assembly assisting at the sacrifice of praise. The dialogue consisted of the sung ending *Per omnia saecula saeculorum*. ℟. *Amen*, concluding the silently recited offertory collect (entitled [*oratio*] *secreta* or [*oratio*] *super oblata*); the dominical salutation *Dominus uobiscum*. ℟. *Et cum spiritu tuo*; and the versicles and responses *Sursum corda*. ℟. *Habemus ad Dominum. Gratias agamus Domini Deo nostro*. ℟. *Dignum et iustum est*, leading into the beginning of the preface and the great prayer of thanksgiving, *Vere dignum et iustum est, aequum et salutare*.[59] How far back did the tradition of anaphoral chant reach? That is, when did the preface, or perhaps the entire great prayer of the eucharist, begin to be sung?[60] Did Roman celebrants in the early third century sing their Greek anaphoras? Did Hippolytus sing the anaphora he presented as a model in *The Apostolic Tradition*? We do not know. Levy suggests that the tradition of anaphoral chant might reach back to the fourth century (if not earlier), to a time when there was still spiritual and artistic commerce between the Greek-singing East and the Latin-singing West.[61] Just possibly the tradition might reach back still further to Jewish customs for the table blessing of the cup and the bread, but we do not know what Jewish tradition (if any) there might have been for singing such a blessing, and we have no way of establishing a direct connection with the Christian rite. We do not even know for certain when the Roman church changed from Greek to Latin in public worship, although the change must have been accomplished by A.D. 400 at the latest. I think that the singing of texts like the prefaces and the collects probably dates from the peace of the church and the building of the great basilicas. Singing would have rendered the words of the liturgy audible in vast spaces, and it would have added solemnity to the developing public ceremonial of a semi-official cult, one soon to be fully sanctioned by law.

The attentive reader of Moeller's *Corpus Praefationum* or Deshusses's *Le Sacramentaire grégorien*[62] would never suspect that the many preface texts there edited were sung at all. Chant is nowhere mentioned; almost never is it indicated that a given preface in a given manuscript carries notation. And yet, it would seem that the preface (as well as the Pater noster after the canon) was sung at all masses, whether public or private, festal or ferial, votive or of the temporal or sanctoral.[63] Such was the case in southern Italy until perhaps beginning around 1050, when reform papacy and Norman infiltration began to spread transalpine customs south of Rome. Beyond doubt, the preface was always sung at *public* masses north and south of the Alps throughout the middle ages. I contend that the silent or recited private mass of the later middle ages has mistakenly been taken as the norm for *private* masses of the early middle ages. Such evidence as we have rather suggests that even the private mass of the early middle ages was a sung mass, though celebrated by a single priest with or without the assistance of a server.[64] The following points support this view.

First, the rubric for a votive mass a priest celebrated on his own behalf typically reads, *Missa quam sacerdos pro se ipso debet cān. [canere]*[65] — not *debet dicere* or *debet celebrare* (which terms might have included singing but need not) but firmly *canere* or *cantare,* and in the title of the most private sort of votive mass! Second, even votive missalettes and mass *ordines* with but a few masses for the dead have a notated common preface in some manuscripts from the very late tenth century, when one might begin to expect to find notation for such passages. Third, in Lo 3511 (a missal from St. Peter's Convent *intra muros,* Benevento), all twelve proper prefaces were copied together in a collection that preceded the notated common preface chants. (Ten of them were notated.) The usual place to have entered the texts of proper prefaces would have been among the propers of the feasts and seasons, where, however, in Lo 3511 they were indicated by incipit only. (Occasionally the scribe forgot to enter the incipit.) Now, if the proper prefaces were sometimes to have been said without note — that is, if we suppose a private mass *without* singing, perhaps a votive mass of the Holy Cross or of the Trinity — the scribe would surely have helped the celebrant by recopying the proper prefaces among the rest of the propers (where he found them if he used an older exemplar) at little cost of time and parchment, thus sparing the celebrant an awkward turn of page after the secret collect. Instead, the celebrant was instructed to turn to the collection where the proper preface for the day was in almost all cases *notated*. (Having done so, the celebrant might still have ignored the notation and merely read the preface, it is true.) The scribe of Lo 3511 would surely have included the proper prefaces among the other mass propers, had it been customary to say the prefaces regularly without note.[66]

Preface Chant Formulas

Whenever and however they originated, the chants for the preface were transmitted for at least five hundred years solely by imitation of often heard musical patterns. As emphasized earlier, the preface chant was sung by the presiding bishop or priest, who gave thanks to God at mass on behalf of the assembly of the faithful. Thus anaphoral chant was clerical chant — heard, subconsciously absorbed, and vocally responded to by acolytes, lectors, subdeacons, and others in minor orders aspiring to the priesthood.[67] The proper sections that were inserted between a fixed opening and a fixed conclusion required the celebrant to adapt the chant formulas, which in the common preface he probably sang from memory, to less familiar words. A consistently punctuated text might ease his task by marking where the clausulae in proper prefaces occurred, but even then mistakes must have been frequent.

All local formulations of preface chants employed the same four pitches, *ut re mi fa* (G a b c) in the same way.[68] A forephrase, ending with an intermediate (or "medial") cadence, was repeated at least once. The forephrases were rounded off by an afterphrase having a different, more final cadence. That final cadence having been sung, an initial figure began a new paragraph; sometimes this figure, or another, was sung after intermediate cadences as well. The last final cadence of the preface led directly into Sanctus.

FORMULAS IN THE BEN 33 PREFACE

The common preface of Ben 33 (see p. xxii above) will serve to illustrate the formulas. The text of the preface in this early eleventh-century missal was carefully punctuated by the original text scribe, although the notation was squeezed in later. Beginning at *gratias agere,* final cadences were marked with the sign ⁏, and most intermediate cadences, with the sign ⁄. The last accent of the intermediate cadence almost always took the notes ab (b) b—as *ángeli* and *dominati-ó-nes* (using the pitch of the transcription on pp. 12–23). Within the final cadence, the last accent was invariably prepared by the fixed notes for the three syllables preceding the accent, as shown below.

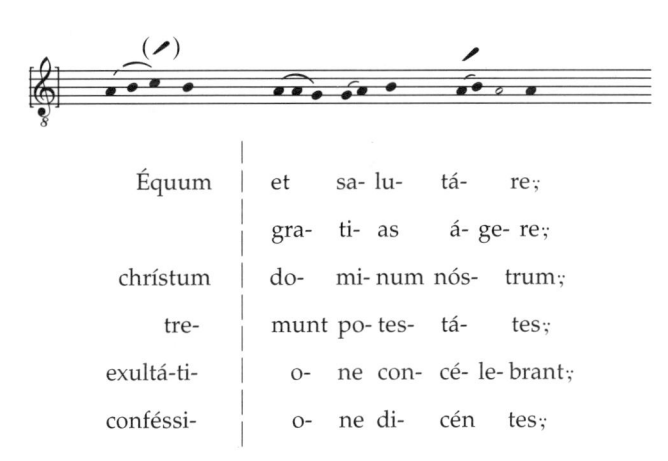

Équum		et	sa- lu-	tá-	re ⁏
		gra-	ti- as	á- ge-	re ⁏
chrístum		do-	mi- num	nós-	trum ⁏
tre-		munt	po- tes-	tá-	tes ⁏
exultá-ti-		o-	ne con-	cé- le-	brant ⁏
conféssi-		o-	ne di-	cén	tes ⁏

When singing an unnotated proper preface, the celebrant looked for the sign ⁏, determined the last accented syllable before the sign, and began the cadence formula three syllables earlier. The shape of the afterphrase before these three preparatory syllables was not altogether fixed: the celebrant might fit tone to text in different ways. The tenor of the afterphrase was *mi* (b). But it is hard to recognize the tenor in this common preface chant because an accented syllable preceding the three preparatory syllables of the cadence was usually sung to *fa* (c). Sometimes an accented syllable near the start of the afterphrase was given a scandicus, *re-mi-fa* (abc), which functioned as a kind of initial figure for the afterphrase. Thus the first part of the afterphrase (preceding the cadence) was not altogether formulaic in the version of Ben 33.

The first syllable of a new paragraph (after a preceding final cadence) was sung to the three-note group *ut-re-mi* (Gab) to begin the first forephrase. A special characteristic of Ben 33 was that the tenors of the *forephrases* remained on *mi* (b), just as in the afterphrase. In the intermediate cadences closing the forephrases, many accented syllables rose above the tenor to *fa* (c). One might even sometimes think that the tenor itself had risen to *fa*, as in fact it did in the forephrases of other versions of the preface chant. What differentiated forephrases from afterphrase in Ben 33 was cadence form and last note: *mi* (b) in the forephrases and *re* (a), one step lower, in the afterphrase.

Notation of Preface Formulas

Notation, even for the common preface, seldom appeared in southern Italy for these chants before the early eleventh century.[69] At first, notation was added to manuscripts not planned for it, as in the common preface of Ben 33. Sometimes only a few sections of the text were notated, in order to help the celebrant over a difficult passage. But even when notation was planned for in advance, it was confined to the common preface in most manuscripts, the proper prefaces being left unnotated. Colored lines or clefs for c and F were seldom used in south Italian altar books and not until the thirteenth century for prefaces, even when they were used for the proper chants of the soloist and schola. The formulas were well known and too simple for the celebrant to need them, the half step usually being located below the highest of the four notes that comprise the vast majority of preface formulas.[70]

Local formulations of the preface chant were notated with the text of the common preface—a text that most celebrants sang by heart—chiefly to provide a visible model to be referred to when unnotated proper prefaces were to be sung and to ascertain and limit divagations from the local melodic norm. The bishop's original freedom to compose passages of the great prayer and especially prefaces to suit particular occasions persisted in a way in the local versions of the preface chant. Just as different bishops' personal sacramentaries contained a varying number and selection of proper prefaces, so chant traditions were differently recorded and fixed in notation locally—only much later. Particularly in the opening dialogue, local variations abounded. Old forms and irrational variants persisted.[71] The notation of the dialogue and especially of the congregational responses must often have recorded what had once been sung in a certain church, rather than what was in fact being sung at the time of copying. But sometimes, too, a later scribe revised the notation in a new missal to bring notation into accord with present practice. So it is that the chants for the dialogue vary greatly, even within the Beneventan zone of southern Italy.

Proper prefaces continued for some time to be copied without notation among other proper prayers, lections, and chants in missals. But beginning in the late twelfth century, proper prefaces were gathered together just before the common preface chants in some south Italian missals. The earliest instance known to me is Lo 3511, where the proper prefaces were notated just before the common preface (see above, p. xxi, and below, pp. 1–2). In this as in other respects, Lo 3511 followed Cassinese practice, which was loyal to the decree of Urban II in 1095 confirming the use of only a limited number of proper prefaces.

Cassinese Preface Chants

To the cavalier and eclectic treatment of preface chants prevailing in sources from the border areas of the Beneventan zone, the Cassinese tradition supplies an outstanding contrast, reflecting the prestige, learning, and power of the abbey of Montecassino in the eleventh and early twelfth centuries and its predominant influence on the liturgy of surrounding areas and associated monastic institutions, however far flung. Cassinese preface chants can be identified in manuscripts dating from around 1071 to around 1325. This consistent tradition was sustained by written exemplars, which in this case were prescriptive as well as descriptive. Abbot Desiderius' deluxe sacramentary, MC 339, the *chef de file* of manuscripts having the special Cassinese preface chants, already presents the outstanding feature of the tradition—namely, two different chants for the same text of the common preface and, by inference, a choice between the two chants for appropriate proper-preface texts. The one chant, rubricked *In dominicis seu festis diebus*, fortunately survives intact in MC 339. The other, *In cotidianis diebus*, was meant primarily for votive masses on weekdays and for ferias. (This version is also found by itself in votive missals and in mass *ordines* bound within other collections.)[72] During the late fourteenth century, both versions were physically replaced in the manuscript MC 339 by the Franciscan Roman-curial forms (which the forms of the Vatican edition closely resemble). The original chant *In cotidianis diebus* was erased to allow for the replacement, but enough of the original can still be read to reconstruct it with the aid of a slightly later manuscript, MC 127, which we know was copied from MC 339. (The original notation for the chant *In dominicis seu festis diebus* was left intact so as not to damage the sumptuous illuminations, and the version that supplanted it was entered elsewhere. See below, pp. 2–3 and 11.) All surviving later Cassinese and Cassinese-derived missals have the two versions in nearly the original form of MC 339; none of the border-area missals used for this edition has more than a single version. In early eleventh-century Benevento,[73] only one type of preface chant is known—that found in the versions of Ben 33 and Ben 40, which differ from each other only slightly. If there was a distinct votive-mass version at this time in Benevento, it has not come down to us.

We have grown accustomed to the notion of festal and ferial tones for the preface and Pater noster largely through Dom Pothier's regularized versions published in the *Toni Communes Missae* (1907) of the Vatican edition.[74] In the Vatican preface tones, the ferial form is but the festal form stripped of its modest ornamentation down to a bare and nearly syllabic skeleton.[75] The Franciscan forms utilized by Pothier in turn derive from the thirteenth-century versions.[76] The idea of differentiating festal from ferial versions may ultimately have been borrowed from Cassinese use, but the Franciscan differentiation in the Vatican edition is of another order. For the Cassinese everyday chant is not just a simplification of the Sunday-festive chant; nor, conversely, is the Sunday-festive chant an ornamentation of the everyday chant. Though both inhabit the tetrachord *ut re mi fa*, they are in several respects different melodies. Their cadences, however, are closely related. The everyday final cadence is indeed a simpler version of the slightly more ornamented festal form. Here are the Cassinese final cadences.

MC 339, *In dominicis seu festis diebus* (= 339^{df})

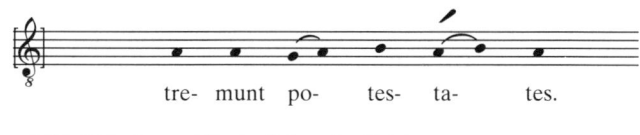

tre- munt po- tes- ta- tes.

MC 339, *In cotidianis diebus* (= 339^c)

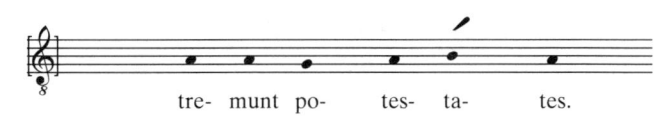

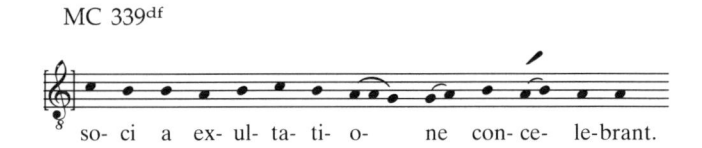

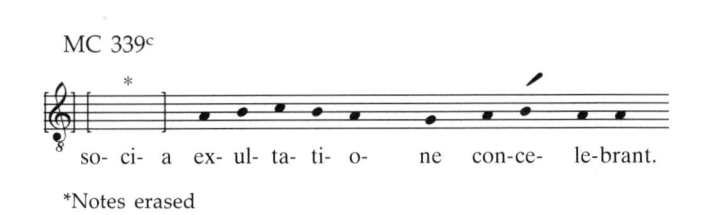

tre- munt po- tes- ta- tes.

MC 339^{df}

so- ci a ex- ul- ta- ti- o- ne con- ce- le-brant.

MC 339^c

so- ci- a ex- ul- ta- ti- o- ne con- ce- le-brant.

*Notes erased

The Sunday-festive Cassinese form has almost exactly the same neumes as the final cadence from Ben 33 quoted on p. xxxix above.

In the two Cassinese versions, intermediate cadences are almost the same, although the approach to them varies and the first intermediate cadences in the common preface show some irregularities. Here are the standard Cassinese forms of the intermediate cadence.

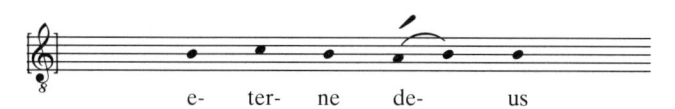

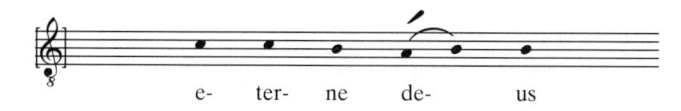

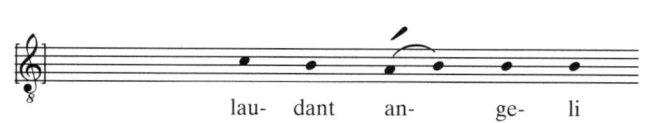

The initial formulas of the two Cassinese chants differ in a striking way, especially in the interior sections of the common preface, as can be seen below, where the initial figures are marked with brackets.

Several observations follow. First, the Sunday-festive initial descends, *mi re-ut*, while the everyday form ascends, either *ut re mi fa* after a preceding final cadence or *re mi fa* after a preceding medial cadence. In either case, the everyday initial leads up to a tenor on *fa* (at the pitch used in the examples, the note c). Second, the tenor of the everyday forephrase is established on *fa*, where as the forephrase of the Sunday-festive version retains an affinity for *mi*; but many accented syllables rise the half step to *fa*. Third, in the Sunday-festive example above, the text is divided "O holy Lord / Father almighty / eternal God," but in the everyday example, "O Lord, holy Father / almighty, eternal God." The first and third observations make it clear that neither preface chant can derive from the other, for an ascending initial figure cannot derive from a descending figure, or vice-versa. And different ways of dividing the text must also stem from once separate oral traditions.

Certain passages in both chants were composed rather than assembled according to formula. Or perhaps these passages should be regarded as codified accidental variation. In the Sunday-festive chant, the beginning of the celebrant's proclamation takes the following shape, the cadence at *gratias agere* being freely composed.

[MC 339^{df}]

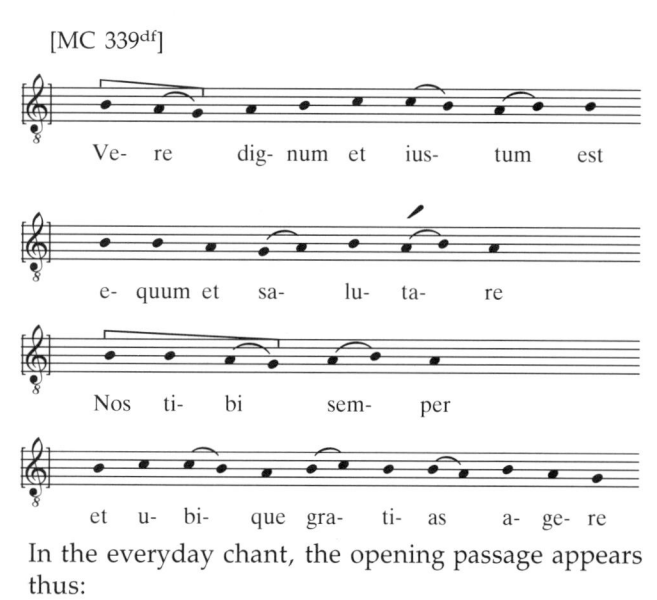

Ve- re dig- num et ius- tum est

e- quum et sa- lu- ta- re

Nos ti- bi sem- per

et u- bi- que gra- ti- as a- ge- re

In the everyday chant, the opening passage appears thus:

MC 426 [= 339^c]

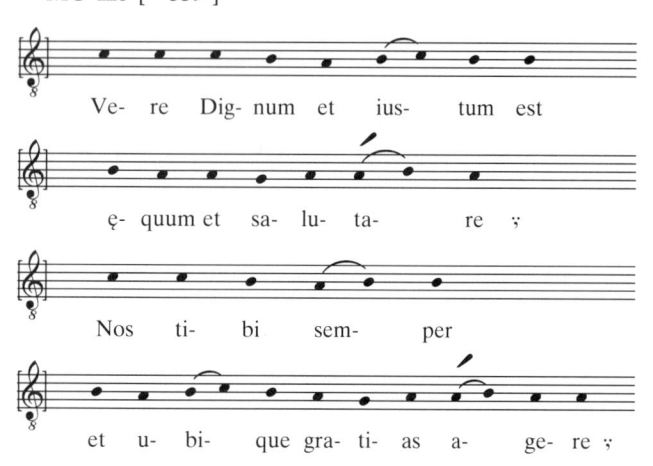

Ve- re Dig- num et ius- tum est

ę- quum et sa- lu- ta- re

Nos ti- bi sem- per

et u- bi- que gra- ti- as a- ge- re

In the Sunday-festive version, the standard descending initial figure begins the two phrases, but the everyday version starts *ex abrupto* on *fa* (the note c), the tenor of the forephrase. The phrase *Cum quibus et nostras uoces*, which introduces the final line of the common preface, is freely composed in the Sunday-festive version.

MC 339^{df}

Cum qui- bus et nos- tras uo- ces

The characteristic notes for this phrase are found only in the Cassinese version *In dominicis seu festis diebus*. They will serve to identify any version of unknown origin as the Cassinese Sunday-festive chant, or as a chant directly derived from it.

The opening dialogue pervasively departs from formula in both Cassinese versions (see p. xl above). The everyday version of the dialogue is not a whit less ornate nor more syllabic than the Sunday-festive version, but different syllables receive neumes of more than one note. The educated and musically literate monks of Montecassino who were in priest's orders might well have kept the respective versions of the celebrant's parts of the dialogue distinct by reading the notes in their altar books. Yet it is hard to understand how an entire monastic community, including semiliterate or illiterate lay brothers even at Montecassino, managed to keep two sets of responses distinct. Nevertheless, the two Cassinese versions of the dialogue in fact retained their separate identifies for more than two hundred years. (See the Cassinese Sources listed at pp. 2–6 below.)

The Three Preface Chants in Lo 3511 from St. Peter's within the Walls, Benevento

It will be instructive to compare the dialogue of the early eleventh-century preface chants found in Ben 33 and Ben 40 (which diverge from each other only slightly) with the dialogue for the festive preface chant in the missal from St. Peter's Convent *intra muros*, Benevento (= Lo 3511^f), dating from the first half of the twelfth century. (See pp. 1–2 and 12–15 below.) The Benevento missal shows Cassinese influence: the chant from *Vere dignum* on is almost the same as the Cassinese Sunday-festive version of MC 339—except precisely for the Cassinese test phrase *Cum quibus et nostras uoces*, which in Lo 3511^f reverts to the regional Beneventan-Salernitan form, nearly as in Ben 33. The dialogue of Lo 3511^f retains many earlier Beneventan forms, but from *(Habemus) ad dominum* through *Gratias agamus domino deo nostro. Dignum et iustum est* follows the Cassinese version. Thus the scribe preserved much of local tradition for the nuns' responses but mostly followed Cassinese usage for the celebrant alone. The chaplains who sang mass for St. Peter's were evidently Cassinese or Cassinese-trained.

Moreover, Lo 3511 followed late twelfth-century Cassinese practice by providing not just one preface chant (as in Ben 33) but three: *In festiuitatibus*, the one that we have just been discussing; *In cotidianis diebus*, modeled upon the Cassinese everyday chant, which we shall discuss immediately below; and a *tonus sollemnior* rubricked *In sollemnitatibus*, which first appeared at Montecassino in the twelfth century and which we shall refer to later. The double Cassinese preface-chant tradition (not very convincingly expanded to a triple preface-chant tradition) was now transplanted to Benevento; but, alas, the chant *In cotidianis diebus* was, at least in part, maladroitly edited. The scribe must have recalled the Cassinese everyday version from memory but based all the intermediate cadences of the copy he made for St. Peter's on two irregular cadences (or free transitional passages) in the opening of the Cassinese everyday version, namely those for *et iustum est* and *et ubique.* In Lo 3511ᶜ, that is, the accent podatus of all medial cadences is notated as *mi-fa* (transcribed bc) instead of *re-mi* (ab) as in most other copies of the Cassinese chant *In cotidianis diebus.* (See pp. 11–13 below.)

Standard Cassinese Everyday Medial Cadence
MC 339ᶜ

lau-dant an- ge- li do- mi- na- ti- o- nes

Lo 3511 Everyday Medial Cadence
Lo3511ᶜ

lau-dant an- ge- li do- mi- na- ti- o- nes

Source of Lo3511ᶜ Version
MC 426 [=339ᶜ]

Ve-re Dig-num et ius-tum est ę-quum et sa-lu- ta- re ⁊

Nos ti- bi sem-per et u- bi- que gra-ti- as a- ge-re ⁊

The scribal editor also exchanged the Cassinese initial figures for the phrases *Nos tibi sem[per]*—*fa fa mi ré-mi mi* (transcribed c c b áb b), as can be seen in the text below, as on pp. 17 and 18. This happier rearrangement kept the phrase division of the festive chant, *Domine sancte / pater omnipotens / eterne deus,* thereby correcting the alternative division *Domine sancte pater / omnipotens ęterne deus* found in the Cassinese everyday text. Consistency in the two chants and conformity with local usage were thus neatly achieved.

The maladroitly revised intermediate cadences were employed not only throughout the common preface but also in the prefaces notated with the everyday chant in the collected proper prefaces (see pp. xxiii–xxxiv, above, and pp. 26–36, below). Inexplicably, the everyday chant was used for the preface text rubricked for the feasts of Christmas, the Purification, and the Annunciation—although the cue *eterne deus* from the common preface and the cued beginning of the conclusion, *Et ideo,* take their notes from the chant *In festiuitatibus*. The scribe certainly erred in choosing the chant version *In cotidianis diebus* for the first proper preface notated in Lo 3511, that for Christmas, and (if the mistake was noticed) must have declined to erase the handsome script and notation. (He ought instead to have chosen the chant *In festiuitatibus*—or for Christmas, the chant *In sollemnitatibus*.) The Trinity preface was also assigned the chant *In cotidianis diebus*. Trinity Sunday was not kept as the octave day of Pentecost in southern Italy, but the propers of the Trinity mass were regularly used for the feast of the Transfiguration of Christ, 6 August, the collects and lections being appropriately changed. This Trinity preface was in fact cued for the feast of the Transfiguration on fol. 261ᵛ (penciled foliation, 262ᵛ) of Lo 3511. The Trinity preface ought also to have been assigned the chant *In festiuitatibus*. (No provision for a votive mass of the Trinity now exists in Lo 3511: such a mass might however have been included at the end of the missal in a section of votive masses, which if once present has since disappeared.)

The two flaws in the edition made for Lo 3511 of the Cassinese *In cotidianis* preface chant—that is, incorrect medial cadences and the misassignment of this version to Christmas (and to the Purification and the Annunciation) and to the Trinity mass of the Transfiguration—suggest that the everyday version of the preface was unfamiliar and was being introduced for the first time to Benevento, or at least to the nuns of St. Peter's within the walls. The divergences from the Cassinese everyday chant do not for the most part reflect well-established Beneventan use: they are mostly to be explained as intentional alterations resulting from the scribe's faulty recollection or misunderstanding of the Cassinese formulas.

THE VERSION *IN SOLLEMNITATIBUS* OF LO 3511

The opening dialogue of a chant rubricked *In sollemnitatibus* is found as the last of three melodies for the common preface in Lo 3511. The version now breaks off after *Sursum corda* because a folio is missing. The Lo 3511 scribe used this version for the proper prefaces of Eastertide, Ascension and its octave, Pentecost and its octave, feasts of the Holy Cross (where the peculiar form taken from the Lo 3511 *In cotidianis diebus* chant is used for the first two intermediate cadences), and finally for the Dedication (where all intermediate cadences, other than those cued from the common preface, use the peculiar Lo 3511 form). These proper prefaces (see pp. 32–35 below) and the surviving opening dialogue (p. 12

below) demonstrate that the chant was intended as a *tonus sollemnior,* that is, a highly ornamented version, which extended its range upwards at the words *ymnum glorię tuę* (as for example in the special conclusion of the Pentecost preface—see p. 34 below). The elaborated cadences of the Easter, Ascension, and Pentecost prefaces are based not upon the chant *In festiuitatibus* of Lo 3511 but upon a chant *In cotidianis diebus*—and, remarkably, upon a chant using the correct Cassinese form of the intermediate cadence. It therefore seems that the Lo 3511 scribal editor did not arrange or even edit the ornamented versions *In sollemnitatibus* for Easter, Ascension, and Pentecost, but copied them straight from a late Cassinese source (see below). But the editor must have composed the confused, semi-solemn confections for the texts of the Holy Cross and the Dedication feast (see pp. 35 and 36).

LATE CASSINESE VERSIONS *IN SOLLEMNITATIBUS*

Corroboration for the existence of such a late Cassinese *tonus sollemnior* comes from two quarters. The missal ZaMR 166 (now in Zagreb; see below, p. 4) has not one but two such chants, namely the third and last of five chants set to the common-preface text.[77] The third preface chant *ī festiuitatibus scōrum* provides a still more solemn version than the third, with descending thirds and accent podatus *fa-sol* (cd) to decorate a tenor on *fa* (c). At Montecassino itself, a fragment (now kept in Compactiones VII) contains the opening dialogue of the preface only.[78] Its most elaborate phrase, for *Sursum corda,* corresponds exactly to the Lo 3511 *In sollemnitatibus* version; the other phrases are similar but not exactly alike. These survivals show that during the twelfth century a *tonus sollemnior* was being evolved in the *Terra Sancti Benedicti* and that it was in part copied and in part imitated elsewhere. These super-festive versions, excluding the dialogue, ornament the Cassinese chant *In cotidianis diebus* rather than the Sunday-festive chant. Their derivation is clear from their internal initial figures, which employ the stepwise rising three or four notes of the Cassinese everyday version. No evidence from the eleventh century for a preface chant *In sollemnitatibus* at Montecassino survives; rather, the evidence is late, inconsistent, and fragmentary, suggesting that the experiments with a *tonus sollemnior* were never canonized by the abbey.[79] The main tradition for prefaces at Montecassino remained the double one: the everyday-votive chant coupled with the Sunday-festive melody.

THE *FRANCISCA* VERSION OF MONTECASSINO 127 AND 339

In its original state, Desiderius' sacramentary did contain a third chant for the common preface, one now thoroughly erased (cf. p. xl above and pp. 2–3, below). It is next to certain that the third preface of MC 127, which is rubricked *Francisca* ("Frankish") reproduces the erased third version of MC 339. Desiderius' policy of rapprochement with the Normans made it expedient and natural for Montecassino to borrow chants and tropes from the Norman-Apulian repertory (as is documented throughout BTC II); and indeed, the *Francisca* preface and the similarly labeled Pater noster and Gloria in excelsis intonation (Bosse 56; see BTC II/2, pp. 46 and 203) may also have been borrowed from the Normans. But so long as actual manuscript evidence to confirm a Norman-Apulian or Norman-Sicilian derivation of the *Francisca* version is lacking,[80] the possibility remains that the version goes back to earlier Frankish intervention in the south, predating the arrival of the Normans, or at least predating their political hegemony in the south.[81]

The simple formulas of the *Francisca* version were applied with rigor to the common-preface text. The dialogue seems to differ radically from other south Italian versions. Within the preface itself, nothing is composed, everything is formulaic. The *Francisca* chant is pure set form.[82] The tenor remains on *mi* in the forephrases as well as in the afterphrase (transcribed as b in the examples below). Accented syllables rise above the tenor to *fa* (the note c). An initial figure ordinarily consists of but one note for the first syllable of a new phrase, a whole step below the tenor, thus:

$$\overset{a\ b\ b}{Nos\ tibi} \ldots, \overset{a\ b\ b\ b\ b}{Domine\ sancte} \ldots, \overset{a\ b\ b}{cum\ quibus} \ldots$$

—but $\overset{a\ a}{ut\ admitti} \ldots$, and $\overset{G\ a\ b\ b}{Vere\ dignum} \ldots$

The intermediate cadence to conclude the forephrase almost always takes the notes

iubeas   de- pre-   xxxxxxxxxxx ca-   xx mur)

but is exceptionally treated at $\overset{á\ b\ b}{seraphim}$, where the accent podatus is broken up. In the medial cadence, an accented syllable on the note c above the tenor immediately precedes the somewhat freely treated notes preparing the last accent of the intermediate cadence. In the afterphrase, the higher note c for an accent is missing, except in the last two cadences: *sócia exultatióne concélebrant* and *súpplici confessióne dicéntes.* The final cadence for the afterphrase, like the Beneventan and Cassinese Sunday-festive forms, has three preparatory syllables leading to the last accent:

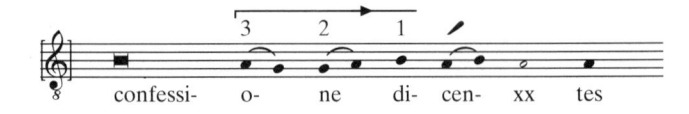

confessi-   o-   ne   di-   cen-   xx   tes

It is surprising that, in a chant labeled *Francisca*, the recitations of the forephrases occur on *mi*, where our preconceived notions of northern French and Norman usage would lead us to expect a tenor raised to *fa*.[83] As a record of the way prefaces were actually sung by eleventh-century "Frankish" priests, the rigorously simple and regular *Francisca* version is suspect. Yet its almost certain presence in Desiderius' sacramentary weighs in its favor: did the great abbot sing this chant when celebrating mass at Robert Guiscard's court? The version disappeared quickly. None of the later Cassinese missals has it.

Border-Area Preface Chants

A group of chants for the common preface, transcribed in the text below (pp. 38–46), derive from the mixed traditions of border areas. Two come from the northern edge of the Beneventan zone, from Subiaco (RoV B 24) and perhaps Gaeta (RoC 1574); a third from north of Rome, possibly Norcia (RoV B 23); and the last presumably from north of the Alps via Montecassino—the *Francisca* chant discussed above, which only in one sense belongs to this group. In the first three, initial and cadential formulas within the anaphoral-chant matrix show a confused, bewildering variety of decoration. In these chants, one can detect reminiscences of earlier Beneventan forms or of the two Cassinese chants; but whether these border-area chants were shaped directly from them or from a common stock of oral formulas current in the south is impossible to say. None of the border-area chants reproduces the tell-tale Cassinese phrase *Cum quibus et nostras uoces*, but many other passages are similar to those of the Cassinese version *In cotidianis diebus*. Specific cadence formulations from the Cassinese everyday-votive, Sunday-festive, or superfestive usages turn up, but with no appearance of consequence or consistency. The version of RoC 1574 even employs the incorrect intermediate cadence of the Lo 3511 *In cotidianis diebus* version, while raising the note immediately preceding the last accent of the final cadence to *fa* (c) from *mi* (b)—but only sometimes! (In addition to the transcriptions, see the summary description for each version on p. 38 and the more extended description of the manuscript sources, pp. 6–7.) These selected preface chants outside the Beneventan and Cassinese traditions illustrate how variously local tradition congealed into written form. All south Italian prefaces, true, were chanted within the tonal field of anaphoral chant; all chiefly or exclusively employ the four notes *ut re mi fa*; all employ one or more consecutive forephrases ending with the same medial cadence and a single following afterphrase with a different cadence; all employ some form of initial figure to begin internal phrases after a preceding cadence. This much they have in common.

Sources of the Cassinese Double Preface-Chant Tradition

It was easy to define the mature Cassinese double tradition for singing the preface, thanks to an abundance of surviving manuscripts disseminated throughout southern Italy and beyond. But to fix immediate sources for the two branches of that tradition and to suggest more distant origins is not so easy. The two branches had different roots, not a common stem. It is not immediately evident what those roots might have been. Desiderius' sacramentary presents the earliest known instance of the Sunday-festive chant in the Cassinese version, but that version must have existed for some time before it was entered in MC 339. Musical content and historical context imply that the Cassinese Sunday-festive chant was related to the early eleventh-century Beneventan tradition disclosed in Ben 33 and Ben 40, as for instance in the phrase *Per quem maiestatem laudant angeli* in Ben 40 and MC 339[df]. (See below, p. 19.) The standard Beneventan initial figure *ut-re-mi re-ut* (Gab aG) appears at Montecassino in the reduced form *mi re-ut* (b AG) or *mi re re-ut* (b a aG). A Lombardic, old Beneventan way of singing the preface was the probable source for the Cassinese Sunday-festive chant.

But the source or sources for the Cassinese everyday-votive preface chant have seemed mysterious. We possess a record of this version that must date from the early years of the eleventh century, MC 426. No earlier source or related melody for this chant— with its tenor on *fa* (c) in the forephrases and its rising-scale initial figures—has been known up to now. I shall now try to show that the Cassinese everyday votive chant may ultimately derive from something like the *Francisca* version, by way of something like the single preface chant fortunately surviving in the votive missal from Canosa in Apulia, now Baltimore, Walters Art Gallery, W.6.

EXCURSUS: The ancient Greek settlement of Canusium throve under the late Roman republic and the early empire, especially after the Via Traiana ran through it. By the first century A.D. there was a large Jewish population. The earliest Christian inscription that can be dated is from 343. There were bishops of Canosa in the fourth century, but the succession is difficult to establish until the diocese was united with Bari in the ninth century. After the Gothic wars and the Lombard invasion of the South, the see remained vacant, and in 591 Pope Gregory the Great charged Felix, bishop of the nearby diocese of Siponto (which included the shrine of St. Michael at Monte Sant'Angelo) to take over the see of Canosa. The see was supposed to have been restored to Canosa by the efforts of the Lombard Theodora, the daughter of Lupo, Duke of Friuli, and the catholic wife of Romuald, duke of Benevento, 671–87. She is also credited with building the first church of San Sabino in Canosa.

The town was repeatedly devastated by the Saracens between 840 and 870. In 867, the emperor Louis II installed a garrison at Canosa as part of this campaign against the intruding Saracen brigands. A Bishop Peter of Canosa fled the Saracens, going into exile at Salerno; his successor Angelarius became bishop of Bari in addition, while still in exile. (The two sees remained united in the person of a single bishop until the Normans occupied Canosa in the late eleventh century.) Reconstruction of the city had begun by 963, when the first Otto came to Italy; and the by now archdiocese of Bari-Canosa reached its greatest extent under Otto II. In 1024–25, Pope John XIX recognized the archepiscopal rights of Canosa-Bari, granting a large jurisdiction. But after the Normans separated the dioceses, Canosa again declined. The church was troubled by internal disputes, and the town was several times destroyed by earthquakes. In 1818, the see was given to nearby Andria to administer.[84]

If the Gregorian repertory of proper chants indeed reached Canosa "ca. 800,"[85] it would certainly have had to have been before 871, when the Franks withdrew from the South. Bishop Peter or his successor might have obtained a copy during their Salerno exile. If such a copy, wherever made, was preserved at Canosa, it must have been preserved "underground" to have survived the disasters of the ninth century. Underground preservation might account for the archaic notation and repertory copied in the eleventh-century missal Baltimore W 6.

The Canosa Missal Preface Compared with *Francisca* and *In Cotidianis Diebus* Versions

The Canosa missal contains selected masses for important feasts, many votive masses, and a common of saints, but almost no Sunday masses and no weekday masses of the temporal cycle. Although copied in the latter part of the eleventh century, the manuscript has archaic features of repertory and of notation. Levy has demonstrated that the selection of choir propers notated in Baltimore W 6 (or some of them) must reach back through intervening copies to a written Frankish chant exemplar from the early ninth century.[86] It would be foolish to claim any such ancestry for the preface chant in Baltimore W 6: prefaces and other items of clerical anaphoral chant were not notated in the ninth century. The importance of the Canosa preface chant lies in this: it makes credible that the *Francisca* preface chant found in MC 127 (or something like it) was actually being sung in southern Italy before it was written down in the mid-eleventh century, and it records a version (or something like the version) of the common preface from which the Cassinese everyday-votive chant might ultimately derive. That is, the Canosa missal transmits a stage midway between the *Francisca* version and the Cassinese everyday-votive version—a stage perhaps fossilized at Canosa during the long period of Saracen disruption, and subsequent Byzantine control during the first part of the tenth century. In order to facilitate comparison between the three versions, transcriptions in modern notation are given immediately below, vertically aligned above a single standardized text. (See IV. Common Preface in the Canosa Missal W 6, pp. 47–49 below; for the *Francisca* chant and the votive chants in MC 426 and elsewhere, see pp. 38–43 below, where the spelling, punctuation, neumes, and liquescent indications of the manuscripts are reproduced.)

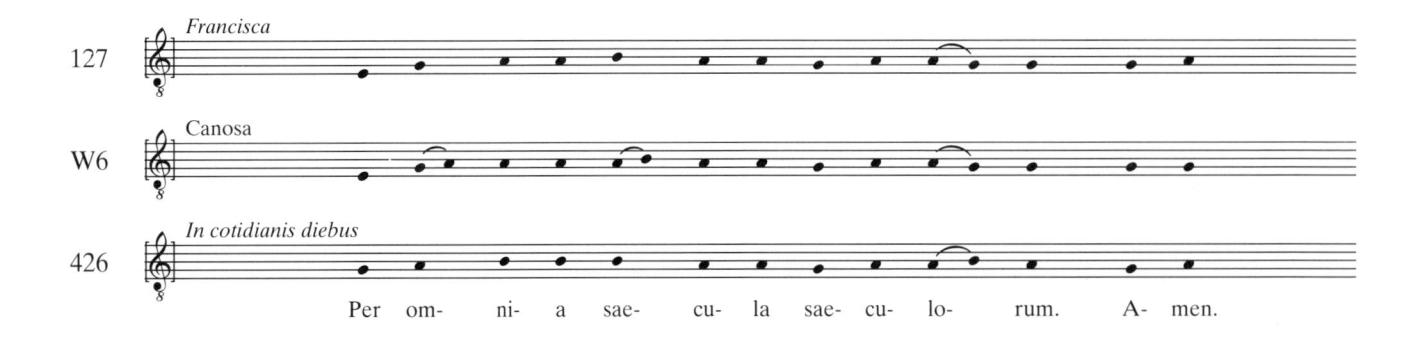

127

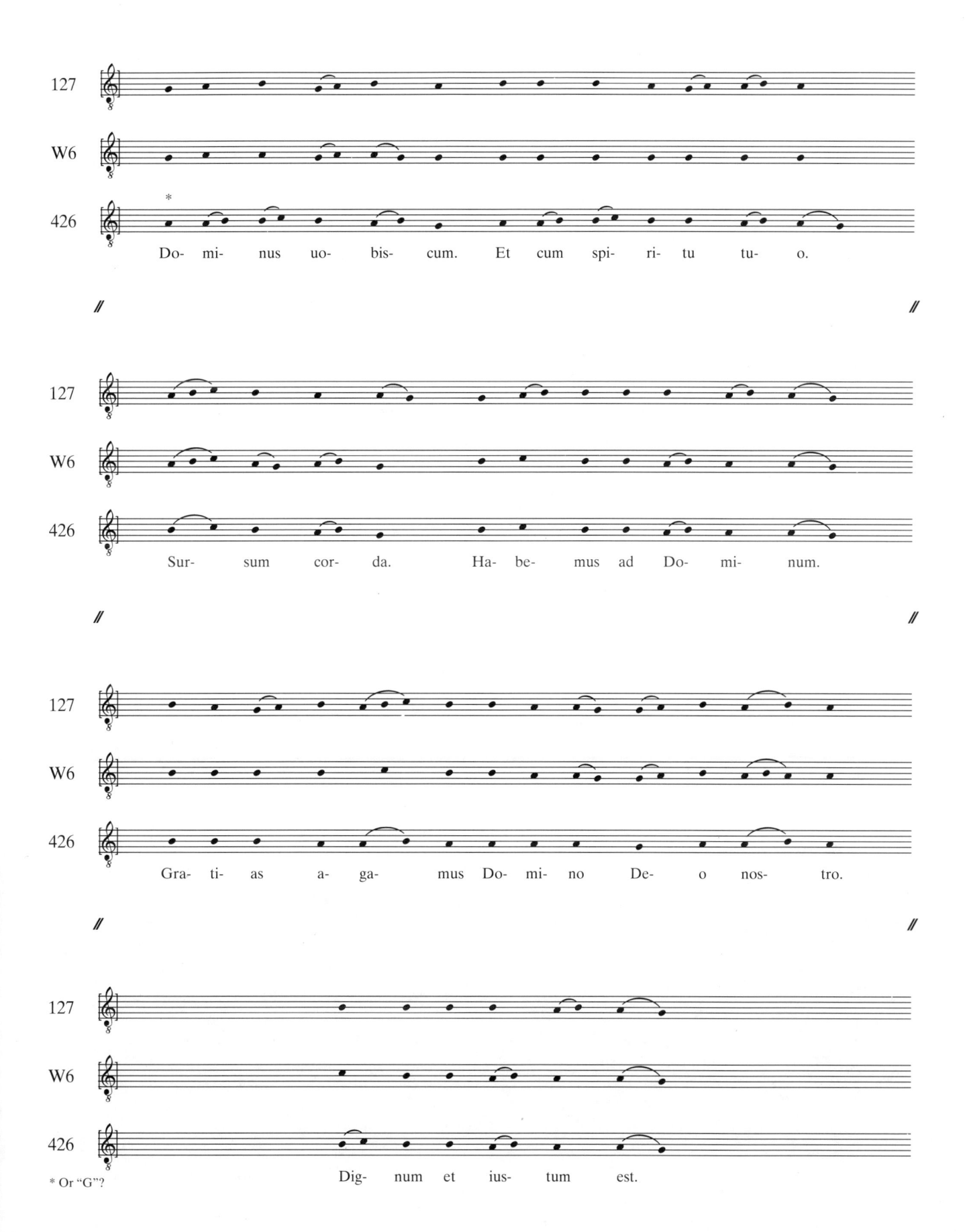

W6

426
Do- mi- nus uo- bis- cum. Et cum spi- ri- tu tu- o.

127

W6

426
Sur- sum cor- da. Ha- be- mus ad Do- mi- num.

127

W6

426
Gra- ti- as a- ga- mus Do- mi- no De- o nos- tro.

127

W6

426
Dig- num et ius- tum est.

* Or "G"?

Ve- re dig- num et ius- tum est, ae- quum et sa- lu- ta- re,

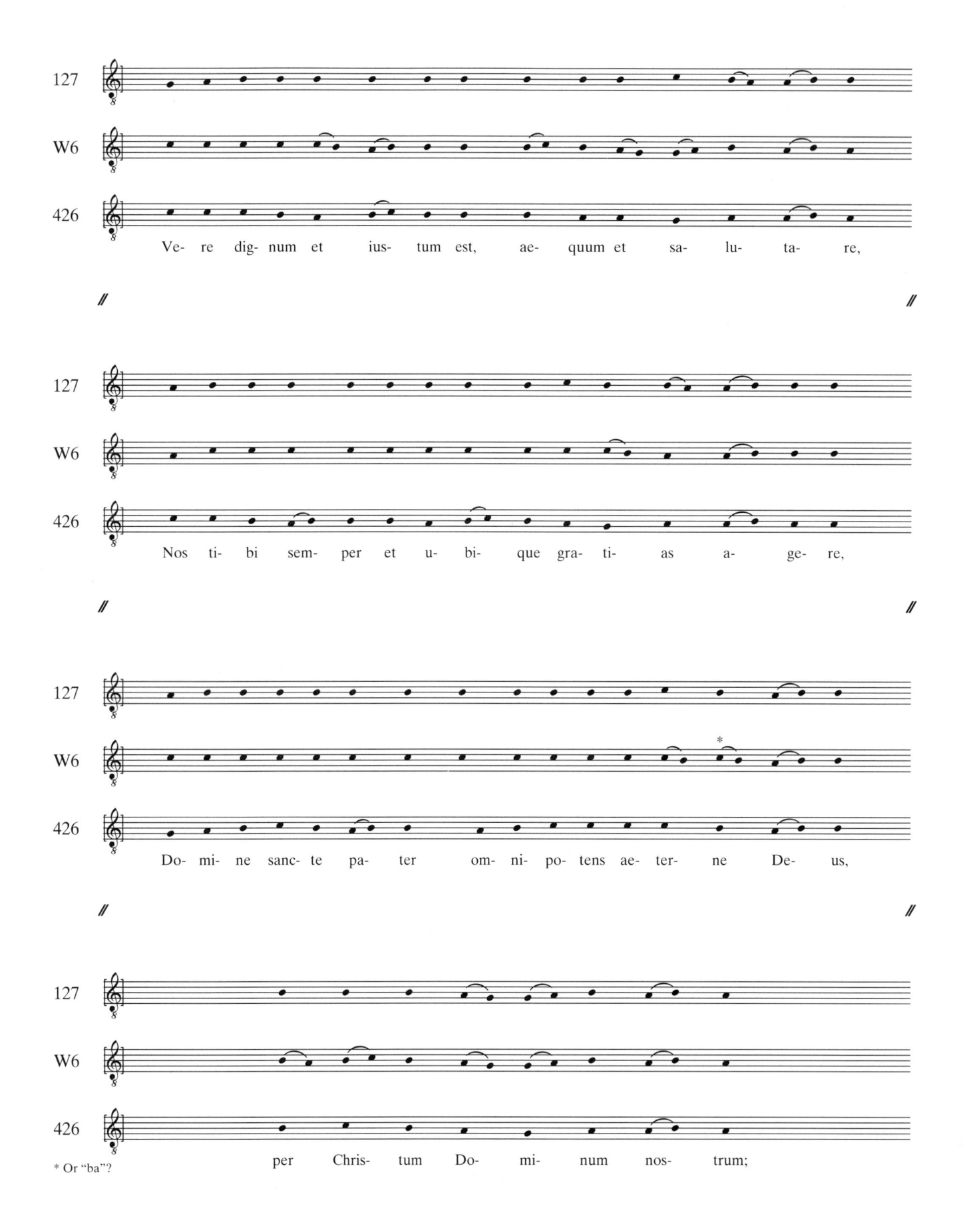

Nos ti- bi sem- per et u- bi- que gra- ti- as a- ge- re,

Do- mi- ne sanc- te pa- ter om- ni- po- tens ae- ter- ne De- us,

* Or "ba"?

per Chris- tum Do- mi- num nos- trum;

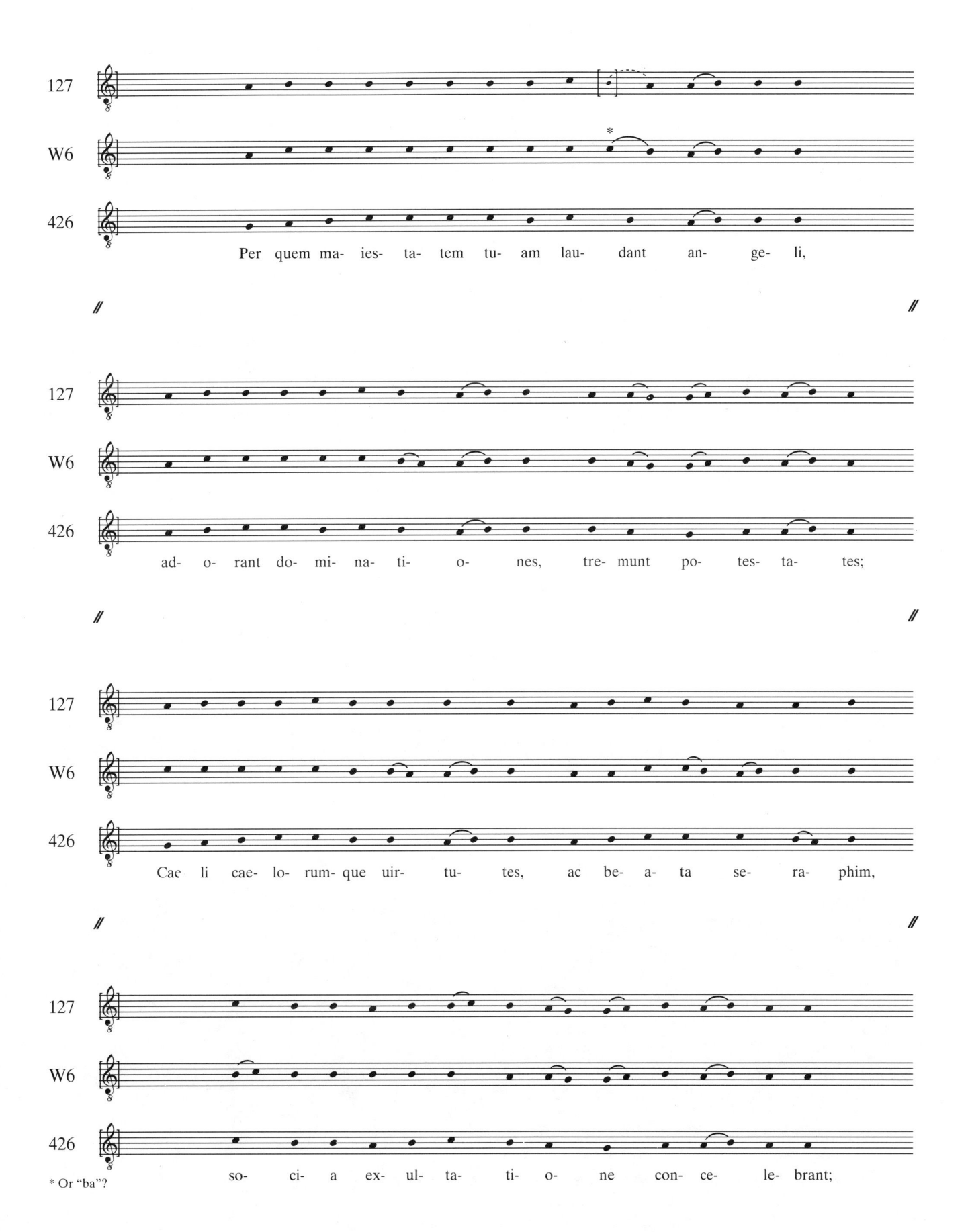

Per quem maiestatem tuam laudant angeli,

adorant dominationes, tremunt potestates;

Caeli caelorumque uirtutes, ac beata seraphim,

*Or "ba"?   socia exultatione concelebrant;

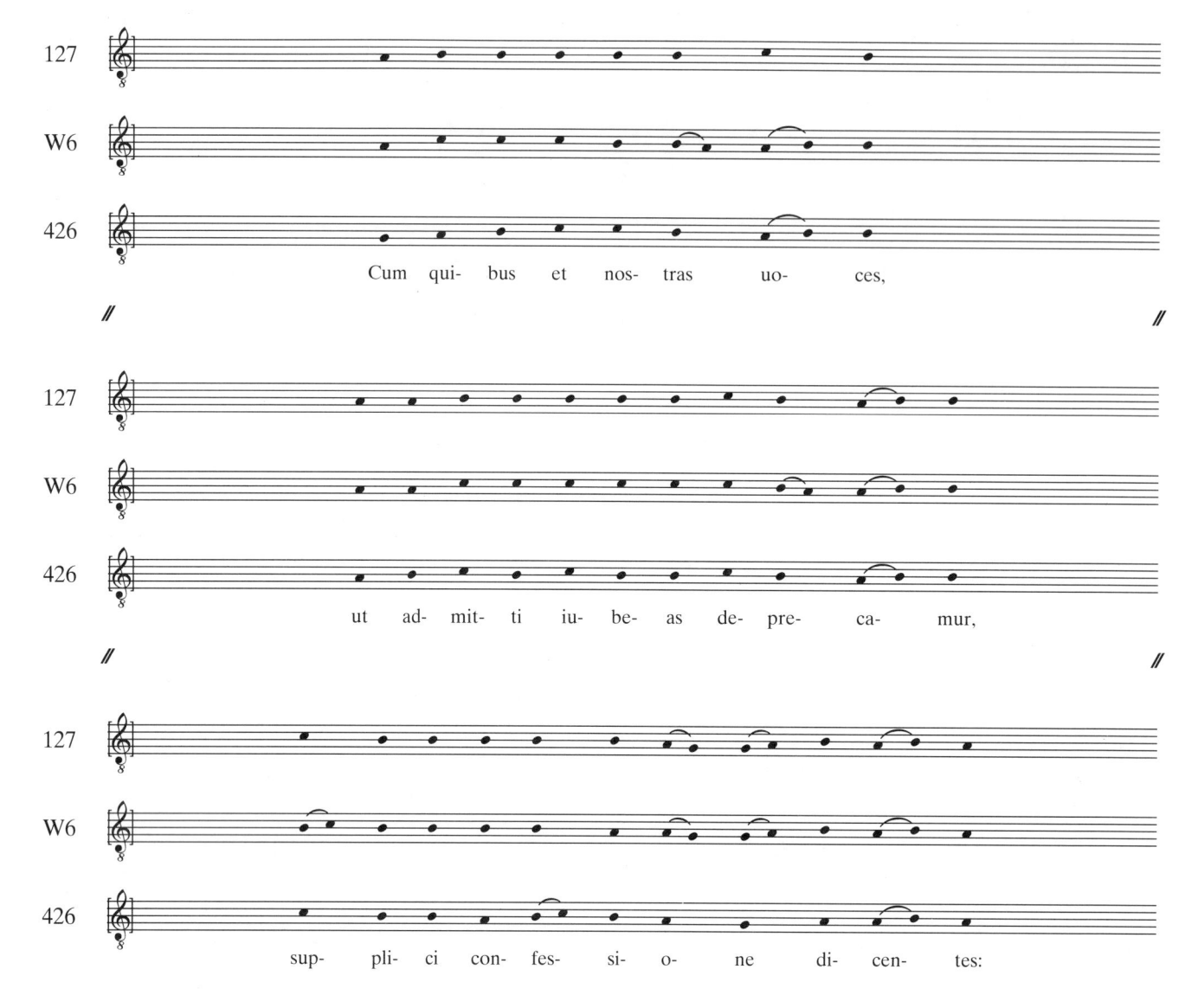

To show the relationships between the three chant versions given above, it may be clearest to proceed backwards (so to speak) by considering first their tenors, then their initial figures, and finally their versions of the opening dialogue. In *Francisca*, the tenor is *mi* (that is, b ; only letter names for notes are used throughout the rest of this discussion to facilitate references to the transcriptions in modern notation above). A few accented syllables rise to c , just before a cadence. In the Canosa missal, the tenor of the forephrases has risen to c at least from *Per quem maiestatem* onwards, and probably from the start.[87] In the Cassinese everyday-votive version, the tenor of the forephrases is unequivocally c throughout.

Although it extensively employs initial figures, the Cassinese everyday-votive version begins *ex abrupto* on the c-tenor at *Vere dignum*. This beginning may have arisen in the following manner. In *Francisca*, the initial figure of all forephrases consists of the single note a, one whole step below the tenor on b, with but two exceptions: the opening *Vere dignum*, beginning G a b (which recalls the frequent use of these notes in the immediately preceding *Francisca* dialogue); and *ūt ādmīttī*, where the low initial is repeated. In the Canosa version of the forephrase, this single note—now a minor third below the tenor on c—remains as the sole initial wherever the text can be read as beginning with a single unaccented syllable before an accent; hence— *Nōs tĩbi semper, Pĕr quẽm maiestatem, ādõrant dominationes, Cũm qũibũs*. But Canosa omits the low initial altogether whenever a phrase starts with a strongly accented syllable:

Vére dignum, Dómine sancte, Caéli caelorumque.
The Canosine suppression of the initial low note when the phrase begins with a strong accent is patently the source of the Cassinese beginning *ex abrupto* on the tenor at *Vere dignum*.

1

In the *Francisca* version, the low initial note was repeated only in the single case ū̆t ā̆dmĭ́ttī̆. Canosa extended this usage to the similarly accented beginning ā̆c bĕā̆tā̆ sĕ̆rā̆phī̆m. Now it is easy to see how the characteristic initial figure of the Cassinese quotidian chant evolved. Once the tenor of the forephrase had risen to c, an intervenient note (b), between the first note (a) and third note (the accented c), replaced the earlier second note (the repeated a), so as to produce a smooth, stepwise rising motion. And so the initial figures for these two phrases came to be sung ac beata[88] and ut admitti, as is the case in MC 426. These three notes came then to be interpreted as an initial figure for beginning a forephrase repeated after a medial cadence. This new internal initial figure

a b c (c)

begins one whole step below the last note of a preceding intermediate cadence. A related initial figure began a whole step below the last note of the *final* cadence, likewise rising up conjunctly to the tenor in the new forephrase. Thus arose the Cassinese four-note initial figure to begin a forephrase following a final cadence: *ut re mi fa* (G a b c) as at *Domine sanc(te)*, *Per quem maies(tatem)*, *Caeli caelo(rumque)*, and *Cum quibus et*. The Canosa missal supplies the crucial link between a fixed initial of a single lower note (as in the *Francisca* chant) and an initial consisting of three or four notes rising by step (as in the Cassinese quotidian melody).

More variants among the three versions are found in the opening dialogue than elsewhere, as is true of preface chants in general. The first two purely monotoned responses in the Canosa missal, *Amen* and *Et cum spiritu tuo*, must however be regarded as the scribe's confession of ignorance. He perhaps misunderstood a series of unheightened virgas in a syllabic context in his exemplar, possibly intended to read *Amen* and *Et cum spiritu tuo*. Or the notes for these words may have been torn out of his exemplar. Apart from these two responses, the Canosa dialogue through *Sursum corda* and the response *Habemus ad dominum* is remarkably similar to the border-area version of these phrases in RoC 1574.[89] The near identity of the celebrant's first three phrases in RoC 1574 and W 6 cannot be coincidental: versions so widely separated in place and time must ultimately reach back to a period when the eucharistic dialogue in southern Italy did indeed begin with the so-called kernel of anaphoral chant—two notes a whole step apart. The rest of the dialogue in the Canosa missal does not match any other chant, although similar bits can be found, dispersed among other versions.

The provincial, archaic missal from Canosa tells us that in Apulia, once upon a time, the preface chant was being sung in a manner related to the rigid formulas of the *Francisca* version as it appears in MC 127. The Cassinese version *In cotidianis diebus* seems to be derived from an intermediate stage of development based on the *Francisca* formulas, of which intermediate stage the Canosa votive missal at present furnishes the only known example. The earliest Cassinese everyday version is found in another votive missal, MC 426, which like Baltimore W 6 contained only selected masses. In these modest sources, the preface form later to be rubricked *In cotidianis diebus* at Montecassino supplied the only preface chant.

*

To form the double preface-chant tradition at Montecassino, Cassinese editors intentionally differentiated a preface chant rooted in Beneventan-Salernitan Lombard usage from another found chiefly in votive missals, recomposing certain passages and editing traditional formulas so as to emphasize their respective differences, and assigning the first to Sunday and festive use and the second to use *In cotidianis diebus*. Scribal discipline maintained the two chants of the double tradition intact for nearly two hundred fifty years, a local triumph of written over oral tradition. Amidst the shifting, variegated, and inconsistent instances of local practice evident in border-area sources, the Cassinese preface chants are recognizable at once. In them, written tradition superseded the celebrant's improvisatory freedom to shape inherited formulas. The proper prefaces, it is true, often remained without notation in Cassinese altar books. But even the proper prefaces, reduced in number to fewer than fifteen by the end of the eleventh century, were sometimes notated.[90] The shift from an oral tradition sporadically and locally recorded to the normative Cassinese written tradition antedates the same shift for the preface chant in northern Europe by half a century or more.[91]

No instances from Rome of notation for the mass preface seem to be known before the latter part of the thirteenth century, when northern and Franciscan forms began to appear in Roman altar books. That the preface was sung at Rome is certain: exactly how it was sung in the eleventh century or earlier is not known. So far as we can tell, at Rome the preface chant still remained the unchallenged domain of oral tradition.

Notes

1. The sixth-century entry for Pope Gelasius (492–96) in the *Liber Pontificalis* (*Le Liber pontificalis: Texte, introduction et commentaire,* ed. Louis Duchesne [Paris, 1886–92]) says that he composed "prefaces"; the term *praefatio* occurs often in the rubrics of the *Hadrianum,* the late eighth-century copy of the Gregorian sacramentary sent to Charlemagne between 784 and 791 from Rome. The Gallican rite employed the term *immolatio* or *contestatio,* as did the Milanese; the Visigothic rite, the term *illatio.* The definition of *praefor* in classical Latin, given above, is drawn from the *Oxford Latin Dictionary,* ed. P. G. W. Glare (Oxford, 1982; fasc. 6, 1977): "1. To say beforehand or by way of preface . . . 2. To recite (a preliminary formula); also, to dictate (a formula to be repeated by others), lead the recitation of. 3. To address with a preliminary prayer."

Certain recent scholars have contended that the term *praefatio* was applied to the entire great prayer—a view hardly borne out by the earliest surviving MSS to contain them, dating from the early seventh century. See Noële Maurice Denis-Boulet, "La Liturgie eucharistique: le canon," *L'Église en prière,* 3d ed., Aimé-Georges Martimort (Paris, 1965), pp. 396–97. Also see Bernard Botte, *Le Canon de la messe romaine* (Louvain, 1935), where St. Cyprian's use of *praefatio* to refer to the dialogue preceding the great prayer is cited, and where Joseph A. Jungmann's speculation that *praefatio* once referred to the entire prayer (in "Praefatio und stiller Kanon," *Zeitschrift für katholische Theologie* 53 [1929]: 66–94) is summarized thus:

> Le préfixe *prae* n'a pas nécessairement le sens temporel; il peut avoir un sens local, de même que dans *praedicare, praecinere, prelegere.* Le sens de *praefatio* dans la liturgie romaine serait non pas celui de formule d'introduction, mais de prière solennelle proférée devant l'assemblée et ce terme ne désignerait pas seulement notre préface actuelle, mais tout le canon. (p. 51)

Manuscript evidence is lacking to support this speculation, which Jungmann reiterates in *The Mass of the Roman Rite,* tr. Francis Brunner, 2 vols. (New York, 1951–55), 2:107. The well-documented use of the word *prex* (or its declined forms) to refer specifically to the preface as well as to the entire prayer of thanksgiving should, it seems to me, have been stressed instead.

I am indebted to Joseph Dyer for several references cited above and in the notes immediately following.

2. The origins of the preceding first versicle and response of the dialogue, *Sursum corda.* ℟. *Habemus ad Dominum,* are unknown. The pair are already found in Hippolytus' model anaphora, preceded by the standard greeting *Dominus uobiscum* and the reply *Et cum spiritu tuo.* (See note 6 below.)

3. See, for instance, the discussion of the cup of blessing at the Jewish fellowship meal in Gregory Dix, *The Shape of the Liturgy* (London, 1945), pp. 50–59, and the contrasting views in Jungmann, *The Mass of the Roman Rite: Its Origins and Development,* 1:7–14, differences that can be traced to conflicting details in the New Testament accounts of the Last Supper. An up-to-date selected bibliography of the euchological literature can be found in Bryan P. Spinks, *The Sanctus in the Eucharistic Prayer* (Cambridge, England, 1991), pp. 235–54; also see pp. 104–25. Paul Bradshaw, *The Search for the Origins of Christian Worship* (New York, 1992), criticizes the shortcomings of many of these studies seriatim but fails to supply a comprehensive bibliography.

The tiny number of texts of anaphoras or quasi-anaphoras that survive from the second and third centuries (just six, according to Bradshaw) and the distressing absence until the fifth century of texts of Jewish prayers (as opposed to existing early descriptions of them) prompted an older generation of scholars to construct hypotheses for the Jewish roots and the early stages of development of the great eucharistic prayer that were based on varying interpretations of these few documents—hypotheses that often conflicted. Bradshaw and Spinks have consequently attacked the very notion that it may ever be possible to ferret out the origins of Christian worship. Instead, they propose an indeterminate multiplicity of early local forms—a proposition for which (it seems to me) the evidence is equally lacking. (The argument and its outcome in fact matters little to our examination of Latin preface texts, which could hardly have been composed before the late fourth century, by which time the language of the liturgy at Rome had shifted from Greek to Latin.)

4. The term *canon*—that is, the "rule" or model according to which the celebrant gave thanks—was used early on for the entire prayer of consecration but was later confined to the section after Sanctus that came to be recited silently. Fernand Cabrol, in his article "Canon romain" in *Dictionnaire d'archéologie chrétienne et de liturgie* (henceforth DACL) 2: cols. 1847–49, makes the following points. (1) In the old Gelasian sacramentary, BAV Reginensis lat. 316, the rubric *Incipit canon actionis* is placed before the dialogue. (2) In the "transparently anachronistic" biography of Pope Xystus (ca. 116–25), which was written in the mid-sixth century, the *Liber Pontificalis* states, "Hic constituit, ut infra actionem sacerdotis incipiens populus hymnum decantaret Sanctus Sanctus." That is, the sixth-century writer regarded Sanctus as having been inserted *infra actionem,* into the giving of thanks. (3) On the other hand, in the eighth-century *Ordo Romanus Primus* the canon is understood as beginning after Sanctus and as finishing before Pater noster. After Sanctus, [the celebrant] *intrat in canonem,* or, in another version, *Quem [Sanctus] dum expleuerit, surgit pontifex solus et intrat in canone.* For further discussion of the silent canon, see DACL 14: cols. 1704–16, s.v. "Préface," by Henri Leclercq, and especially Botte, *Le Canon de la messe romaine,* pp. 51–52.

Notions as to where the *canon actionis* began and the relative importance of the sections before and after Sanctus were expressed graphically in the manuscripts by the size and degree of elaboration employed for three initial letters—namely those beginning the phrases *Per omnia saecula saeculorum. Amen,* **Vere** *Dignum,* and **Te igitur.** The *P* at the start of the sung ending of the secret (the silently recited offertory collect) was written large and decorated in earlier manuscripts in order to stress the importance of the dialogue as the beginning of the great prayer. (In some later manuscripts, the large *P* survives, even after the other two beginnings had acquired higher status. For instance, see the dialogue before the preface from the Beneventan missal Lo 3511, easily available in David Hiley, *Western Plainchant* [Oxford, 1993], pl. 12.) A little later, the letters *VD* superposed, illuminated, and lavishly decorated to occupy an

lii

entire page, abbreviate and emphasize the invariable beginning of the celebrant's chant in the Roman rite, *Vere dignum et iustum est,* the true beginning of the prayer of consecration. The presence of a proper preface among the mass propers of a sacramentary or missal was signaled by the superposed letters *VD* placed against the left margin and written a little larger than the rest of the text. At the same time, the letters served as a substitute or cue for the first phrases of the common preface (usually ending *aeterne Deus*) that led into the proper preface of the day (See pls. 2 and 3, below.) In some manuscripts (beginning in the tenth century if not before, and regularly in later missals) *Te igitur,* the start of the silent canon, was increasingly emphasized, an entire page often being reserved for the two words. The *T* often appears as a tau cross bearing the dying body of the Lord, a representation of the sacrifice of Calvary. Examples are legion. Consequently, from the twelfth century on, the letter *P* beginning the dialogue rarely received special treatment. The elaboration of *VD* tended to be reduced as that of the *T* of *Te igitur* grew. (See the extensive section "II. Le sigle VD," in DACL 1: cols. 159–63, s.v. "Abréviations" [with illustrations] by Henri Leclercq, and Walter Howard Frere, *The Anaphora or Great Eucharistic Prayer* [London, 1938], p. 65, n. 1.)

5. The scriptural sources of the Sanctus acclamations are Isa. 6:3; Rev. 4:8; Matt. 21: 8,9; Mark 11:8–10; Luke 19:37,38; John 12:12,13; and Ps. 118 (Vulgate 117): 25,26. See Spinks's exhaustive but inconclusive study cited above, *The Sanctus in the Eucharistic Prayer,* where he suggests east Syria (not Egypt, as often thought) as the region where Sanctus was introduced into the great prayer.

6. The earliest surviving text of a complete anaphora or prayer of consecration does not contain Sanctus. The text appears in a treatise from the first quarter of the third century, *The Apostolic Tradition,* by the Roman priest, first antipope, and martyr, St. Hippolytus. Hippolytus' text, in a fourth-century Latin translation from the original Greek (which has been lost), is easily available in Frere, *Anaphora,* pp. 47–53; for Frere's views on the introduction of Sanctus, see pp. 57–88. For more recent editions of Hippolytus' prayer, see Gregory Dix, Ἀποστολικὴ Παράδοσις : *The Treatise on the Apostolic Tradition of St. Hippolytus of Rome* (London, 1937); Bernard Botte, *La Tradition apostolique de saint Hippolyte: Essai de reconstitution,* Liturgiewissenschaftliche Quellen und Forschungen 39 (Münster, 1966); and Joseph A. Jungmann, "Prex Eucharistica in 'Traditione Apostolica'," in *Prex Eucharistica: Textus e Variis Liturgiis Antiquioribus Selecti,* 2d ed., ed. Anton Hänggi and Irmgard Pahl, Spicilegium Friburgense 12 (Freiburg, Switzerland, 1968, 1978), pp. 80–81. Also see Jungmann, *The Mass of the Roman Rite,* 1:29. Hippolytus' authorship has been attacked, then vigorously and successfully defended, and more recently again questioned by Bradshaw.

How the great prayer developed at Rome from Hippolytus' example (in Greek) of the way to pray it into the settled patchwork of the early seventh-century Roman canon is not known—except for bits of information, chiefly in Ambrose's and Gregory's letters; scholarly attempts to reconstruct the fractured and rearranged Latin text of the Roman prayer as it might once have existed in the fourth and fifth centuries again differ sharply. Pierre M. Gy, "Le Sanctus romain et les anaphores orientales," *Mélanges offerts au R. P. Bernard Botte, O.S.B.* (Louvain, 1972), pp. 167–74, attempts to date the introduction of Sanctus no earlier than the end of the fourth century, on the grounds that the liturgical Sanctus was never mentioned by western writers before around A.D. 400. Gy also thinks that the enumeration of angels and heavenly powers in the Roman and Ambrosian conclusions of the common preface and the fixed conclusions for proper prefaces before Sanctus (see pp. xxii–xxiii below) show that the western Sanctus derived from eastern liturgies by reason of the similarity of enumeration to that found in eastern *ante-Sanctus* passages. Perhaps so; the arguments advanced seem weak.

The "confused compilation" (Frere, *The Anaphora,* p. 135) of the text of the great prayer as Gregory left it remained in all important features from *Te igitur* onwards as the unaltered and unalterable canon of the Roman mass, right down to the reforms of the second Vatican council. See DACL, s. v. "Canon romain," by Fernand Cabrol (as at n. 4, above); Jungmann, *The Mass of the Roman Rite,* 1:40–57; and the extensive bibliography (to 1966) in *Prex Eucharistica,* pp. 424–26.

7. But the reverse was not the case. From the tenth century onwards, certain solemn prayers of blessing and particularly those sung by a bishop—as at ordinations, the consecration of a church, and (very much earlier) the blessing of oils on Maundy Thursday—were converted to preface forms utilizing the melodic formulas of the preface chant, perhaps on the early model of the blessing of the paschal candle and the new fire in the Exultet of the Easter vigil. None of these blessings converted into prefaces led to Sanctus, except in the dry mass of the Pian missal for the blessing of branches on Palm Sunday.

8. See *Prex Eucharistica,* pp. 429–38, where all the variable texts within the Latin canon after Sanctus are printed together.

9. Certain west Syrian, Maronite, and Ethiopian liturgies employed different anaphoras or consecration prayers for specified different occasions: "Notum est in hac Ecclesia [i.e., Syro-Antiochena] multas anaphoras, usque octaginta, partim ex lingua graeca translatas, partim in lingua syriaca usque saeculum xiv redactas, in usu fuisse, non autem omnes ubique; neque hodie multae de facto adhibentur." (Alphonse Raes, "Anaphorae Orientales," in *Prex Eucharistica,* p. 264; see also pp. 264–415, and especially see his *Anaphorae Syriacae* [Rome, 1939].)

10. See Noële Maurice Denis-Boulet, "Sources de la messe romaine" and "Le Canon à voix basse," in *L'Église en prière,* 3d ed., ed. Aimé-Georges Martimort (Paris, 1965), pp. 30, 95–96, and 103, and pp. 393–94, where the passages from *Ordo Romanus Primus* quoted in n. 3 above are cited, as well as the corresponding passage from the fifth *Ordo Romanus* (dating from the second half of the ninth century), *. . . et tacito intrat in canonem.*

11. Deshusses speculates that in seventh-century Rome separate *libelli* containing prefaces may have been used to supplement the collection later entitled the Gregorian sacramentary, even for papal masses:

> La question des préfaces romaines n'a jamais été tirée tout à fait clair. Leur absence presque totale dans le sacramentaire papal semble postuler l'existence de séries indépendantes, telles que celle de notre manuscrit [Trent, Museo Provinciale d'Arte, Cod. 1590]. ("Le Sacramentaire grégorien de Trente," *Revue bénédictine* 78 [1968]: 273, n. 2).

> On sait que la question des préfaces dans l'ancienne liturgie garde une certaine obscurité. L'antique sacramentaire dit léonien contient un très grand nombre de préfaces (deux ou trois cents). Le Gélasien ancien et le Gélasien du VIIIe siècle, eux aussi, en sont abondamment pourvus. Par contre le sacramentaire grégorien n'en possède que quelques rares échantillons. Il est bien peu probable que seule la messe du Latran ait ig-

noré les préfaces propres, et il est beaucoup plus vraisemblable qu'a côté du sacramentaire grégorien, il existait au Latran un livret de préfaces, dont on usait conjointement avec lui.

The second quotation is from Jean Deshusses's masterly comparative edition, *Le Sacramentaire grégorien: Ses principales formes d'après les plus anciens manuscrits,* 2d ed., 3 vols., Spicilegium Friburgense 16, 24, and 28 (Freiburg, Switzerland, 1971–88), vol. 2 (2d ed, 1988), p. 28, hereafter "Deshusses." In any event, only fourteen prefaces are found in the Hadrianum sent to Charlemagne. By the end of the eleventh century the number of prefaces was officially limited to ten. See Noële Maurice Denis-Boulet, "Les Préfaces du missel romain," *L'Eglise en prière,* ed. Martimort, p. 398, and below, p. xxi.

12. The title of the old Gelasian collection, BAV Reginensis 316, in Chavasse's transcription (see n. 20) reads: *In nomine Domini nostri Jesus Christi salvatoris, incipit liber sacramentorum Romanae Ecclesiae ordinis anni circuli.* Here, *liber sacramentorum* clearly means "a book of the sacraments." The title of the Hadrianum edition of the Gregorian sacramentary in the nearly contemporary copy Cambrai 164 (as printed by Deshusses) reads IN NOMINE DOMINI HIC SACRAMENTORUM DE CIRCULO ANNI EXPOSITO A SANCTO GREGORIO PAPA ROMANO EDITUM EX AUTHENTICO LIBRO BIBLIOTHECAE CUBICULI SCRIPTUM. Here the word *liber* must be supplied—*hic [liber] sacramentorum,* where *sacramentorum* can still be understood as the genitive plural of *sacramentum.* But the title used for an early revision of the base text (the so-called Trent version of the Gregorian sacramentary, the *Tridentinum*) already has *hoc sacramentorum,* where *sacramentorum* must be read as a neuter nominative singular. (Even in the Hadrianum title—at least in the latter part of the title, which was perhaps added in Francia—*editum* and *scriptum* also suppose a neuter nominative singular.) Next, naturally, came the form *sacramentorium* and finally the normalized form *sacramentarium.*

Also see Antoine Chavasse, "Le Titre du Grégorien, selon H et O," as revised in *La Liturgie de la ville de Rome du Ve au VIIIe siècle,* pp. 261–68, Présentation d'Adrien Nocent, Studia Anselmiana 112, Analecta Liturgica 18 (Rome, 1993), and earlier in *Revue des sciences religieuses* 57 (1983):50–56.

13. See Alfred Stuiber, *Libelli Sacramentorum Romani. Untersuchungen zur Entstehung des sogenannten Sacramentarium Leonianum* (Bonn, 1950), especially pp. 79–82. For a succinct but thorough review of Roman sacramentaries and of those derived from or based upon Roman models, see Jean Deshusses, "Les Sacramentaires: État actuel de la recherche," *Archiv für Liturgiewissenschaft* 24 (1982): 19–46.

14. See the article by Deshusses cited in n. 13 above, pp. 28 and 30. One of the extra prayers found in certain masses of the old Gelasian sacramentary is thought to have been recited *super sindonem,* after the gospel and before the offertory.

15. See DACL 5: cols. 245–344 and especially 256–61, s.v. "Epîtres," by G. Godu. Also see the pseudo-Jerome letter in *[Patrologia Latina] Patrologiae Cursus Completus,* Series Latina (henceforth PL), ed. J. P. Migne, 222 vols. (Paris, 1844–55), 30:501.

16. The only pure sacramentary in Beneventan script to survive from the eleventh and twelfth centuries in more or less complete form seems to be Montecassino 339, Desiderius' sacramentary. Virginia Brown has kindly directed my attention to what is described as part of a sacramentary, Monte Vergine, Biblioteca dell'Abbazia 4, pp. 4–144, in G. Mongelli, *Archivi. Archivi d'Italia e rassegna internazionale degli archivi,* 2d ser., vol. 26 (1959), pp. 155 and 162–65. Whereas Mongelli says "sec. XIII fine," Brown dates the MS "saec. xii." (See E. A. Lowe, *The Beneventan Script,* 2d ed., prepared and enlarged by Virginia Brown, 2 vols., Sussidi eruditi, 33 and 34 [Rome, 1980], vol. 2, *Handlist of Beneventan MSS,* p. 96.) Mongelli's description makes plain that the manuscript is not a pure sacramentary: some introits and other chants are included. The list of masses for saints' days now surviving in the fragment is like those feasts kept in Benevento. (Two other fragments, now in Rimini and Frosinone, may possibly have belonged to sacramentaries; the descriptions existing are too sparse to allow one to say.)

17. The most recent of several editions of the text is that of L. Cunibert Mohlberg, *Sacramentarium Veronense,* Rerum Ecclesiasticarum Documenta, Series Maior, Fontes 1 (Rome, 1956). For a thorough but pedestrian study of the contents of the MS (with a full bibliography), see D. M. Hope, *The Leonine Sacramentary: A Reassessment of Its Nature and Purpose* (Oxford, 1971). Also see the first volume of Emmanuel Bourque's dated but informative *Étude sur les sacramentaires romains,* 3 vols., pt. 1, *Les Textes primitifs,* Studi di Antichità Cristiana, 20 (Rome, 1948). Stuiber, *Libelli Sacramentorum Romani* (especially pp. 77–85), shows how the collection must have derived from Roman *libelli missarum.* Deshusses, "Les Sacramentaires," pp. 24–25, gives a concise description of the collection, as does Antoine Chavasse in his revised edition of the study "Évangéliaire, épistolier, antiphonaire et sacramentaire. Les livres romains de la messe, au VIIe et VIIIe siècle," in *La Liturgie de la ville de Rome* (Rome, 1993), pp. 167–72, which first appeared as an article in *Ecclesia Orans* 6 (1989):177–255. In an earlier, more exhaustive and provocative study, "Le Sacramentaire, dit Léonien, conservé par le Veronensis LXXXV (80)" in *La Liturgie de la ville de Rome,* pp. 69–107, and earlier in *Sacris Eruditi* 27 (1984):151–90 (in which Chavasse assumes the reader's acquaintance with the collection and turns at once to its problematical aspects), Chavasse proposes that the collection with its idiosyncratic, limited, and largely extramural sanctoral was originally assembled for the use of Pope John III (561–74), while that pope was prudently staying outside the city (from around 568 to perhaps 571) at the cemetery of SS. Tiburtius and Valerian—that is, the cemetery *Praetextatus* on the Via Appia. The *Liber Pontificalis* says:

> Tunc sanctissimus papa retinuit se in cymiterio sanctorum Tiburtii et Valeriani et habitavit ibi multum temporis et etiam episcopos ibidem consecravit.

Chavasse's case is strong; but the evidence might also be taken as derived from or related to pilgrim itineraries of this and a slightly later date (which are also mentioned in passing by Chavasse).

18. See, for instance, "Les Sacramentaires," p. 36, where Deshusses notes the erection of a Vatican oratory in honor of our Lady and All Saints by Gregory III (731–41) as a particular witness to an early stage in this development.

> [À Rome] au VIIIe siècle, comme au VIIe, il apparaît bien que chaque église continue à célébrer en toute liberté *ses* offices, *ses* fêtes, selon sa pratique traditionnelle. Rien ne permet de supposer qu'on éprouve le besoin de célébrer des fêtes qui ne se rattachent pas à telle église, par son titre ou par la présence de reliques.
>
> Mais sous le pape Grégoire III . . . , un fait nouveau se produit, qui est rapporté par le *Liber Pontificalis.* Le pape fait construire dans la basilique vaticane un oratoire particulier en l'honneur de Notre-Dame et de tous les saints. . . . On cesse de limiter la célébration aux fêtes propres à une église particulière et l'on vient à célébrer en un même lieu toutes les fêtes inscrites au sanctoral.

Also see Pierre Jounel, "Le Culte collectif des saints à Rome du viie au ixe siècle," *Ecclesia Orans* 6 (1989):285–300. Of Gregory III's foundation of the oratory *sanctae Dei Genitricis semperque virginis Mariae, sanctorumque apostolorum, omnium sanctorum martyrum ac confessorum, perfectorum iustorum, toto in orbe terrarum requiescentium,* which he dates to a synod of 731 that condemned iconoclasm, Jounel says:

> C'était la première fois qu'on célébrait les saints d'une manière collective et en dehors du lieu où reposaient leurs corps. Elle fut à l'origine de la diffusion du culte local des saints et de l'établissement d'un calendrier plus ou moins prolixe. (p. 289)

19. The missing end of the manuscript was discovered in Paris, PaN lat. 7193, fols. 41–56. See E. A. Lowe, "The Vatican ms. of the Gelasian Sacramentary and Its Supplement at Paris," *Journal of Theological Studies* 27 (1925–26): 357–73. To it (or to a copy of it) belongs a bifolio called the *Index de Saint-Thierry,* bound at the beginning of Rheims, Bibl. munic. MS 8.

20. The outstanding study of the old Gelasian sacramentary remains Antoine Chavasse, *Le Sacramentaire gélasien (Vaticanus Reginensis 316): Sacramentaire presbytéral en usage dans les titres romains au viie siècle* (Paris-Tournai, 1958). In spite of occasional circularities of argument and certain minor views overturned by later scholarship (sometimes by Chavasse himself), this book is still the most illuminating and penetrating study of eucharistic liturgy in seventh-century Rome. Jean Deshusses, who is responsible for the model edition of the texts of the Gregorian sacramentaries, says of Chavasse's study:

> Cet ouvrage, de toute première importance, étudie a fond non seulement le sacramentaire gélasien, mais, à son occasion, les autres sacramentaires romains, constituant, sans aucun doute, la meilleure étude d'ensemble sur tous les problèmes qu'ils soulèvent. C'est sur lui que s'appuieront le plus possible les pages qui vont suivre. (*Le Sacramentaire grégorien* 1:33, n. 7).

Also see Deshusses' laudatory citations of Chavasse's work in "Les Sacramentaires," pp. 28–46 and passim. For a negatively critical view of Chavasse's work in general (though of this volume only in passing), see James W. McKinnon, "Antoine Chavasse and the Dating of Early Chant," *Plainsong and Medieval Music* 1 (1992):123–47.

Chavasse cited the sacramentary text according to the edition by H. A. Wilson, *The Gelasian Sacramentary* (Oxford, 1894); the later edition is L. Cunibert Mohlberg, *Liber Sacramentorum Romanae Aecclesiae Ordinis Anni Circuli (Cod. Vat. Reg. lat. 316 / Paris Bibl. Nat. 7193, 41/46),* Rerum Ecclesiasticarum Documenta, Series Maior, Fontes 4 (Rome, 1960). Mohlberg's edition was used by Chavasse in his later compressed overview of the old Gelasian collection in "Évangéliaire, épistolier, antiphonaire et sacramentaire," as revised in *La Liturgie de la ville de Rome* (Rome, 1993), pp. 187–205, and earlier in *Ecclesia Orans* 6 (1989):177–255.

21. Surviving ninth-century library catalogues list sacramentaries *secundum gelasianum* and *secundum gregorianum.* Unlike the term "Leonine," the term "Gelasian" thus has the sanction of early usage, although it is just as inaccurate. Pope Gelasius I (492–96) wrote prolifically. Individual liturgical pieces of his may indeed be contained in the Leonine and Gelasian collections, but it is impossible that he should have made, or ordered made, the collection that bore his name. See Bernard Moreton's published doctoral thesis, *The Eighth-Century Gelasian Sacramentary: A Study in Tradition* (Oxford, 1976). Moreton cites several articles by Antoine Chavasse, including "Le Sacramentaire gélasien du viiie siècle: ses deux principales formes," *Ephemerides Liturgicae* 73 (1959): 249–98, but does not cite, include in his bibliography, or appear to have used Chavasse's thorny, minute analysis of texts and concordances, *Le Sacramentaire dans le groupe dit "Gélasiens du viiie siècle." Une compilation raisonée. Étude des procédés de confection et Synoptiques nouveau modèle,* Instrumenta Patristica 14 A-B. 2 vols. Vol. 1, *Études particulières;* vol. 2, *Synoptiques et tableaux spéciaux.* (Steenbruggen, 1984). For a just appreciation and criticism of this work with an indispensable guide to its contents and a set of concordances between its two volumes, see Martin Klöckener, "Sakramentstudien zwischen Fortschritt und Sackgasse. Entschlüsselung und Würdigung des zusammenfassenden Werkes von Antoine Chavasse über die Gelasiana des 8. Jahrhunderts," *Archiv für Liturgiewissenschaft* 32 (1990):207–30.

22. The Gallican *immolationes* and *contestationes* and the Visigothic *illationes* tended toward florid style and discursive length. Milanese prefaces—usually also entitled *contestationes*—while heavily influenced by Roman custom (like the rest of the Milanese canon) retain some peculiarities of probable Gallican origin.

23. The first ascriptions to Gregory the Great are from the eighth century. Henry Ashworth, in "The Liturgical Prayers of St. Gregory the Great," *Traditio* 15 (1959):107–61, adduces seven such instances from the eighth and ninth centuries. The contents of this sacramentary originally began *ex abrupto* (as Deshusses remarks) with the Christmas vigil mass, preceded only by the invocation (dutifully copied in the Hadrianum), *IN NOMINE DOMINI.* The preceding *ordo missae* and *canon missae* and the texts for ordinations of the Hadrianum seem to have been added under Leo II (682–83) or shortly thereafter. The famous long title of most copies of the Gregorian sacramentary, *HOC* [or *HIC*] *SACRAMENTORIUM* [or *LIBER SACRAMENTORUM*] *DE CIRCULO ANNI EXPOSITO A SANCTO GREGORIO PAPA ROMANO EDITUM . . .* must have been added to the copies made at Charlemagne's court, just before A.D. 800.

24. See Chavasse's vivid and poetic description, "La Fortune du vieux sacramentaire gélasien," the concluding chapter of *Le Sacramentaire gélasien,* pp. 679–92.

25. The supplement was formerly thought to have been the work of Alcuin, Charlemagne's liturgical adviser, who was indeed the author of prayers and a preface that were later combined with the Hadrianum. But Deshusses has proved that the supplement to the Hadrianum was the work of Benedict of Aniane; see Jean Deshusses, "Le 'Supplément' au sacramentaire grégorien: Alcuin ou s. Benoît?," *Archiv für Liturgiewissenschaft* 9 (1965):47–71, and his summary account in *Le Sacramentaire grégorien,* 1:64–70 (see immediately below), where the complete text of the supplement is given, pp. 351–605. Concerning the collection of prefaces toward the end of the supplement, Deshusses writes:

> La série des préfaces relève, dans l'ordre, toutes celles qui figuraient dans les Gélasiens francs, mais en les soumettant à une revision très poussée: beaucoup sont corrigées, d'autres entièrement recomposées, voire remplacées par des pièces toutes nouvelles. De nouveaux textes ont été élaborés pour que chaque férie de Carême ait sa préface propre . . . [L]es préfaces . . . doivent remonte . . . à la fin du VIIIe siècle. (p. 68)

He goes on to say that Benedict borrowed phrases from Visigothic sources for many of the prefaces he himself composed. See *Le Sacramentaire grégorien: ses principales formes d'après les plus anciens manuscrits,* 2d ed., 3 vols., Spicilegium Friburgense 16 (Freiburg, Switzerland, 1979)—hereafter, simply "Deshusses."

26. Deshusses 3:62–63. Also see "Les Sacramentaires," p. 33, where Deshusses briefly entertains the rather different notion that the original core of the Gregorian sacramentary was only a collection made early in the seventh century by some Lateran official from existing *libelli,* from which later seventh-century adaptations would have been made for papal use (the Tridentinum) and for titular-presbyteral use (the Paduense, for St. Peter's: see n. 27 below.) In defense of this notion, Deshusses recalls the undoubtedly tedious and repetitive nature of many prayers of the Gregorian sacramentary (especially the secret and post-communion collects) and questions whether a pope would have composed, assembled, or formally approved such a collection.

> ... [L]'on est tenté de dire: si un Grégoire ne pouvait être l'auteur d'un livre bâti d'une manière si pauvre, peut-on croire qu'un de ses successeurs de la première moitié du viie siècle, voulant composer ou faire composer au Latran un livre officiel, aurait obtenu un se piètre résultat? (p. 33)

I should answer "yes." Only two of the ten popes consecrated after Gregory and before 650 were Romans. (One of the two, Severinus, survived his consecration by only two months.) Although several of them had served in the Lateran bureaucracy and (usually) the administrative diaconate, Gregory was the last pope to have enjoyed a Roman education in rhetoric and law (except possibly for Severinus). The abrupt disappearance of the quantitative aspect in the clausulae—later called *cursus*—of Roman prayers that can definitely be dated to the seventh century (see below, pp. xxxiv–xxxvii) can likewise be explained by the change in the Lateran personnel and the papal entourage. If the composition of the "Gregorian" core dates from the years after Gregory (as Deshusses thinks), one would hardly be justified in denying the papal character of the collection because its formulas lack variety and literary quality. Declining papal *latinitas,* strictly or broadly understood, would sufficiently account for the faults of the Gregorian collection.

Furthermore, Chavasse has properly reminded us that a complete stational sacramentary for an entire year, collected from existing papal and Lateran sources, would especially be needed by the liturgical replacement or vicar for the pope (bishop or *archipresbyter?*) during vacancies in the see and extended absence or exile of the pontiff from Rome, when the free exercise of the papal *ius liturgicum* was in abeyance. In the seventh century, such extended vacancies of over a year occurred 9.xi.618 to 22.xii.619, 13.x.638 to 27.v.640 (just before Severinus' pontificate of two months), 18.vi.653 (when Martin I was deposed, exiled and in effect martyred under the emperor Constans II) to 9.viii.654, and ii.i.681 to 16.viii.682. If the assembled core of the Gregorian sacramentary in fact resulted from the exigencies of such a vacancy or such vacancies, it need not have been a *pope* who "assembled or formerly approved" the collection. (See Antoine Chavasse, "Le Sanctoral et le temporal grégoriens, vers 680. Distribution et origine des pièces utilisées," as revised in *La Liturgie de la ville de Rome* [Rome, 1993], pp. 185 and 271–72, and earlier in *Ecclesia Orans* 3 [1986]: 263–288.) According to his latest views expressed in the article just cited, Chavasse proposed as late a date as 681–82 for the completion of the core of the Gregorian sacramentary—that is, during the last lengthy vacancy of the see before Leo II.

27. Pre-Hadrianic *Roman* adaptations form the basis of two heavily supplemented later copies of the Gregorian sacramentary that still survive. The early ninth-century manuscript Padua, Bibl. Capit. D 47, generally called Paduensis (or *[Sacramentarium] Paduense*), must reach back to a Roman edition that originated between 650 and 680 and that was intended for a priest as celebrant (not the pope or his episcopal delegate) in one of the titular churches of Rome. For this Roman edition, Sunday and weekday masses, a common of saints, *pascha annotina* (the anniversary of last year's Easter, kept especially by those baptized the year before), the Invention of the Cross (3 May), and the Passion of St. John Baptist (29 August) were added to the "Gregorian" core. At the same time, the unneeded papal, episcopal functions of ordination, consecration of the oils, etc., were deleted—if indeed they were already present in the core. (Palimpsest fragments of a sacramentary with *comes,* now Montecassino MS 271 and dated no later than 700, reflect this core. See Deshusses 1:45, 58–60. Later supplementary material added after the exemplar left Rome or when PdC D 47 was copied does not concern us.) Chavasse, (*Le Sacramentaire gélasien*) seconded by Deshusses, thinks this presbyteral edition of the Gregorian sacramentary may have been prepared for St. Peter's at the Vatican, possibly when the emperor Constans II visited Rome and attended mass in St. Peter's on Sunday 9 July and Sunday 16 July in the year 663. Pope Vitalian himself celebrated on the second Sunday. (See Deshusses 1:607–84 and 3:79–83, and Deshusses, "Les Sacramentaires," pp. 44–45. But see Chavasse's later and somewhat differently oriented discussion of the Paduensis, "Le Sacramentaire grégorien: les additions et remaniements introduits dans le témoin P," in *Le Liturgie de la ville de Rome* [Rome, 1993], pp. 297–320, and earlier in *Traditio et Progressio, Studi liturgici in onore del Prof. Adrien Nocent,* Studia Anselmiana 95, Analecta Liturgica 12 [Rome, 1988], pp. 125–48.)

A second pre-Hadrianic Roman adaptation of the Gregorian sacramentary forms the basis of Trent, Museo Provinciale d'Arte, cod. 1590 (*olim* Castello del Buon Consiglio, without shelfmark), where a papal Roman core similar to that of the Hadrianum was supplemented at a later time with material from a Gelasian sacramentary of the eighth century. The Roman core of the Tridentinum had been brought up to date but to a slightly later date than the Paduense—that is, after Leo II (682–83) and before Sergius I (687–706). The core seems to have been supplemented and revised into its present form by the addition of masses for Sundays, weekdays, votive intentions, a common of saints, and of other items, mainly at Salzburg in the early years of the ninth century. (See Deshusses 1:71–72; 3:183–88; and especially the supplement of seventy-one prefaces printed at 2:343–55, nos. 3740–3810—here called *contestationes* and mostly found in Gelasian sacramentaries of the eighth century. Also see Deshusses, "Les Sacramentaires," pp. 43–44, and especially Jean Deshusses, "Le Sacramentaire grégorien de Trente," *Revue bénédictine* 73 (1968): 261–82.) The text of the Trent sacramentary has been separately edited and published by F. Dell'Oro, *Sacramentarium Tridentinum,* Monumenta Ecclesiae Tridentinae saeculo xiii antiquiora, vol. 2A = Collana di monografie edita dalle Società per gli Studi Trentini 38, 2 (Trent, 1985).

28. Sieghild Rehle, "Missale Beneventanum (Codex VI.33 des Erzbischöflichen Archivs von Benevent)," *Sacris Eruditi* 21 (1972–73): 323–405, and *Missale Beneventanum von Canosa (Baltimore, Walters Art Gallery, MS W6),* Textus Patristici et Liturgici 9 (Regensburg, 1972).

29. *Le Missel de Bénévent VI-33*, introduction by Jacques Hourlier, tables by Jacques Froger, Paléographie musicale (hereafter PM), vol. 20 (Bern and Frankfort am Mainz, 1983), p. 13*: "livre de la liturgie romano-franque." In *Corpus Praefationum* 1:lxxxii–lxxxiii (to be discussed at length in the text following and in n. 32, below), Moeller dismisses Ben 33 with generalities.

> Il représente, comme tous les sacramentaires de la même familie, un type mixte de fonds gélasien, mais grégorianisé *de manière différente que* l'Hadrianum *supplémenté* [by Benedict of Aniane]. (my italics)

Hourlier, having disposed of the prefaces in this missal with the statement, "Nous n'insisterons pas sur le grand nombre de Préfaces" (PM 20, p. 14*), continues:

> Les Oraisons et Préfaces ne semblent pas avoir encore attiré la curiosité des liturgistes. Dom Jacques Froger avait réalisé un gros travail de comparaison, dont le résultat le plus clair est que *Bénévent VI–33 utilise l'Hadrianum, parfois avec des différences, et le Supplément d'Aniane; il utilise aussi un gélasien-franc,* sans suivre complètement l'un des témoins connus de ce Sacramentaire. Reste à savoir si le travail de compilation est le fait du copiste de Bénévent, ou plutôt de son modèle. (p. 15*; my italics)

30. Not even the celebrated sacramentary of Desiderius, one of the most important products of the Cassinese scriptorium, has been properly studied as to its contents. The student will look in vain among the listings of *Corpus Praefationum* for the number of proper prefaces in this MS or their incipits. The works cited in the bibliography for this sacramentary, MC 339, in Brown, *Handlist* (see n. 16 above) deal with script or music; none deal with euchology.

31. Deshusses 1:51.

32. *Corpus Praefationum* (hereafter CP), ed. Edmond (Eugène) Moeller, 5 vols., Corpus Christianorum, Series Latina, 161, 161A, 161B, 161C, and 161D (Tournai, 1980–81). There are actually more than 1,674 entries for prefaces, because additions to Moeller's original collection were assigned the preceding entry number plus bis.

33. Shelfmarks and *fonds* are not always accurate. The old Gelasian sacramentary is referred to as "Vat. lat. 316"—which if so requested at the Biblioteca Apostolica Vaticana would produce a very different manuscript than the famous Reginensis, which must be requested as "Regin. lat. 316" and should have been referred to by Moeller as "BAV Regin. lat. 316" (or "Vatican Library, Regin. 316"). Hence, I suppose, Moeller's siglum *V* for the old Gelasian sacramentary. (Or does it stand for *Vetus?*) The Leonine sacramentary, often referred to as the *Veronense,* is more understandably given the siglum *L.*

34. See n. 11, above.

35. Conflicting statements about the number of prefaces in the Hadrianum can be found. There is in fact a total of fourteen different proper prefaces used in twenty-four masses. (Some prefaces appear with the same or nearly the same wording in more than one mass.) Four of these prefaces were retained from older papal votive masses—namely, those for the ordination of a priest, for a marriage, for the blessing of oils on Maundy Thursday, and for the anniversary of the pope's ordination. There remain ten for the temporale and sanctorale, or nine proper prefaces, if the common preface (which appears within the canon at the beginning of the sacramentary) is excluded from the count. The prefaces in the Hadrianum are the following, numbered as in Deshusses' edition:

#3	common preface	
#38, 51	Christmas I and III Quia incarnati uerbi	
#45	St. Anastasia Qui ut de hoste generis humani	
#46	Christmas II Quia nostri saluatoris hodie lux	
#89	Epiphany Quia cum unigenitus tuus in substantia	
#335	Maundy Thursday, oils Qui in principio inter cetera	
#379, 385	Easter vigil and day Te quidem omni	
#394, 417	Easter Monday and Thursday Te quidem omni	
#499	Ascension Qui post resurrectionem	
#522, 528	Pentecost vigil and day Qui ascendens	
#591, 596	St. Peter [and St. Paul] vigil and day Te dne suppliciter exorare ut gregem	
#768, 772	St. Andrew, vigil and day Quia (Qui) tua dne praeconia non tacemus	
#821	Dedication of a church Per te supplices deprecamur	
#826	In natale papae Vt quia in manu tua	
#830	In ordinatione presbyteri Qui dissimulatis peccatis humanae fragilitatis	
#835	Ad sponsas uelandas Qui foedere nuptiarum	

There are 222 separately numbered formulas in Deshusses' edition of Benedict of Aniane's supplement, 1:495–575, #1516–1737. See n. 25, above.

36. Two categories were excluded for lack of space and in order not to duplicate others' work: pontificals, which have many prayers of blessing that were converted to preface form and supplied with a preface chant, and the liturgical rolls (*rotuli*) and other manuscripts containing the Exultet at the Easter vigil. Thomas Forrest Kelly is preparing a study of Italian Exultet chants and texts. Richard Gyug will soon publish his work on south Italian pontificals written in Beneventan script.

37. Chants for the preface are barely noticed in most euchological studies. The reader would be lucky to find a remark that a given manuscript with prefaces "has

neumes"; unfortunately, it would too often be the case that other manuscripts described in the same study also have neumes, but unnoticed. (Richard Gyug's editions of south Italian missals and pontificals will supply an honorable exception to the general neglect of music and notation.)

38. "Im Proprium de Tempore stimmt das Missale von Canosa weitgehend mit diesem Codex [Ben 33] überein, besonders was die Heiligenfeste betrifft"; Rehle, *Missale Beneventanum von Canosa,* p. 21. The prefaces contained in Ben 33 are conveniently listed on p. 47* of the introduction to the facsimile edition, PM 20.

39. See above, p. xx, and under Beneventan Sources below, p. 2. For Urban II's decree confirming the limitation of the number of prefaces, see Botte, *Le Canon de la messe romaine,* p. 19. and CP 1:v. That the decree was generally observed is evident from the drastically reduced number of proper prefaces copied in missals from the twelfth century onwards. As a twelfth-century sacramentary from an abbey in the region of Narbonne puts it,

Has viiii prefactiones tenet et custodit sancta romana Ecclesia . . . x^a addita est a papa Urbano II in sollempnitatibus beate Marie.

(Bibliothèque municipale d'Avignon, ms. 178, fols. 87^r and 88^v, as quoted by Victor Leroquais, *Les Sacramentaires et les missels manuscrits des bibliothèques publiques de France,* 4 vols. [Paris, 1924], vol. 1, p. 255.) Leroquais also mentions (vol. 1, p. 361) that "copie de la prétendue lettre de Pélage aux évêques de Germanie et des Gaules relative aux préfaces de la messe" was included in a missal from Saint-Remi de Reims, Bibliothèque municipale de Reims, ms. 226 (C. 135).

40. For the twelfth-century missal Lo 3511, formerly Ben 29, from St. Peter's Convent within the walls of Benevento, see below, pp. xlii and 1–2; for ZaMR 166, a Cassinese-derived missal sent to Dalmatia, see pp. 4–5 below (with a complete list of proper prefaces contained in both missals).

41. In his translation of preface texts for the 1549 Book of Common Prayer, Thomas Cranmer used this proper-preface conclusion to end his version of the common preface as well as the proper prefaces (except one). As printed in John Merbecke's *Book of Common Prayer Noted* of 1550, the common preface reads:

The preface.
Priest. The lorde be with you.   Auns[er]. And with thy spirit.
Priest. Lift up your hertes.   Auns. We lift them up unto the lorde.
Priest. Let us geve thankes to our lorde god.   Auns. It is mete and right so to do.

It is very meete right & 'our bounden dutie, that we should at all times, and in all places geve thankes to the o lorde, holy father almightie everlastynge god. Therefore with angels and archangels, and with all the holy companye of heaven, we laude and magnifie thy glorious name ever more praysyng the and saying.

Cranmer joined the shortened beginning of the common preface down through *aeterne Deus* to a free and slightly compressed version of the proper-preface conclusion. (Cranmer disposed of the untranslatable word *salutare*—which I have unwillingly left as "salutary" in the translations for want of anything better—by replacing *aequum et salutare* with the famous phrase "our bounden duty," thereby producing the admirable rhythm

. . . meét, ríght, ănd oūr boúndĕn dútў

but failing to suggest the concepts of health and salvation in the omitted *salutare.*)

42. Thomas Cranmer's compressed translation in the 1549 Book of Common Prayer (as printed in John Merbecke's *Book of Common Prayer Noted* of 1550) reads:

It is very meete, right, and our bounden dutie that we should at all times, and in all places, geve thankes to the o lorde almightie, everlastyng god, which arte one god, one lord, not one onely person, but thre persons in one substaunce, for that which we beleve of the glory of the father, the same we beleve of the sonne, and of the holy ghost, without any difference of inequalitie, whome the angels and arch. etc.

Cranmer either took it for granted that the celebrant would know the conclusion *Quam laudant angeli et archangeli* (which is nowhere found in the Book of Common Prayer) and would be able to supply a translation; or, more likely, Cranmer forgot to furnish the printer the full ending to expand his draft of the translation.

43. Already in 1949, well before the Second Vatican Council, Alfred Stuiber had attacked the concept of *Bittpräfationen* in his *Libelli Sacramentorum Romani,* pp. 65–71 and especially p. 69 (see n. 13 above).

For Schmidt's article cited by Moeller, see *Sacris Erudiri* 4 (1952): 163, no. 66.

44. Cranmer's 1549 translation (as printed in Merbecke's *Book of Common Prayer Noted* of 1550) reads:

[It is very meete right and our bounden dutie, that we should at all tymes, and in all places geve thankes to the o lorde, holy father almightie everlastynge god.]
But chefly are we bound to prayse the, for the glorious resurrection of thy sonne
    Jesus Christ oure lorde,
for he is the very paschal lambe which was offered for us
    and hath taken away the synnes of the world,
    who by his death hath destroyed death,
    and by his rysing agayn, hath restored to us everlastyng life.
Therefore with angels etc.

45. Rehle's edition, *Missale Beneventanum von Canosa,* sheds no light. Nothing could be wider of the mark than her statement (p. 21), "Dies [the mistaken spelling *Cor.* instead of *Col.* in both missals of the title for the lesson pericope for the Invention of the Holy Cross] beweist, dass VI, 33 and MS W6 letztenendes auf eine gemeinsame Vorlage zurückzuführen sind."

46. Cranmer's translation, as printed in the *Book of Common Prayer Noted* of 1550, reads:

Through thy most deare beloved sonne Jesus Christ our lorde,
who after his most glorious resurrection
    manifestly appeared to all his disciples,
and in their sight ascended up into heaven to prepare a place for us,
    that where he is, thether might we also ascend
    and reigne with him in glory.
Therefore with angels etc.

Cranmer's explication, correction, and expansion of the bold if not heretical phrase *ut nos diuinitatis suae tribueret esse participes* is based on John 14:2b and 3b: "I go to prepare a place for you. . . . that where I am, there ye may be also." Cranmer's version is preferable (it seems to me) to any literal translation of the Latin.

47. Cranmer did not try to translate the Latin text but composed a new and lengthy preface for Whitsunday (i.e., Pentecost), employing several passages lifted almost directly from scripture. As Cranmer printed it among the 1549 Prayer Book prefaces, the Whitsun preface was perhaps his only failure. Succeeding revisions have ruined it.

48. See André Mocquereau, "Le Cursus et la psalmodie," PM 4, pp. 27–40 (introductory survey; the rest is tendentious); E. Vacandard, "Le Cursus: son origine, son histoire, son emploi dans la liturgie," *Revue des questions historiques* 78 (Paris, 1905): 59–102; H. A. Wilson, "The Metrical Endings of the Leonine Sacramentary," *Journal of Theological Studies* 5 (1904): 386–95 and 6 (1905): 381–91; L. Laurand, "Le Cursus dans le sacramentaire léonien," in *Questions liturgiques et paroissiales* (Louvain, 1914), pp. 215–18; Laurand, "Ce qu'on sait et ce qu'on ignore du cursus," in *Manuel des études grecques et latines,* 2d ed. by A. Lauras, vol. 4 (Paris, 1949), pp. 270–96; and especially DACL 3: cols. 3193–3205, s.v. "Cursus," by Henri Leclercq. See also the citations in Wilson's article of earlier works dating from the last twenty years of the nineteenth century by Duchesne, Meyer, Norden, and Valois.

49. Hope, *The Leonine Sacramentary,* p. 154.

50. See D. S. Raven, *Latin Metre* (London, 1965), pp. 169–72. The first three examples of the most common Ciceronian clausulae on p. 171 are in fact the purely quantitative equivalents of the fifth and sixth-century cadences, which came to be called *cursus planus, cursus tardus,* and *cursus uelox.* (See the text following.) Raven never uses the word *cursus* and mercifully avoids the Greek names for the metrical feet he discusses.

51. Actually the postcommunion collect *ad completa* for the feast of the Annunciation in the Hadrianum, Deshusses 1:#143.

52. See Wilson, "The Metrical Endings of the Leonine Sacramentary," where the liturgical clausulae are examined almost entirely in their quantitative aspect. For the quantities of Latin syllables, one of the many Latin grammars —or better, Raven's *Latin Metre*—should be consulted. In brief, syllables in classical Latin may be long "by nature"—that is, by the nature of the vowel—or "by position"—roughly speaking, by the positioning of two or more consonants between the end of the vowel of one syllable and the start of the vowel of the next. There are exceptions.

53. Moreover, this cadence has been dubbed *cursus dispondaïque.* See an earlier edition of the work cited in n. 48 above by L. Laurand, *Manuel des études grecques et latines,* fasc. 6, *Grammaire historique latine* (Paris, 1918):

Cursus dispondaïque (accent sur la 2ᵉ et la 6ᵉ syllable): ordinairement quadrisyllable, accentué sur la pénultième précédé d'un mot accentué, lui aussi, sur la pénultième: *consolatióne respirémus.* (p. 628)

54. See Dag Norberg, "Les Débuts de la versification rhythmiques," chap. 6 of *Introduction à l'Étude de la versification latine médiéevale,* Studia Latina Stockholmiensia 5 (Stockholm, 1958), pp. 87–135.

55. Cf. Gy, "Le Sanctus romain et les anaphores orientales."

56. The first two lines (as printed on p. xxxiii, above) have three main accents each. The paired third and fourth lines and the paired fifth and sixth lines have each of them two main accents.

57. In general the statement holds, but I can suggest an exception. In his often-cited article, "The Liturgical Prayers of St. Gregory the Great" (1959: see n. 23, above), Dom Henry Ashworth for the first time demonstrated that Gregory himself could not have compiled the sacramentary that bears his name. But Ashworth also tried to show that Gregory *was* the author of "not more than 82" prayers of the "245 proper to the Gregorianum"—that is, not found in any earlier collection. To demonstrate Gregory's authorship, Ashworth assembled passages from Gregory's sermons and other writings that use phrases found in these prayers. (The case for some of these identifications is weak, especially when resting on paired quotations of well-known scripture. In some cases Ashworth's examples seem convincing.) Ashworth quotes a sermon of Gregory's to his bishops assembled at the Lateran (in the baptistery?—*in fontes Lateranenses:* Homily 17 on the gospels, PL 76, 1149 BC) which concludes with a collect *not* found in any sacramentary and which therefore may reasonably be ascribed to Gregory.

Haec, fratres, uobiscum sollicite cogitate, haec et proxima uestris impendite: omnipotenti Deo fructum uos reddere de negotio quo accepistis, parate. Sed ista quae dicimus, melius apud uos orando, quam loquendo obtinebimus:

Oremus

Deus, qui nos pastores in populo uocắrĕ uŏlŭĭ́stĭ,

praesta quaesumus ut quod humano ore dicimur,

in tuis oculis ếssĕ uălĕắmŭ́s:

per dominum nostrum. . . .

Ashworth nowhere mentions the cursus. Yet this prayer of Gregory's is unusual in that it employs two examples of the *cursus laxus* and no other form of cursus. (The sermon is one of the several Gregory tells us he dictated in advance and then had read by a notary in his presence at the assembly or service. See Antoine Chavasse, "Les *Episcopi*, dans la liturgie de l'*Urbs,* au VIIᵉ et au VIIIᵉ siècle," in *La Liturgie de la ville de Rome* [Rome, 1993], pp. 337–42 and especially p. 340.)

Looking for similar formations, I examined the 79 separate prayers that Ashworth thinks are by Gregory. (Duplicates raise the count to Ashworth's 82.) Almost all of them, whether or not by Gregory, show quantitative-accentual cursus formations. (The prayers for the feast of St. Gregory himself, introduced between A.D. 687 and 706, have the largest number of irregular cursus formations of the lot!) A surprisingly large proportion of clausulae have the *cursus laxus.* I count 44 prayers (of the 79 Ashworth thinks are by Gregory) that have no *cursus laxus,* though many other cursus forms; 31 prayers that have one *cursus laxus;* and 4 that have two *cursus laxus,* including the prayer for the bishops' synod quoted above. Nearly half of the 39 examples use the quantitative pattern -́ ͜ ͜ -́ ͜ found twice in that prayer. Moreover, the prayers having the *cursus laxus* are mostly clustered at certain times of the year. The collects for four "pre-Lenten" saints—Sebastian, Vincent, Agatha, and Valentine (pp. 126–28 of Ashworth's article)—all have the *cursus laxus.* There are other clusters for Easter week and Eastertide, and for the Ascension and Pentecost, skipping the Eastertide saints. Furthermore, the evidence Ashworth adduces from Gregory's writings in support of Gregory's authorship of the prayers is strong for all those having the *cursus laxus,* although my judgment in this regard is of necessity subjective. See Antoine Chavasse, "Le Sanctoral et le temporal grégoriens, vers 680. Distribution et origine des pièces utilisées," and especially section VIII, "Les Pièces du sacramentaire *Gr*H(OP) attribuées à Grégoire Iᵉʳ, par H. Ashworth," in *La Liturgie de la ville de Rome,* pp. 283–94 (Rome, 1993), and earlier in *Ecclesia Orans* 3 (1986):263–88.

In view of the questionable ascriptions of many of the seventy-nine prayers to Gregory, the only conclusions that can fairly be made now are that Gregory did know and use the quantitative-accentual cursus in most of his liturgical prayers—in spite of his protestations that a Christian might profitably ignore the classical quantities—and that Gregory was especially fond of the *cursus laxus.*

58. Except for purely accentual or irregular instances, mostly of *cursus uelox,* and except for Gregory I's well-known addition to the *Hanc igitur* section of the canon—

diesque nostros in tua pácĕ dīspōnăs   p

atque ab aeterna damnatiōnĕ nōs ērĭpī ˘   t

et in electorum tuorum iubeas grĕ́gĕ nŭmĕrā́rĭ̆   ℓ

—attested by the *Liber Pontificalis* and by the Venerable Bede (see Botte, *Le Canon de la messe romaine,* pp. 36–37), I count only seven instances of *cursus planus* and *cursus tardus,* scattered throughout the long text.

59. See above, p. xvi. For the term *anaphoral chant,* see the excursus in BTC II/1, p. xvi, and Levy, "The Byzantine Sanctus and Its Modal Tradition in East and West," *Annales musicologiques* 6 (1958):7–67.

60. Since 1970, when the reformed Roman missal restored an audible canon—or rather, introduced a choice among audible canons—it has often been asserted that "originally" the entire eucharistic *prex* was sung, not just the preface. If so—whatever "originally" may mean—when did the continuation of the *prex* after Sanctus begin to be recited silently? No clear answers are forthcoming. Already in the seventh century, the words of institution were recited silently in the Gallican and Visigothic rites. Dix, in *The Shape of the Liturgy,* p. 483, n. 3, states without documentation that "silent recitation was the rule at Rome before c. A.D. 700" and that the practice had begun two centuries earlier in the east. On the silent canon in the Carolingian period, see Amalar, *Lib. off.* 3, 23, 8–12, as found in Jean Michel Hanssens, ed., *Amalarii Episcopi Opera Liturgica Omnia,* 3 vols., Studi e testi, 138–40; vol. 2, *Liber Officialis,* Studi e testi, 139 (Vatican City, 1948), pp. 331–33. On Florus, see PL 119:43. Also see n. 10 above.

61. Levy, "Byzantine Sanctus," pp. 38 and 67. For Hippolytus' anaphora, see n. 6 above.

62. See notes 11 and 32 above.

63. There must have been exceptions for deaf celebrants, bishops and popes intruded directly from the lay state into their sees, and foreign celebrants unacquainted with local chant—to mention only a few such possible cases.

64. Here the vexed question of whether the celebrant of a private mass also sang the choir propers that were notated in full missals is not at issue: I only assert that before around 1050 in southern Italy, those parts of the mass sung by the celebrant at a "solemn" or normal celebration were also sung by him at a private mass.

65. Thus, for instance, in the partial and votive missal Baltimore, Walters Art Gallery W.6 (the Canosa missal), fol. 11ʳ. (Klaus Gamber transcribed this rubric *Missa quam sacerdos pro se ipso debet facere* [CLLA 1:244, no. 445], perhaps not believing that a private votive mass ought to be sung.) Also see the rubrics for the same type of mass in Deshusses 2:80, formula 60: MISSA QUAM SACERDOS PRO SE CANERE DEBET, and 85, formula 62: MISSA . . . CANTARE DEBET.

66. Preface texts were certainly read silently or recited without note after 1300 or so (sooner in some places), when it came to be expected that every priest ought to celebrate a private mass daily or even (abusively) several times a day, besides participating or possibly celebrating a conventual, capitular, or parish mass if a monk, friar, canon, or parish priest. In consequence, side altars to accommodate private masses were multiplied in monastic, collegiate, and cathedral churches, and simultaneous celebrations within the same acoustical space became frequent.

67. Or to the administrative diaconate, from which order bishops and especially popes were often chosen.

68. More often notated in the manuscripts as F G a b-flat—or else C D E F or c d e f—when fixed in pitch. Present-day transcriptions almost always use G a b c , following the Vatican *Cantorinus;* BTC II/3 adheres to this usage except when the manuscript source prescribes another pitch.

69. Except for the lengthy and special form of the preface chant used for the Exultet at the Easter vigil, sung by a deacon. Deacons did not ordinarily sing prefaces and must have needed help from notation when singing a text used but once a year on an occasion of the highest liturgical importance.

70. Late south Italian *toni sollemniores* extend higher, beyond the four notes, as do many versions of the phrase *Et ideo* with which the most often used proper-preface conclusion begins. (See below, p. 24.) The low note for the first syllable of the ecphonesis, *Per omnia saecula saeculorum,* does not normally recur in the preface.

71. A congregation, even when chiefly or entirely composed of monks, nuns, canons, or the clergy assisting the celebrant in the sanctuary, could not see the notation for congregational responses, if indeed they were capable of reading it. The book where the responses were notated reposed on the altar or in the hands of the celebrant or his immediate assistants, its notation invisible to those responding (except perhaps to an assisting deacon). All congregations in fact sing by heart what they know, although changes creep in. Moreover, the celebrant might alter his part of the dialogue in turn, to suit the way the responses were locally being sung, despite the notation in his altar book.

72. The version *In cotidianis diebus* first appears in a much earlier votive missal, MC 426, dating from around the year 1000. See John Boe, "The Neumes and Pater Noster Chant of Montecassino Codex 426," *Miscellanea Cassinese, Monastica I* (Montecassino, 1982), pp. 219–35. Also see RoV C 32, discussed below, p. 6.

73. Or in Benevento and the neighboring diocese of Salerno, if Ben 33 should come from the Salerno area. See below, p. 1.

74. And in the *Cantorinus seu Toni Communes Officii et Missae* (1911) and in all succeeding editions of the *Missale Romanum* until the new Roman missal of 1970.

75. For a description of the tones of the Vatican edition, see Bruno Stäblein's article "Präfation" in the first edition of MGG. Also see John Boe, "The Ordinary in English: Anglican Plainsong Kyrials and Their Sources," 3 vols. (Ph.D. diss., Northwestern University, 1969), 1:84–91 (in need of revision).

76. See Peter Wagner's discussion of the preface tones in *Einführung in die gregorianischen Melodien* (hereafter, EGM), 3 vols.; Part 3, *Gregorianische Formenlehre: Eine choralische Stilkunde* (Leipzig, 1921), pp. 69–80. The chant books of the Dominican order derived from Cistercian models and probably served as the direct source for the Franciscan chant books. Also cf. the single preface tone copied twice in a Chartres missal dating from the second quarter of the thirteenth century, *Missale Carnotense (Chartres Codex*

520), MMA 4, ed. David Hiley (Kassel, 1992), vol. 2, fols. 237ʳ–238ʳ (the original version) and vol. 1, fols. 226ᵛ–228ʳ (a later copy of the earlier version with clefs and lines, nearly two hundred years later than the first but nearly identical to it).

77. The first part of the missal, which includes the prefaces, originated in southern Italy but not at Montecassino (although the missal is based on a Cassinese exemplar) and was taken to Dalmatia, where its second part was added. See Richard F. Gyug, "Tropes and Prosulas in Dalmatian Sources of the Twelfth and Thirteenth Centuries," *La Tradizione dei tropi liturgici*, Atti dei convegni sui tropi liturgici, [Paris, 1985 and Perugia, 1987], ed. Claudio Leonardi and Enrico Menestò (Spoleto, 1990), pp. 409–38 and especially pp. 423–25.

78. The fragment is to be identified with Alban Dold's "Missal II." See Alban Dold, "Umfangreiche Reste zweier Plenarmissalien des 11. und 12. Jh. aus Montecassin," *Ephemerides Liturgicae* 53 (1939): 111–67.

79. There is no *tonus sollemnior* in the later Cassinese or Cassinese-derived missals Vat 6082 and Ott 576.

80. Through the courtesy of David Hiley, I have been able to examine his microfilms of the Norman-Sicilian full missal Palermo Archivio Storico e Diocesano 8 and Palermo, Bibl. Naz. XIV.F.16. None of the preface texts in them is notated. Mr. Hiley tells me that neither the sacramentary Madrid 52 nor the gradual Vitrina 20-4 has notated prefaces.

81. Such a northern and hence "Frankish" stimulus might have been felt at any of three junctures: (1) at the time of Henry II's visit to Montecassino in 1022; (2) earlier, under the Ottonian dynasty, possibly when Otto II made his brilliant but eventually disastrous military expedition to the south in 981–82; or (3) conceivably at the time of the emperor Louis II's five years in the south (866–71), when he defeated the Saracens at Bari but was thereafter held captive in Benevento by his treacherous Lombard allies—the eventful five years when the Frankish repertory of Gregorian chant might have spread through the Beneventan principality. See BTC I, pp. xiii–xiv.

82. See BTC II/3, pp. 94–95 and 99, below.

83. Cf. the Sarum preface chant with tenor on *fa* throughout, presumably derived from northern French and Norman usage.

84. See *Dictionnaire d'histoire et de géographie écclesiastiques* 11: cols. 760–62, and the *Enciclopedia Italiana* 8:762–64, s.v. "Canosa," from which works the summary above is mainly drawn.

85. See Kenneth Levy, "Charlemagne's Archetype of Gregorian Chant," *Journal of the American Musicological Society* 40 (1987): 1–30, and especially p. 15: "I would venture . . . the . . . following propositions: 1. that the Gallo-Gregorian Offertory *Factus est repente* reached Italy from the Frankish north by ca. 800 . . ." ("Italy"—but perhaps not Canosa?)

86. Levy, "Charlemagne's Archetype," pp. 15–17.

87. Missing custodes and ambiguous heightening of neumes in W 6 allow for a reading of the opening forephrases with a tenor of b . But the resulting inconsistent treatment of the tenor—at first b and later c—is unlikely. See p. 48 below for an optional transcription of the beginning section using the lower tenor. (If it were so sung, the first part of the Canosa preface would be still closer to the *Francisca* version.)

88. The notes *ac beata seraphim* ᵃ ᵇᶜᵇ[ᵃ ᵇ ᵇ] in *Francisca* are not an initial figure but only a preparation for an irregular medial cadence after a long recitation. See the transcription above, p. xlix.

89. See Border-Area Sources, p. 39, below; for the entire version, see pp. 38–44, below. In RoC 1574, the preface, with notation from the late twelfth or early thirteenth centuries, is found as part of a mass ordo inserted in a monastic compendium.

90. Lo 3511 is the surviving almost complete example—not altogether successful and not altogether Cassinese. Also see a proper preface for Pentecost notated in RoV B 24, transcribed below on p. 46. (But cf. Ben 19 and 20.)

91. See Peter Wagner's citations of Cistercian and Carthusian prefaces referred to above and in n. 76.

lxi

The South Italian Sanctus Repertory

Sanctus Repertories in the Manuscripts
Grouping of sources

The south Italian Sanctus trope repertory survives in manuscripts dating from the eleventh and twelfth centuries from the three centers of Benevento, Montecassino, and Rome. For the most part, Sanctus tropes came from north of the Alps, sometimes by way of the Normans in southern Italy, or else imitated northern styles. There were but few native south Italian Sanctus tropes in general use.

*

In Lombard southern Italy until at least A.D. 1025, Sanctus was sung to anaphoral-chant melodies without tropes. In these melodies, the kernel G a b was repeated, prolonged, or developed. (When, somewhat later, the melodies came to be notated, the melodic kernel often read C D E , F G a , or c d e .) The melodic kernel was usually but by no means always present in the opening acclamations *Sanctus, Sanctus, Sanctus*. In semirecitative form with tenor on b—sometimes raised to c—the kernel is often found in internal phrases and especially at *Benedictus qui uenit in nomine Domini*.[1] Such melodies are the only ones notated as incipits (and occasionally complete) at the end of certain prefaces in south Italian missals and sacramentaries.[2] No Sanctus tropes are ever found in these altar books.

The northern, Frankish custom of interpolating Sanctus with explanatory or exclamatory tropes began to be introduced on certain occasions and in certain places in the south where the Roman rite was followed and Gregorian chants sung.[3] Kyrie verses and Gloria in excelsis tropes had been sung earlier, some of them locally composed and others imported.[4] But the Sanctus, imbedded in the prefatory chant of the celebrant and leading straight into the so-called canon of the mass, was not usually troped in south Italy until after around 1050.[5] More Sanctus tropes—including Hosanna pros(ul)as under the general term—were introduced later in the eleventh century culminating in the inflated collection of Benevento 35 (soon after 1100?) and those in Ben 34 (mid-twelfth century?) where the pieces were partly distributed among the propers and partly collected together at the end of the manuscript.

These sources now contain sixteen and fourteen Sanctus melodies, respectively. Ben 35 must once have contained eighteen Sanctus and probably more, before at least two leaves were removed between the present folios 195 and 196 and between folios 198 and 199. The modest collection of the Roman St. Cecilia gradual, Bod 74, which was completed in the year 1071, has nine S⟨AN⟩C⟨TV⟩S CV⟨M⟩ V⟨E⟩R⟨SIBVS⟩; the Cassinese troper, Urb 602, roughly contemporary with Ben 35, twelve Sanctus; and the twelfth-century Cassinese winter-gradual MC 546, six. Earlier south Italian graduals had only two to six Sanctus.[6]

The accumulated Sanctus-trope repertory found in manuscripts from southern Italy dating from 1071 to 1175 consists of four groups: (1) a sharply restricted number of well-known European Sanctus tropes (using the word *tropes* in the limited sense and excluding Hosanna pros[ul]as), just two of which were in general use; (2) several north or central Italian Sanctus tropes, some of which seem to have reached Benevento by way of Rome; (3) a small group of famous European Hosanna prosulas or prosas that mostly arrived towards the end of the eleventh century, one of which quickly became generally popular, another being sung only at Benevento; and (4) late south Italian imitations of northern Sanctus tropes and Hosanna pros(ul)as, the latter nearly contemporary with the introduction to south Italy of their models.[7] Sometimes it is hard to tell south Italian pieces from pieces whose source must be in northern or central Italy, especially when an origin at Montecassino can be surmised. Confections from Benevento are more easily identified.

European Tropes for Sanctus

The earliest and most widely distributed Sanctus trope imported to southern Italy was *Deus pater ingenitus*, sung with Thannabaur 154.[8] It was included for Easter Day in Ben 40, as already mentioned—one of only two additions to Sanctus in that earliest surviving Benevento gradual. *Deus pater ingenitus* is the first item in the Bod 74 Sanctus collection and the first in the Cassinese collections of Urb 602 and MC 546. It was included in one of the two small collections of Ben 34 but not among the propers. It is not among the Sanctus surviving in Ben 35. The trope is found in both east and west Frankish manuscripts and in northern and central Italian manuscripts. Its trinitarian text was attached to the three opening acclamations, like that of many Sanctus tropes.

lxiii

Sanctus.
> Deus pater ingenitus.

Sanctus.
> Filius dei unigenitus.

Sanctus dominus.
> Spiritus paraclitus ex utroque procedens.

Dominus sabaoth.
Pleni sunt . . .
(Urb 602)

In all the south Italian manuscripts that contain *Deus pater ingenitus* (and only in them), the probably Cassinese Hosanna prosula *Qui uenisti carnem sumens* is subjoined.[9]

The only other European trope for Sanctus widely sung in southern Italy, the trinitarian *Admirabilis splendor*, appears third in the Cassinese collections Urb 602 and MC 546. It is also found in Bod 74 (where the wandering verse *Indefessas uoces* functions as a tiny Hosanna prosula) and in Ben 35 and Ben 34. In the last-named manuscripts it was assigned to the propers for Christmas Day with a unique trope element added. It was entered across the bottom margins of two facing pages of a later supplement to Ben 38.[10] In Italy, *Admirabilis splendor* was sung with Thannabaur 74, to which Sanctus the Italian melody for the trope is related. (Elsewhere, *Admirabilis splendor* was usually sung with Thannabaur 111.) It does not appear in east Frankish sources; but its wide and early distribution throughout western Europe and Italy implies a tenth-century origin.

Sanctus
> Ammirabilis splendor
> immarcessibilisque lux
> pater deus

Sanctus
> Verbum quod erat
> in principio apud deum

Sanctus   Dominus   deus sabaoth
> Paraclitus sanctusque spiritus

Pleni sunt cęli et terra gloria tua
Osanna in excelsis
> Cui omne flectitur genu
> et omnis lingua proclamat dicens

Benedictus   qui uenit in nomine domini
Osanna ———————————— in excelsis ————
> ℞ **Indefessas uoces**
> **nostras exaudies** in excelsis ————

(Bod 74)

Two other Sanctus tropes from north of the Alps, written in quantitative verse, found their way into the Cassinese troper Urb 602, presumably by way of the Normans then established in southern Italy who were beginning their conquest of Sicily. The pieces seem not to have been generally copied. *Summe pater de quo* (in flawed hexameters), sung with Thannabaur 56 and coupled with the older transalpine prosa *[Hosanna] Omnes tua gratia*, is found only in Urb 602. Concordances are exclusively Norman-Sicilian and French, mainly from the north of France.[11] *Perpetuo numine* (in pentameters-hexameters), in addition to its place in Urb 602, was entered among the propers for Pentecost in Ben 34 with the variant opening line *Perpetuo lumine*. This trope, the most popular of the European tropes associated with the widely sung Sanctus melody Thannabaur 49, must have originated in France and spread thence into Germany and Italy and throughout Europe.[12]

Italian Tropes for Sanctus

The Sanctus trope *Altissimeque rector* (or *Altissime creator* in the Montecassino redaction) appears in all the chief south Italian sources in an astonishing variety of versions and layouts. This Sanctus is second in the Cassinese collections of Urb 602 and MC 546. In the manuscripts that contain it—all of them Italian—it is associated with an unusual Sanctus melody, Thannabaur 92, which is never found except together with this trope. It is probable that two versions of a preexistent hymn were restructured as a Sanctus trope and that the melody for Sanctus was then drawn from phrases of the hymn melody.[13] The putative hymn and its arrangements as a Sanctus trope may have originated in southern Italy rather than north of Rome; but neither the hymn nor the trope originated at Montecassino, where the Sanctus-trope text was subjected to typically Cassinese corrections and revision before being received. Probably they did not originate at Benevento either, where the arrangement is first known from Ben 35, where it probably had been borrowed with other matter from Roman collections. Thus the Sanctus trope is Italian and earlier than 1071. It is impossible to be more precise. (The Hosanna prosula *Conditor alme*, always attached to this Sanctus trope, is not found elsewhere.)

> Sanctus
> Sanctus
> Sanctus
> dominus deus sabaoth
> Altissimeque rector
> poli sede redemptor
> parce peccata cuncta
> domine misericors   nobis indignis

Pleni sunt cęli et terra   gloria tua
Osanna ————————————— in excelsis
Repleti sumus
> quam non meremur   propter peccata
> quę gessimus   gloriam tuam nobis dona

> Benedictus qui uenit in nomine domini
> Ebreorum proles ore concrepauerunt
>
> Osanna ——————————————— in excelsis
>
> ℣ Conditor alme domine
>   poli rector
>   telluris gubernator
>   mari sustentor
>   miserere
>   plasmę tuę
>   quem formasti de humo
>   ad tuam imaginem
>   misericors
>
> (Bod 74)   in excelsis

No other tropes for Sanctus enjoyed the same universal distribution in south Italy as the three texts given above, two of them European and one Italian in origin.[14] However, two other Sanctus tropes, whose immediate source was northern or central Italy, appear in some but not all south Italian collections. These are *Deus fortis* (the first verses of which may be transalpine) and *Quem cherubim atque seraphim*. Three other north or central Italian pieces appear only once or twice in south Italy. *Mundi fabricator* was probably borrowed from Nonantola for Ben 35, its only southern source. Why *Immortalis et uerus* should turn up in Ben 34 is a mystery, unless it was copied from a now-missing folio of Ben 35. Another north Italian trope, *Pax in caelo* (=*Laudatur trina maiestas*), unexpectedly appears in Bod 74. From this Roman collection or some other it was borrowed for Ben 35. I now discuss these five Italian pieces.

Deus fortis, sung like *Deus pater ingenitus* with Thannabaur 154 in the south, is found in versions of various lengths all over northern Italy. The first half of the trope is European (though not found in Aquitanian manuscripts), but the characteristic second half, beginning [4] *Te laudat/Te adorat/Te glorificat*, is found only in Italy, and I therefore classify the trope in the extended form used in south Italy as "Italian." These longer versions incorporate lines reminiscent of Te Deum laudamus that must preserve an Eastertide post-Sanctus from a non-Roman liturgy, perhaps a Gallican *immolatio*. (For the text, see the commentary below, p. 70.)[15]

Quem cherubim atque seraphim, sung with Thannabaur 63 in the south and generally in the north of Italy, must have originated north of Rome. It is not found outside the peninsula. At Montecassino it was split into two Sanctus tropes. The one consisted of two introductory citations of angelic praise and a concluding trinitarian doxology for use on feasts of St. Michael the Archangel (*In Sci angli*); the other consisted of the three verses beginning *Cui pueri Hebraeorum* with the Hosanna prosula **Hebraeorum pueri ramos** for Palm Sunday.[16]

Mundi fabricator, sung with Thannabaur 223, was probably copied for Ben 35 (the only southern Italian manuscript to have it) from a Nonantola collection.[17] In CT 7, Iversen lists seven concordances from northern Italy and two from Norman Sicily—a rare case of an Italian piece having been borrowed for Norman use. There are no French concordances.

Immortalis et uerus is known elsewhere only from Mod 7, RoV C 52, and PdC A 47. It may have been included in the Ben 35 anthology (but entered on one of the now missing folios of that Sanctus collection) and thence transferred to Ben 34.[18]

Pax in caelo, sung with a version of Thannabaur 60 (?=66,67), begins with Vs [2] *Laudatur trina maiestas* in two central Italian manuscripts, Mod 7 and RoV C 52. Where or why it was adapted from its original and much more suitable guise as a set of trope elements introducing the lines of Gloria in excelsis (in which guise it first appeared at Breme-Novalesa, in the Piedmont) or why and where its original first verse beginning *Pax in caelo* was restored to the Sanctus trope text, as now found in Bod 74, cannot be said.[19]

European Hosanna Prosas and Prosulas

One imported European Hosanna prosa, **Laudes Deo ore pio**, was copied nearly as often as the European Sanctus tropes *Deus pater ingenitus* and *Admirabilis splendor*, although it arrived later. The Hosanna prosa was sung with a variant of Sanctus Thannabaur 213 but without trope. **Laudes Deo ore pio** was copied into Ben 38 over part of the erased old Beneventan mass for Pentecost sometime during the last third of the eleventh century, but with Thannabaur 223 rather than Thannabaur 213, the customary southern melody. In Ben 35, Sanctus Thannabaur 213—broken off by a lacuna in the manuscript—almost certainly concluded with this prosa, seeing that it is found in the later manuscript Ben 34. It appears in both surviving Cassinese collections, Urb 602 and MC 546. In the latter, a winter gradual, there are only six Sanctus, of which Thannabaur 213 with **Laudes Deo ore pio** is the fourth. In Urb 602, the phrases of the prosa were distributed in a unique manner throughout the base Sanctus text just as if they were a Sanctus trope, though retaining their prosa melody.[20]

The well-known Aquitanian prosas **Hosanna Plasmatum populum** and **Hosanna Dulcis est cantica** were composed for insertion into the first and second *Hosanna in excelsis* of the base text. The prosas were copied in the earliest surviving Benevento gradual, Ben 40, among the propers of an alternative mass for the Milanese saints Nazarius and Celsus, but garbled and attached to a seemingly unique Sanctus melody.[21] The pair were copied more correctly in Ben 35 with the usual Italian Sanctus melody, Thannabaur 197 (here untroped), and copied again in Ben 34 with the addition of the unique single trope element *Caelestia sidera*. The two miniature prosas, set to the same melody and together forming a larger prosa, were perhaps composed at different times in Aquitaine, where they were sung with Thannabaur 89. (See the concordances in CT 7.) The prosas are not found at Montecassino nor elsewhere in Italy outside of Benevento (except in Mod 7) nor elsewhere in Europe save in Aquitaine and its borders, as at Apt and in Catalonia.[22] In the first text, *Hosanna* retains its Hebrew meaning of "Save now!"; in the second, it is the name for the song described.

> Sanctus. Sanctus. Sanctus
> Dominus deus sabaoth.
> Pleni sunt celi et terra gloria tua.
>
> **Osanna plasmatum populum**
> **et qui uerum   fore promit ore christum**
> **et qui cosmi   satorem permanentem**
> in excelsis.
>
> Benedictus qui uenit in nomine domini.
>
> **Osanna dulcis est cantica**
> **melliflua   nimisque laudabilia**
> **organica   trinum et unum laudemus**
> **omnes in hac aula.**
>
> **Suscipe cum agmina   angelorum carmina.**
> **Sit dicat nunc osanna**
> in excelsis.
> (Ben 35)

[The second line should properly read *Te qui uerum   fore promit ore christum*; and *sit* in the last line should read *ut*.]

The prosa *[Hosanna] Omnes tua gratia*, which follows the Sanctus trope *Summe pater de quo* with Thannabaur 56 (see above), was copied for Urb 602 from a Norman source.[23] The prosa is older than the trope and the Sanctus. It appears with other tropes and other Sanctus melodies in the Winchester tropers and throughout Francia. It is a miniature prosa having four melodic incises, the second and third of which are repeated with matching text, the fourth being repeated only in part.

Hosanna Saluifica tuum plasma, the last of the European pieces for Hosanna to be considered here, was sung with Sanctus melody Thannabaur 226, Var., but without trope. Through concordances and parallel variants in the slightly later Norman-Sicilian manuscripts, it can be shown that the Cassinese editor of Urb 602 must have borrowed *Hosanna Saluifica tuum plasma* from a Norman-Puglian source. From Montecassino it was borrowed for Ben 34.[24] The piece is a short prosa with four melodic incises, each repeated with matching text. The theme of the prosa is God's salvation of fallen man.

> Benedictus qui uenit in nomine domini.
>
> **Osanna saluifica tuum plasma.**
> **qui   creasti   simul   omnia.**
> **Temet laus   decet honor et gloria**
> **rex   ęterne   in sęcula.**
>
> **Qui de patris gremio**
> **genitus   aduenisti summo.**
>
> **Redimere   perditum**
> **hominem sanguine proprio.**
>
> **Quem   deceperat lucifer**
> **fraude nequam callidissime**
> **serpentino coniugis   dente.**
>
> **Quem   expulerat propere**
> **hoc   in ceno   criminę**
> **paradysi cardine   adque limine.**
>
> **Tu dignare saluare/**
> **Iesu christe benigne**
> in excel ———————————————— sis.
> (Urb 602)

South Italian Hosanna Prosulas Imitating Northern Models

Native composition of tropes and prosulas to decorate and expand Sanctus and Hosanna in excelsis began relatively late in southern Italy, generally not until the second half of the eleventh century. Most of them were written down towards the end of the century, a date later than that for native composition of Kyrie verses and Gloria tropes. A Hosanna prosula may have been the first native south Italian addition to a Sanctus text—if indeed *Qui uenisti carnem sumens* is Cassinese. This carefully wrought text, attached to Thannabaur 154 with the tropes *Deus pater ingenitus* or *Deus fortis* (see above), occurs mainly in south Italian manuscripts, including all the chief sources except Ben 38. (The only concordances not from south Italy are Mod 7 and RoV C52.) Indirect, persuasive, but in the end nonconclusive evidence leads me to think that the piece was written at Montecassino.[25] It is modeled on prosas and prosulas from north of the Alps that have short lines of varying lengths making up a verset whose tune is repeated with the different words of a parallel verset having lines of the same or nearly the same length and accentuation.

> Benedictus qui uenit in nomine domini.
> Osanna ————————————————
>
> **Qui uenisti carnem sumens ex matre./**
> **pro totius mundi salute./**
> **Tu nos ab hoste potenter libera./**
>
> **Et exaudi cunctos famulos tuos./**
> **Vt possimus laudes promere**
> **tibi uoce indefessa. Osanna**
> In excelsis.   (Urb 602)

lxvi

The Hosanna prosula *Pie Christe descendisti* imitates the just discussed *Qui uenisti carnem sumens* in structure. It is set to a version of the same prosula tune. This prosula is only found in three south Italian sources: Urb 602, where it is assigned to Sundays; Ben 34, where it is sung after Thannabaur 223 without trope; and Ben 35, with Sanctus Thannabaur 223 troped with the unicum *Quem cherubim et seraphim non cessant* (see below).[26]

> Benedictus qui uenit in nomine domini.
>
> **Pie christe   descendisti ad terram**
> **mundum tuam facturam saluas**
> **inferni portas confringes fortiter.**
>
> **dyra iura   ipsa dextra conculcans**
> **sanctos sursum leuans ad etheram.**
> **Vt tibi semper decantent.**
>
> Osanna in excelsis.
>
> (Ben 35)

Five other Hosanna prosulas are joined exclusively to their particular Sanctus tropes. They are listed in the summary below, with page numbers for the BTC II/3 main text. All are south Italian except perhaps the first, which—like its host trope *Altissimeque rector*—may have originated elsewhere in Italy. The words of the miniature prosula *Indefessas uoces* turn up in other contexts.

	BTC II/3
Conditor alme domine (with *Altissimeque rector*)	12
Gloria Christe omnes resurgamus (with *Corona iustitiae*)	29
Hosanna cuncta procedens (with *Inuisibiliter penetrauit rex*)	48
Hebraeorum pueri ramos (with *Quem cherubim atque seraphim* + *Cui pueri Hebraeorum*)	93
Indefessas uoces (with *Admirabilis splendor*)	3

Local South Italian Sanctus Tropes

Leaving the Hosanna prosulas, I now turn to tropes for Sanctus composed in south Italy. These native products fall into three subcategories, according to where they were written. In the first subcategory are two Roman pieces; in the second, one from Montecassino; and in the third, five pieces assembled at Benevento especially for the Sanctus collection of Ben 35.

Two pieces, *Quam pulchra est* (for the Assumption of the Blessed Virgin) and *Inuisibiliter penetrauit rex* (for the Ascension), seem to have been borrowed from Roman use for Benevento, according to a typical pattern of transmission. *Quam pulchra est* (rubricked *In scę̄ MARIĘ* in Bod 74) was sung with Thannabaur 62. The incomplete version of Ben 35 breaks off in the middle of an added fourth trope element that begins *Surge propera columba mea*.[27] The piece is known only from these two sources. *Inuisibiliter penetrauit rex* with its prosula *Hosanna cuncta procedens*, sung with Thannabaur ?64 (cf. 60, 66, 67), was included in the Ascension Day propers of Ben 34. This manuscript is nearly a century later than the other source for the piece, Bod 74.[28] (*Inuisibiliter penetrauit rex* does not now appear in Ben 35 but was almost certainly entered on one of the now missing folios of that Sanctus collection and thence copied into Ben 34.) Several phrases of the trope were borrowed from well-known tropes for Gloria in excelsis (see the commentary), a procedure like that used to piece together the first Kyrie in the Bod 74 collection, *Incarnate quoque*.[29]

The Cassinese subcategory of native south Italian Sanctus tropes (my second subcategory) contains just one item: the unicum *Pater Deus qui caret initio*.[30] Entered in Urb 602, where many pieces were borrowed from the Norman repertory, it can nevertheless be attributed to Montecassino on internal stylistic grounds. The melody shows characteristics of other unica written by "the falling-fourth composer of Urb 602," as I call him. In some respects, the words of this trope resemble those of a rare text also found in Urb 602, the verbose Gloria trope *Assit honor*.[31]

The third subcategory of south Italian Sanctus tropes consists of those assembled at Benevento for the collection of Ben 35, presumably around or just after 1100.

	BTC II/3
Antra modicis deserti nati, Th 45 fol. 195ʳ	22
Quem cuncti angeli, Th 86 fol. 196ᵛ	102
Ante thronum Domini, Th 178 fol. 197ʳ⁻ᵛ (prosula?)	20
Quem cherubim et seraphim non cessant (with prosula *Pie Christe descendisti*), Th 223, fols. 197ᵛ–198ʳ	64
Corona iustitiae (with prosula *Gloria Christe omnes resurgamus*) Th 152 (=154), fol. 198ᵛ	29

The first text in this list is for the Nativity of St. John Baptist. The next three pursue the general theme of the angels praising God, a theme found in the stereotyped concluding phrases of the prefaces that precede Sanctus. In **Ante thronum Domini** (the second of the three) all four lines are inserted in succession between the last *Osanna* and *in excelsis* of the base text and are sung to the same motive drawn from the Sanctus melody. Perhaps this piece should be regarded as a local attempt to create a prosula for an indigenous melody, relying on what Iversen calls *versus technique* and Levy calls *variation versus*. The last piece, *Corona iustitiae*, with its special Hosanna prosula *Gloria Christe omnes resurgamus*, was probably meant as a trope for Eastertide or for Easter Day itself—or just possibly for the protomartyr Stephen or another saint. Its Sanctus melody, Thannabaur 152, is a rearrangement of the famous international Sanctus Thannabaur 154 that was sung elsewhere in south Italy with the trope *Deus pater ingenitus* (followed by the Hosanna prosula *Qui uenisti carnem sumens*) and with the Eastertide trope *Deus fortis* (see above). *Deus fortis* is missing from Ben 34 and was probably also missing from Ben 35, supplanted by the newer *Corona iustitiae*. The newer Sanctus utilizes the melody of the older prosulas *Qui uenisti carnem sumens* and *Pie Christe descendisti* (see above) for its prosula *Gloria Christe omnes resurgamus*. The scribe of Ben 34 was aware of the connection, for he placed *Corona iustitiae* with its *Gloria Christe omnes resurgamus* immediately after *Deus pater ingenitus* with its attendant *Qui uenisti carnem sumens*. The editor or scribe of Ben 34 made a judicious choice among the unica of Ben 35 when he chose *Corona iustitiae*, the best of a bad lot.

All the "new" pieces of Ben 35 are marked by some of the faults abundantly evident in *Antra modicis deserti nati*, set proudly at the head of the Sanctus collection. *Antra modicis deserti nati* was cobbled together by a semiliterate cleric who rummaged through appropriate liturgical sources for resonant phrases to plunder without regard to meaning or meter—in this case, two office hymns for St. John Baptist, identified by Iversen.[32] Based on her identification, the format and apparatus employed in the BTC commentary, p. 61, shows the derivation of every word of the trope. In *Antra modicis deserti nati*, sense was dissolved into pious gabble.

The Sanctus Trope Repertory Compared with Other Ordinary Trope Repertories

The Sanctus trope repertory of southern Italy was evidently established later than repertories for other tropes of the ordinary. In spite of the imposing size of the largest surviving collection, that of Ben 35, the core repertory of Sanctus tropes and Hosanna prosulas in general use remained small. This core included three Sanctus tropes (the first three in the collections of Urb 602 and MC 546) and three Hosanna prosulas (*Laudes Deo ore pio*, *Qui uenisti carnem sumens*, and its daughter prosula *Pie Christe descendisti*). The collecting zeal of the Ben 35 compiler enriched the local repertory with various pieces that stem from central and northern Italy, many of them doubtless drawn by the compiler from the Roman collections available to him. With little judgment and less skill the compiler also assembled five "new" pieces for his collection, only one of which was copied in Ben 34. Thus the imposing size of the Ben 35 Sanctus collection, even in its present incomplete state, is in a sense deceptive.

At Montecassino, two deftly chosen borrowings for Urb 602 from the Norman-Puglian repertory took local root and were eventually transplanted to Benevento, where *Perpetuo numine* (*lumine*) and the independent prosa **Hosanna Saluifica tuum plasma** were copied in Ben 34. Neither the northern *Summe pater de quo* with the prosa *[Hosanna] Omnes tua gratia* nor the Cassinese composition *Pater Deus qui caret initio* found their way into the Ben 34 collection.

Viewed *in toto*, the south Italian repertory of Sanctus tropes is broad but shallow: only a few of the large number of pieces included in it were sung for long in many places, and these few pieces—six, or less—were most of them imports from the north. Within this core repertory, only the prosulas *Qui uenisti carnem sumens* and *Pie Christe descendisti* modeled upon it are likely to have originated in the south. This situation contrasts with that found in other ordinary trope repertories. Of the approximately thirty-five Kyries with verses in the same manuscripts, nine come from north of the Alps (plus one Roman imitation); five are Italian and possibly Cassinese; eight more are Italian but hardly southern; six are native to Rome; and six more are local Benevento compilations.[33] The core repertory of nine tropes that are regularly included for Gloria in excelsis in these and other south Italian manuscripts comprises five European tropes (counting one "fringe" piece) against three local tropes (or four, if one piece of debatable origin should in fact come from southern Italy).[34] The much smaller repertory of verses and tropes for Agnus Dei in south Italian manuscripts is harder to assess: most of the repertory seems to have been borrowed from north of Rome, with a few southern additions. In the case of both Kyrie eleison and Gloria in excelsis, at least a third of the core repertory was local and early. The reasons for this state of affairs are complex: at least it is clear that, in general, Sanctus continued to be sung without tropes long after it had become customary on festive occasions to sing Gloria in excelsis with added *laudes*. As suggested earlier, the availability of a great many proper prefaces in south Italian altar books—at least until after 1085—tended to diminish the need for tropes specific to a particular occasion and altogether removed the motif of "introducing Sanctus." Furthermore, the tenacity of the south Italian anaphoral-chant tradition of untroped Sanctus melodies, closely related to the preceding preface chants, tended to slow the spread of northern Sanctus melodies and tropes, which were often foreign to the southern melodic tradition.

Economic decline, political unrest, sack by invading armies, monastic decay and the rise of the mendicant orders, the change of chant at Rome and the destruction of the old books under Nicholas III (1277–80), and the removal of the papacy to Avignon obscure the fate of liturgical tropes in southern Italy during the later thirteenth and the fourteenth centuries. One can speculate that the passing fashion for Sanctus tropes disappeared quickly, but that Hosanna prosulas, which lent themselves to rhythmical verse forms and rhyme schemes, increased in popularity for a time. Nonetheless we are lucky to have an abundance of manuscripts from Benevento and a sufficient number from Montecassino and Rome to determine the repertory of Sanctus tropes and Hosanna pros(ul)as in southern Italy during the eleventh and early twelfth centuries.

Ordering of the Sanctus Repertory in South Italian Collections

In the more comprehensive Sanctus collections, certain principles underlying the arrangement of individual pieces and some of the sources drawn upon can be distinguished. These collections are the twelve Sanctus in the Cassinese troper Urb 602, dated just before 1100; the nine in the Roman gradual Bod 74, completed in 1071; the sixteen in Ben 35, from around or just after 1100—the largest collection and originally even larger; and the fourteen in Ben 34, from the mid-twelfth century, six of which Sanctus were distributed among the propers of important feasts.[35]

The Cassinese Collections

The Cassinese arrangement of Urb 602 is the easiest to understand and the most rational, although not the earliest. Table 2 shows how troped Sanctus were assigned by rubric to important feasts, including the local saints Benedict and Maur, according to the calendrical order of their primary assignment, beginning with Christmas and ending with Pentecost. Two Sanctus with pros(ul)as but no tropes were assigned to Sundays, at the end of the collection. (There are no Sanctus melodies having neither tropes nor prosulas in Urb 602.) The three Sanctus tropes most often found in south Italian manuscripts—*1 Deus pater ingenitus, 2 Altissime creator = Altissimeque rector*, and *3 Admirabilis splendor*—were placed first. (The same priority was accorded these three pieces in the collection of six Sanctus in MC 546, a later Cassinese winter gradual. See table 3.) These three pieces constitute the core of the south Italian Sanctus trope repertory.

Kyrie verses and Gloria in excelsis tropes were arranged similarly in Urb 602. The original assignments of the first Kyries have been obscured by erasure (see BTC II/1, p. xxxii, table 3), but the assignments of Gloria tropes are clear (see BTC II/2, p. xvii, table 3). All feasts assigned any kind of ordinary trope are listed by order of feast in BTC II/1, p. xiv, table 1. St. Maur (disciple of St. Benedict and second abbot of Montecassino, *natale* 15 January), Palm Sunday, and the Apparition of St. Michael the Archangel on 8 May were assigned troped Sanctus only. On the other hand, the first mass of Christmas and the feasts of the Annunciation and the Nativity of St. Mary were not assigned special Sanctus, though they were assigned other ordinary chants.

TABLE 2. Sanctus Trope and Pros(ul)a Assignments by Rubric in Urb 602

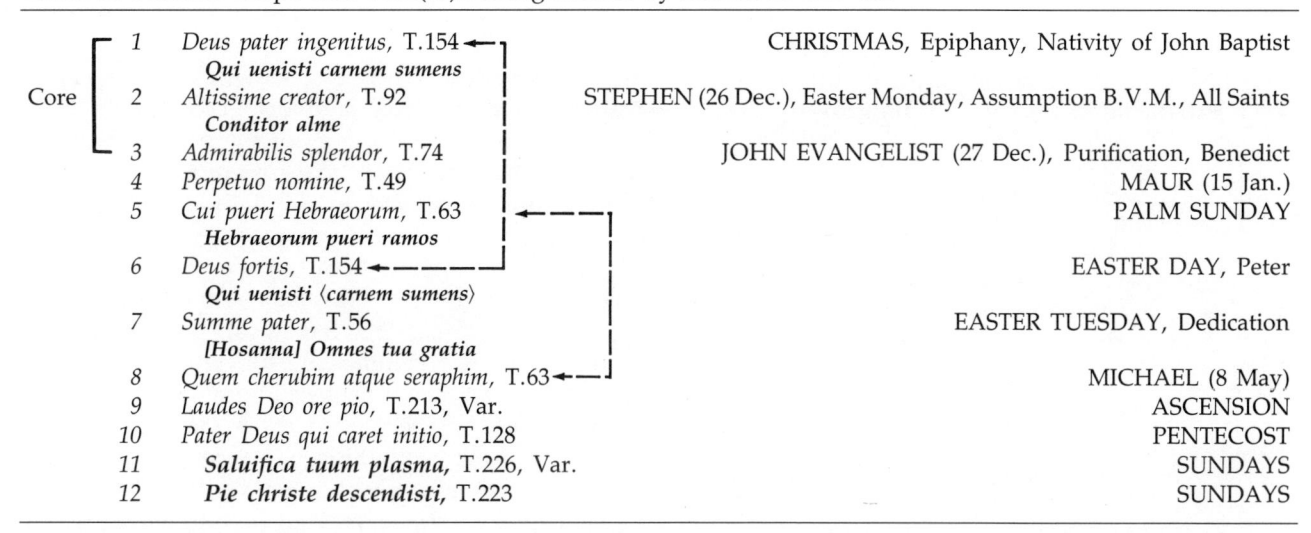

Core	1	*Deus pater ingenitus*, T.154	CHRISTMAS, Epiphany, Nativity of John Baptist
		Qui uenisti carnem sumens	
	2	*Altissime creator*, T.92	STEPHEN (26 Dec.), Easter Monday, Assumption B.V.M., All Saints
		Conditor alme	
	3	*Admirabilis splendor*, T.74	JOHN EVANGELIST (27 Dec.), Purification, Benedict
	4	*Perpetuo nomine*, T.49	MAUR (15 Jan.)
	5	*Cui pueri Hebraeorum*, T.63	PALM SUNDAY
		Hebraeorum pueri ramos	
	6	*Deus fortis*, T.154	EASTER DAY, Peter
		Qui uenisti ⟨carnem sumens⟩	
	7	*Summe pater*, T.56	EASTER TUESDAY, Dedication
		[Hosanna] *Omnes tua gratia*	
	8	*Quem cherubim atque seraphim*, T.63	MICHAEL (8 May)
	9	*Laudes Deo ore pio*, T.213, Var.	ASCENSION
	10	*Pater Deus qui caret initio*, T.128	PENTECOST
	11	**Saluifica tuum plasma**, T.226, Var.	SUNDAYS
	12	**Pie christe descendisti**, T.223	SUNDAYS

NOTE: Feasts given in full capital letters reflect chronological order within the church year. For pieces with more than one assignment, feasts are given in their original rubrical order.

Item *6 Deus fortis*, rubricked for Easter Day in Urb 602, was copied almost as often as the three items in the core repertory. (See table 2, above.) *Quem cherubim atque seraphim*, a pan-Italian trope, which elsewhere included the elements beginning *Cui pueri Hebraeorum*, was for this collection split into two Sanctus: one for Palm Sunday and one for St. Michael. The lines of the famous Hosanna prosa **Laudes Deo ore pio** were segmented and distributed throughout the Sanctus text as a trope for the Ascension. This unique arrangement was in accordance with the Urb 602 rationale of employing Sanctus tropes for feasts (sometimes with subjoined prosulas) and Hosanna pros(ul)as alone for Sundays.

Two tropes were probably borrowed from the Norman-Puglian repertory: *4 Perpetuo numine* and certainly *7 Summe pater de quo*. Although its origin seems to have been in Aquitaine, the immediate source employed for the prosa *11* **Hosanna Saluifica tuum plasma** in Urb 602 is uncertain.

The unicum *10 Pater Deus qui caret initio* was especially composed for the Urb 602 collection. Aside from this lengthy piece, the collection fairly represents the south Italian repertory: three core items plus the pan-Italian extended version of *Deus fortis*, enriched by an Italian trope split into two Sanctus and by two non-Italian pieces. Two Hosanna pros(ul)as were added, one foreign and the other native. (The unica of the Ben 35 collection—they could hardly have been known to the editor of Urb 602—happily do not appear.) I regret the absence of the twin prosas **Hosanna Plasmatum populum** and **Hosanna Dulcis est cantica**, among the first to have been copied at Benevento. I cannot explain the absence in Urb 602 of any Sanctus melodies without trope or prosula, such as items 5 and 6 in the MC 546 collection (see table 3). After all, ten verseless Kyrie melodies were included in Urb 602.

TABLE 3. Sanctus in MC 546 (no rubrics)

Core	1	*Deus pater ingenitus*, T.154
		Qui uenisti carnem sumens
	2	*Altissime creator*, T.92
		Conditor alme
	3	*Admirabilis splendor*, T.74
	4	*Laudes Deo ore pio*, T.213, Var.
	5	T.32
	6	T.49

NOTE: MC 546 is a winter gradual, the propers of which run from Advent to the beginning of the Easter vigil mass. The sanctoral ends with the feast of the Annunciation on 25 March. A corresponding summer gradual (which if it existed has not survived) may have contained more ordinary chants, especially those with tropes for Eastertide and Pentecost.

The Roman Collection in Bodmer 74

The Sanctus collection in Bod 74 is the earliest of the four collections that concern us. All nine of these Sanctus have tropes of some sort, just as the rubric *Incipiunt SC̄S · SC̄S · CV̄ V̄R* says. There are no Sanctus without verbal additions in Bod 74; there are no Sanctus with prosas or prosulas only; and such prosulas as appear subjoined to tropes do not qualify as "prosas" according to the distinctions followed in BTC II/3.[36] I am unable to discover a rationale for the order of the collection, except that it begins with *Deus pater ingenitus*, the first item of the south Italian core repertory in the Cassinese collections. In the Bod 74 collection the other two items of the core repertory are scattered: *5 Altissimeque rector* (not the Cassinese version *Altissime creator*) and *9 Admirabilis splendor*. The widespread Italian trope *5 Deus fortis* is also included. Of the others, only *7 Quem cherubim atque seraphim* appears in Urb 602, split into two separate Sanctus, as mentioned above.[37] This trope and *8 Pax in caelo* (= *Laudatur trina maiestas*) have concordances in north and central Italian manuscripts containing other material found in Roman collections. (See table 4.)

Two pieces have concordances only with Benevento: *3 In Sce MARIE Quam pulchra est* (with Ben 35) and the Ascension trope *6 Inuisibiliter penetrauit rex* (with Ben 34). The Benevento manuscripts are later, and the Beneventan versions were almost certainly based on Roman versions like those found in Bod 74, not vice versa. To the fourth Sanctus in Bod 74 were appended the Easter verses beginning *Hodie Dominus Iesus Christus resurrexit a mortuis*, which are found in various liturgical contexts in several south Italian manuscripts. The assignment in Bod 74 of the text as a "post-Sanctus" is unique.[38]

We may well ask what items are not found in the Bod 74 Sanctus collection. The four unica of the later manuscript Ben 35 (plus *Corona iustitiae*, probably copied from Ben 35 into Ben 34) are obviously missing. None of the Cassinese borrowings from the Norman repertory nor the Cassinese unicum *Pater Deus qui caret initio* is present; nor are any of the Cassinese textual or melodic variants for core-repertory Sanctus found. Thus it is almost certain that the Bod 74 editor did *not* get his Sanctus collection or any part of it from Montecassino. Where, then, did he find his pieces? I believe that he (or a previous Roman editor) got most of them from central Italian collections now lost, whose contents resembled the Ravennate collection of Mod 7 or the Sanctus collection in RoV C 52.[39] The Roman editor also arranged three pieces from pre-existing sources in the liturgy: *3 Quam pulchra est, 4 Hodie Dominus Iesus Christus resurrexit a mortuis*, and *6 Inuisibiliter penetrauit rex*—all mentioned above in connection with their Benevento concordances.

TABLE 4. Sanctus in Bod 74, with North and Central Italian Concordances

Bodmer 74 (9 collected Sanctus)	Mod 7 (11 collected Sanctus + 3 in propers)	RoV C 52 (11 collected Sanctus)	To 18 (6 collected Sanctus + 2 in propers)
*1 *Deus pater ingenitus*, T.154	—	8th	Christmas Day
Qui uenisti carnem sumens	Ascension (with T.223 and *Cuius in laude*)	—	—
2 *Deus fortis*, T.154	Christmas Day, Easter	2d	1st
3 *Quam pulchra est*, T.62	—	—	—
4 [V *Hodie Dominus Iesus Christus*], T.?64 (cf. 60,66,67)	—	—	—
*5 *Altissimeque rector*, T.92	10th	—	5th
Conditor alme	10th	—	5th
6 *Inuisibiliter penetrauit rex*, T.?64 (cf. 60,66,67)	—	—	—
Hosanna cuncta procedens	—	—	—
7 *Quem cherubim atque seraphim*, T.63	2d	5th	2d
8 [1] *Pax in caelo*, T.60 (?=66,67)	—	—	—
[2] *Laudatur trina maiestas*	1st	6th	—
*9 *Admirabilis splendor*, T.74	6th	4th	—
Indefessas uoces	3d (with T.46 and *Immortalis et uerus*)	—	—

*South Italian core repertory

The presence of nine troped Sanctus in such an early collection at Rome is unexpected and noteworthy. If there were other such Roman collections, as would seem likely, they remain lost to us.

The Benevento 35 Collection

The collection of sixteen Sanctus in Ben 35 is the largest from southern Italy still extant but the most frustrating to consider. Apart from the pieces surviving in fragmentary form, at least three and perhaps as many as six Sanctus have been lost. Thus it is always possible to suppose that a piece now missing from the collection might once have been included, and consequently it is difficult to draw firm conclusions about the Sanctus sung at Benevento around the time this manuscript was copied. Even though the text and melodies of certain Sanctus found in the later gradual Ben 34 resemble those in Cassinese sources, several others were certainly copied into Ben 34 in Beneventan—not Cassinese—versions, either from Ben 35 itself or from another local version very much like it.

On the basis of the content and ordering of the Sanctus in Ben 34, two pieces can be retrospectively proposed as prime candidates for inclusion on the missing folios of Ben 35: *Deus pater ingenitus* with the prosula *Qui uenisti carnem sumens*[40] and *Quem cherubim atque seraphim* + *Cui pueri Hebraeorum*, which appears as one item in both Bod 74 and Ben 34—not two as in Urb 602.[41]

In the collection of Ben 35, *11 Admirabilis splendor* immediately follows *10 Mundi fabricator* (see table 5). This exceptional order demands attention. In Cassinese collections, *Admirabilis splendor* comes third, after the other pieces of the south Italian core repertory. (In Bod 74, *Admirabilis splendor* is last.) The Italian trope *Mundi fabricator* is found in seven central Italian manuscripts, three of which are from Nonantola, and in the two earliest surviving Norman-Sicilian manuscripts. (In the Sicilian manuscripts it supplies the single, anomalous instance of an Italian trope borrowed for inclusion in the Norman repertory.)[42] It appears in no other south Italian source except Ben 35. Of all the sources, it is only Ben 35 and the two manuscripts from Nonantola, RoC 1741 and RoN 1343, that place the tropes *Mundi fabricator* (with Thannabaur 223) and *Admirabilis splendor* (with Thannabaur 74) adjacent in that order. (See table 5.) In a third, slightly later Sanctus collection from Nonantola in the manuscript BoU 2824, they still appear in that order but separated by three Sanctus melodies without tropes. This similarity of ordering suggests that the omnivorous editor of Ben 35 must have collected *Mundi fabricator* from a Nonantolan source or from a copy of one.[43]

In its present state, the Sanctus collection of Ben 35 concludes with *14 Pax in caelo* (=*Laudatur trina maiestas*), *15 Corona iustitiae*, and *16 Quam pulchra est*, broken off by the second lacuna. Now *Laudatur trina maiestas* as a Sanctus trope has *Pax in caelo* as its first

lxxi

TABLE 5. The Ben 35 Sanctus Collection compared with Bod 74, Ben 34, Mod 7, and Nonantolan MSS

Mod 7 (Cf. RoV C52 and To 18 in table 4)	Bodmer 74* (See table 4 for MS order)	Benevento 35	Benevento 34 (See table 6 for MS order)	RoC 1741 (Nonantola)	RoN 1343 (Nonantola)
‡*Immortalis et uerus*	—	1 †*Antra modicis deserti*, T.45	—	T.111 Var.; 9th	8th
		2 T.111	?		
		3 ‖T.109			
7th		4 T.223 (=10 below)	*Pater lumen*, T.216 Var; 3d	*Pater lumen*, T.216 Var; 3d	3d
7th		5 T.216 Var.			
		6 T.213 Var. #			
		[*Laudes Deo ore pio*?]	*Immortalis et uerus*, T.46	T32 Var.; 11th	12th
	?	LACUNA (of 1 folio?)	Epiphany		
3rd	5th				
10th	5th	7 #*Altissimeque rector*, T.92 ?	2d	—	—
		Conditor alme	2d		
T.197, 9th		8 T.197	*Caelestia sidera*, T.197	RoC 1741 (in MS order)	RoN 1343 (in MS order)
9th		*Hosanna*[1] *Plasmatum populum*	Dedication	1 *Deus fortis*, T.154	1 *Deus fortis*, T.154
9th		*Hosanna*[2] *Dulcis est cantica*	Dedication	2 *Pater ingenitus*, T.154	2 *Pater ingenitus*, T.154
				3 *Pater lumen*, T.216 Var.	3 *Pater lumen*, T.216 Var.
		9 †*Quem cuncti angeli*, T.86		4 *Deus pater ingenite*, T.154	4 *Deus pater ingenite*, T.154
8th		10 *Mundi fabricator*, T.223 (=4 above)		5 *Mundi fabricator*, T.223	5 *Mundi fabricator*, T.223
6th	9th	11 *Admirabilis splendor*, T.74	Christmas Day	6 *Admirabilis splendor*, T.74	6 *Admirabilis splendor*, T.74
	Indefessas uoces			7 *Quem cherubim atque seraphim*, T.63	
		12 †*Ante thronum Domini*, T.178		8 T.60	7 T.60
		13 †*Quem cherubim et seraphim*, T.223 Var.	T.223 (no trope); 3d	9 T.111 Var.	8 T.111 Var.
		Pie Christe descendisti	3d	10 T.9	9 T.9 Var.
Laudatur trina maiestas	8th (as in Ben 35)	14 [1] *Pax in caelo*, T.60 (? =66,67)		11 T.32 Var.	10 T.9
T.66; 1st		[2] *Laudatur trina maiestas*		12 T.57	11 *Quem cherubim atque seraphim*, T.63
			§8th		12 T.32 Var.
		15 §*Coronа iustitiae*, T.152 (=154)	§8th		
	§3d	§*Gloria Christe omnes resurgamus*			
—, T.223; Ascension		16 §*Quam pulchra est*, T.62#	*Deus pater ingenitus*, T.154; 7th	*Deus pater ingenite*, T.154; 4th	4th
Qui uenisti carnem sumens	*Deus pater ingenitus*, T.154; 1st	LACUNA (of a quaternion?)	*Qui uenisti carnem sumens*		
Christmas Day, Easter	*Qui uenisti carnem sumens*				
	Deus fortis, T.154; 2d		*Inuisibiliter penetrauit rex*, T.64	*Deus fortis*, T.154; 1st	1st
	Inuisibiliter penetrauit rex, T.64; 6th		(cf. 60,66,67)		
	(cf. T.60,66,67)		Ascension		
—	*Hosanna cuncta procedens*		*Hosanna cuncta procedens*; Ascension		
—	*Quem cherubim atque seraphim*, T.63; 7th		*Quem cherubim atque seraphim*, T.63; 1st	*Quem cherubim atque seraphim*, T.63; 6th	11th
			Hebraeorum pueri ramos		
			Also:		
			T.80; 5th (in Ben 38)		
			#T.226 Var.; 6th		
			Hosanna Saluifica tuum plasma		
		Montecassino	*Perpetuo numine* (34: *lumine*), T.49; Pentecost		

*Arrows pointing from the Bod 74 column call attention items in Ben 35 that may have been borrowed from a Roman collection like that of Bod 74.
†One of four unica in Ben 35.
‡Also in RoV C 52 and PdC A 47. These central Italian versions differ from that of Ben 34.

‖The incipit of T.109 is found in two missals, the Cassinese MC 127 and ZaMR 166 derived from a Cassinese model.
#Now incomplete.
§The only two sources known for *Corona iustitiae* with *Gloria Christe omnes resurgamus* and *Quam pulchra est*, respectively.

line only in Bod 74 and Ben 35. The Marian trope *Quam pulchra est* is likewise known only from these two manuscripts, and the respective versions of the two tropes in Bod 74 and Ben 35 are remarkably similar.[44] The ordinary collection of Ben 35 was copied at least thirty years after Bod 74 was completed in 1071. It is out of the question that these texts should have been copied into Bod 74 from Ben 35 or another Beneventan exemplar: rather, Ben 35 (or just possibly an earlier Beneventan manuscript, now lost) must have been copied from a Roman exemplar. The end of the Ben 35 collection, as it survives, thus has two pieces copied from Roman models, items *14* and *16*, separated by a new local composition, *15 Corona iustitiae*.

There are five of these "new" local compositions in Ben 35, four of them unica: items *1, 9, 12, 13*, and *15* in table 5. The last, *15 Corona iustitiae*, was later copied into Ben 34, as just remarked. The Ben 35 collection opens in typical fashion with one of these "new" compositions and the worst: *Antra modicis deserti*. The remaining new pieces were interspersed among older, borrowed Sanctus.

In summary, in the present truncated Sanctus collection of Ben 35, two of the three pieces in the south Italian core repertory survive in non-Cassinese, Beneventan versions. (The third piece of the core repertory may have been entered on a now-lost folio.) Two pieces came from a Roman collection and one piece from Nonantola. Of five "new" pieces compiled for the collection, four remained forever unica and a fifth was copied only in Ben 34. The proximate source for two (or three?) independent Hosanna pros(ul)as and the four tropeless Sanctus melodies inserted as items 2 through 5 near the start of the collection cannot now be guessed. Thus the collection of sixteen Sanctus in Ben 35, at least in the present state of the manuscript, turns out upon inspection to be less compendious than it first appeared.

TABLE 6. Sanctus in Ben 34 Collections and Distributed among the Propers†

Admirabilis splendor, T.74	Christmas Day (fol. 20^{r-v})
Immortalis et uerus, T.46	Epiphany (fol. 35^{r-v})
Caelestia sidera, T.197	Dedication (fol. 176^{r-v})
Hosanna¹ Plasmatum populum	
Hosanna² Dulcis est cantica	
Inuisibiliter penetrauit rex, T.64 (cf. 60,66,67)	Ascension (fol. 181^{r-v})
Hosanna cuncta procedens	
Perpetuo numine (34: *lumine*), T.49	Pentecost (fol. 190^{r-v})
T.213 Var.	All Saints (fols. 240^v–241^r)
Laudes Deo ore pio	

FIRST COLLECTION (fols. 282^v–284^r, followed by Agnus Dei)

1   *Quem cherubim atque seraphim*, T.63
       Hebraeorum pueri ramos
*2   *Altissimeque rector*, T.92
       Conditor alme
3   T.223
       Pie Christe descendisti
4   T.32
5   T.80

SECOND COLLECTION (fols. 285^r–286^r, after a lacuna "of three folios"‖ and before two Agnus Dei and several Kyrie melodies without verses)‡

            ?

6¹   #T.226 Var.
       #Hosanna Saluifica tuum plasma
*7²   *Deus pater ingenitus*, T.154
       Qui uenisti carnem sumens
8³   *Corona iustitiae*, T.152 (=154)
       Gloria Christe omnes resurgamus

---

*The three tropes of the south Italian core repertory.
†For the possible sources of certain Sanctus in Ben 34, see table 5, preceding.
‡Colored lines and clefs were not entered originally with the neumes of the second collection; clefs now present were added later. Missing folios just before the second collection may have consisted of more Agnus Dei plus the beginning of the second group of Sanctus, or they may have contained Sanctus chants only.
‖According to Mallet and Thibaut.
#Now incomplete.

The Distribution of Sanctus in Benevento 34

The twelve troped Sanctus in Ben 34 were distributed in a largely random manner: six among the propers and six in two discrete collections towards the end of the manuscript. Two Sanctus melodies without trope or prosula conclude the first collection. (See table 6, above.) The feasts whose propers received Sanctus tropes were Christmas Day, the Epiphany, the feast of Dedication of the church, Ascension Day, Pentecost, and All Saints' Day. Of these assignments, only that of *Inuisibiliter penetrauit rex* to Ascension Day is especially apt. None of the rubrical assignments in Urb 602—in cases where pieces were common to both manuscripts—was followed.

The first Sanctus collection of Ben 34 contains two tropes, one independent prosula, and the two abovementioned Sanctus melodies without trope or prosula (folios 282ᵛ–284ʳ). A collection of Agnus Dei beginning on folio 284ᵛ is interrupted by a lacuna of three folios (according to Mallet and Thibaut). Folio 285ʳ picks up the middle of **Hosanna Saluifica tuum plasma.** Two more troped Sanctus follow on the verso of folio 285 and on folio 286: the famous *Deus pater ingenitus* with **Qui uenisti carnem sumens** and then *Corona iustitiae* with **Gloria Christe omnes resurgamus,** probably composed for Ben 35. There is now no way to ascertain how many pieces the second collection once contained. The second collection was an afterthought, in turn followed by additional Agnus Dei melodies and several verseless Kyries.

The collection of Ben 34 seems mainly to have drawn upon sources from within the city of Benevento and secondarily on sources from Montecassino.[45] Cassinese influence upon the Sanctus repertory of Ben 34 amounts to less than might be expected—certainly less than in the repertories of proper tropes, of Kyrie verses, and of Gloria tropes. (See BTC I, pp. xx, xlv; BTC II/1, pp. xiii, xxxi–xxxiv; and BTC II/2, pp. x–xix.) However, the version of *Admirabilis splendor* copied in Ben 34 was based in part upon a Cassinese model rather than upon Ben 35 or Ben 38. And *Perpetuo numine*—in south Italy a trope found only at Montecassino and in Ben 34—begins in Ben 34 with the non-Cassinese wording *Perpetuo lumine,* an incipit otherwise known only from the manuscripts PaN 495 and Pst 121. *Inuisibiliter penetrauit rex* must ultimately derive from Rome and was probably copied from a Roman rather than from a Beneventan exemplar—unless it was present on a now-missing folio of Ben 35. *Immortalis et uerus,* assigned to the propers of the Epiphany, has concordances only with Mod 7, PdC A 47, and RoV C 52—uncommon concordances for Ben 34 but frequent for ordinary chants in Ben 35 and Bod 74. (*Immortalis et uerus* might have been copied from Ben 35 into Ben 34—see above.) The twin prosas **Hosanna Plasmatum populum** and **Hosanna Dulcis est cantica** were very likely copied from Ben 35, with one trope element, *Caelestia sidera,* added.[46] *Altissimeque rector* employs the non-Cassinese version of the text, but the first four elements were distributed in the base text more or less as in Urb 602 rather than as in Bod 74. (However, the remaining fragment of the Ben 35 version of this trope implies the same distribution of text as in Ben 34, so that Ben 35 might have been the source of the Ben 34 version. But there are other differences between the two versions; see the commentary and main text, pp. 55 and 12.)

Within the second small group of collected Sanctus in Ben 34, the non-Cassinese wording *Filius eius* (instead of *Filius dei,* as in Urb 602 and MC 546) is employed in *Deus pater ingenitus,* although its melodic variants tend to resemble those of Urb 602. Similarly, *Quem seraphim atque seraphim* + *Cui pueri Hebraeorum* does not follow Cassinese usage, in which the text was split into two separate Sanctus (see above). In Ben 34 the trope elements are kept together within a single Sanctus, and the prosula is expanded with new lines.

Two pros(ul)as have no companion tropes: *Pie Christe descendisti* (in the first Sanctus collection after two troped Sanctus and before two tropeless Sanctus) and **Hosanna Saluifica tuum plasma** (its surviving concluding fragment placed before the two troped Sanctus of the second collection). One cannot say what pieces might have preceded **Hosanna Saluifica tuum plasma** in Ben 34. Its fragmentary text is so remarkably similar to that of Urb 602 that it must either have been copied from Urb 602 or from an identical Cassinese exemplar. On the other hand, the prosa **Laudes Deo ore pio,** in the Ben 34 propers for All Saints' Day, does not use the special Cassinese element [2.ᴹᶜ] *Cęli regi terrę* nor the Urb 602 disposition of the piece as a trope for Sanctus rather than as a Hosanna prosa. These two Sanctus with Hosanna pros(ul)as and no trope (it will be remembered) concluded the Urb 602 collection, where they were assigned to Sundays.

The striking omission from the surviving Sanctus of Ben 34 is *Deus fortis.* Just possibly it was included on a now missing folio preceding the second collection. In Urb 602, *Deus fortis* was assigned to Easter Day. It was often sung in north and central Italy but is not found in the surviving collection of Ben 35, where *Corona iustitiae* may have been regarded as a replacement for it (see above). Possibly the Ben 34 scribe omitted *Deus fortis* (if he did omit it) for the same reason.

It is altogether likely that four of the pieces contained in Ben 34 but not now found in the Sanctus collection of Ben 35 as it survives were indeed present on the now-missing folios of Ben 35: namely, **Laudes Deo ore pio,** *Immortalis et uerus, Deus pater ingenitus,* and *Quem cherubim atque seraphim.* (To these four, the twin prosas **Hosanna Plasmatum populum** and **Hosanna Dulcis est cantica** could be added, although the trope element *Caelestia sidera* added to their Sanctus chant in Ben 34 is unique.) Furthermore, it is possible that the folios in Ben 35 which I suggest contained these pieces were the very ones used as copy exemplars for Ben 34—and then mislaid, never to be returned to the temporarily dismembered codex Ben 35.

Just one Sanctus in Ben 34 is clearly borrowed from a Cassinese source: the incomplete **Hosanna Saluifica tuum plasma.** The version in Ben 34 of *Admirabilis splendor* also owes something to Cassinese influence. Otherwise, the editor of Ben 34 drew mostly on local tradition for older Sanctus tropes and Hosanna pros(ul)as, probably using the collection of Ben 35 as his main source. If my suppositions about the contents of the missing folios of Ben 35 are even partly correct, then the Ben 34 scribe need not have much used Roman or other central Italian sources directly: he would have found the pieces that originated in these repertories at hand, for the most part already collected in Ben 35.

Notes

1. See Kenneth Levy, "The Byzantine Sanctus and Its Modal Tradition in East and West," *Annales musicologiques* 6 (1958–63):7–67, and the excursus on anaphoral chant in BTC II/1, p. xvi. The anaphoral-chant Sanctus found in south Italian MSS—many of them popular throughout Italy—include these melodies numbered in Peter Josef Thannabaur's index *Das einstimmige Sanctus der römischen Messe in der handschriftlichen Überlieferung des 11. bis 16. Jahrhunderts,* Erlanger Arbeiten zur Musikwissenschaft, vol. 1 (Munich, 1962)—henceforth "Thannabaur." They are listed here in the order of their appearance in BTC II/3: Thannabaur 74, 92, 45, 152, 154, ?64, 223, 60 (? = 66,67), 63, 86, 56 (a Norman melody), 41, 109, 216, Var., plus two such melodies that were not included in Thannabaur's index, designated "BTC-Scs 1" and "BTC-Scs 2."

2. Thus Thannabaur 154 (see BTC II/3, p. 68 and 71, *Deus pater ingenitus*) in Montecassino, Compactiones VI; Thannabaur 41 (see BTC II/3, p. 116) in three sources: RoC 1574, p. 36, RoV B 23, fol. 143^v, and MC 339, pp. 132 and 134; and Thannabaur 109 (see BTC II/3, p. 120) in MC 127, p. 313. Also see pp. xvii, xxi, and xxxi above.

3. See the sketched Historical Background in BTC I, pp. xii–xiv, and BTC II/1, pp. xxiv–xxv.

4. See BTC II/1, pp. xiii and xxiv–xxxvii, and BTC II/2, pp. x–xv.

5. The earliest examples known to me of the genre in southern Italy are Ben 40, fol. 26^r, *Deus pater ingenitus* with the prosula *Qui uenisti carnem sumens* and Thannabaur 154, and fol. 104^{r-v}, **Hosanna Plasmatum populum** and **Hosanna Dulcis est cantica** with BTC-Scs 3 (related to a variant of Thannabaur 111). See BTC II/3, pp. 63, 24; 71, 38; and 123, 128.

6. Ben 40 has the two just mentioned in n. 5 above; Ben 38 has six Sanctus in a later supplement at the end of the MS, only the first of which, Thannabaur 74, is troped, with *Admirabilis splendor*—plus one more, Thannabaur 223 with the Hosanna prosa **Laudes Deo ore pio,** entered over the erased old Beneventan mass for Pentecost. If there was a collection of ordinary chants at the end of Ben 39, it has disappeared.

According to Jean Mallet and André Thibaut, *Les Manuscrits en écriture bénéventaine de la Bibliothèque Capitulaire de Bénévent,* 2 vols. (Paris, 1984–), vol. 2 (in press), a folio is missing between fols. 195 and 196 and a quaternion between fols. 198 and 199. (This information was kindly communicated to me in advance of publication by Dom Mallet.)

7. Hosanna prosulas or prosas are usually inserted between or replace the final *Hosanna* and *in excelsis* of the Sanctus text. Supposedly the prosula text was underlaid to the melisma at the end of Hosanna, but many instances escape this definition. At least one set of paired versets sung to the same musical phrase, repeated, is usually present. Longer texts having two or more such sets of paired versets, each to a different melody, are designated *prosa* in BTC II/3; but a distinction between *prosa, prosula,* and *prosunzola* (in Bod 74) is not evident from the normal abbreviation *ps* used in south Italian MSS. Usually their style is easy to distinguish from that of Sanctus tropes, but an adequate single definition to cover all pros(ul)as is impossible to frame. See the discussion by Gunilla Iversen, ed., *Corpus Troporum VII, Tropes du Sanctus,* Studia Latina Stockholmiensia 34 (Stockholm, 1990), pp. 29–34—referred to hereafter as CT 7. Also see Editorial Methods above, pp. xii–xiv.

8. See BTC II/3, pp. 71 and 38. Further references to CT 7 and other works, as well as a complete listing of south Italian sources, are given in the individual commentary just cited and in later citations. Note especially the appearance of Thannabaur 154 as a post-preface incipit in the Cassinese altar-book fragment listed under Sources, p. 3 below.

9. In Urb 602, *Qui uenisti carnem sumens* is also cued as a Hosanna prosula to be sung after the trope *Deus fortis* with Thannabaur 154. The isolated concordances for *Qui uenisti carnem sumens* in the Italian MSS Mod 7 and RoV C 52 are hard to account for. In both cases, the prosula follows the single-element trope *Cuius in laude* (otherwise unknown in Italy, and elsewhere known only from two northern French sources) sung with Thannabaur 223. Both Mod 7 (perhaps from Forlimpopoli, near Ravenna) and RoV C 52 (central Italy?) share many ordinary tropes with the south Italian repertory and especially with Bod 74; but their respective versions of texts and melodies vary greatly.

10. See BTC II/3, pp. 53 and 3. For the wandering verse *Indefessas uoces,* see CT 7, nos. 1F, 62D, and 63A.

11. See BTC II/3, pp. 110 and 106. For the prosa *[Hosanna] Omnes tua gratia,* see below.

12. See BTC II/3, pp. 93 and 83. The Sanctus melody, Thannabaur 49, appears without trope in MC 546 and Ben 38.

13. See BTC II/3, pp. 55 and 12, for a detailed study of text and music, with concordances.

14. The Hosanna prosa *Laudes Deo ore pio* (see below) rivaled the popularity of these three texts, but *Laudes Deo ore pio* is not found in Bod 74.

15. Also see BTC II/3, p. 32. The trope appears in Bod 74 and in Urb 602. In the latter MS it is rubricked *In resurrectione domini. Et sci petri.* It is not found at Benevento, where it seems to have been replaced by a local product perhaps meant for Easter, *Corona iustitiae* (see below).

16. See BTC II/3, pp. 98 and 93.

17. See BTC II/3, pp. 82 and 64. The grounds for thinking the Ben 35 scribe copied a Nonantola source are circumstantial but compelling. In the Sanctus collection of Ben 35, *Admirabilis splendor* (the eleventh piece now surviving) immediately follows *Mundi fabricator*. This placement for *Admirabilis splendor* is exceptional: in the Cassinese collections it comes third. Now these two pieces appear in the order of Ben 35 and adjacent *only* in two MSS from Nonantola, RoC 1741 and RoN 1343—and in Ben 35. (In a third, slightly later Sanctus collection from Nonantola, BoU 2824, they still appear in that order but are separated by three Sanctus melodies without tropes.) There are other connections between the Nonantola tropers and the Ben 35 ordinary collection: see for instance BTC II/2, pp. 25 and 29–31. The similarity of ordering leads me to think that the editor of Ben 35 borrowed *Mundi fabricator* from a Nonantola collection. Also see below, p. lxxi.

18. See BTC II/3, pp. 74 and 46.

19. For various forms of this text, including the original Gloria trope, see BTC II/3, pp. 90 and 76. As a Gloria trope it appears in Ox 222 and RoC 3830, both from Breme-Novalesa. In Mod 7 it is found both as Gloria trope and Sanctus trope. Mark Alan Leach first pointed out the origins of the text in his dissertation, "The *Gloria in excelsis Deo* Tropes of the Breme-Novalesa Community and the Repertory in North and Central Italy," 2 vols. (University of North Carolina at Chapel Hill, 1986), 1:36 (table 2) and 300–304; 2:97–100.

20. See BTC II/3, pp. 79 and 57, and the references to the articles by Atkinson and Iversen.

21. Ben 40, fol. 104[r–v]; see BTC II/3, Appendix I, pp. 123 and 128, where notice is taken of Atkinson's important article "Text, Music." The Sanctus, BTC-Scs 3, is similar in some respects to Thannabaur 111, Var, pp. 129 and 149.

22. See BTC II/3, pp. 63 and 24.

23. See BTC II/3, pp. 110 and 106.

24. See BTC II/3, pp. 104 and 104.

25. See BTC II/3, pp. 71 and 38.

26. See the commentary for *Pie Christe descendisti*, pp. 84–86, and p. 64.

27. See BTC II/3, pp. 96 and 90.

28. See BTC II/3, pp. 77 and 48.

29. See BTC II/1, pp. 44–47 and 110. In the MS, the verse begins *Incarnatum quoque*.

30. See BTC II/3, pp. 87 and 72.

31. See BTC II/2, pp. 5–7 and 3. For "the falling-fourth composer," see the commentary for BTC-Ky 1 and the references given in BTC II/1, pp. 81–82.

32. *Vt queant laxis*, AH 50, no. 96, and *Almi prophetae progenies*. AH 27, no. 137. Also see CT 7, pp. 75–76 (no. 8).

33. See BTC II/1, pp. xxv–xxxvii.

34. See BTC II/2, pp. xi–xv.

35. See notes 5 and 6 above. Also see BTC II/1, pp. xii–xiii. In the earliest Beneventan graduals, Sanctus tropes are entered incidentally, not systematically. Their inclusion among the propers is modeled upon the sometime presence of the base ordinary texts in the propers of the Easter vigil mass, along with the preface(s) and the canon.

36. See Editorial Methods, pp. xii–xiii above.

37. The two Sanctus were assigned to Palm Sunday and St. Michael—neither of which days was given other ordinary tropes. See above, p. lxv.

38. See BTC II/3, pp. 77 and 48 (Thannabaur ?64 [cf. 60, 66, 67]) and Appendix II, pp. 124 and 131, where all the sources for the Easter verses are listed and the texts given in full.

39. See note 9 above. Mod 7, dated to the second half of the eleventh century and thought to come from Forlimpopoli or elsewhere in the Ravenna area, contains five of the six non-original Sanctus in Bod 74. It does not have *Deus pater ingenitus* but does have the prosula text *Qui uenisti carnem sumens*. Mod 7 also contains four other texts not found in Bod 74 but found in either Ben 35 or in Ben 34. It has only one text—the Hosanna prosula *Agie altissime*—not known from south Italian manuscripts. The Mod 7 versions of texts common to Bod 74 are generally similar but are far from identical, and their ordering is quite different from that of Bod 74.

The collection of central Italian fragments in BoC 7 contains three texts found in Bod 74 and four not found anywhere in south Italy. To 18 (twelfth-century, from Bobbio) has a total of eight (or nine?) texts for Sanctus: four of these are in Bod 74 and two others are found at Benevento. Three (or possibly four) texts are not found in southern Italy. Finally, RoV C 52 (see n. 9, above) has six pieces found in Bod 74. The other three appear in manuscripts from Benevento.

But the trope versions in these manuscripts—especially the melodies of Mod 7 and RoV C 52, which I have examined—often vary greatly from those in Bod 74. There can be no question of direct copying in either direction, but only of the sharing of a repertory, undoubtedly through the mediation of several manuscripts now lost.

40. See above, p. lxiii, and n. 8.

41. See above, p. lxv, and BTC II/3, pp. 98 and 93.

42. See above, p. lxv, n. 17, and the citations from Hiley's articles under References on p. 83 of BTC II/3. See especially David Hiley, "The Chant of Norman Sicily: Interactions between the Norman and Italian Traditions," in *Atti del XIV Congresso della Società Internazionale di Musicologia, Trasmissione e recezione delle forme di cultura musicale*, II. Study Sessions 7, Tradizioni periferiche della monodia liturgica medioevale in Italia, ed. by Lorenzo Bianconi, F. Alberto Gallo, Angelo Pompilio, and Donatella Restani (Turin, 1990), pp. 92–107.

43. One of the versions of Gloria in excelsis, Bosse 39 (Gloria A) copied in Ben 35 may come from Nonantola, and possibly the Gloria trope *Quem nouitate*, also in Ben 35. See BTC II/2, pp. 22–31.

Admirabilis splendor in Ben 35 is much closer to the version of Bod 74 than to any Nonantolan version. On the other hand, melody and words of *Mundi fabricator* in Ben 35 closely resemble the Nonantolan version of RoC 1741, fols. 37[v]–38[r]. Where the two versions diverge, the customary carelessness and inattention of the Ben 35 text-scribe in providing for syllable underlay, coupled with Beneventan misunderstanding of Nonantolan notation, would suffice to explain the variants.

44. See above, p. lxvii, and note 27.

45. Cf. the description of Ben 34 in the General Introduction to BTC I, p. xvi.

46. The melodic alterations for [1.¹] . . . *et qui [uerum] fore promit ore Christum* almost certainly stem from the inadvertent omission of the word *uerum* by the text scribe of Ben 34. See BTC II/3, pp. 63 and 24.

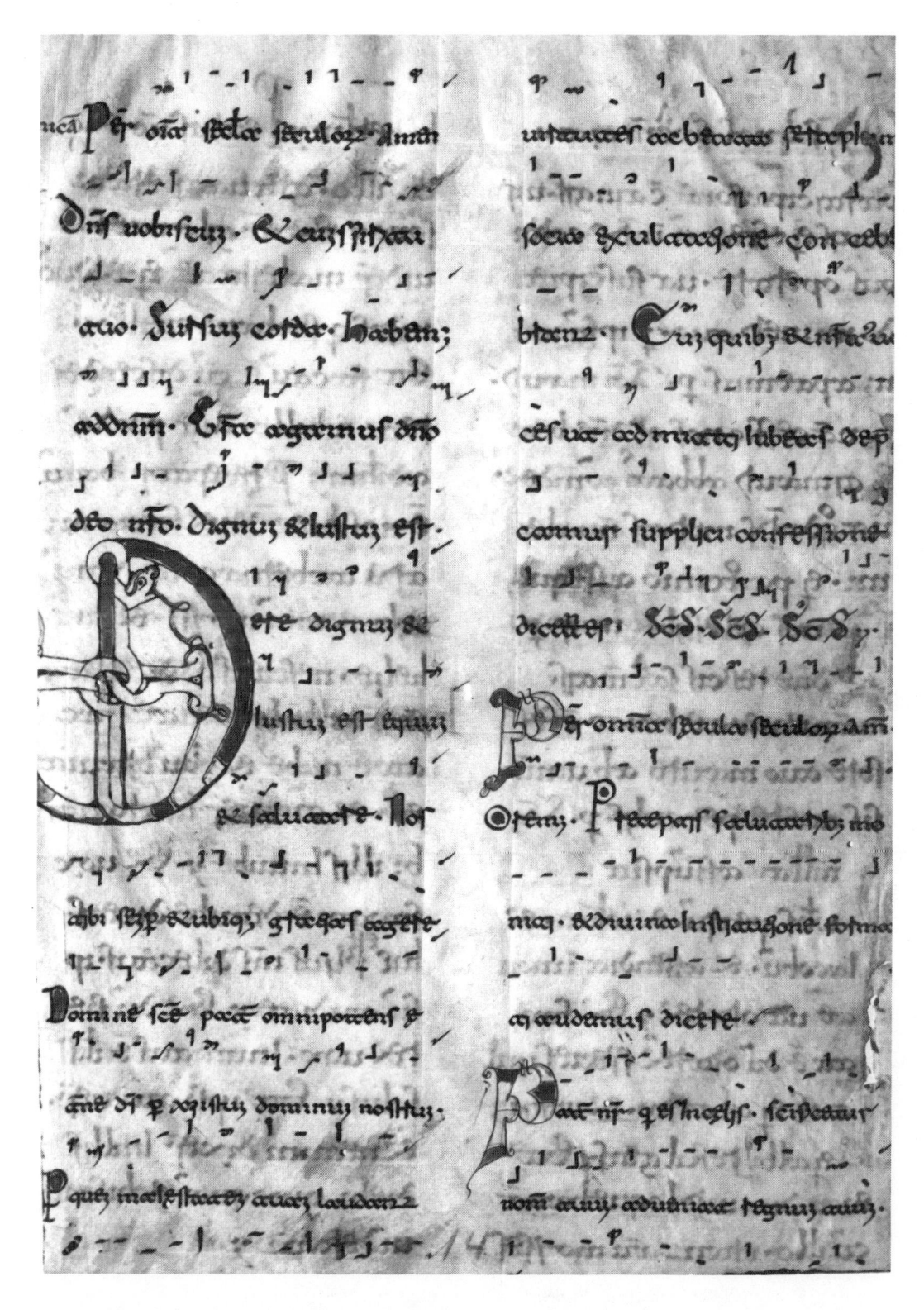

Plate 1. Montecassino, Archivio della Badia, leaf formerly in Compactiones VI Dialogue, common preface (CP 687), Sanctus incipit (Thannabaur 154), followed by the exordium and first phrases of Pater noster, all with standard Cassinese Sunday and festal chant, nearly identical to that in MC 339. Precisely diastematic Cassinese notation *in campo aperto*, ?1060–85. A line of music and text and the text missing beneath the lowest neumes has been cut off. From a sacramentary, missal, or gradual.

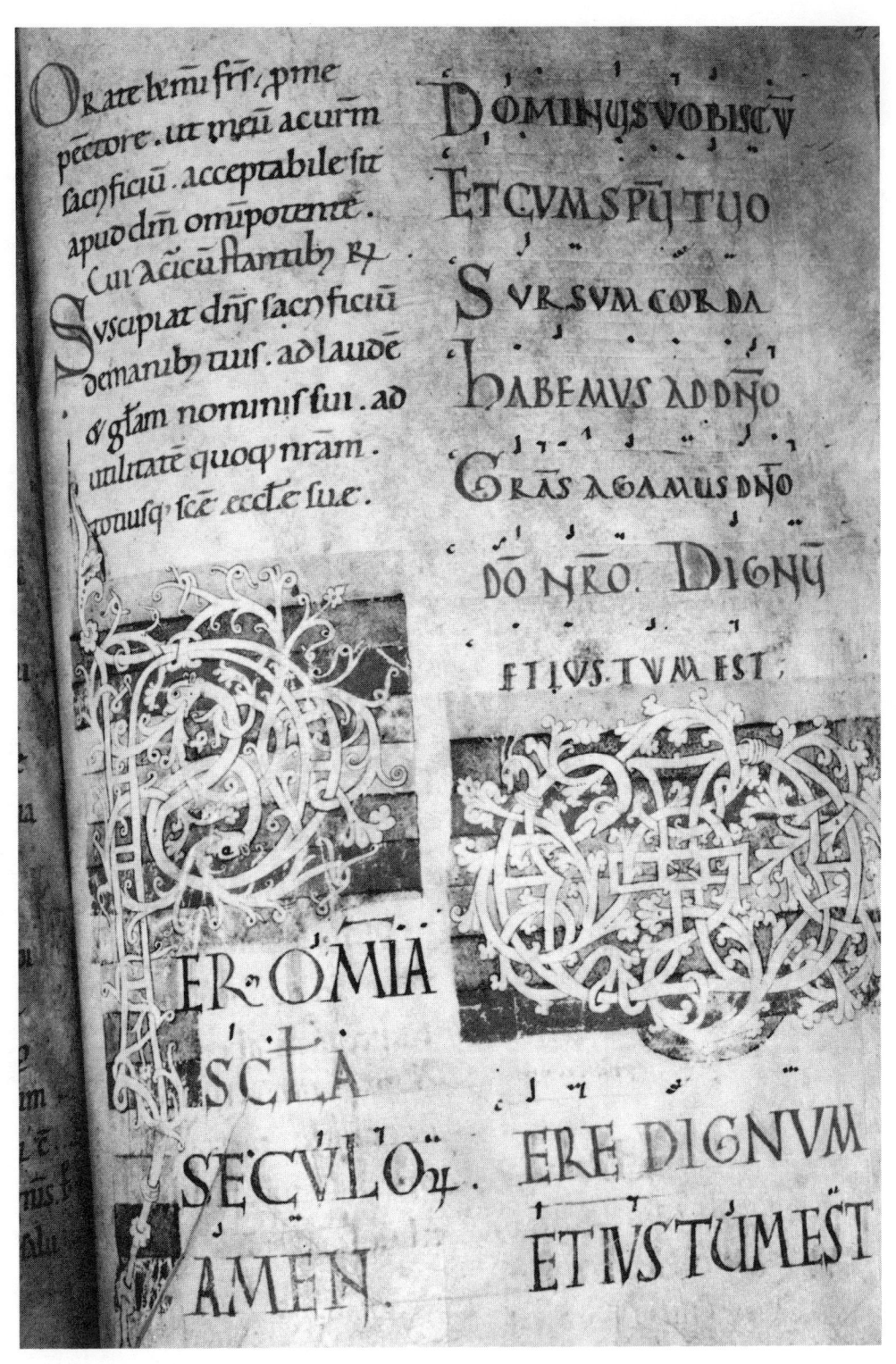

Plate 2. Rome, Biblioteca Vallicelliana, MS B 23, fol. 143ʳ
Dialogue and beginning of common preface (CP 687), preceded by the celebrant's
bidding *Orate . . . fratres* and his ministers' response *Suscipiat dominus sacrificium de
manibus tuis* at the offertory. Originally notated *in campo aperto* with heighted neumes
blending central Italian and Beneventan features. The clef for c (or C?) was later
added and later still the intermittent red F (or f?) line. The single preface chant in
a monastic missal in use at San Bartolomeo, Norcia, in the early twelfth century.

Plate 3. Rome, Biblioteca Vallicelliana, MS B 23, fol. 143ᵛ

Continuation of the notated common preface begun on fol. 143ʳ, followed by an unnotated preface for Lent, *Qui corporali ieiunio* (CP 863), and the notated proper-preface conclusion *Et ideo . . . dicentes,* leading into an entire notated Sanctus (Thannabaur 41). The notes of Sanctus were heighted so as to begin e ee d (or E EE D) in relation to the preface but the Sanctus was supplied with an F clef and red line, so that it now begins a aa G . The prayer *Aperi domine os meum* and *Te igitur* (fol. 144ʳ) with the rest of the canon follow.

Manuscripts and Publications Cited

List of Manuscript Sigla

The following list identifies and provides a summary description for each manuscript source cited by siglum in BTC II/3. Sources for transcriptions in the main text of BTC II/3 are marked below with asterisks. For detailed descriptions of the principal sources, consult the General Introduction in BTC I, pp. xvi–xix.

Apt 17	Apt, Basilique de Sainte Anne, MS 17(5). Troper-proser. Apt, middle 11c. See CT 5.
Apt 18	Apt, Basilique de Sainte Anne, MS 18(4). Troper-proser. Southeast France (?), late 10c, or "ca. 1000." See CT 5.
Ba 5	Bamberg, Staatsbibliothek, MS Lit. 5 (Ed. V. 9). Tonary, troper, proser. Reichenau, 1001.
Baltimore W 6	Baltimore, Walters Art Gallery, MS W.6. A votive full missal with selected masses from temporal and sanctoral. Copied for use at Canosa in Apulia in the middle or late 11c, in part from an archaic monastic exemplar. See Rehle, *Missale Beneventanum von Canosa*.
Barc 1408/9	Barcelona, Biblioteca Central, Fragment 1408, ix. Septimania, 11/12c.
BAV	Vatican, Biblioteca Apostolica Vaticana.
Ben 19/20	Benevento, Biblioteca Capitolare, MSS 19 and 20. *Pars hiemalis* and *pars aestiua*, respectively of a *liber typicus* (mixed breviary-missal) for non-monastic use. Benevento, 12c. Common prefaces in both parts and appropriately divided proper prefaces have nearly the same verbal text as Lo 3511. Some chants are the identical; others differ from those in Lo 3511 and even between the companion volumes. (See p. lxii above.)
Ben 21	Benevento, Biblioteca Capitolare, MS 21. Office antiphoner. Benevento (not San Lupo), 12c.
(Ben 29)	= Lo 3511
Ben 33	Benevento, Biblioteca Capitolare, MS 33. Full missal. South Italian, late 10c or early 11c. Used in the diocese of Salerno by the 13c. Facsimile, Paléographie musicale, vol. 20.
*Ben 34	Benevento, Biblioteca Capitolare, MS 34 (*olim* 25). Gradual. Benevento, early or middle 12c. Facsimile, Paléographie musicale, vol. 15.
*Ben 35	Benevento, Biblioteca Capitolare, MS 35 (*olim* 26). Gradual. Benevento, early 12c.
*Ben 38	Benevento, Biblioteca Capitolare, MS 38 (*olim* 27). Gradual. Benevento, shortly before 1050.
*Ben 40	Benevento, Biblioteca Capitolare, MS 40 (*olim* 29). Gradual. Benevento, probably Santa Sofia, before 1050. Facsimile, *Benevento, Biblioteca Capitolare 40, Graduale*, Codices Gregoriani, 1991.
BoC 7	Bologna, Civico Museo Bibliografico Musicale, MS Q7 (=86). Liturgical fragments. Italian, 11–12c.
*Bod 74	Cologny-Geneva, Bibliotheca Bodmeriana, MS 74. Gradual with old Roman chant. Rome, Santa Cecilia, 1071. Facsimile, *Das Graduale von Santa Cecilia in Trastevere*.
BoU 2748	Bologna, Biblioteca Universitaria, MS 2748 (716). Processional, proser, kyrial. Brescia, 12c.
BoU 2824	Bologna, Biblioteca Universitaria, MS 2824. Troper, proser. Nonantola, San Silvestro, late 11c.
Cai 75	Cambrai, Bibliothèque Municipale, MS 75 (76). Troper, kyrial, gradual. Arras, St. Vaast, middle 11c.
Cai 164	Cambrai, Bibliothèque Municipale 164 (159). Sacramentary of Hildoard. A direct copy of the Hadrianum, the Roman edition of the Gregorian sacramentary sent to Charlemagne by the pope. Written 811–12, perhaps at Cambrai.

CC 473	Cambridge, Corpus Christi College, MS 473. Troper, proser. Winchester, Old Minster, 996–1006.
Du 6	Durham, University Library, MS Cosin. V. V. 6. Gradual, kyrial, proser. Canterbury, Christ Church (?), late 11c (after 1066) or early 12c.
Hu 4	Huesca, Biblioteca de la Catedral, MS 4. Troper, proser. San Juan de la Peña, middle 12c.
Lo 13	London, British Library, Royal MS 8 C. XIII. Troper-proser. London?/St. Benoît-sur-Loire, late 11c.
*Lo 3511	(= Ben 29) London, British Library, Egerton MS 3511 (*olim* Benevento, Biblioteca Capitolare, MS 29). Full missal based on a Cassinese model. Benevento, San Pietro *intra muros*, early or middle 12c.
Ma 288	Madrid, Biblioteca Nacional, MS 288 (C 151). Troper, proser. Cappella Palatina of Ruggero I (Sicily); later Palermo. Early 12c.
Ma 289	Madrid, Biblioteca Nacional, MS 289 (C 153). Troper, proser. Cappella Palatina of Ruggero I or II; Palermo, ca. 1140?
Ma 19421	Madrid, Biblioteca Nacional, MS 19421 (C 88). Troper, proser. Catania, third quarter of 12c.
MaA 51	Madrid, Biblioteca de la Real Academia de la Historia, MS 51. San Millán de la Cogolla, late 11c or early 12c.
MC 127	Montecassino, Archivio della Badia, MS 127. Full missal. Montecassino and Albaneta, 1058–87 ("tempore Desiderii descriptus").
MC 271	Montecassino, Archivio della Badia, MS 271 (palimpsest, lower writing). Fragments of a pre-Hadrianic Gregorian sacramentary with lectionary written no later than 700, probably earlier, but not before 668. Descended "du Grégorien gélasianisé de Saint-Pierre [au Vatican]," but probably written in north Italy (Ravenna?).
MC 339	Montecassino, Archivio della Badia, MS 339. Sacramentary of Desiderius, abbot of Montecassino, 1058–87.
MC 426	Montecassino, Archivio della Badia, MS 426. Votive missal from the Montecassino region (but not the abbey itself), having partial notation for some propers. Late 10c or early 11c.
MC 506	Montecassino, Archivio della Badia, MS 506. Hymnal, almost entirely unnotated. "The lower script of the palimpsest portion is Beneventan, saec. x/xi."
*MC 546	Montecassino, Archivio della Badia, MS 546. Gradual (winter). Montecassino, late 12c or early 13c.
Mod 7	Modena, Biblioteca Capitolare, MS O. I. 7. Gradual with tropes and proses. Forlimpopoli (region of Ravenna), late 11c.
Mod 16	Modena, Biblioteca Capitolare, MS O. I. 16. Kyrial, cantatory, processional. Modena, early 13c.
Msrt 73	Montserrat, Biblioteca del Abadia, MS 73. Troper-proser. Septimania (Toulouse?), 12c.
Mza 77	Monza, Biblioteca Capitolare, MS c.14/77. Gradual, kyrial, proser. Monza, late 12c.
Ott 145	Vatican, Biblioteca Apostolica Vaticana, MS Ott. lat. 145. Monastic miscellany including *Mandatum* with alternative old Beneventan chants. Benevento, Santa Sofia, early–middle 11c.
Ott 576	Vatican, Biblioteca Apostolica Vaticana, MS Ott. lat. 576. Full missal. South Italian, late 12c–early 13c.
Ox 222	Oxford, Bodleian Library, MS Douce 222. Troper, prosulary, proser. Breme-Novalesa, middle 11c (Planchart) or late 11c (Leach).
Ox 775	Oxford, Bodleian Library, MS Bodley 775. Troper, proser. Winchester, Old Minster, 1050.
PaA 1169	Paris, Bibliothèque de l'Arsenal, MS 1169. Troper-proser. Autun, St. Nazaire, 996–1024.
PaN 495	Paris, Bibliothèque Nationale, n.a. latin, MS 495. Troper, proser. Gerona, 12c.
PaN 778	Paris, Bibliothèque Nationale, fonds latin, MS 778. Troper, proser. Narbonne, 12c.
PaN 887	Paris, Bibliothèque Nationale, fonds latin, MS 887. Troper, sequentiary, proser. Aquitanian, 11c.
PaN 903	Paris, Bibliothèque Nationale, fonds latin, MS 903. Gradual, troper, proser. St. Yrieix, before 1031. Facsimile of gradual, Paléographie musicale, vol. 13.

PaN 909	Paris, Bibliothèque Nationale, fonds latin, MS 909. Troper, sequentiary, proser. Limoges, St. Martial, 11c.	PdC A 47	Padua, Biblioteca Capitolare, MS A 47. Gradual with tropes and proses, kyrial. Ravenna, 12c.
PaN 1086	Paris, Bibliothèque Nationale, fonds latin, MS 1086. Processional, troper, proser, kyrial. Limoges, St. Leonard, late 12c–early 13c.	PdC D 47	Padua, Biblioteca Capitolare, MS D 47. Pre-Hadrianic Gregorian sacramentary, Deshusses' type II, known as the *Paduense*, encased in material borrowed from 8th-c. Gelasian sacramentaries. Written in the 2d quarter or middle of the 9c, probably in northeast France or possibly northern Italy.
PaN 1087	Paris, Bibliothèque Nationale, fonds latin, MS 1087. Gradual. Cluny, ca. 1075.		
PaN 1107	Paris, Bibliothèque Nationale, fonds latin, MS 1107. Full missal, kyrial, proser. St. Denis, after 1254.	Pia 65	Piacenza, Biblioteca Capitolare, MS 65. Tonary, hymnal, gradual, troper-proser, antiphoner, theoretical writings. Piacenza, cathedral, late 12c.
PaN 1118	Paris, Bibliothèque Nationale, fonds latin, MS 1118. Troper, tonary, sequentiary, proser. Auch (?), 985–96.	Pst 121	Pistoia, Biblioteca Capitolare, MS C 121. Troper, proser. Pistoia, 11c.
PaN 1120	Paris, Bibliothèque Nationale, fonds latin, MS 1120. Troper, proser. Limoges, St. Martial, ca. 1000.	Reg 316	= Reginensis 316 = [Sacramentarium] Reginense. Vatican, Biblioteca Apostolica Vaticana, MS Regin. lat. 316. The old Gelasian sacramentary. Reproduces a Roman but nonpapal collection of mass prayers edited in the latter part of the 7c for priests in titular and suburban churches, but copied with Frankish additions at Chelles, east of Paris, middle 8c.
PaN 1137	Paris, Bibliothèque Nationale, fonds latin, MS 1137. Cantatory, sequentiary, proser. Limoges, 11c.		
PaN 1139	Paris, Bibliothèque Nationale, fonds latin, MS 1139. Proser, troper, miscellany. Region of Limoges, 11c–13c.		
PaN 1177	Paris, Bibliothèque Nationale, n. a. latin, MS 1177. Cantatory, prosulary, proser. Southern France, late 11c.	RoC 1574	Rome, Biblioteca Casanatense, MS 1574. Monastic compendium: psalter, antiphoner, hymnal, mass ordo, etc. From the northern border of the Beneventan zone, perhaps Gaeta. Notation of preface chant 12c or early 13c; parts of the MS are earlier.
PaN 1235	Paris, Bibliothèque Nationale, n. a. latin, MS 1235. Gradual, tonary, hymnal, troper. Nevers, St. Cyr, 12c.		
PaN 1871	Paris, Bibliothèque Nationale, n. a. latin, MS 1871. Troper, sequentiary, proser. Moissac, St. Pierre, 11c.	RoC 1741	Rome, Biblioteca Casanatense, MS 1741 (C.VI.2). Troper, proser, processional. Nonantola, 11c.
PaN 7185	Paris, Bibliothèque Nationale, fonds latin, MS 7185. Miscellany, including works of Boethius on arithmetic and music and various fragments of notation. St. Benoît-sur-Loire, early 12c.	RoC 3830	Rome, Biblioteca Casanatense, MS 3830. Three fragmentary sections from a cantatory, troper, and proser. North Italy, early 12c.
		RoN 1343	Rome, Biblioteca Nazionale, MS 1343 (Sessorianus 62). Troper, proser, processional. Nonantola, 11c.
PaN 7193	Paris, Bibliothèque Nationale, fonds latin, MS 7193. Folios 41–56 supply the missing end of BAV Reg. 316, the old Gelasian sacramentary, copied at Chelles, east of Paris, ca. middle 8c.		
		RoV B 8	Rome, Biblioteca Vallicelliana, MS B 8. A monastic missal, assembled in the late 11c, partly from an older sacramentary, for use at Sant'Eustizio, Val Castoriana, near Norcia.
PaN 9449	Paris, Bibliothèque Nationale, fonds latin, MS 9449. Gradual-troper-proser. Nevers, St. Cyr, middle 11c.		
PaN 10508	Paris, Bibliothèque Nationale, fonds latin, MS 10508. Troper, proser, cantatory, theoretical treatises. St. Évroult, early 12c.	RoV B 23	Rome, Biblioteca Vallicelliana, MS B 23. Monastic full missal. San Bartolomeo, Norcia, early 12c.

RoV B 24　Rome, Biblioteca Vallicelliana, MS B 24. Sacramentary in Roman minuscule script, with two prefaces using Beneventan notation added. Subiaco, 1075.

RoV C 32　Rome, Biblioteca Vallicelliana, MS C 32. A monastic manual, chiefly for ministrations to the ill and the dying, with offices and masses for the dead. Region of Montecassino, late 11c.

RoV C 52　Rome, Biblioteca Vallicelliana, MS C 52. Gradual, troper, proser, kyrial. The former ascription to Norcia, Sant' Eustizio, cannot stand without support of script, illumination, or sanctoral (Supino Martini, *Roma e l'area grafica romanesca*, p. 335). Benedictine, perhaps Tuscany, early 12c.

SG 484　St. Gall, Stiftsbibliothek, MS 484. Troper, proser-sequentiary. St. Gall, 965–1000.

SP B 79　Vatican, Biblioteca Apostolica Vaticana, Archivio di San Pietro, MS B 79. Office antiphoner with old Roman chant, with appended pieces for the ordinary of the mass. Rome, San Pietro, early 13c.

To 18　Turin, Biblioteca Nazionale Universitaria, MS 897 (F.IV.18). Gradual with tropes, proser. Bobbio, early 12c.

Trent 1590　= Tridentinus 1590. Trent, Museo Provinciale d'Arte (Castello del Buonconsiglio), MS 1590. Gregorian sacramentary based on a pre-Hadrianic papal Roman core dated 685–87, supplemented in the early 9c at Salzburg and probably copied somewhere in northern Italy for use at Trent, first half 9c.

Tsa 135　Tortosa, Archivio de la Catedral, MS 135. Troper, proser, kyrial, written for the cathedral of Tortosa, 1228–64.

*Urb 602　Vatican, Biblioteca Apostolica Vaticana, MS Urb. lat. 602. Troper, proser, processional. Montecassino, late 11c.

Vat 4770　Vatican, Biblioteca Apostolica Vaticana, MS Vat. lat. 4770. Full missal, unnotated. Central Italy, late 10c to early 11c.

Vat 6082　Vatican, Biblioteca Apostolica Vaticana, MS Vat. lat. 6082. Full missal. Montecassino or San Vincenzo al Volturno, early 12c.

Vce 161　Vercelli, Biblioteca Capitolare, MS 161. Gradual, kyrial, proser. Vercelli, middle or late 11c.

Vich 105　Vich, Museo Episcopal, MS 105 (CXI). Troper, proser. Vich, middle 11c.

Vich 106　Vich, Museo Episcopal, MS 106 (Rip. 31). Troper, proser, liturgical plays. Vich, 12c.

Vro 90　(= Vro 85) Verona, Biblioteca Capitolare, MS XC (85). Collectanea with tropes. Monza or Mantua, ca. 900.

Vro 107　(= Vro 100) Verona, Biblioteca Capitolare, MS CVII (100). Troper, proser. Mantua, San Benedetto, ca. 1000.

ZaMR 166　Zagreb, Nacionalna i Sveučilišna Biblioteka, Metropolitana Raria MS 166. Full missal, Region of Montecassino; later, Dalmatia, 12c.

List of Cited Works with Abbreviations

The following list is intended to include all works cited in BTC II/3, as well as short reference forms used in the Commentary and the Notes.

AH = *Analecta Hymnica Medii Aevi*. Edited by Clemens Blume and Guido M. Dreves. 55 vols. Leipzig, 1886–1922.

AH 2 = Guido Maria Dreves, ed. *Hymnarius Moissiacensis. Das Hymnar der Abtei Moissac im 10. Jahrhundert*. Analecta Hymnica Medii Aevi, vol. 2. Leipzig, 1887.

AH 7 = Guido Maria Dreves, ed. *Prosarium Lemovicense. Die Prosen der Abtei St. Martial zu Limoges, aus Troparien des 10., 11. und 12. Jahrhunderts*. Analecta Hymnica Medii Aevi, vol. 7. Leipzig, 1889.

AH 17 = Guido Maria Dreves, ed. *Hymnodia Hiberica. Liturgische Reimofficien aus spanischen Brevieren. Im Anhange: Carmina Compostellana, die Lieder des s.g. Codex Calixtinus*. Analecta Hymnica Medii Aevi, vol. 17. Leipzig, 1894.

AH 27 = Clemens Blume, ed. *Hymnodia Gotica. Die mozarabischen Hymnen des alt-spanischen Ritus*. Analecta Hymnica Medii Aevi, vol. 27. Leipzig, 1897.

AH 47 = Clemens Blume and Henry Marriott Bannister, eds. *Tropi Graduales. Tropen des Missale im Mittelalter I: Tropen zum Ordinarium Missae*. Analecta Hymnica Medii Aevi, vol. 47. Leipzig, 1905.

AH 50 = Guido Maria Dreves, ed. *Hymnographi Latini. Lateinische Hymnendichter des Mittelalters. Zweite Folge*. Analecta Hymnica Medii Aevi, vol. 50. Leipzig, 1907.

AM = *Antiphonale Monasticum pro Diurnis Horis juxta Vota RR. DD. Abbatum Congregationum Confoederatum Ordinis Sancti Benedicti. A Solesmensibus Monachis restitutum.* Paris, Tournai, and Rome, 1934.

Amalarius, Symphosius. *Liber Officium.* In *Amalarii Episcopi Opera Liturgica Omnia,* vol. 2, edited by Jean Michel Hanssens. Studi e testi, 139. Vatican City, 1948.

Apel, Willi. *Gregorian Chant.* Bloomington and Indianapolis, 1958.

Ashworth, Henry. "The Liturgical Prayers of St. Gregory the Great." *Traditio* 15 (1959): 107–61.

Atkinson, Charles M. "Music as 'Mistress of the Words': *Laudes deo ore pio.*" In *Liturgische Tropen: Referate zweier Colloquien des Corpus Troporum in München (1983) und Canterbury (1984),* edited by Gabriel Silagi, pp. 67–82. Münchener Beiträge zur Mediävistik und Renaissance-Forschung, 36. Munich, 1985.

———. "Text, Music, and the Persistence of Memory in *Dulcis Est Cantica.*" In *Recherches nouvelles sur les tropes liturgiques,* edited by Wulf Arlt and Gunilla Björkvall, pp. 96–117. Studia Latina Stockholmiensia, 36. Stockholm, 1993.

Bailey, Terence. *Antiphon and Psalm in the Ambrosian Office.* Musicological Studies, 50/3. Ottawa, 1994.

Bailey, Terence, and Paul Merkley. *The Antiphons of the Ambrosian Office.* Musicological Studies, 50/1. Ottawa, 1989.

Bannister, Henry Marriott. *Monumenti vaticani di paleografia musicale latina.* 2 vols. Codices e Vaticanis Selecti, Phototypice Expressi, 11. Leipzig, 1913.

Benevento, Biblioteca Capitolare 40, Graduale. Edited by Nino Albarosa and Alberto Turco, with prefatory essays by Jean Mallet and André Thibaut, Rupert Fischer, and Thomas Forrest Kelly. Codices Gregoriani. Padua, 1991.

Boe, John. "The Beneventan Apostrophus in South Italian Notation, A.D. 1000–1100." *Early Music History* 3 (1983): 43–66.

———. "Gloria A and the Roman Easter Vigil Ordinary." *Musica Disciplina* 36 (1982): 5–37.

———. "Hymns and Poems at Mass in Eleventh-Century Southern Italy (Other than Sequences)." In *Atti del XIV Congresso della Società Internazionale di Musicologia, Trasmissione e recezione delle forme di cultura musicale.* Edited by Lorenzo Bianconi, et al. III. Free Papers, pp. 515–41. Turin, 1990.

———. "The 'Lost' Palimpsest Kyries in the Vatican Manuscript Urbinas latinus 602." *Journal of the Plainsong & Mediaeval Music Society* 8 (1985): 1–24.

———. "The Neumes and Pater Noster Chant of Montecassino Codex 426." In *Miscellanea Cassinese, Monastica I,* pp. 219–35. Montecassino, 1982.

———. "The Ordinary in English: Anglican Plainsong Kyrials and Their Sources." 3 vols. Ph.D. diss., Northwestern University, 1969.

Bosse, Detlev. *Untersuchung einstimmiger Melodien zum "Gloria in excelsis Deo."* Forschungsbeiträge zur Musikwissenschaft, vol. 2. Regensburg, 1955.

Botte, Bernard. *Le Canon de la messe romaine.* Louvain, 1935.

———. *La Tradition apostolique de saint Hippolyte: Essai de reconstitution.* Liturgiewissenschaftliche Quellen und Forschungen, 39. Münster, 1966.

Bourque, Emmanuel. *Étude sur les sacramentaires romains.* 3 vols. Pt. 1, *Les Textes primitifs,* Studi di Antichità Cristiana, 20. Rome, 1948. Pt. 2, *Les Textes remaniés,* t. 1, *Le Gélasien du viiie siècle,* Bibliothèque Théologique de Laval. Québec, 1952. Pt. 2, t. 2, *Le Sacramentaire d'Hadrien . . . et les Grégoriens mixtes,* Studi di Antichità Cristiana, 25. Rome, 1958.

Bradshaw, Paul. *The Search for the Origins of Christian Worship.* New York, 1992.

Brown, *Handlist* = Virginia Brown, *Handlist of Beneventan MSS.* Sussidi eruditi, 34. Rome, 1980. (= E. A. Loew, *The Beneventan Script,* 2d ed. Prepared and enlarged by Virginia Brown, vol. 2).

Brunner, Lance. "Catalogo delle sequenze in manoscritti di origine italiana." *Rivista italiana di musicologia* 20 (1985): 191–276.

———. "A Perspective on the Southern Italian Sequence: the Second Tonary of the Manuscript Monte Cassino 318." *Early Music History* 1 (1981): 117–64.

BTC I = *Beneventanum Troporum Corpus I: Tropes of the Proper of the Mass from Southern Italy,* A.D. 1000–1250. Edited by Alejandro Enrique Planchart. Recent Researches in the Music of the Middle Ages and Early Renaissance, vols. 16–18. Madison, 1994.

BTC II = *Beneventanum Troporum Corpus II: Ordinary Chants and Tropes for the Mass from Southern Italy,* A.D. 1000–1250. Edited by John Boe. Recent Researches in the Music of the Middle Ages and Early Renaissance, vols. 19–27. Madison, 1989–.

Part 1: Kyrie eleison. Part 2: Gloria in excelsis. Part 3: Preface Chants and Sanctus. Part 4: Pater noster Chants and Agnus Dei with Ite missa est.

Cabrol, Fernand. "Canon romain." In DACL 2: cols. 1847–49.

Cantorinus seu Toni Communes Officii. [Edited by Joseph Pothier.] Vatican City, 1911.

CAO = *Corpus Antiphonalium Officii.* Edited by René-Jean Hesbert. 6 vols. Rerum Ecclesiasticarum Documenta, Series Maior, Fontes 7–12. Rome, 1963–79.

Chavasse, Antoine. "Les *Episcopi*, dans la liturgie de l'*Urbs*, au VIIe et au VIIIe siècle." In *La Liturgie de la ville de Rome*, pp. 337–42.

———. "Evangéliaire, épistolier, antiphonaire, sacramentaire. Les livres romains de la messe, au VIIe et VIIIe siècle." In *La Liturgie de la ville de Rome*, pp. 153–229. First published in *Ecclesia Orans* 6 (1989): 177–255.

———. *La Liturgie de la ville de Rome du Ve au VIIIe siècle. Une liturgie conditionée par l'organisation de la vie in Urbe et extra muros.* Présentation d'Adrien Nocent. Studia Anselmiana, 112; Analecta Liturgica, 18. Rome, 1993.

———. *Le Sacramentaire dans le groupe dit "Gélasiens du viiie siècle." Une compilation raisonée. Étude des procédés de confection et Synoptiques nouveau modèle.* 2 vols. Vol. 1, *Études particulières*; vol. 2, *Synoptiques et tableaux spéciaux.* Instrumenta Patristica, 14A–B. Steenbruggen, 1984.

———. "Le Sacramentaire, dit Léonien, conservé par le Veronensis LXXXV (80)." In *La Liturgie de la ville de Rome*, pp. 69–107. First published in *Sacris Erudiri* 27 (1984): 151–90.

———. "Le Sacramentaire gélasien du viiie siècle: ses deux principales formes." *Ephemerides Liturgicae* 73 (1959): 249–98.

———. *Le Sacramentaire gélasien (Vaticanus Reginensis 316): sacramentaire presbytéral en usage dans les titres romains au viie siècle.* Paris-Tournai, 1958.

———. "Le Sacramentaire grégorien: les additions et remaniements introduits dans le témoin P." In *La Liturgie de la ville de Rome*, pp. 297–320. Published earlier in *Traditio et Progressio. Studi liturgici in onore del Prof. Adrien Nocent*, pp. 125–48. Studia Anselmiana, 95; Analecta Liturgica, 12. Rome, 1988.

———. "Le Sanctoral et le temporal grégoriens, vers 680. Distribution et origine des pièces utilisées." In *La Liturgie de la ville de Rome*, pp. 267–95. Published earlier in *Ecclesia Orans* 3 (1986): 263–88.

———. "Le Titre du Grégorien, selon H et O." In *La Liturgie de la ville de Rome*, pp. 261–68. First published in *Revue des sciences religieuses* 57 (1983): 50–56.

CLLA = Klaus Gamber, *Codices Liturgici Latini Antiquiores.* See s.v. Gamber.

CP = *Corpus Praefationum.* Edited by Edmond (Eugène) Moeller. 5 vols. Corpus Christianorum, Series Latina, 161, 161A, 161B, 161C and 161D. Tournai, 1980–81.

CT = *Corpus Troporum.* Stockholm, 1975–93.

CT 4 = Gunilla Iversen, ed. *Corpus Troporum IV. Tropes de l'Agnus Dei.* Studia Latina Stockholmiensia, 26. Stockholm, 1980.

CT 5 = Gunilla Björkvall, ed. *Corpus Troporum V. Les deux tropaires d'Apt, mss. 17 et 18: Inventaire analytiques des mss. et édition des textes uniques.* Studia Latina Stockholmiensia, 32. Stockholm, 1986.

CT 7 = Gunilla Iversen, ed. *Corpus Troporum VII. Tropes du Sanctus.* Studia Latina Stockholmiensia, 34. Stockholm, 1990.

DACL = *Dictionnaire d'archéologie chrétienne et de liturgie.* 15 vols. Edited successively by Fernand Cabrol, Henri Leclercq, and Henri Marron. Paris, 1907–53.

Dell'Oro, F. *Sacramentarium Tridentinum.* Monumenta Ecclesiae Tridentinae saeculo xiii antiquiora, vol. 2/A = Collana di monografie edita dalle Società per gli Studi Trentini, 38, 2. Trent, 1985.

Denis-Boulet, Noële Maurice. "Le Canon à voix basse." In *L'Église en prière*, 3d ed. Edited by Aimé-Georges Martimort, pp. 393–94. Paris, 1965.

———. "La Liturgie eucharistique: le canon." In *L'Église en prière*, 3d ed., pp. 396–97.

———. "Les Préfaces du missel romain." In *L'Église en prière*, 3d ed., p. 398.

———. "Sources de la messe romaine." In *L'Église en prière*, 3d ed., pp. 30–103.

Deshusses = Jean Deshusses. *Le Sacramentaire grégorien: Ses principales formes d'après les plus anciens manuscrits.* 2d ed. 3 vols. Spicilegium Friburgense 16, 24, and 28. Freiburg, Switzerland, 1971–88.

Deshusses, Jean. "Messes d'Alcuin." *Archiv für Liturgiewissenschaft* 14 (1972): 7–41.

———. "Le Sacramentaire grégorien de Trente." *Revue bénédictine* 78 (1968): 261–82.

---. *Le Sacramentaire grégorien* . . . . (See first entry above under "Deshusses.")

---. "Les Sacramentaires: État actuel de la recherche." *Archiv für Liturgiewissenschaft* 24 (1982): 19–46.

---. "Le 'Supplement' au sacramentaire grégorien: Alcuin ou s. Benoît?" *Archiv für Liturgiewissenschaft* 9 (1965): 48–71.

Di Franco, Maria Clara, and Viviana Jemolo. "Nuove testimonanze di scrittura beneventana." *Studi medievali*, 3d ser., 8 (1967): 864–66.

Diaz y Diaz, Manuel. *El Codice Calixtino de la Catedral de Santiago. Estudio codicologico de contenido.* Santiago de Compostela, 1988.

Dictionnaire d'histoire et de géographie ecclésiastiques. Edited by Alfred Baudrillart, Albert Vogt, and Urbain Rouziès. Now edited by R. Aubert. Paris, 1912–.

Dix, Gregory. Ἀποστολικὴ Παράδοσις : *The Treatise on the Apostolic Tradition of St. Hippolytus of Rome.* London, 1937.

Dold, Alban. "Umfangreiche Reste zweier Plenarmissalien des 11. und 12. Jh. aus Montecassin." *Ephemerides Liturgicae* 53 (1939): 111–67.

L'Église en prière. Introduction à la liturgie. 3d ed. Edited by Aimé-Georges Martimort. Paris, 1965. (The Édition nouvelle, 1–4, Paris, 1983, was not available for BTC II/3.)

EGM = Peter Wagner, *Einführung in die gregorianischen Melodien.* See s.v. Wagner.

Enciclopedia Italiana di scienze lettere ed arti. 15 vols. Rome, 1929. Reprinted, Rome, 1949, with 9 vols. of appendices and supplements, Rome 1938–78.

Ferretti, Paolo M. "I Manoscritti musicali gregoriani dell'Archivio di Montecassino." *Casinensia* (1929): 190–91.

Fiala, V. "Der Ordo Missae im Vollmissale des Cod. Vat. lat. 6082." In *Zeugnis des Geistes: Festgabe zum Benediktus-Jubiläum 547–1947*, pp. 180–224.

Frere, Walter Howard. *The Anaphora or Great Eucharistic Prayer. An Eirenical Study in Liturgical History.* London, 1938.

Gamber, Klaus. CLLA = *Codices Liturgici Latini Antiquiores.* 2d ed. 2 vols. Spicilegii Friburgensis Subsidia 1. Freiburg, Switzerland, 1968.

Gautier, Léon. *Histoire de la poésie liturgique au moyen âge: les tropes.* Paris, 1886.

Godu, G. "Épîtres." In DACL 5, cols. 245–344.

Das Graduale von Santa Cecilia in Trastevere (Cod. Bodmer 74). Edited by Max Lütolf. 2 vols. Cologny-Geneva, 1987.

Gy, Pierre M. "Le Sanctus romain et les anaphores orientales." In *Mélanges offerts au R. P. Bernard Botte, O. S. B.*, pp. 167–74. Louvain, 1972.

Gyug, Richard. "Tropes and Prosulas in Dalmatian Sources of the Twelfth and Thirteenth Centuries." In *La Tradizione dei tropi liturgici, Atti dei convegni sui tropi liturgici* [Paris 1985 and Perugia 1987]. Edited by Claudio Leonardi and Enrico Menestò, pp. 409–38. Spoleto, 1990.

Hanssens, Jean Michel, ed. *Amalarii Episcopi Opera Liturgica Omnia.* 3 vols. Studi e testi, 138, 139, and 140. Vatican City, 1948–50.

Hiley, David. "The Chant of Norman Sicily: Interaction between the Norman and Italian Traditions." In *Atti del XIV Congresso della Società Internazionale di Musicologia, Trasmissione e recezione delle forme di cultura musicale.* 3 vols. [Bologna, 1987]. Edited by Lorenzo Bianconi, Angelo Pompilio, and Donatella Restani. II. *Study Sessions, Tradizione periferiche della monodia liturgica mediovale in Italia*, pp. 92–105. Turin, 1990.

Hiley, David, ed. *Missale Carnotense (Chartres Codex 520).* 2 vols. Monumenta Monodica Medii Aevi, vol. 4. Kassel, 1992.

Hiley, David. "The Norman Chant Traditions—Normandy, Britain, Sicily." *Proceedings of the Royal Musical Association* 107 (1980–81): 1–33.

---. "Ordinary of Mass Chants in English, North French and Sicilian Manuscripts." *Journal of the Plainsong & Mediaeval Music Society* 9, pts. 1–2 (1986): 1–128.

---. *Western Plainchant: A Handbook.* Oxford, 1993.

Hippolytus. *The Apostolic Tradition.* See Dix, Ἀποστολικὴ Παράδοσις, and Botte, *La Tradition apostolique de Saint Hippolyte.*

Hoffman, Hartmut, and Rudolf Pokorny. *Das Dekret des Bischofs Burchard von Worms: Textstufen, frühe Verbreitung, Vorlagen.* Monumenta Germaniae Historica, Hilfsmittel, 12. Munich, 1991.

Hope, D. M. *The Leonine Sacramentary: A Reassessment of Its Nature and Purpose.* Oxford, 1971.

Hudovsky, Zoran. "Missale Beneventanum MR 166 della Biblioteca Metropolitana a Zagrabia." *Jucunda Laudatio* 3 (1965): 306–14.

Ireland = Donald W. Ireland. "The Tropes to the Sanctus and Agnus Dei in Three Norman-

Sicilian Manuscripts of the 12th–13th Centuries." 2 vols. M. Phil. Thesis, University of Leeds, 1985.

Iversen, Gunilla. "Music as *Ancilla Verbi* and Words as *Ancilla Musicae*: On the Interpretation of the Musical and Textual Forms of Two Tropes to *Osanna in excelsis: Laudes deo* and *Trinitas, unitas, deitas*." In *Liturgische Tropen: Referate zweier Colloquien des Corpus Troporum in München (1983) und Canterbury (1984)*, edited by Gabriel Silagi, pp. 45–66. Beiträge zur Mediävistik und Renaissance-Forschung, 36. Munich, 1985.

———. "On the Iconography of Praise in the Sanctus and Its Tropes." In *De Musica et Cantu. Studien zur Geschichte der Kirchenmusik und der Oper, Helmut Hucke zum 60. Geburtstag*. Edited by Peter Cahn and Ann-Katrin Heimer, pp. 275–308. Hildesheim, 1993.

———. "Osanna Dulcis Est Cantica. On a Group of Compositions Added to the Osanna in excelsis." In *Cantus planus: IMS Study Session à Tihany 1987*. Edited by László Dobszay, pp. 275–96. Budapest, 1990.

———. "Pax et Sapientia: A Thematic Study on Tropes from Different Traditions." In *Pax et Sapientia: Studies in Text and Music of Liturgical Tropes and Sequences in Memory of Gordon Anderson*, edited by Ritva Jacobsson, pp. 23–58. Studia Latina Stockholmiensia, 29. Stockholm, 1986.

———. "Sur la géographie des tropes du Sanctus." In *La Tradizione dei tropi liturgici, Atti dei convegni sui tropi liturgici* [Paris 1985 and Perugia 1987]. Edited by Claudio Leonardi and Enrico Menestò, pp. 39–62. Spoleto, 1990.

Jounel, Pierre. "Le Culte collectif des saints à Rome du viie au ixe siècle." *Ecclesia Orans* 6 (1989): 285–300.

Jungmann, Josef A. *The Mass of the Roman Rite: Its Origins and Development (Missarum Sollemnia)*. Translated by Francis A. Brunner. 2 vols. New York, 1951–55.

———. "Praefatio und stiller Kanon." *Zeitschrift für katholische Theologie* 53 (1929): 66–94.

———. "Prex Eucharistica in 'Traditione Apostolica'." In *Prex Eucharistica*, q. v., pp. 80–81.

———. "Um die Herkunft der Trinitatispräfation." *Zeitschrift für katholische Theologie* 81 (1959): 461–65.

Kähler, Ernst. *Studien zum Te Deum und zur Geschichte des 24. Psalms in der Alten Kirche*. Göttingen, 1958.

Kelly, Thomas Forrest. *The Beneventan Chant*. Cambridge, England, 1989.

———. *The Exultet in Southern Italy*. Oxford, forthcoming.

Klöckener, Martin. "Sakramentarstudien zwischen Fortschritt und Sackgasse. Entschlüsselung und Würdigung des zusammenfassenden Werkes von Antoine Chavasse über die Gelasiana des 8. Jahrhunderts." *Archiv für Liturgiewissenschaft* 32 (1990): 207–30.

Lang, A. P. "Leo der Grosse und die Dreifaltigkeitspräfation." *Sacris Erudiri* 9 (1957): 116–62.

———. "Leo der Grosse und die liturgischen Texte der Oktavtages von Epiphanie." *Sacris Erudiri* 11 (1960): 12–84.

Laurand, L. "Ce qu'on sait et ce qu'on ignore du cursus." In *Manuel des études grecques et latines*. 2d ed. 8 vols. Edited by A. Lauras, vol. 4, pp. 270–96. Paris, 1949.

———. "Le Cursus dans le sacramentaire léonien." In *Questions liturgiques et paroissiales*, pp. 215–18. Louvain, 1914.

Leach, Mark Alan. "The *Gloria in excelsis Deo* Tropes of the Breme-Novalesa Community and the Repertory in North and Central Italy." 2 vols. Ph.D. diss., University of North Carolina, Chapel Hill, 1986.

Leclercq, Henri. "Abréviations" [with illustrations]. In DACL 1, cols. 159–63.

———. "Cursus." In DACL 3, cols. 3193–3205.

———. "Préface." In DACL 14, cols. 1704–16.

Levy, Kenneth. "The Byzantine Sanctus and Its Modal Tradition in East and West." *Annales musicologiques* 6 (1958–63): 7–67.

———. "Charlemagne's Archetype of Gregorian Chant." *Journal of the American Musicological Society* 40 (1987): 1–30.

———. " 'Lux de Luce': The Origin of an Italian Sequence." *Musical Quarterly* 57 (1971): 40–61.

Liber Pontificalis = *Le Liber Pontificalis: Texte, introduction et commentaire*. 2 vols. Edited by Louis Duchesne. Paris, 1886–92.

Liber Vesperalis Mediolanensis = *Liber Vesperalis juxta Ritum Sanctae Ecclesiae Mediolanensis*. [Edited by Gregorio Suñol.] Rome, 1939.

Loew [Lowe], E. A. [Elias Avery]. *The Beneventan Script*. 2d ed. Prepared and enlarged by Virginia Brown. 2 vols. Sussidi eruditi, 33–34. Rome, 1980.

———. "The Vatican ms. of the Gelasian Sacramentary and Its Supplement at Paris." *Journal of Theological Studies* 27 (1925–26): 357–73.

Mallet, Jean, and André Thibaut. *Les Manuscrits en écriture bénéventaine de la Bibliothèque Capitulaire de Bénévent.* 2 vols. Vol. 1, *Manuscrits 1–18.* Documents, études et repertoires publiés par l'Institut de Recherche et d'Histoire des Textes. Paris, 1984–.

Martimort, Aimés-Georges, ed. *L'Église en prière,* q. v. supra.

McKinnon, James W. "Antoine Chavasse and the Dating of Early Chant." *Plainsong and Medieval Music* 1 (1992): 123–47.

Melnicki [-Landwehr], Margareta. *Das einstimmige Kyrie des lateinischen Mittelalters.* Regensburg, 1955.

MGG = *Die Musik in Geschichte und Gegenwart.* Edited by Friedrich Blume. 14 vols. Kassel, 1949–68.

MGH = Monumenta Germaniae Historica. 1826–.

MMMA = Monumenta Monodica Medii Aevi. Kassel, 1956–.

MMMA 17 = Charles Atkinson, ed. *Sanctus-Melodien mit ihren Tropen.* Monumenta Monodica Medii Aevi, vol. 17. Kassel, forthcoming.

Mocquereau, André. "Le Cursus et la psalmodie." [Introductory survey.] PM 4, pp. 27–40.

Mohlberg, L. Cunibert. *Liber Sacramentorum Romanae Aecclesiae Ordinis Anni Circuli (Cod. Vat. Reg. lat. 316 / Paris Bibl. Nat. 7193, 41/46).* Rerum Ecclesiasticarum Documenta, Series Maior, Fontes 4. Rome, 1960.

———. *Sacramentarium Veronense.* [The Leonine Sacramentary.] Rerum Ecclesiasticarum Documenta, Series Maior, Fontes 1. Rome, 1956.

Mongelli, G. *Archivi. Archivi d'Italia e rassegna internazionale degli archivi.* 2d ser., vol. 26. 1959.

Moreton, Bernard. *The Eighth-Century Gelasian Sacramentary: A Study in Tradition.* Oxford, 1976.

New Grove = *The New Grove Dictionary of Music and Musicians.* Edited by Stanley Sadie. 20 vols. London, 1980.

Norberg, Dag. *Introduction à l'étude de la versification latine médiévale.* Studia Latina Stockholmiensia, 5. Stockholm, 1958.

Odermatt, Ambros. *Ein Rituale in beneventanischer Schrift. Roma, Biblioteca Vallicelliana, Cod. C 32, Ende des 11. Jahrhunderts.* Spicilegium Friburgense, 26. Freiburg, Switzerland, 1980.

PL = [Patrologia Latina.] Patrologiae Cursus Completus. Series Latina. Edited by J. P. Migne. 222 vols. Paris, 1844–55.

Peirce, Elizabeth. "An Edition of Egerton MS. 3511: A Twelfth-Century Missal of St. Peter's in Benevento." Thesis, University of London, 1964.

Planchart = Alejandro Enrique Planchart. *The Repertory of Tropes at Winchester.* 2 vols. Princeton, 1977.

PM = Paléographie musicale, collection fondée en 1889 par Dom André Mocquereau: Les principaux manuscrits de chant grégorien, ambrosien, mozarabe, gallican, publiés par les moines de Solesmes. 21 vols. Solesmes, 1889–.

PM 4 = *Le Codex 121 de la Bibliothèque d'Einsiedeln (x^e–xie siècle): Antiphonale Missarum Sancti Gregorii.* Paléographie musicale, vol. 4. Solesmes, 1894; Bern, 1974.

PM 15 = *Le Codex VI.34 de la Bibliothèque capitulaire de Bénévent avec prosaire et tropaire.* Paléographie musicale, vol. 15. Solesmes, 1937.

PM 20 = *Le Missel de Bénévent VI.33.* Introduction par Dom Jacques Hourlier, tables par Dom Jacques Froger. Paléographie musicale, vol. 20. Bern and Frankfurt, 1983.

PM 21 = *Les Témoins manuscrits du chant bénéventain.* Edited by Thomas Forrest Kelly. Paléographie musicale, vol. 21. Solesmes, 1992.

Prex Eucharistica: Textus e Variis Liturgiis Antiquioribus Selecti. 2d ed. Edited by Anton Hänggi and Irmgard Pahl. Spicilegium Friburgense, 12. Freiburg, Switzerland, 1968, 1978.

Raes, Alphonse. "Anaphorae Orientales." In *Prex Eucharistica,* 2d ed., pp. 98–415.

———. *Anaphorae Syriacae.* Rome, 1939.

Raven, D. S. *Latin Metre.* London, 1965.

Rehle, Sieghild. "Missale Beneventanum (Codex VI. 33 des Erzbischöflichen Archivs von Benevent)." *Sacris Erudiri* 21 (1972–73): 323–405.

———. *Missale Beneventanum von Canosa (Baltimore, Walters Art Gallery, MS W6).* Textus Patristici et Liturgici, 9. Regensburg, 1972.

Schildbach, Martin. *Das einstimmige Agnus Dei und seine handschriftliche Überlieferung vom 10. bis zum 16. Jahrhundert.* Erlangen-Nuremberg, 1967.

Schmidt, Hermann. "De Lectionibus Variantibus in Formulis Identicis Sacramentariorum Leoniani, Gelasiani et Gregoriani." *Sacris Erudiri* 4 (1952): 103–73.

Spinks, Bryan P. *The Sanctus in the Eucharistic Prayer.* Cambridge, England, 1991.

Stuiber, Alfred. *Libelli Sacramentorum Romani: Untersuchungen zur Entstehung des sogenannten Sacramentarium Leonianum.* Bonn, 1950.

Supino Martini, Paola. *Roma e l'area grafica romanesca (secoli X–XII).* Biblioteca di scrittura e civiltà, 1. Alessandria, 1987.

Thannabaur, Peter Josef. *Das einstimmige Sanctus der römischen Messe in der handschriftlichen Überlieferung des 11. bis 16. Jahrhunderts.* Erlanger Arbeiten zur Musikwissenschaft, vol. 1. Munich, 1962.

Toni Communes Missae. [Edited by Joseph Pothier.] Vatican City, 1907.

Vacandard, E. "Le Cursus: son origine, son histoire, son emploi dans la liturgie." *Revue des questions historiques* 78 (1905): 59–102.

Wagner, Peter. *Einführung in die gregorianischen Melodien.* Part 1: *Ursprung und Entwicklung der liturgischen Gesangsformen bis zum Ausgang des Mittelalters.* Leipzig, 1895; 3d ed., 1911. Part 2: *Neumenkunde. Paläographie des liturgischen Gesanges.* 2d ed. Leipzig, 1912. Part 3: *Gregorianische Formenlehre: Eine choralische Stilkunde.* Leipzig, 1921.

———. *Die Gesänge der Jacobusliturgie zu Santiago de Compostela aus dem sog. Codex Calixtinus.* Freiburg, 1931.

Wilson, H. A. *The Gelasian Sacramentary.* Oxford, 1894.

———. "The Metrical Endings of the Leonine Sacramentary." *Journal of Theological Studies* 5 (1904): 386–95; 6 (1905): 381–91.

The Manuscript Sources of Preface Chants in Part 3

Beneventan Sources

Ben 33   11–23

SOURCE: *Benevento 33, fol. 80ʳ⁻ᵛ (the common preface, inserted in the Easter vigil mass after two special post-Lenten prayers of blessing—the second, of meat, b̄en. carnis in pascha. Deus uniuerse carnis . . .—the preface leading into the complete Sanctus text without notation and followed by *Te [igitur]* of the canon). Notation *in campo aperto* was added, but very early, to a text not meant for it: The neumes are cramped and the diastematy inexact. The manuscript is a late tenth or early eleventh-century full missal, not from Benevento itself but very possibly from the diocese of Salerno, the city on the coast directly south of Benevento that was the sometime capital of the Beneventan duchy-principality and the later capital of an independent fraction of it. The missal contains old Beneventan pieces for Holy Week but the Gregorian repertory of notated propers for the rest of the year.

REFERENCES: Brown, *Handlist*, p. 21 (with further bibliography); Gamber, CLLA, no. 430; Kelly, *The Beneventan Chant*, p. 300; Mallet and Thibaut, *Les Manuscrits* 1:90 and the extensive note discussing episcopal indulgences entered in the margins of the folio having the preface; PM 20 (facsimile of the MS), especially fol. 80ʳ⁻ᵛ and the colored frontispiece of fol. 80ᵛ; and Rehle, "Missale Beneventanum Codex VI.33."

Ben 40   11–22

SOURCE: *Benevento 40, fol. 27ʳ⁻ᵛ (the common preface, inserted among the old Beneventan chant propers for Easter Day, after the conclusion *quem queritis non est hic surrexit sicut dixit alleluia* of the otherwise missing offertory *Angelus domini* and before the exordium and Pater noster in turn followed by the fully notated *Libera nos* and *Pax domini*). Notated *in campo aperto* in exactly the same hand and style and with the same approximate diastematy as the rest of the gradual. No Sanctus text is appended. An unusual location for the common preface: if present at all in a gradual, the common preface would normally have been found as part of a complete *ordo missae* within the Easter vigil mass, rather than in the mass of Easter Day, when the ancient proper preface for Easter, *Te quidem* (CP 1527), would presumably have been sung. For the Easter vigil, Ben 40 (the oldest of the surviving graduals now at Benevento) has the offertory *Omnes qui in christo baptizati estis* and the communion *Ymnum canite agni mundi* but no *ordo missae* and no preface. As with Ben 33, it is hard to tell whether this preface was chanted only in the old Beneventan rite, or whether it was also chanted at masses where Gregorian chant was sung, as is perhaps implied by strong reminiscences of this version in the opening dialogue of a much later Benevento version, the Sunday and festal chant in the missal Lo 3511, described next below. Perhaps the same prefaces and mass canon were used in old Beneventan and Roman-Gregorian rites in the early eleventh century.

REFERENCES: Brown, *Handlist*, p. 22 (with further bibliography); Kelly, *The Beneventan Chant*, pp. 302–03; and Mallet and Thibaut, "Notes codicologiques," in *Benevento Biblioteca Capitolare 40, Graduale*, p. vii. Also see the description of the MS in BTC I, p. xvii.

Lo 3511   11–25, 26–37

SOURCE: *London, B. L. Egerton MS 3511, fols. 170ᵛ–174ᵛ, as correctly foliated in light pencil and cited throughout BTC II/3. (The proper prefaces of Christmas/Purification/Annunciation, of the Epiphany, of Lent, of Easter, Ascension, Pentecost, Holy Cross, Holy Trinity, of the Assumption/Nativity of St. Mary, the unnotated preface of the Apostles, the notated preface of the Dedication of a church, and the unnotated preface of the dead precede the common-preface chants *In cotidianis diebus* [=3511ᶜ below], *In festiuitatibus* [=3511ᶠ], and *In sollemnitatibus* [=3511ˢ, incomplete], and the proper-preface conclusion *Et ideo . . . dicentes* with the chant *In sollemnitatibus* [see below, pp. 11–37]. All these prefaces are placed after the celebrant's offertory prayers, which conclude with the bidding and response *Orate pro me fr⟨atre⟩s. ut meum ac u⟨estru⟩m sacrificium acceptabile fiat apud d⟨eu⟩m om⟨n⟩ipotentem. Cui respondendum est. Sit d⟨omi⟩n⟨u⟩s in corde tuo et in ore tuo. suscipiatque sacrificium acceptum de ore tuo et de manibus tuis pro nostra om⟨n⟩iumque salute* ⁊ and before the remainder of the canon of the mass, of which the folio with *Te igitur* and its immediate continuation has been ripped off.) Notated with accurate diastematy *in campo aperto*.

All three chants for the common preface are based on Cassinese models, though not in every particular. The salutation and the dialogue responses of the chant *In festiuitatibus* (and to a lesser degree, of the chant *In cotidianis*) mostly adhere to local Benevento tradition, as a comparison of lines 40, 3511ᶠ, and 339ᵈᶠ (the Cassinese equivalent), or of the everyday Cassinese version C 32 will show. (See p. 12 below.) From the beginning of the celebrant's chant *Vere dignum* onwards, the Cassinese version is preferred in Lo 3511 to older Benevento usage. The fragmentary common preface *In sollemnitatibus*, now extending only through *Sursum corda* of the opening dialogue but reconstructible from the proper prefaces employing it and from their conclusion *Et ideo . . . dicentes,* also seems to have been based on a Cassinese model that does not however survive in exactly this form. A more highly ornamented twelfth-century Cassinese version does survive in fragmentary form (through *Dignum et iustum est* of the dialogue) in a twelfth-century leaf now found in Montecassino Compactio VII and in complete form as the third common preface in ZaMR 166, which derives from a twelfth-century Cassinese model (see below).

The missal Lo 3511, written in the mid-twelfth century for and perhaps at the convent of San Pietro *intra muros,* Benevento, was based on a Cassinese exemplar (as is evident above). The prefaces were included within an *ordo ad celebrandum missa* [sic] inserted immediately after the Easter vigil mass. The missal is the earliest south Italian manuscript presently known to contain an entire set of *notated* proper prefaces grouped together. The proper prefaces for Christmas, Epiphany, Lent (or rather, Maundy Thursday), Easter, Ascension, and Pentecost are followed by brief passages rubricked *Infrac.* or *Infra actionem,* usually beginning *Communicantes,* to be inserted in the canon on these occasions. In addition, Maundy Thursday, Easter, and Pentecost have an insertion for *Hanc igitur oblationem* in the canon; Maundy Thursday has another insertion for the passage *Qui pridie* as well.

Most of the proper prefaces are introduced in the MS by the variously interlaced zoomorphic initials *VD,* for **Vere Dignum,** the standard beginning of the preface in the Roman mass. The twelve proper prefaces are transcribed under II. Proper Prefaces in the Missal Lo 3511 from St. Peter's *intra muros,* Benevento, pp. 26–36 below, where they are arranged according to the chant version they employ. (1) The prefaces for votive masses (here including the preface for the Holy Trinity as well as the unnotated preface for the dead, the chant for the latter an arrangement by the present editor) and also—strange to say—the preface for Christmas with its octave, the Purification, and the Annunciation employ the chant *In cotidianis diebus.* (2) The prefaces for the Epiphany, the Assumption and Nativity of St. Mary, and the unnotated preface for feasts of the Apostles (the present arrangement for the Apostles again by the present editor) employ the chant *In festiuitatibus.* (3) The prefaces for Easter and Eastertide, the Ascension, Pentecost, Holy Cross, and the Dedication of a church employ the chant *In sollemnitatibus.* The scribe did not apply cadential formulas belonging to the three versions consistently; he mixed cadences inappropriately. Furthermore, the scribe misinterpreted the notes of the medial cadence of the Cassinese *In cotidianis* tradition, although he employed the curious forms resulting with a certain consistency. (See above, pp. xlii–xliii.)

REFERENCES: Brown, *Handlist,* p. 53 (with further bibliography); Gamber, CLLA no. 452; Hiley, *Western Plainchant,* pp. 428–29 and pl. 12 (with an excellent reproduction of the last surviving page of the prefaces, fol. 174^v); and Elizabeth Peirce, "An Edition of Egerton MS. 3511: A Twelfth-Century Missal of St. Peter's in Benevento," (Thesis, University of London, 1964).

Cassinese Sources

MC 339   11–25

SOURCE: *Montecassino 339, fols. 63^v–66^v = pp. 130–36. (The common-preface chants are preceded by Gloria in excelsis intonations with tropes on fol. 63^r = p. 129 and by three Gloria intonations without tropes and a Credo intonation at the top of fol. 63^v = p. 130, the preface chants in their turn being followed by the continuation of the text of the canon within the Easter vigil mass.) The original notation was *in campo aperto.* The deluxe manuscript, known as the sacramentary of Desiderius, abbot of Montecassino (1058–87), once contained a series of three chants for the opening dialogue and common preface, of which only the first—rubricked *In dominicis seu festis diebus* (hence 339^{df} below)—survives intact. (See pp. 23 and 116 for the Sanctus incipit attached to this version.) What must have been a sumptuously illuminated leaf with gold ground for the words VERE DIGNVM ET IVSTVM EST has been torn out between the present fols. 63 and 64, that is, between pp. 130 and 131.

The neumes for the second chant were erased and replaced by a version resembling the 1907 Vatican-edition ferial preface. The replacement version was entered in Metz notation of the late thirteenth or early fourteenth centuries using three lines, the topmost of which is red. The original rubric *In cotidianis diebus* and the original verbal text however remain, along with the still legible concluding section of chant beginning *per christum dominum nostrum. Per quem maiestatem . . .* through the Sanctus incipits and the proper-preface conclusion *Et ideo . . . Cumque omni . . .* (p. 18, line 339^c—also see pp. 24 and 117.) These passages of the everyday version are very close to the versions found in the votive missals MC 426 and RoV C 32; the now-missing opening section in 339^c must have been similar.

In the manuscript in its present state, a rewritten version of the Sunday and festal opening dialogue and common preface follows (fols. 65^v–66^v = pp. 134–36), which resembles the festal forms of the Franciscan codex BAV Regin. lat. 2048 adopted for use in the papal curia, forms similar to the 1907 Vatican-edition festal tone. This rewritten version was meant to replace the unerased original notation of the first version of the manuscript (described above), which was probably left unerased in order to avoid damaging the illumination and gold ground of the now-missing folio.

What the original third version in MC 339—now very thoroughly erased in order to accommodate the rewritten festal version just described—might have been can be guessed: either a tonus sollemnior like the version *In sollemnitatibus* of Lo 3511, or more probably a *Francisca* version ("Frankish," not "Franciscan"!) like that found in MC 127, the Cassinese missal that faithfully copies the version *In dominicis seu festis diebus* of MC 339. (See the description of MC 127 below.)

REFERENCES: Boe, "Ordinary in English," 1:84–91; Brown, *Handlist,* pp. 82–83 (with sparse bibliography); Paolo M. Ferretti, "I Manoscritti musicali gregoriani dell' Archivio di Montecassino," *Casinensia* (1929): 190–91; and Wagner, EGM 3:69–80. Also see BTC II/3, pp. xl–xlii.

MC Compactiones 16

SOURCE: (*)Montecassino Compactiones, a single loose folio bearing the faint numeration "14" at bottom center, formerly in the packet of fragments labeled Compactio VI. (The dialogue and the common preface, ending with a notated Sanctus incipit [Thannabaur 154—see below], are preceded by the fragmentary marginal rubric . . . inicā and immediately followed by the exordium and two and a half lines of the Pater noster.) The notation, *in campo aperto,* is precisely diastematic. Script and notation both are from the very late eleventh or the early twelfth century. Two lines of text and one line of neumes have been trimmed off the bottom of the leaf. The leaf is probably not from a missal: the preface and Sanctus incipit are immediately followed by the exordium introducing the Pater noster without intervening canon, as in the gradual Ben 40 (see above). The text showing through from the other side of the leaf, insofar as it can be made out from a photograph, appears in part to consist of a south Italian proper preface for the feast of the Transfiguration of Christ. The words *Hic est filius meus dilectus ipsum audite* can be read but not as part of a lesson for the Transfiguration. At CP 1265, a preface for the Transfiguration where these words occur is reproduced from two sources: BAV Vat. lat. 4770 (an Abruzzi missal with many south Italian concordances) and Ben 33, fol. 117^{r-v}.

This version of the dialogue and preface is identical in nearly every respect with the MC 339 chant *In dominicis seu festis diebus,* except for the standard pes ab for the ending *dicen*tes, instead of bb as in MC 339, and except for the different Sanctus incipit (Thannabaur 154 instead of Thannabaur 41). The version from Compactio VI has been drawn upon to supply the phrase missing in MC 339^{df}, *VERE DIGNVM ET IVSTVM EST.*

REFERENCES: Brown, *Handlist,* p. 92; also see BTC II/3, pp. 68 and 72. For the text of the Transfiguration preface mentioned above, see Rehle, "Missale Beneventanum Codex VI.33," p. 376. See pl. 1, p. lxxvii above.

MC 127 25, 38–43

SOURCE: *Montecassino 127, fols. 157^r–159^v = pp. 323–28. (Various proper prefaces without notation, notated chants for the fixed proper-preface conclusion *Et ideo . . . dicentes* and *Quem laudant angeli . . . clamare dicen*tes, and three chants for the common preface follow the celebrant's offertory prayers and precede *Te igitur* of the canon.) The chants were originally notated *in campo aperto* with precise diastematy, but a red line for F was added on fol. 158^v = p. 326 for the dialogue and start of the common preface through *et salutare* of the version labeled *Dominicalis,* so as to place the chant in the C hexachord. Had it been entered elsewhere, the red line would probably have been added similarly; nevertheless, I have transcribed passages where lines were never added in the G hexachord for ease of comparison with chants from other sources.

This large Cassinese missal, which mostly dates from the late eleventh century (*tempore Desiderii descriptus,* according to Iguanez's inventory) was used at the monastery of Santa Maria di Albaneta, dependent on nearby Montecassino. The choir propers were written smaller than the prayers and lections, but no space was left for neumes and for the most part they were never entered. However, music for the celebrant and his ministers was supplied. Notated prefaces begin with two versions of the proper-preface conclusion *Et ideo . . . dicentes* (as stated earlier: fols. 157^{r-v} = pp. 323–24). The first of these, which is almost identical with that of MC 339^{df}, corresponds with the *Dominicalis* common-preface chant of MC 127. The second, merely rubricked $\overline{Al}$., matches the 339^c version almost exactly, if compared to the additions in red ink in 339^c for *Et* and *hymnum*. A different conclusion for certain proper prefaces, including that of the Trinity, *quem* (or *Quam,* for the Trinity) *laudant angeli. cherubin quoque et seraphim non cessant clamare dicentes. Scs.*, again corresponds with the *Dominicalis* common-preface version. (See p. 25 following. For the notated Sanctus incipit, see pp. 120 and 120.) Although erasures and corrections were attempted, the original versions until this point in the manuscript can usually be made out.

The first of three common-preface chant versions that follow, *Cotidiana,* was thoroughly erased and the later Franciscan-Roman curial ferial tone substituted (see under MC 339, above). The second of the common-preface chants (fol. 158^r = p. 325), rubricked *Francisca* ("Frankish," not "Franciscan") at the bottom of fol. 157^v = p. 324, was also partially erased and corrected, but the original can usually be read. (See pp. 38–43 below.) The unerased third version, for Sundays and rubricked *Dominicalis,* facing and following the full-page illuminated and entwined initial *VD* on fol. 159^r = p. 327, is in almost every respect identical to the version *In dominicis seu festis diebus* of MC 339 (see 339^{df}, above and below). The striking similarity of these two versions of the Sunday and festal chant and the nearness in time and place of origin of MC 127 and MC 339 render it practically certain that all the common prefaces of MC 127 are faithful copies of originals in Desiderius' sacramentary, and consequently that the *Francisca version of MC 127 must supply the third original preface of MC 339, otherwise irrecoverable. (Also see pp. xlvi–li, above.)

REFERENCES: Brown, *Handlist,* p. 70 (with further bibliography); M. Inguanez, *Miscellanea cassinese* 21 (1941): 51, no. 42, and in *Studi medievali,* n.s. 14 (1941): 145 ff. and pl. on p. 218.

Vat 6082

SOURCE: BAV Vat. lat. 6082, fol. 143^v–145^r. (The common-preface chant versions are followed by the proper-preface conclusion *Et ideo . . . dicentes. Scs. Scs. Scs.* on fol. 145^r, which is in turn followed by the rest of the canon.) Precisely heightened notation *in campo aperto*. Dating from the twelfth century, this deluxe notated full missal comes from Montecassino or its environs, not from San Vincenzo al Volturno. (Fiala's ascription of the MS to that abbey, repeated by Gamber in CLLA, cannot be sustained. See below.) In its present state, the MS has two chants for the common preface: the first, labeled *In cotidianis diebus* (fol. 143ᵛ to the bottom of the folio, broken off after *Per quem maiestatem . . .*); and another, now without rubric, the dialogue of which begins on fol. 144ʳ (fol. 144ᵛ, *Vere dignum . . . salutare* in gold), ending on fol. 145ʳ with a notated Sanctus incipit (see pp. 117 and 114 below). As mentioned, the conclusion for proper prefaces, *Et ideo . . . dicentes* follows, but without notation for its appended Sanctus incipit. The second common-preface chant is for the most part identical with the version *In dominicis seu festis diebus* of MC 339, with the exceptions following: five times a single note is found where there is a clivis or pes in 339ᵈᶠ; the standard pes ab is used for the accented syllable of *dicentes* instead of the singular bb in 339ᵈᶠ; and the first syllable of *deprecamur* is sung to c instead of b . The similarity of this version to its Desiderian model after an interval of some seventy-five years is remarkable. The first version of Vat 6082 for everyday use is also almost the same, so far as it goes, as the Cassinese version found in the votive missals MC 426 and RoV C 32, except that *Gratias agamus do-* was copied one step higher.

REFERENCES: Brown, *Handlist,* p. 152 (with further references); V. Fiala, "Der Ordo Missae im Vollmissale des Cod. Vat. lat. 6082," in *Zeugnis des Geistes. Festgabe zum Benediktus-Jubiläum 547–1947* (Beuron, 1947), pp. 180–224; and Gamber, CLLA, no. 455. In BTC II/3, see p. xliv and p. lxi, n. 79.

ZaMR 166

SOURCE: Zagreb, Metropolitanska Knjižnica, MR 166, on deposit in the Nacionalna i Svbučilišna Biblioteka, pp. 188–93 and 202–5. (Five notated common-preface chant versions, the first of which follows prayers for the celebrant at the offertory blessing of incense and censing, which conclude with the bidding and its responses, *Orate pro me fr⟨atre⟩s. Et respond̄ os hec. Orent pro te om⟨ne⟩s s⟨an⟩c⟨t⟩i d⟨e⟩i. āl. Sit d⟨omi⟩n⟨u⟩s in ore tuo et i⟨n⟩ corde tuo. suscipiatque sacrificium acceptum de ore tuo et de manibus tuis pro n⟨ost⟩ra om⟨n⟩iumque salute. Item p̄p̄h̄.*) The first three common-preface chants are followed by fifteen unnotated proper prefaces (see below). Two more notated chants for the common preface then follow, the second of which with its Sanctus incipit is in turn followed by the rubrics and texts: *Quando ichoat sacerdos secᵉta [?] dicatur hec ōr.*

S⟨an⟩c⟨tu⟩s d⟨eu⟩s. S⟨an⟩c⟨tu⟩s fortis. S⟨an⟩c⟨tu⟩s immortalis miserere nobis.
Agios otheos. Agios yschirros. Agios athanatos. Eleyson ymas.

Aperi os meum d⟨omi⟩ne ad benedicendum . . . pop⟨u⟩lo tuo.

Infra āc in Natl dn̄i. Communicantes et diem sacratissimum . .

with the series of *Communicantes* insertions in the canon for the great feasts (and other insertions *infra actionem*) but broken off before *Te igitur* and the rest of the canon.

According to Gyug (see below), ZaMR 166

> . . . is composed of parts of two . . . missals. The first . . . (pp. 1–326) is a twelfth century collection of votive masses from southern Italy, perhaps intended for a church with a particular veneration of Sts. Sabina and Seraphina (see MR 166 pp. 113–114). The script resembles Cassinese Beneventan but must have originated outside Monte Cassino, perhaps in a dependency on the periphery of the Beneventan zone that retained features of an earlier generation. The script is not the Bari-type otherwise found most often in Dalmatia; the decorated initials are the mixture of pink animals and white vines expected in late-eleventh or early-twelfth-century Cassinese products. . . . The second part of the codex, pp. 327–354, containing masses for the Sanctoral, is probably Dalmatian from the twelfth century.

The presence of so many as five chants for the common preface in a single altar book is exceptional. The verbal text for all of them was carefully written out in a similar format, with similar abundant late Beneventan abbreviations, and by the same hand. The first three, grouped together after the celebrant's offertory texts, are in fact the Cassinese chant versions (1) *In dominicis seu festis diebus* and (2) *In cotidianis diebus* as they appear in MC 339 and many other Cassinese altar books (see above), plus (3) a less well-documented tonus sollemnior for the highest feasts, like that in MC Compactio VII and (in variant form and incomplete) in Lo 3511 (see above). However, the second and third version were incorrectly, though perhaps intentionally, rubricked (2) *Item in minimis festis sc̄orum* and, most inappropriately, (3) *In cotidianis diebus.* (The first of the series bears the neutral rubric *Item p̄p̄h̄.*) Moreover, the neumes of these three prefaces, though precisely heightened and entirely deployed in accordance with the rules of Beneventan notation, seem to have been written by a less than expert scribe imitating a Cassinese model: the neumes are slightly coarse and irregular in shape. On the other hand, the last two common-preface chants (following the fifteen unnotated proper prefaces) are neumed by a firm, fluent hand that had mastered the technique. But the fourth version (the first of the two last), which is correctly rubricked *Item ī dn̄icis diebus,* is almost exactly the same as the first of the ZaMR 166 preface chants, except only for its opening dialogue (a mixture of versions, which begins like the *Francisca* chant of MC 127) and different though equivalent neume forms and varying applications of liquescence. From *Vere dignum* onwards, this fourth common-preface chant is in fact a more accurate copy of the standard Cassinese version than the first. The fifth and otherwise unknown last version, *Item ī festiuitatibus sc̄orum,* provides a still more solemn tone than the mislabeled third version, by means of descending leaps of a third and recitations on c with accent-clives that rise to d .

Taken together, the preface chants in ZaMR 166 confirm the Cassinese derivation for the MS suggested by Gyug and others. The standard Cassinese preface versions—those for everyday use and for Sundays and feasts—appear intact, as well as a less familiar form of the Cassinese tonus sollemnior. But the slightly amateurish notation of the first three versions and, above all, the incorrect rubrics for the second and third versions would never have been penned, or (if penned) would never have been permitted to remain in a manuscript coming from the great abbey itself. The prefaces of ZaMR 166 are indeed based on a Cassinese model, but a model copied and expanded at some remove from its source.

TABLE 7. Proper Prefaces in ZaMR 166, pp. 193–201

		Rubric	Corpus Praefationum		Lo 3511
1	193–94	Prepha de natle.	1322	=	no. 1
2	194	Preph In epypha.	1294	=	no. 2
3	194	In qadrag.	863	=	no. 3
4	194–95	In sabbo sco. et dom. [Easter]	1527	=	no. 4
5	195	De cruce.	1200	=	no. 7
6	195–96	de pentecost.	813	=	no. 6
7	196	De ascensio.	1165	=	no. 5
8	196–97	In Scę marię.	?Et beatę marię semper uirginis laudes reddentes debitas . . .	≠	no. 9, CP 366
9	197	De aplis.	1484 = 1457	=	no. 10
10	197–98	De trinitate.	879	=	no. 8
11	198–99	de aplis.	914		—
12	199	De dedicationem.	203	(=)	no. 11, CP 74, 1st half
13	199–200	Pro sacerdote	?Tu pius es domine ut facturam tuam . . .		—
14	200–01	[Pro defunctis]	1077		—
15	201–02	[Pro defunctis]	699	=	no. 12

The unnotated proper prefaces in ZaMR 166 are mostly word for word the same as those in Lo 3511 (see pp. xxi–xxii and table 7 above). The order in which they are presented in ZaMR 166 varies slightly; the punctuation differs; and a few words vary in texts common to both missals, notably in the preface for the Dedication. The proper prefaces of Lo 3511 and of ZaMR 166 are distant cousins having a common Cassinese ancestor—as can also be shown for the common preface chants.

REFERENCES: Brown, *Handlist,* p. 177 (with further bibliography); Richard F. Gyug, "Tropes and Prosulas in Dalmatian Sources of the Twelfth and Thirteenth Centuries," in *La Tradizione dei tropi liturgici,* Atti dei convegni sui tropi liturgici, Paris 1985 and Perugia 1987, ed. Claudio Leonardi and Enrico Menestò (Spoleto, 1990), pp. 409–38 and especially pp. 423–25; and Zoran Hudovsky, "Missale Beneventanum MR 166 della Biblioteca Metropolitana a Zagrabia," *Jucunda Laudatio* 3 (1965): 306–14.

Ott 576

SOURCE: BAV Ottob. lat. 576, fols. 225ʳ–226ʳ (two common-preface chants, the second of which is followed by the proper-preface conclusion *Et ideo . . . dicentes,* within an *ordo missae* placed after the Easter Day mass in the second part of the MS, which is now bound separately). Clefs and sometimes a red line were used in the choir propers but not for the prefaces, the notation for which was left *in campo aperto.* The missal dates from the late twelfth and early thirteenth centuries. According to Brown, *Handlist,* fols. 2–220 are late twelfth-century and fols. 1 and 221–377 are thirteenth-century; according to Bannister, the missal was copied from a Cassinese exemplar somewhere south of Montecassino by several text scribes and several notators. The hands of "at least five text scribes and eight notators are discernible." Copied at least 125 years after Desiderius' sacramentary, MC 339, the missal is the latest of the altar books cited in BTC II.

The first common-preface chant, *In cotidianis diebus* (fol. 225ʳ⁻ᵛ) is the same as the everyday versions of MC 426, RoV C 32, and MC 339 (where legible), except for a single passage varying in pitch and except for certain different though equivalent neume forms. (Any other slight variant found in Ott 576 from one of these versions can be found in at least one of the others, except for the end of the response . . . et iustum est.) From *Vere dignum* onwards, the second version, *In dominicis et in sollemnitatibus* (fols. 225ᵛ–226ʳ) is also remarkably similar to the version *In dominicis seu festis diebus* in MC 339. The discrepancies from MC 339 are as follows:

gratias agere; per christum dominum; tremunt; deprecamur; dicentes. S⟨an⟩c⟨tu⟩s. S⟨an⟩c⟨tu⟩s. S⟨an⟩c⟨tu⟩s.

REFERENCES: Bannister, *Monumenti vaticani,* no. 368; Brown, *Handlist,* p. 266. In BTC II/3, see the commentary for Thannabaur 213, Var., p. 80 below, where the proper-preface conclusion *Et ideo . . . dicentes* and the attached third Sanctus incipit are transcribed in the C hexachord in letter notation. Also see Thannabaur 41, p. 117, where the Ott 576 ending of the common preface *In dominicis et in sollemnitatibus* and its Sanctus incipit are transcribed in letter notation in the F hexachord.

MC 426   *11–23*

SOURCE: *Montecassino 426, fol. 32ʳ⁻ᵛ = pp. 61–62 (a single common preface, preceded by votive masses for the days of the week and immediately followed by *Te igitur* of the mass canon). Neumes *in campo aperto* from the late tenth or early eleventh centuries were added to a text not intended to receive notation. Diastematy is only approximate and custodes were not always used. Insecure pitches can, however, be determined by comparing the same formulas as used elsewhere. This scruffy votive missal, the earliest known witness to the Cassinese *In cotidianis* preface tradition, comes from the Montecassino region, though hardly from the great abbey itself, and bears the *ex libris* of the nearby dependent monastery of Santa Maria di Albaneta. Fourteen pieces of the so-called choir propers show partial notation posterior to the verbal text but in a different neumatic hand than that found in the preface and Pater noster.

REFERENCES: John Boe, "The Neumes and Pater Noster Chant of Montecassino Codex 426," in *Monastica I*, Miscellanea Cassinese (Montecassino, 1982), pp. 219–35; Brown, *Handlist*, pp. 85–86 (with further references).

RoV C 32   11–23

SOURCE: *Rome, Bibl. Vallicelliana C 32, fol. 91^{r-v} (a single common preface in an *ordo missae* that follows the office and masses for the dead and immediately precedes the remainder of the canon of the mass, which in turn is followed by votive masses for the days of the week, in a slightly later hand). Notated *in campo aperto* with accurate diastematy in the late eleventh or early twelfth century. A monastic manual—a compendium largely devoted to services for the ill and the dying, to the burial service, and to the office and masses for the dead. The preface is notated in the Cassinese *In cotidianis diebus* tradition, thus confirming the assignment of the MS to "the region of Montecassino" made by Gamber.

REFERENCES: Brown, *Handlist*, p. 128 (with further references); Gamber, CLLA, no. 1593; and Ambros Odermatt, *Ein Rituale in beneventanischer Schrift. Roma, Biblioteca Vallicelliana, Cod. C 32. Ende des 11. Jahrhunderts.* Spicilegium Friburgense, 26 (Freiburg, Switzerland, 1980)—an exhaustive study and complete edition of the verbal text of the MS.

Border-Area Sources in Roman Minuscule

RoV B 24   38–43, 46

SOURCE: *Rome, Bibl. Vallicelliana B 24, fols. 1^r–2^r (a single common preface at the very beginning of the MS, followed by the entire unnotated Sanctus text, two private prayers for the celebrant rubricked *Dum canitur Scs*, and the illuminated *Te igitur* of the mass canon) and fol. 29^v (proper preface for Pentecost, in the Pentecost vigil mass). Precisely diastematic Beneventan notation without lines but with custodes and an F clef contemporary with the notation, on fol. 1^{r-v}, which clef situates the chant in the soft F hexachord with implied b-flat. The sacramentary, in roman minuscule script, is from Subiaco, St. Benedict's first foundation twenty miles east of Rome. The sacramentary was completed in 1075 for John of Farfa, then the new abbot John V of Subiaco. The sole notation in the MS, namely for the common and the Pentecost prefaces, was probably added between 1110 and 1130. It thus represents early twelfth-century usage. The only non-Beneventan notational element is the central Italian liquescent pes ✓ sometimes employed.

REFERENCES: Supino Martini, *Roma e l'area grafica romanesca*, pp. 170, 174 (with extensive bibliography for the MS in n. 24), and 175. Supino Martini supplies part of the colophon with the date 1075, the scribe's name, *quidam scriptor nomine Guittone*, and the donor's name, *iubente domino Iohanne gloriosissimus abbas ex venerabili monasterio S. Benedicti qui ponitur Sublaco*. In BTC II/3 see pp. xxxi and xlv.

RoC 1574   38–44

SOURCE: *Rome, Bibl. Casanatense 1574, pp. 33–37, as numbered at the top of the leaves (a single common preface within a mass ordo that begins at p. 30; the canon continues on p. 40 after items from the office inserted by the binder). Notated *in campo aperto* in crude diastematic Beneventan notation of the late twelfth or early thirteenth century. The notation was crammed in above the text, written in mixed uncials and ordinary minuscule of a considerably earlier date than the notation. The MS is a monastic compendium including psalter (p. 76), office antiphoner with small, neat Beneventan notation above the text in ordinary minuscule (p. 188), hymnal with many notated first stanzas (p. 231), chapters, readings, and gospel antiphons for the Sundays after Pentecost (p. 298), collects, and an office and mass for the common of saints, etc. A note in an eighteenth-century hand asserts the MS belonged to Sant'Angelo di Gaeta; nothing is known of its earlier history, except that it must have originated in the northern border of the Beneventan zone. The preface, a mixture of the older Beneventan tradition (certain phrases in the dialogue resemble those in Baltimore W 6—see below) and later Cassinese *In cotidianis diebus* forms, ends with a completely notated Sanctus (Thannabaur 41, see References below) and the conclusion for proper prefaces, *ET IDEO . . . SINE FINE DICENTES*.

REFERENCES: Brown, *Handlist*, p. 124 (with further bibliography). In BTC II/3, see pp. lxiii, 116–19, and 114.

RoV B 23   38–45

SOURCE: *Rome, Bibl. Vallicelliana B 23, fol. 1 43^{r-v}. (A single notated common preface, the unnotated proper preface for Lent, . . . *Eterne deus. Qui corporali ieiunio . . .*, and the notated proper-preface conclusion *Et ideo . . . dicentes* leading into an entire notated Sanctus [Thannabaur 41] are all inserted after the celebrant's bidding *Orate fratres . . .* and the reply ℟. *Suscipiat dominus sacrificium de manibus tuis . . .* at the end of the offertory prayers of the Easter vigil mass, and before the celebrant's private prayer *Aperi domine os meum ad benedicendum nomen sanctum tuum . . .* and *Te igitur* with the rest of the canon.) The preface, proper-preface conclusion, and Sanctus were notated originally *in campo aperto*, probably not long after the verbal text had been completed, with clearly heightened neumes blending central Italian and Beneventan features. Puncta were not slanted according to Beneventan rules, but Beneventan liquescent forms predominate. Later, c clef (or C clef?) and yellow line, and still later, an intermittent red line for f or F were added, beginning at *Dominus uobiscum* and continuing through the preface and the proper-preface conclusion. Thus *dicentes* reads e de d (or possibly E DE D). The notes of Sanctus were heighted so as to begin e ee d (or E EE D) in relation to the preface conclusion, but the Sanctus was supplied with an F clef and a red line, so that *Sanctus* in fact reads a aa G . (See pl. 2.) The chant propers, although written smaller than the celebrant's texts, were never notated; but some passages in the lessons have notation.

This early twelfth-century monastic full missal has been variously assigned to the abbeys of Sant'Eutizio, Val Castoriana (near Norcia) or San Bartolomeo di Trisulti (southwest of Subiaco in the Ernici range west of Sora, east of Anagni, and north of Frosinone), or to the "region of Macerata." On the basis of marginal additions, including one previously unnoticed, Supino Martini convincingly proposes the monastery of San Bartolomeo, Norcia, as the source.

REFERENCES: Kelly, *The Beneventan Chant*, p. 48; Gamber, CLLA, no. 1425; and Supino Martini, *Roma e l'area grafica romanesca*, pp. 224–25 (with an extensive bibliography). In BTC II/3, see pl. 2 and pp. 116 and 114.

RoV B 8

SOURCE: Rome, Bibl. Vallicelliana B 8, fols. 170^v–171^r (a single common preface, immediately following the erased folios 168^v–170^r—which were rewritten in gothic script with the celebrant's private mass prayers, these in turn following fol. 167, the standard title of the older Gregorian sacramentary the preface text belonged to: [see pp. xviii–xx and p. lv, n. 23]:

IN NOMINE DN̄I INCIP̄ LIBER SACRAMENTORVM
DE CIRCVLI ANNI. ⟨EXPOSITVS A⟩
SC̄ GḠ PAPA ROMANO. QVALITER
MISSA ROMANA CAELEBRATVR.

—the preface itself immediately preceding the large illuminated T of *Te igitur* that begins the rest of the canon of the mass). The name of the scribe, *scriptor ubertus infelix,* is tucked within the angle on the right-hand side of the T-cross. The erased but still partly legible notation of the single common preface (written in uncial script) and the erased but completely legible notation for the exordium and Pater noster (following the canon on fol. 173^{r-v}) employ a variety of adiastematic French notation also seen in MSS from certain Roman monasteries touched by Cluniac reform and in MSS from Farfa and wherever the impulse of the monastic reformer Guillaume de Volpiano (otherwise known as William of Dijon) was felt. Unfortunately, extensive erasures and the adiastematic character of the notation that remains legible render a transcription impossible. It is nevertheless clear that this preface chant did not resemble either of the two main Cassinese traditions, nor the *Francisca* tradition, nor any Beneventan usage. The choir propers found elsewhere in the missal are not notated, but certain lessons have incidental notation, sometimes primitively diastematic, and one case, *Heloi lema sabacthani . . .* in the St. Matthew passion for Palm Sunday (fol. 139^r), fully Beneventan.

Written mostly in a local variety of roman minuscule script (as described by Supino Martini), the monastic missal was assembled in the latter part of the eleventh century for use at the abbey of Sant'Eutizio, Val Castoriana, near Norcia. However, I think that the original *ordo missae* (fols. 167–74) with its preface was removed from an older sacramentary and inserted in the traditional spot in the Easter vigil mass en bloc. Supino Martini does not mention the sacramentary title nor (as usual) the musical notation—that on fols. 170^v–171^r contrasting with the notation elsewhere in the MS. She ascribes the other uncial rubrics to Ubertus. Bischoff, however (as quoted by Gamber), says, "früherer Ansatz: 9/10 Jh; 2, 2 Hälfte des 11. Jh."

REFERENCES: Gamber, CLLA, no. 1415 (with further bibliography); Supino Martini, *Roma e l'area grafica romanesca,* pp. 202–5 (with bibliography in n. 10).

Source from Apulia

Baltimore W 6   47–49

SOURCE: *Baltimore, Walters Art Gallery, MS W.6, fols. 66^v–68^r (a single common preface notated with chant sui generis, following *Orate pro me fratres . . . R. Sit dominus in corde tuo . . . pro nostra omniumque salutem, quem.*—which in turn follow nineteen votive masses, the preface preceding the page-size T of *Te igitur* of the canon). Notated *in campo aperto* with approximate diastematy and occasional custodes in a peculiar and presumably archaic variety of Beneventan notation that uses the Metz sign ⌒ in place of the standard level-punctum and but few and often irregular signs for liquescence. One quilisma occurs.

The votive full missal begins with a kalendar enriched by Canosine, Beneventan, and Byzantine saints. It contains masses for fifty selected feasts and special Sundays from the temporal and a common of saints, but lacks masses for ordinary Sundays after Epiphany and after Pentecost and masses for Lenten weekdays. Some of the proper chants have notation, as does the Pater noster after the canon. Thirty-one masses have proper prefaces: nine of the votive masses plus two votive masses for days of the week and the votive mass of the Trinity, and nineteen of the masses of the temporal and sanctoral. None of the common masses for saints or the votive masses added at the end of the missal have proper prefaces. No purely episcopal functions or masses to be sung only by a bishop are included: the book was clearly meant for use by a priest in the town or diocese of Canosa in Apulia. The missal was perhaps copied in part from an archaic monastic exemplar, though as copied must date from the middle or late eleventh century.

REFERENCES: Kenneth Levy, "Charlemagne's Archetype of Gregorian Chant," *Journal of the American Musicological Society* 40 (1987): 1–30, especially 15–16; Sieghild Rehle, *Missale Beneventanum von Canosa,* Textus Patristici et Liturgici 9 (Regensburg, 1972).

Addenda

Ben 19/20

SOURCE: Benevento 19, fol. 106ʳ–108ʳ, and Benevento 20, fol. 146ᵛ–149ᵛ—*olim* Benevento 7 and Benevento 8. (*Pars hiemalis* and *pars aestiua,* respectively, of a *liber typicus* or mixed breviary-missal for non-monastic use. In Ben 19, the notated proper prefaces of Christmas, of Lent, of the Apostles, of the Dedication of a church, and the Easter preface of Holy Saturday precede two common-preface chants, *In cotidianis diebus* and *In festiuitatibus*; in Ben 20, the notated proper prefaces of Easter Day, Ascension, Pentecost, Holy Cross, Holy Trinity, the Assumption/Nativity of St. Mary, of the Apostles [again], of the Dedication of a church [again], and the unnotated preface of the dead once again precede two common-preface chants rubricked *In cotidianis diebus* [nearly identical, apart from liquescents, with the everyday chant in Ben 19 and in Lo 3511] and *In Sollemnitatibus* [a different version of the same festal formulas that were rubricked *In festiuitatibus* in Ben 19, not a true *tonus sollemnior* such as is found in Lo 3511]. In both Ben 19 and Ben 20, the prefaces [with the associated *Communicantes* insertions] are followed by the remainder of the canon of the mass, beginning with the large zoomorphic T of *Te igitur,* where a tonsured figure, identified as STEPHANUS SAC<ERDOS>—perhaps the donor—kneels beside the T-cross.)

The two MSS come from twelfth-century Benevento, like the contemporary missal from St. Peter's Convent *intra muros,* Lo 3511. (See above, pp. xlii–xliv, 1–2, and 26 below.) The prefaces of Lo 3511, supplied with the usual Beneventan indications for liquescence, were probably notated earlier than those of Ben 19/20, where liquescents are remarkably sparse. At least, Lo 3511 is closer to its Cassinese model. The verbal texts of the prefaces found in both parts are the same as the corresponding texts in Lo 3511; but the preface chants, notated *in campo aperto* with accurate diastematy by a different scribe for each volume, vary considerably, even where the companion volumes share texts.

In general, the music scribe of Ben 19 adhered to the versions found in Lo 3511, including the peculiar Lo 3511 everyday medial cadence, a bć (b) b , now employed as well for many proper prefaces with festal chant, even when Lo 3511 retained the correct Cassinese medial cadence (as in the prefaces for Easter, Ascension, and Pentecost). But in those for Christmas and the Holy Trinity, the Ben 19 scribe used the standard festal form of the final cadence, aG Ga b áb (a) a , instead of the final cadence *In cotidianis diebus* inexplicably found with these proper prefaces in Lo 3511. (See pp. xl–xliii above.)

The opening dialogue (where local variants abound) and the common preface *In festiuitatibus* in Ben 19 are identical with those in Lo 3511 except for one note. But the scribe of Ben 20—although for his chant *In cotidianis diebus* he copied Lo 3511 (or Ben 19 or some intermediate version)—must have written his version of the festal chant *In Sollemnitatibus* from memory. Sometimes he notated local Benevento versions recorded earlier in Ben 40 and Ben 33 (see p. 1 above), but he used the distinctive Cassinese notes for the phrase *Cum quibus et nostras uoces . . . deprecamur,* where Ben 19 followed the version of Lo 3511 that conformed to local tradition. The three chants for the proper-preface conclusion *Et ideo . . . dicentes*—in Ben 19 appended to the Christmas proper preface and also appended to the common preface *In cotidianis diebus* in both Ben 19 and Ben 20—alternate between festal and everyday forms, although none approaches the highly neumatic style employed for this conclusion found in Lo 3511 for use with the Lo 3511 *tonus sollemnior.*

The Sanctus incipits in Ben 19/20 are all without notation.

REFERENCES: Brown, *Handlist,* pp. 19–20; Ferdinand Cabrol, "Le Chant du Pater à la messe," *Revue grégorienne* 14 (1929): 12; CLLA, no. 460; Kelly, *The Beneventan Chant,* p. 299 and pl. 5 (Ben 20, fol. 226ʳ); Mallet and Thibaut, *Les Manuscrits en écriture bénéventaine de la Bibliothèque Capitulaire de Bénévent,* vol. 2 (forthcoming); and PM 21, pls. 5–20 and pp. 334–37.

(I am greatly indebted to Dom Jean Mallet, o.s.b., who supplied film strips of the Ben 19/20 prefaces. I regret that they were not available in time to incorporate chants from these MSS in the edition and that I neglected these MSS on visits to Benevento because they did not contain tropes—the inclusion of prefaces in BTC II/3 not yet having been planned.)

Vat 7231

SOURCE: BAV Vat. lat. 7231, fol. 47ʳ–51ᵛ. (A partially notated votive missal with ritual for the sick, dying, and departed. The notated proper prefaces of Christmas, of the Epiphany, of Lent, of Easter, Holy Cross, Ascension, Pentecost, the Apostles, the Trinity, and St. Mary precede two common-preface chants without rubric—versions *sui generis* of the chants *In cotidianis diebus* and *In dominicis seu festis diebus* [or *In festiuitatibus*] as found in MC 339 and Lo 3511 [see pp. 1, 2, and 11–25] and Ben 19/20 [see immediately above] and elsewhere. The proper-preface chants use the standard festal cadences, often retaining *mi* = b as tenor in forephrases but with accented syllables rising to *fa* = c. [See *New Grove,* s.v. "Sources," p. 626, for a facsimile of the Trinity preface.] The distinctive Cassinese notes are used for the phrase *Cum quibus et nostras uoces . . . deprecamur* of the festal preface. *Et ideo . . . dicentes* is cued without elaboration after most proper prefaces with the standard initial figure, but the full text of the conclusion was added in the margin of fol. 48ʳ only, next to the Easter preface and without notation. The first two of the three notated Sanctus incipits, appended to the common-preface chants mentioned above, both read—

Gaba ba   Gaba ba   bc b
S<an>c<tu>s. S<an>c<tu>s. S<an>c<tu>s.

—at the pitch used for the transcriptions from MC 339 and Lo 3511 below. The third Sanctus incipit was originally appended to a third preface chant, the notes of which were expunged and replaced with a version of the Franciscan-curial festal chant, written in gross rectangular notes from the late fourteenth century, with lines for c and F and an F clef, so that *ut* = F . The text *Vere dignum* of the original third chant (a *tonus sollemnior?*) was given a striking zoomorphic initial V and a somewhat cruder T-cross for *Te igitur,* immediately following the unerased Sanctus incipit, still remaining in the original notation without liquescents:

Gab ba   Gab ba   Gab ba
S<an>c<tu>s. S<an>c<tu>s. S<an>c<tu>s.

The prefaces, placed within a mass ordo (the verbal text of which must ultimately derive from a twelfth-century Cassinese missal), are found in succession without the usual intervenient *Communicantes* insertions into the canon for high feasts. In addition to numerous private prayers for the celebrant before, after, and during mass, the ordo contains six Gloria in excelsis intonations with trope incipits [see BTC II/2, p. xii, table 1, under Order C] and an intonation for the Credo. Two unrubricked Pater noster chants with their exordia follow the canon, the first of which is followed by the completely notated embolism *Libera nos . . . quesumus,* with a very different application of the formulas than is found in Ben 40 [see BTC II/4].)

The mass ordo was copied as part of a votive missal of different origin, missing its first and last folios and now beginning with an extensive series of prayers and chants for the sick, dying, and departed and including the burial service, the entire office for the dead, and several masses (with numerous alternative collects) for the departed. The unnotated preface for the dead on fol. 36ᵛ is followed by a pool of six communion chants for use at masses of the dead on the six ferial days of the week. Votive masses of the Virgin follow the mass ordo, which in turn are followed by a votive mass of the Holy Spirit and a common of saints, presumably for votive use. Some of the propers are notated, but not all.

The scribe, although he employs late Cassinese abbreviations and suspensions, was ill lettered, writing *Abemus adominum* and *confexione* (for *confessione*). The prefaces are entitled *Propheta* throughout. The missal was probably copied early in the thirteenth century. The notation employs the provincial, Metz-like form of the punctum found in the Canosa missal, Baltimore W 6, with a rich repertory of liquescent neumes—which were however often misplaced over syllables where not even initial liquescence is possible. Perhaps the scribe liked their decorative effect. Diastematy of the original notation *in campo aperto* is rigorously accurate. The Cassinese exemplar copied by the music scribe perhaps dated from the early or middle twelfth century, although passages may derive from local or Beneventan use.

REFERENCES: Bannister, *Monumenti vaticani di paleografia musicale latina,* p. 132, n. 374, and pl. 78b; Brown, *Handlist,* p. 152; BTC II/2, pp. x, xii (table 1), and xviii; and *New Grove,* s. v. "Sources," pp. 626 (facsimile of fol. 49ᵛ) and 627.

Mass Preface Chants
for the Celebrant
from Southern Italy

I. Beneventan and Cassinese Common Prefaces

(*Corpus Praefationum, Textus* and *Apparatus* no. 687; also see CP 1:xii–xxiii and the description of manuscripts in the BTC list of Sources immediately preceding.)

Early Eleventh-Century Beneventan Tradition

33: The Beneventan preface chant is characterized by two notes, Ga , for the second syllable of *Amen;* by the regular use of the three-note group Gab to begin new fore-phrases; and by the three-note group abc for an important accent early in the afterphrase. The tenor remains b , but accented syllables often rise to c . Nearly the same as the old Beneventan version of 40, below.

40: The earliest preface chant undoubtedly from the city of Benevento. Similar to 33 but with many small variants. In the passages *Per quem maiestatem . . .* and *ut ammitti iubeas,* the tenor is c .

Twelfth-Century Mixed Traditions in Lo 3511 from San Pietro intra muros, Benevento

3511[f]: *In festiuitatibus.* The opening dialogue through *Habemus* resembles that of 40 in many particulars; the rest of the dialogue and almost all the preface are based on the Sunday and festival Cassinese model seen in 339[df] below. Only from *Cum quibus* to the end (the notes illegible after *supplici*) does 3511[f] again diverge, recalling the chant of 40.

3511[s]: *In sollemnitatibus.* The common preface breaks off after *Sursum corda,* owing to the loss of the folio having the illuminated *Te igitur* on the reverse; but the proper-preface conclusion *Et ideo . . . dicentes* (fol. 174[v]—see pp. 24–25 below) and several notated proper prefaces in Lo 3511 use the formulas of this *tonus sollemnior.* An editorial reconstruction of the remainder of the common preface according to this version is given below, pp. 36–37. See Late Cassinese Versions *In sollemnitatibus,* p. xliv above, for two related twelfth-century versions. Also see under ZaMR 166, p. 4 above.

3511[c]: *In cotidianis diebus.* (Lowest staff of the transcriptions following.) Belongs to the same family of everyday votive prefaces as the Cassinese versions 426 and C32, but not copied directly from a Cassinese model or else systematically revised. Cf. the 3511[c] division of text *Domine sanctę [/] pater omnipotens [/] ęternę deus* (as in the Cassinese Sunday and festal forms) with *Domine sancte pater [/] omnipotens eterne deus* in the everyday votive versions of 426 and C32. Also cf. the related interchange of initial figures between *Nos tibi semper* and *Domine sancte.* In the course of the preface, the Cassinese everyday medial cadence closing the forephrase, b áb b (b) , was altered to a bć b (b) , as for instance at *laudant angeli.*

The Cassinese Sunday and Festal Tradition

339[df]: *In dominicis seu festis diebus.* The only preface surviving as originally notated in the renowned sacramentary of Desiderius, Abbot of Montecassino, 1058–87—perhaps prepared for use at the consecration of the new basilica at Montecassino in 1071 (see Cassinese Sources, p. 2 above). In any case, this is the earliest surviving copy of the most widespread and durable south Italian preface chant. The descending initial notes b aG to begin interior phrases; the notes ab ab for *iustum* in the opening dialogue; and the composed, non-formulaic, and unexpected transitional phrase

$$\overset{G\ \ b\ a\ b\ \ \ c\ \ a\ a\ G}{Cum\ quibus\ et\ nostras\ uoces}$$

characterize this version in all its many derivatives, as, for instance, in MC 127, Vat 6082, ZaMR 166, and Ottob. 576 (see Sources, above). In the following transcription, the opening phrase of the preface, *Vere dignum et iustum est,* missing in MC 339, is borrowed from the version in the leaf belonging to Montecassino Compactio VI, which is otherwise identical with the version of MC 339.

The Cassinese Tradition for Votive Masses and Everyday Use

339[c]: *In cotidianis diebus.* The original notation can be made out only from . . . *christum dominum nostrum* (p. 18 below) onwards through the incipit of Sanctus Thannabaur 41 and *Et ideo . . . Cumque omni* of the proper-preface conclusion. What survives closely resembles the versions of 426 and C32, listed below. (See Cassinese Sources, pp. 2–3 above.)

426: Without rubric. The earliest known Cassinese preface for votive masses, the notation dating from the late tenth or early eleventh centuries. The version is characterized by the internal initial figure G a b to begin new phrases, as at *Domine sancte, Per quem maiestatem, Cęli celorumque,* and *Cum quibus* (as opposed to b aG in the Cassinese Sunday and festal version); frequent recitations on c ; and consistently simple medial and final cadences (c b áb b and a G a áb a , respectively). The opening dialogue for the everyday version is less stable and in later copies especially subject to variation, perhaps already reflecting a mixture of traditions. (See Cassinese Sources, pp. 5–6 above.)

C32: Very close to the version of 426, although copied a century later. (See Cassinese Sources, p. 6 above.)

33 (f. 80ʳ) Per om- ni- a sę- cu- la sę- cu- lo- rum. ℟. A- men.

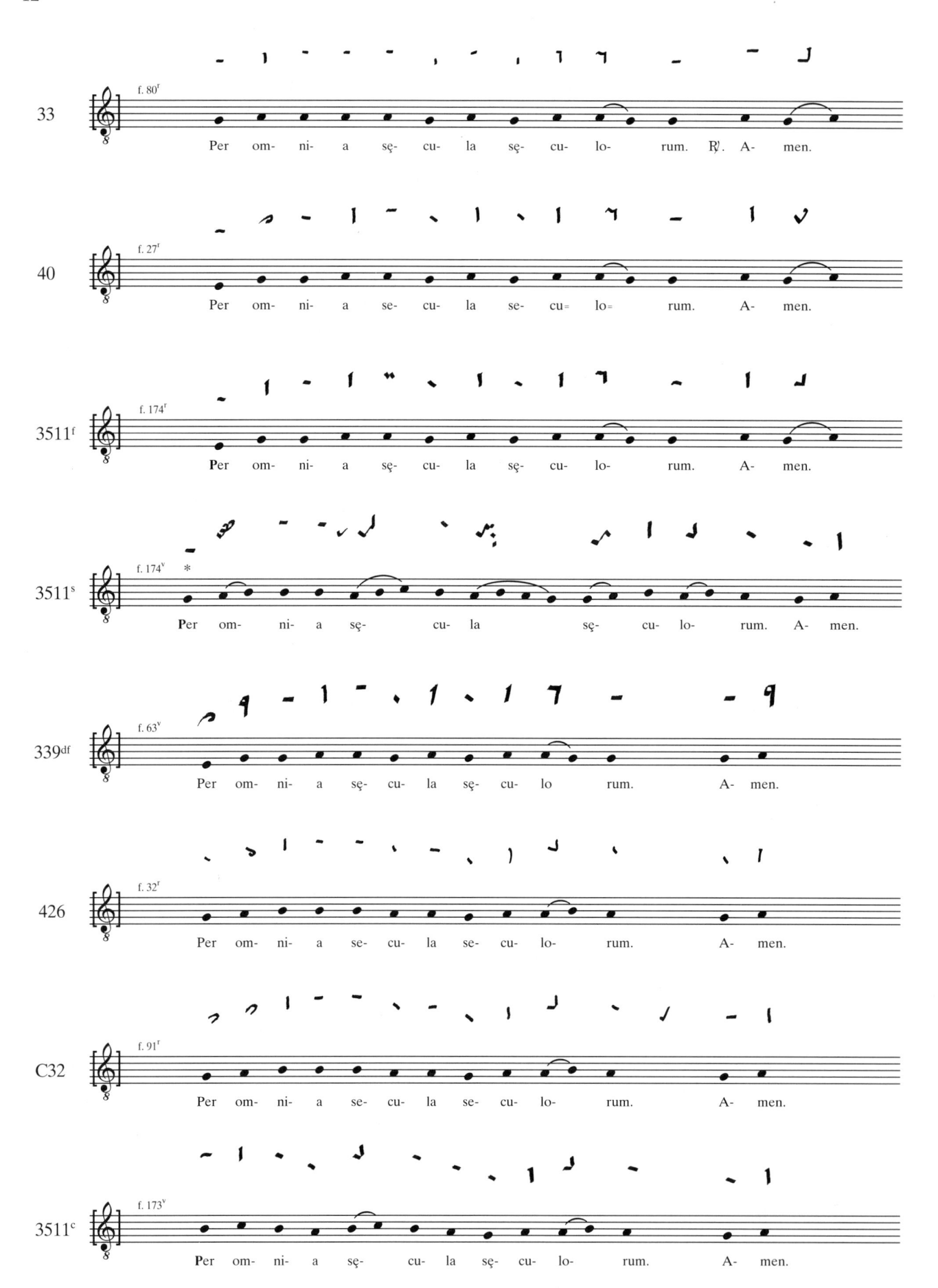

40 (f. 27ʳ) Per om- ni- a se- cu- la se- cu= lo= rum. A- men.

3511ᶠ (f. 174ʳ) Per om- ni- a sę- cu- la sę- cu- lo- rum. A- men.

3511ˢ (f. 174ᵛ) * Per om- ni- a sę- cu- la sę- cu- lo- rum. A- men.

339ᵈᶠ (f. 63ᵛ) Per om- ni- a sę- cu- la sę- cu- lo rum. A- men.

426 (f. 32ʳ) Per om- ni- a se- cu- la se- cu- lo- rum. A- men.

C32 (f. 91ʳ) Per om- ni- a se- cu- la se- cu- lo- rum. A- men.

3511ᶜ (f. 173ᵛ) Per om- ni- a sę- cu- la sę- cu- lo- rum. A- men.

*Or "E"; diastematy inaccurate. If custos after *omnia* is disregarded, the notes for *Per omnia sę-* can be read "E Ga a a abc."

33 Do- mi- nus uo- bis- cum. ℟. Et cum spi- ri- tu tu- o ;

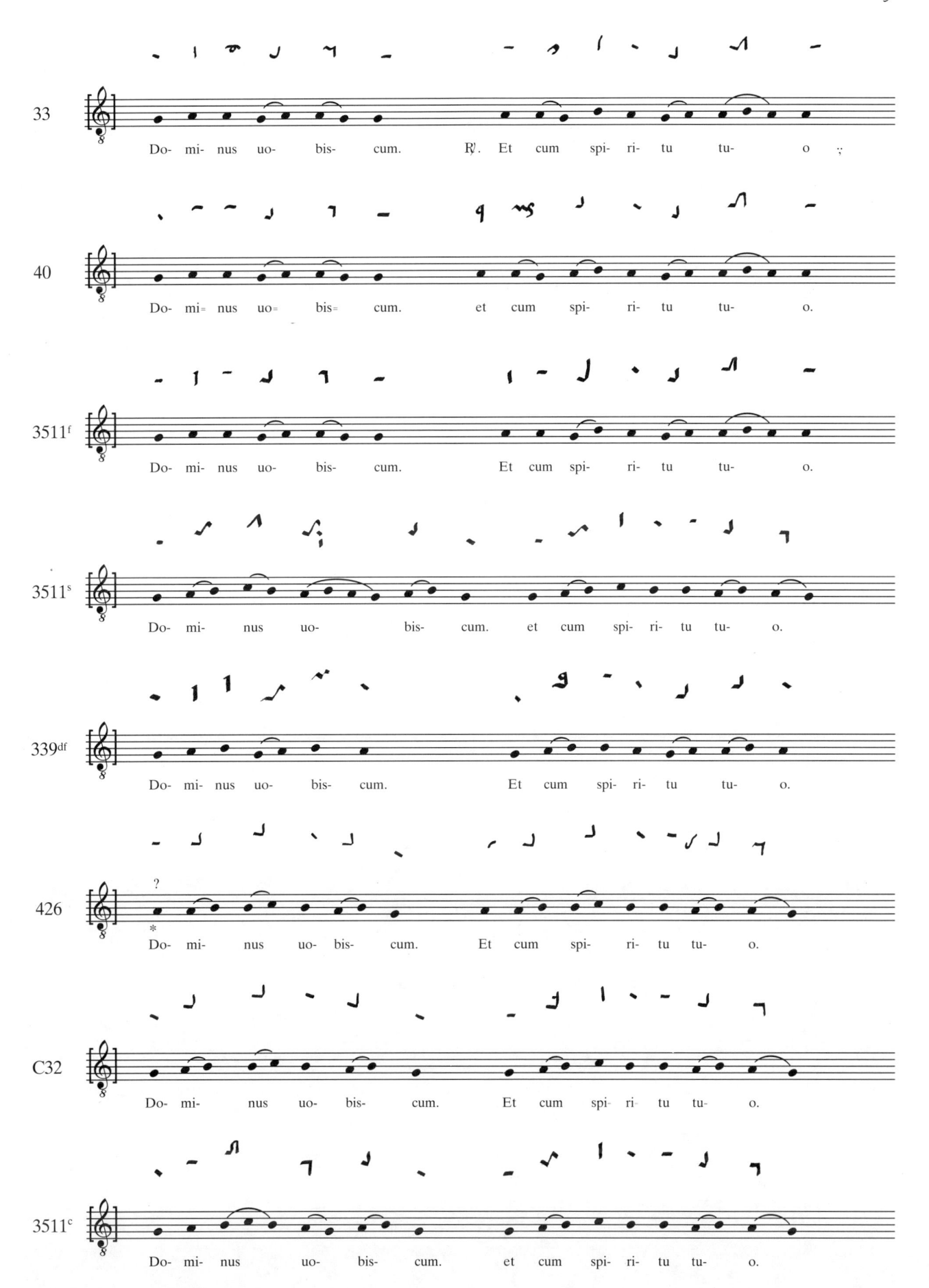

40 Do- mi= nus uo= bis= cum. et cum spi- ri- tu tu- o.

3511ᶠ Do- mi- nus uo- bis- cum. Et cum spi- ri- tu tu- o.

3511ˢ Do- mi- nus uo- bis- cum. et cum spi- ri- tu tu- o.

339ᵈᶠ Do- mi- nus uo- bis- cum. Et cum spi- ri- tu tu- o.

426 Do- mi- nus uo- bis- cum. Et cum spi- ri- tu tu- o.

C32 Do- mi- nus uo- bis- cum. Et cum spi- ri- tu tu- o.

3511ᶜ Do- mi- nus uo- bis- cum. et cum spi- ri- tu tu- o.

*Inexact diastematy. The note can be read "G."

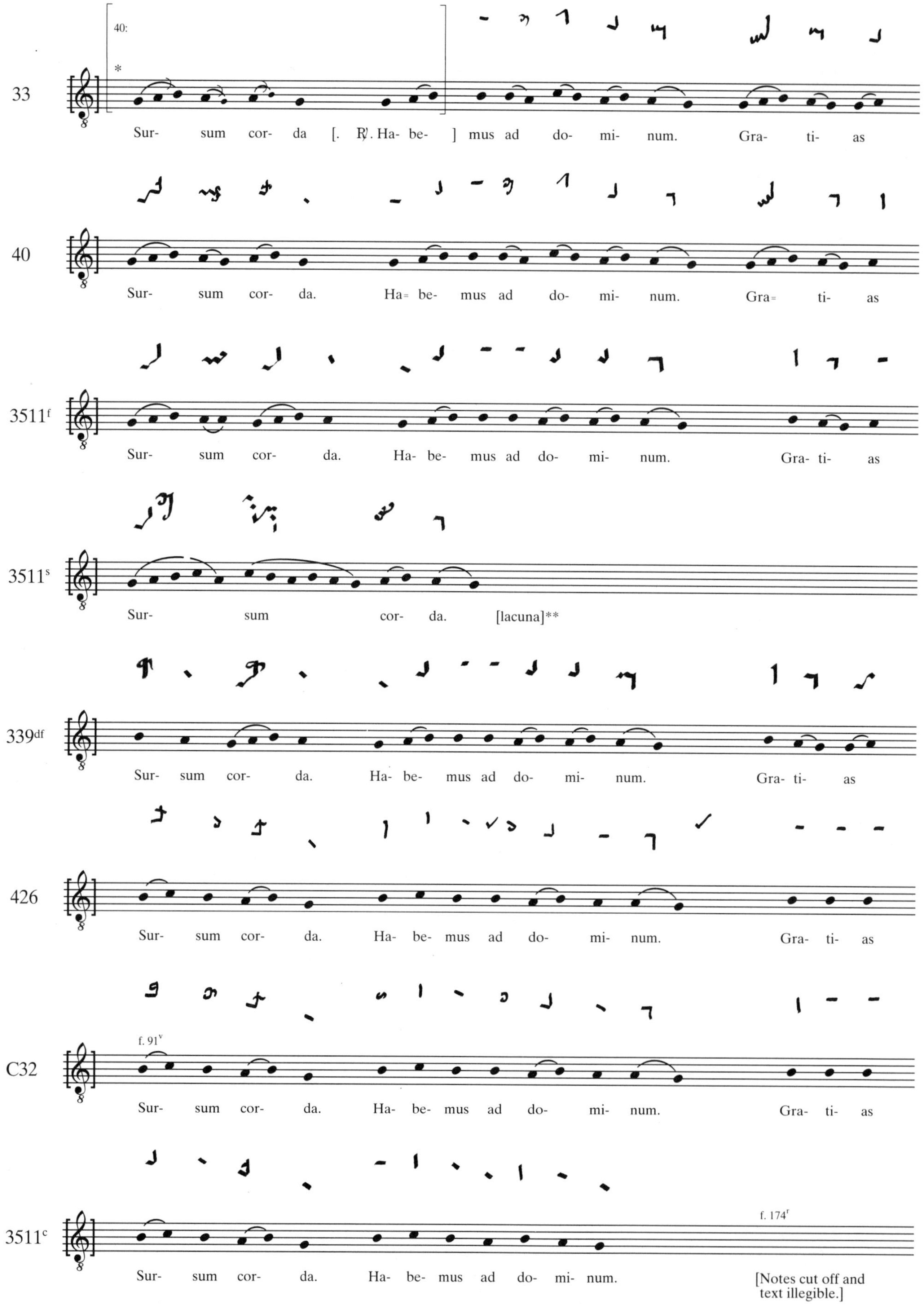
40:
*
33
Sur- sum cor- da [. ℟. Ha- be-] mus ad do- mi- num. Gra- ti- as
40
Sur- sum cor- da. Ha= be- mus ad do- mi- num. Gra= ti- as
3511f
Sur- sum cor- da. Ha- be- mus ad do- mi- num. Gra- ti- as
3511s
Sur- sum cor- da. [lacuna]**
339df
Sur- sum cor- da. Ha- be- mus ad do- mi- num. Gra- ti- as
426
Sur- sum cor- da. Ha- be- mus ad do- mi- num. Gra- ti- as
f. 91v
C32
Sur- sum cor- da. Ha- be- mus ad do- mi- num. Gra- ti- as
3511c
f. 174r
Sur- sum cor- da. Ha- be- mus ad do- mi- num.
[Notes cut off and text illegible.]

*Notes and syllables within brackets are no longer legible, except for evident liquescents. The neumes above are borrowed from Ben 40.
**The end of the dialogue and the solemn preface are missing, together with the continuation of the canon, *Te igitur*—the *T* presumably large and illuminated.

15

33 a- ga- mus do- mi- no de- o nos- tro. ℟ Dig- num et ius- tum est.

40 a= ga= mus do- mi- no de= o nos= tro. Dig- num et ius= tum est.

[sic]

3511f a- ga- mus do- mi- no de- o nos- tro. Dig- num et ius- tum est.

339df a- ga- mus do- mi- no de- o nos- tro. Dig- num et ius- tum est.

426 a- ga- mus do- mi- no de- o nos- tro. Dig- num et ius- tum est.

C32 a- ga- mus do- mi- no de- o nos- tro. Dig- num et ius- tum est.

3511c Dig- num et ius- tum est.

*The note is no longer visible.

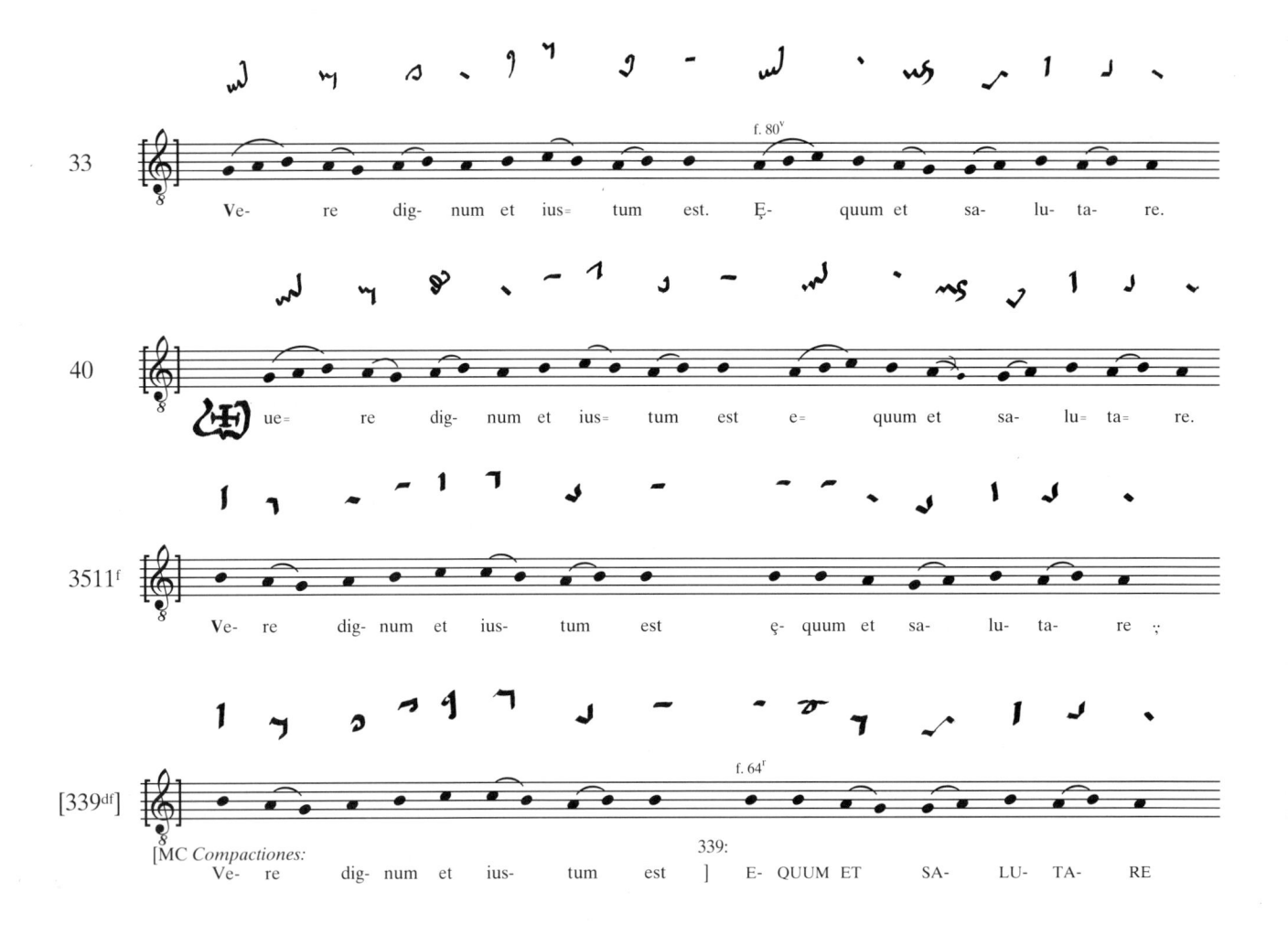

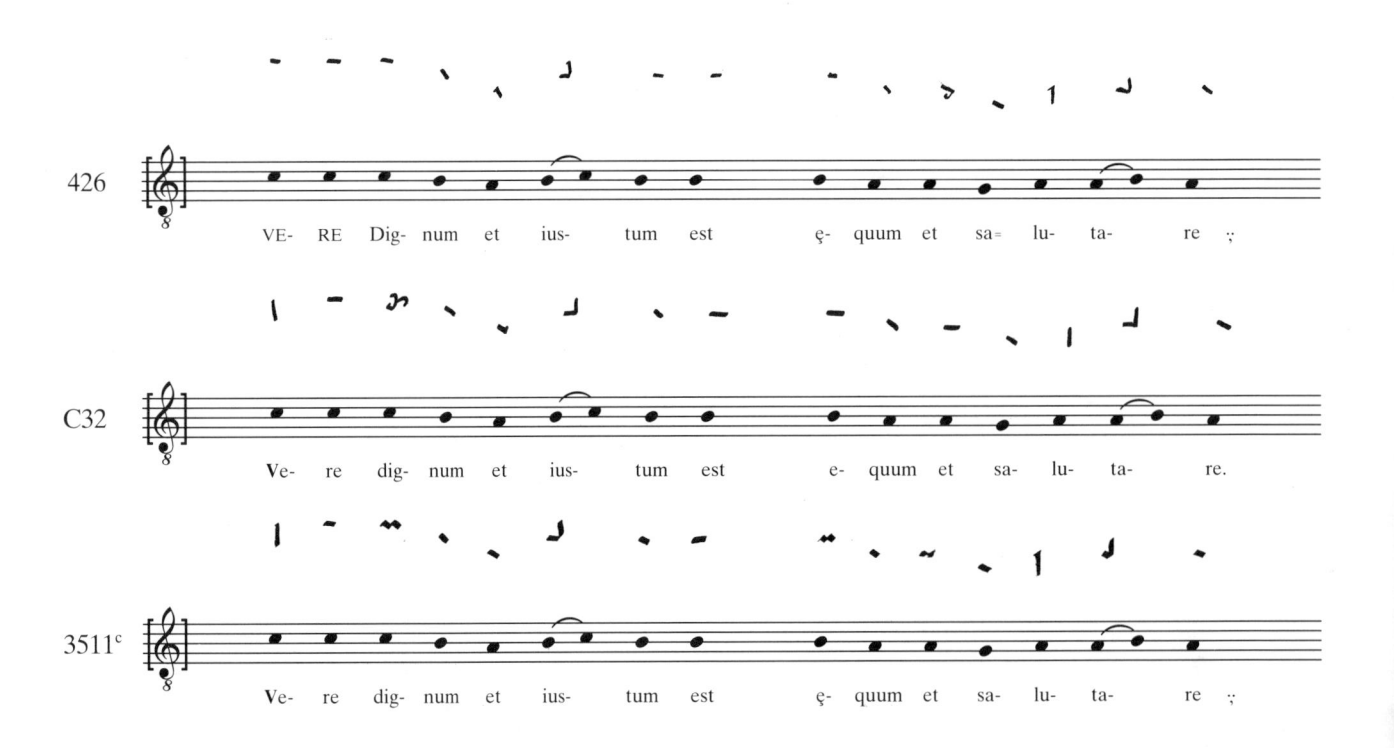

16

33 Ve- re dig- num et ius= tum est. E- quum et sa- lu- ta- re.

40 ue= re dig- num et ius= tum est e= quum et sa- lu= ta= re.

3511ᶠ Ve- re dig- num et ius- tum est ę- quum et sa- lu- ta- re ⁖

[339ᵈᶠ] [MC *Compactiones:* 339:
Ve- re dig- num et ius- tum est] E- QUUM ET SA- LU- TA- RE

426 VE- RE Dig- num et ius- tum est ę- quum et sa= lu- ta- re ⁖

C32 Ve- re dig- num et ius- tum est e- quum et sa- lu- ta- re.

3511ᵉ Ve- re dig- num et ius- tum est ę- quum et sa- lu- ta- re ⁖

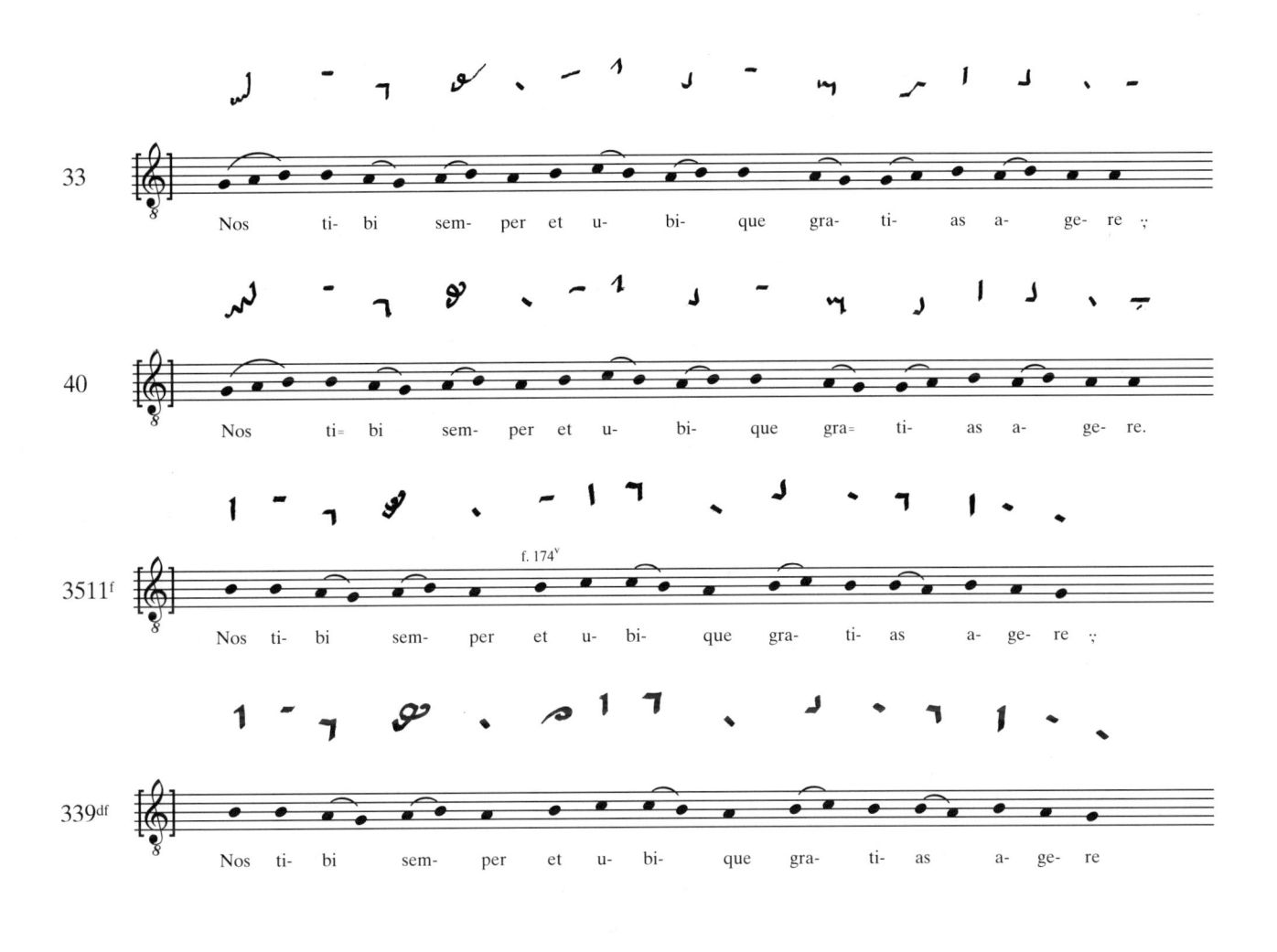

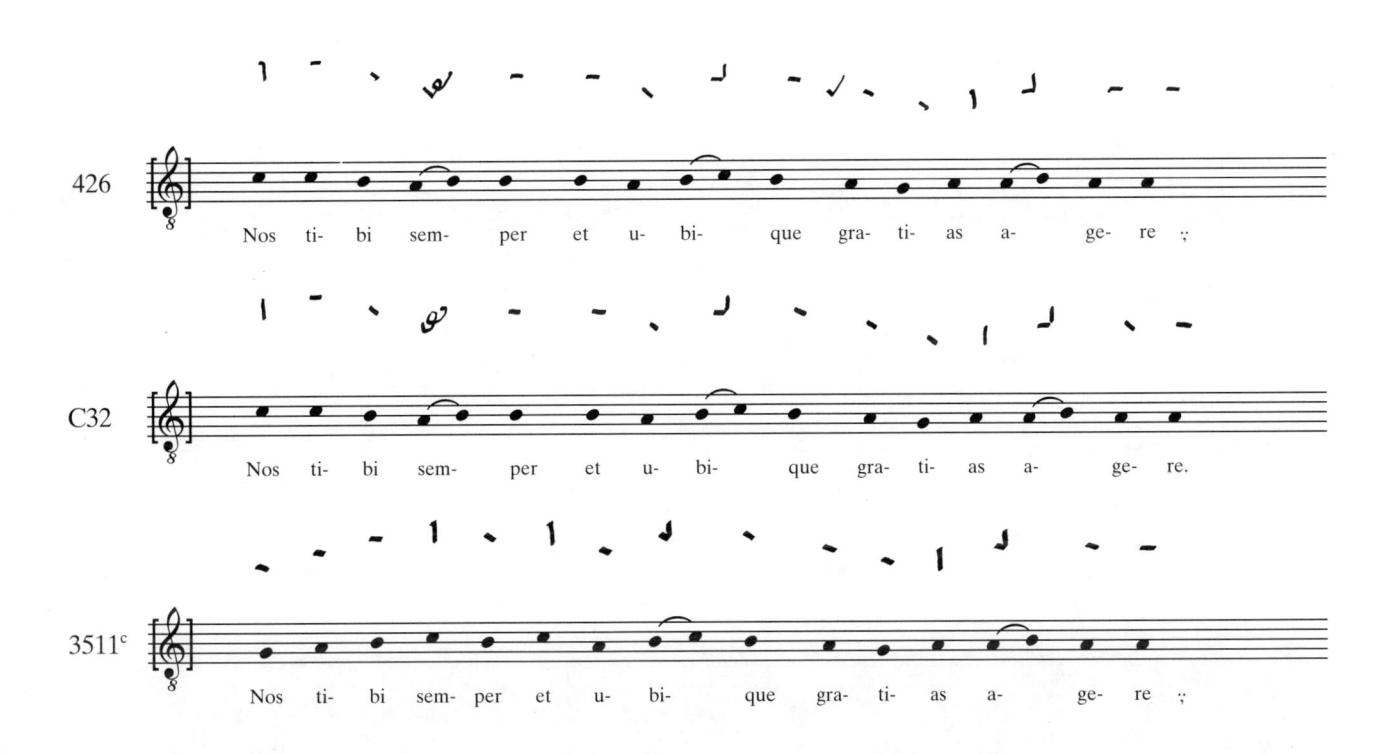

17

33 Nos ti- bi sem- per et u- bi- que gra- ti- as a- ge- re ;

40 Nos ti= bi sem- per et u- bi- que gra= ti- as a- ge- re.

3511ᶠ f. 174ᵛ Nos ti- bi sem- per et u- bi- que gra- ti- as a- ge- re ;

339ᵈᶠ Nos ti- bi sem- per et u- bi- que gra- ti- as a- ge- re

426 Nos ti- bi sem- per et u- bi- que gra- ti- as a- ge- re ;

C32 Nos ti- bi sem- per et u- bi- que gra- ti- as a- ge- re.

3511ᶜ Nos ti- bi sem- per et u- bi- que gra- ti- as a- ge- re ;

18

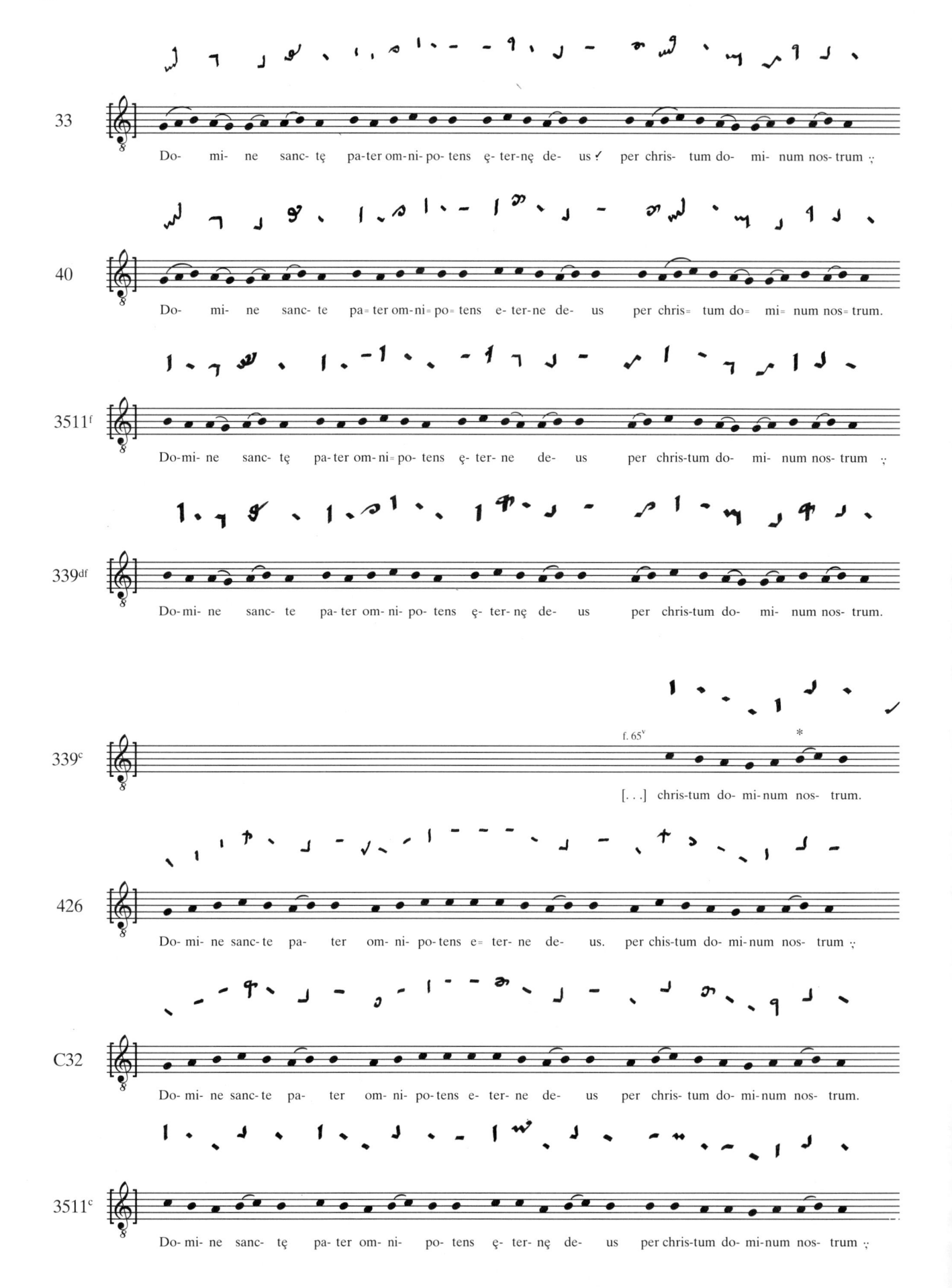

*The scribe erred in positioning the neumes for *nostrum* and the custos following so as to imply the pitches transcribed above. All other Cassinese versions *in cotidianis diebus* have the equivalent of "ab a" for *nostrum*.

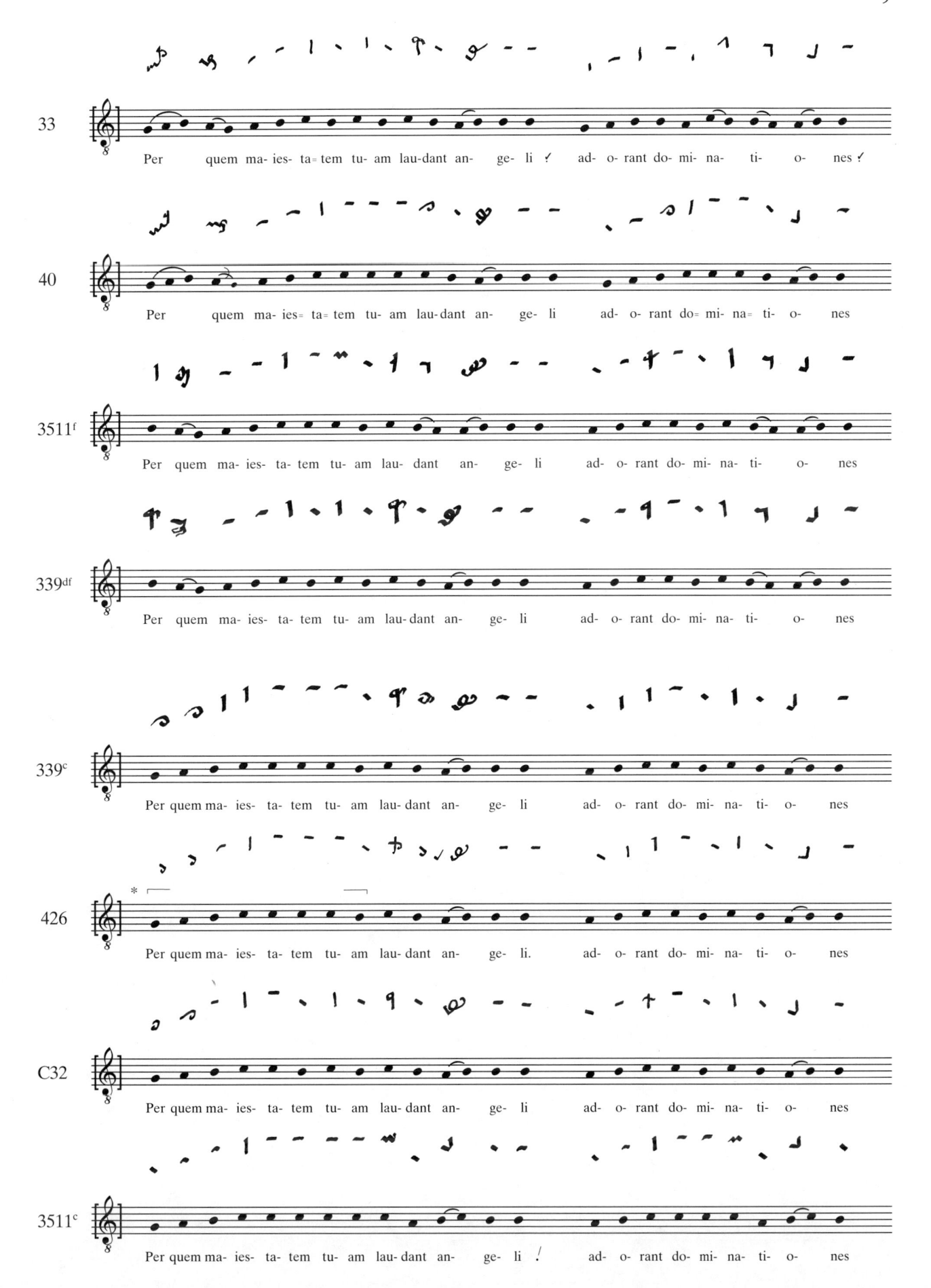

33 Per quem ma- ies- ta= tem tu- am lau- dant an- ge- li ⸭ ad- o- rant do- mi- na- ti- o- nes ⸭

40 Per quem ma- ies= ta- tem tu- am lau- dant an- ge- li ad- o- rant do- mi- na= ti- o- nes

3511ᶠ Per quem ma- ies- ta- tem tu- am lau- dant an- ge- li ad- o- rant do- mi- na- ti- o- nes

339ᵈᶠ Per quem ma- ies- ta- tem tu- am lau- dant an- ge- li ad- o- rant do- mi- na- ti- o- nes

339ᶜ Per quem ma- ies- ta- tem tu- am lau- dant an- ge- li ad- o- rant do- mi- na- ti- o- nes

426 Per quem ma- ies- ta- tem tu- am lau- dant an- ge- li. ad- o- rant do- mi- na- ti- o- nes

C32 Per quem ma- ies- ta- tem tu- am lau- dant an- ge- li ad- o- rant do- mi- na- ti- o- nes

3511ᶜ Per quem ma- ies- ta- tem tu- am lau- dant an- ge- li ⸭ ad- o- rant do- mi- na- ti- o- nes

*Pitches for the notes within brackets are uncertain. The transcription given above, after the parallel versions 339ᶜ and C32, is likely; but other readings are possible.

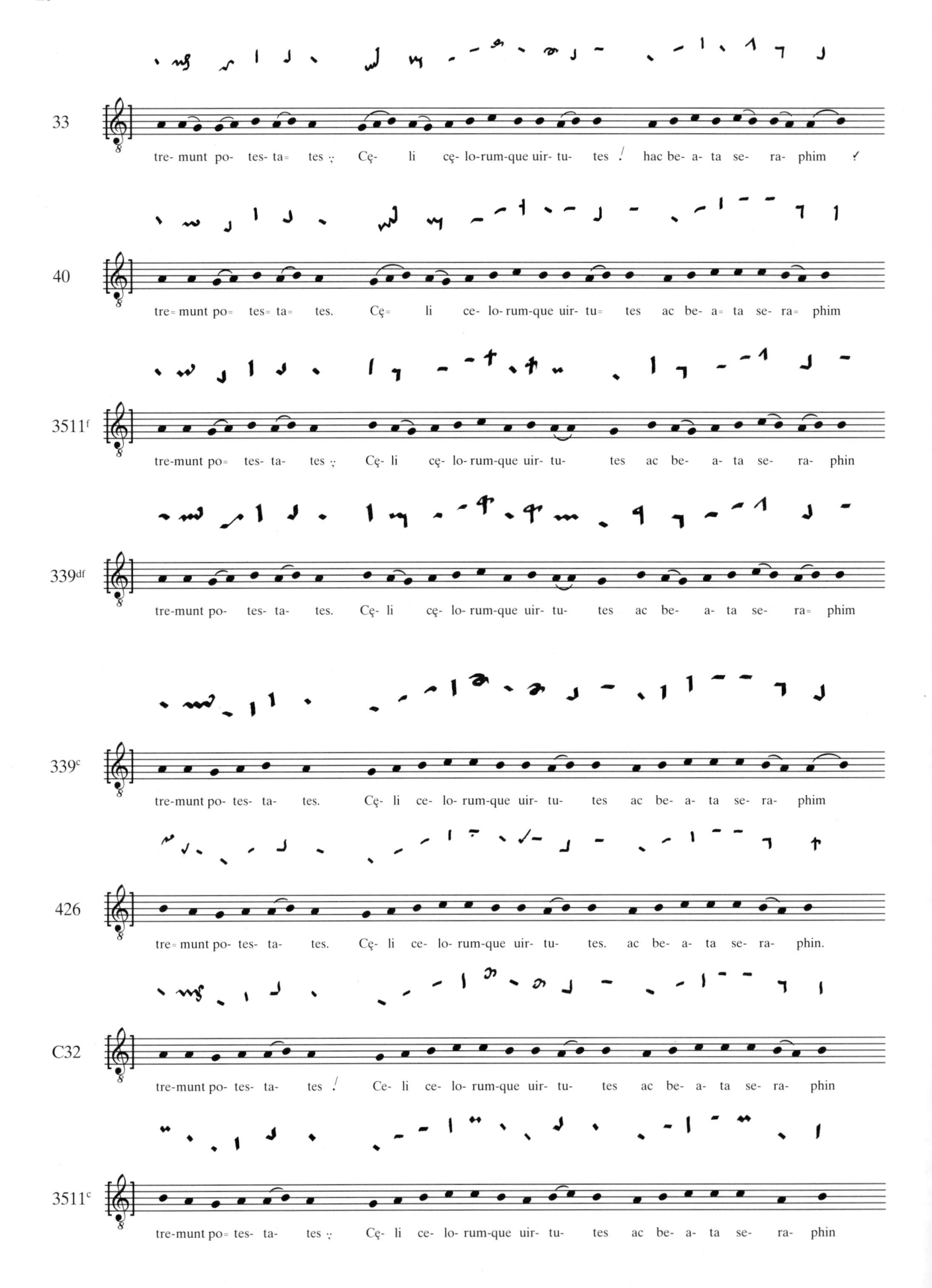

33 tre-munt po- tes- ta= tes ; Cę- li cę- lo-rum-que uir-tu- tes ! hac be- a- ta se- ra- phim

40 tre=munt po= tes= ta= tes. Cę= li ce- lo-rum-que uir-tu= tes ac be- a- ta se- ra- phim

3511ᶠ tre-munt po- tes- ta- tes ; Cę- li cę- lo-rum-que uir-tu- tes ac be- a- ta se- ra- phin

339ᵈᶠ tre-munt po- tes- ta- tes. Cę- li cę- lo-rum-que uir-tu- tes ac be- a- ta se- ra= phim

339ᶜ tre-munt po- tes- ta- tes. Cę- li ce- lo-rum-que uir-tu- tes ac be- a- ta se- ra- phim

426 tre-munt po- tes- ta- tes. Cę- li ce- lo-rum-que uir-tu- tes. ac be- a- ta se- ra- phin.

C32 tre-munt po- tes- ta- tes ! Ce- li ce- lo-rum-que uir-tu- tes ac be- a- ta se- ra- phin

3511ᶜ tre-munt po- tes- ta- tes ; Cę- li ce-lo-rum-que uir-tu- tes ac be- a- ta se- ra- phin

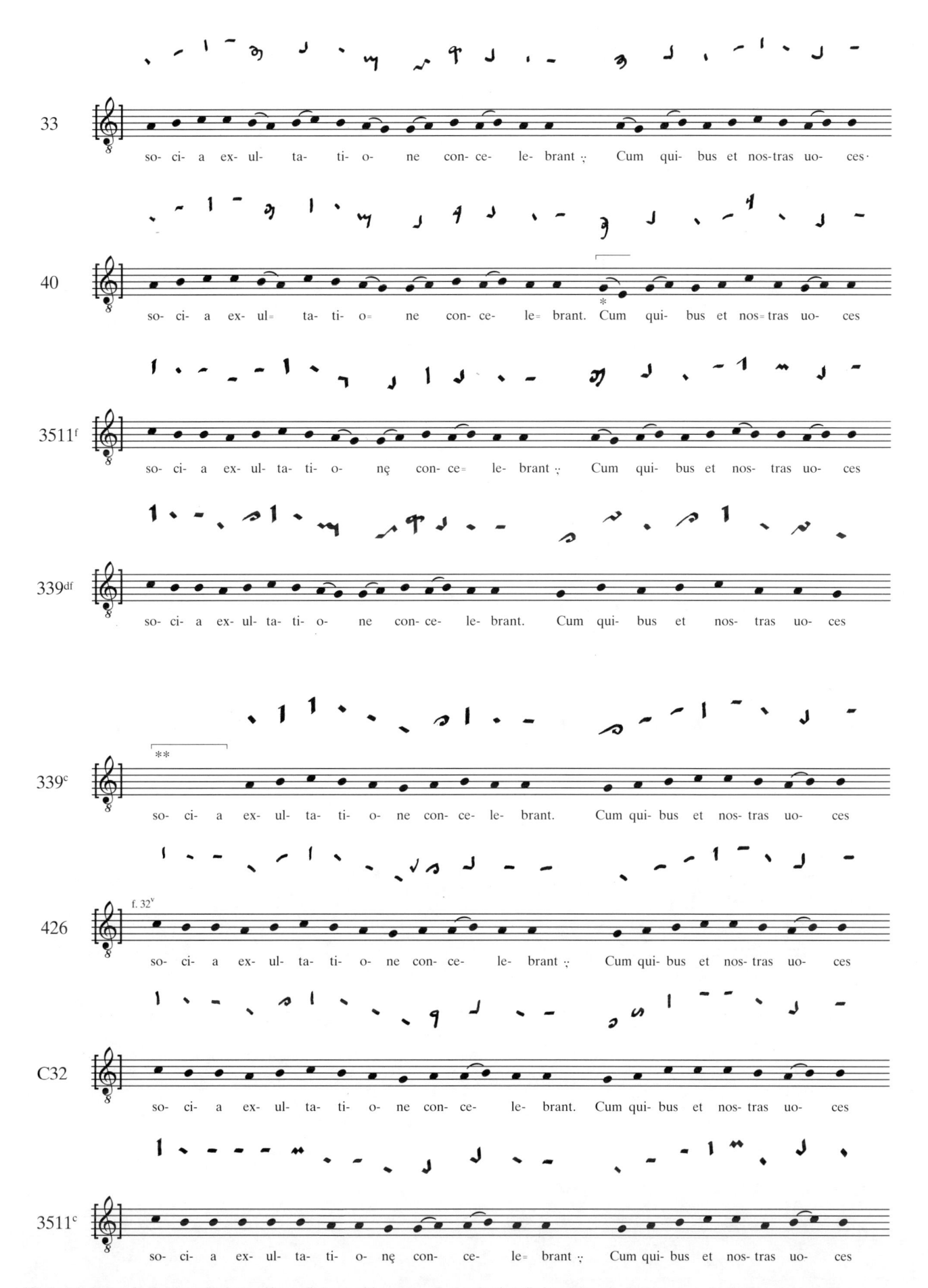

Sic: the notes between brackets transcribe the unambiguous diastematy of the passage, reflecting what the scribe intended to write. But he was wrong: he should have heightened the neumes to read as in the transcription of 33, directly above.

**Completely erased.

22

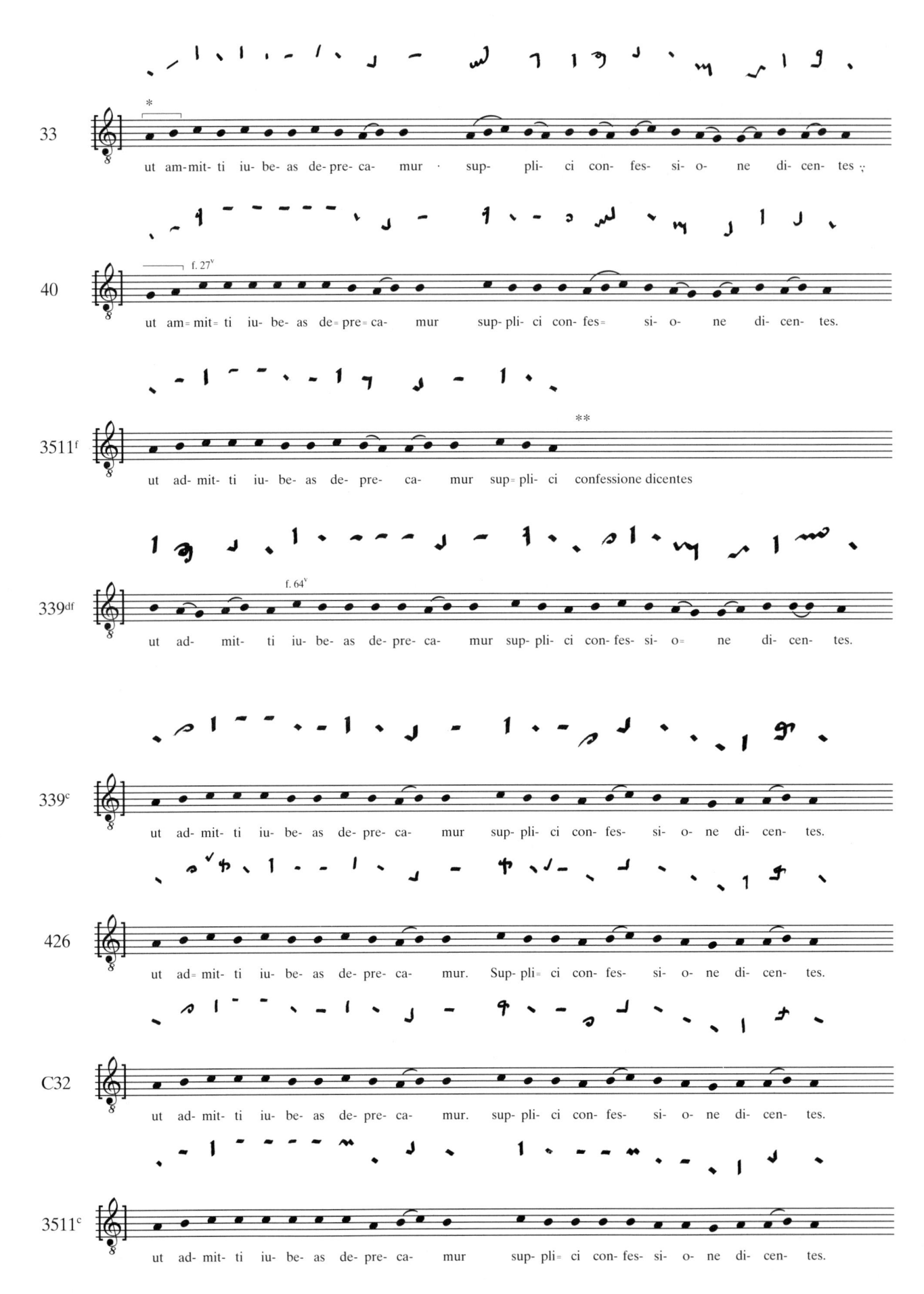

33 ut am-mit-ti iu-be-as de-pre-ca-mur · sup-pli-ci con-fes-si-o-ne di-cen-tes;

40 ut am=mit-ti iu-be-as de-pre-ca-mur sup-pli-ci con-fes=si-o-ne di-cen-tes.

3511ᶠ ut ad-mit-ti iu- be- as de- pre- ca- mur sup=pli- ci confessione dicentes

339ᵈᶠ ut ad- mit- ti iu-be- as de-pre-ca- mur sup-pli-ci con-fes-si-o= ne di-cen-tes.

339ᶜ ut ad-mit-ti iu-be-as de-pre-ca-mur sup-pli-ci con-fes- si-o-ne di-cen-tes.

426 ut ad=mit-ti iu-be-as de-pre-ca-mur. Sup-pli=ci con-fes- si-o-ne di-cen-tes.

C32 ut ad=mit-ti iu-be-as de-pre-ca-mur. sup-pli-ci con-fes- si-o-ne di-cen-tes.

3511ᶜ ut ad-mit-ti iu-be-as de-pre-ca- mur sup- pli-ci con-fes-si-o-ne di-cen- tes.

*Diastematy uncertain: the two notes can be read "G a."
**Notation stained and illegible.

33

    Scs. SCS. scs. Dns ds sabaoth. pleni sunt cęli et terra gla tua. osanna in excelsis. Benedictus qui uenit in nomine dni. osanna in excelsis:;

339df

S(an)c(- tu)s.   S(an)c(- tu)s.   S(an)c(- tu)s.

339c

S(an)c(- tu)s.   S(an)c(- tu)s.   S(an)c(- tu)s.

426

    S̄   S̄   S.

C32

    Scs. Scs. Scs. Dominus ds

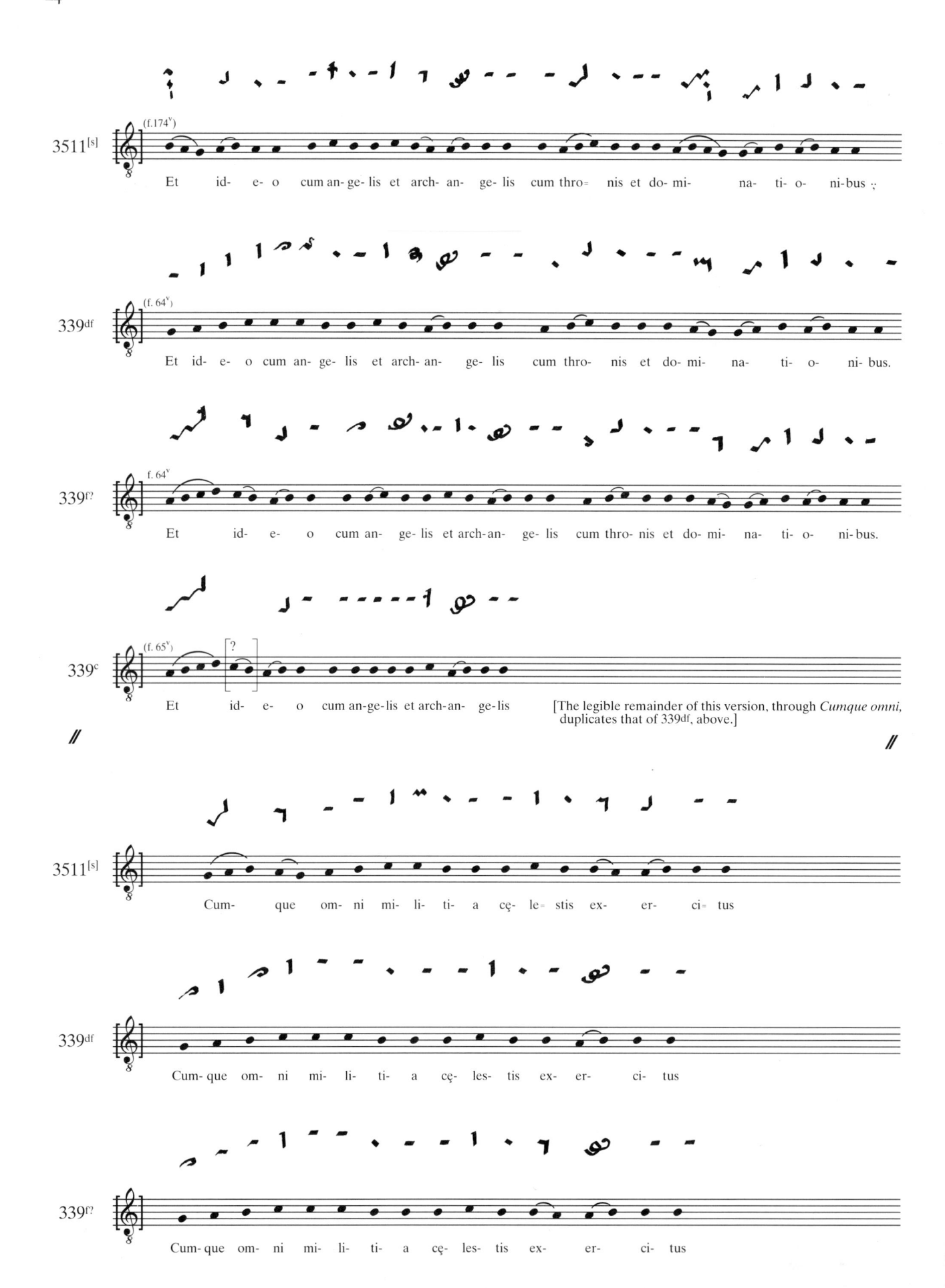

24

3511[s] (f.174ᵛ) Et id- e- o cum an- ge- lis et arch- an- ge- lis cum thro= nis et do- mi- na- ti- o- ni- bus ;

339df (f. 64ᵛ) Et id- e- o cum an- ge- lis et arch- an- ge- lis cum thro- nis et do- mi- na- ti- o- ni- bus.

339f? f. 64ᵛ Et id- e- o cum an- ge- lis et arch- an- ge- lis cum thro- nis et do- mi- na- ti- o- ni- bus.

339c (f. 65ᵛ) Et id- e- o cum an- ge- lis et arch- an- ge- lis [The legible remainder of this version, through *Cumque omni*, duplicates that of 339df, above.]

3511[s] Cum- que om- ni mi- li- ti- a cę- le= stis ex- er- ci= tus

339df Cum- que om- ni mi- li- ti- a cę- les- tis ex- er- ci- tus

339f? Cum- que om- ni mi- li- ti- a cę- les- tis ex- er- ci- tus

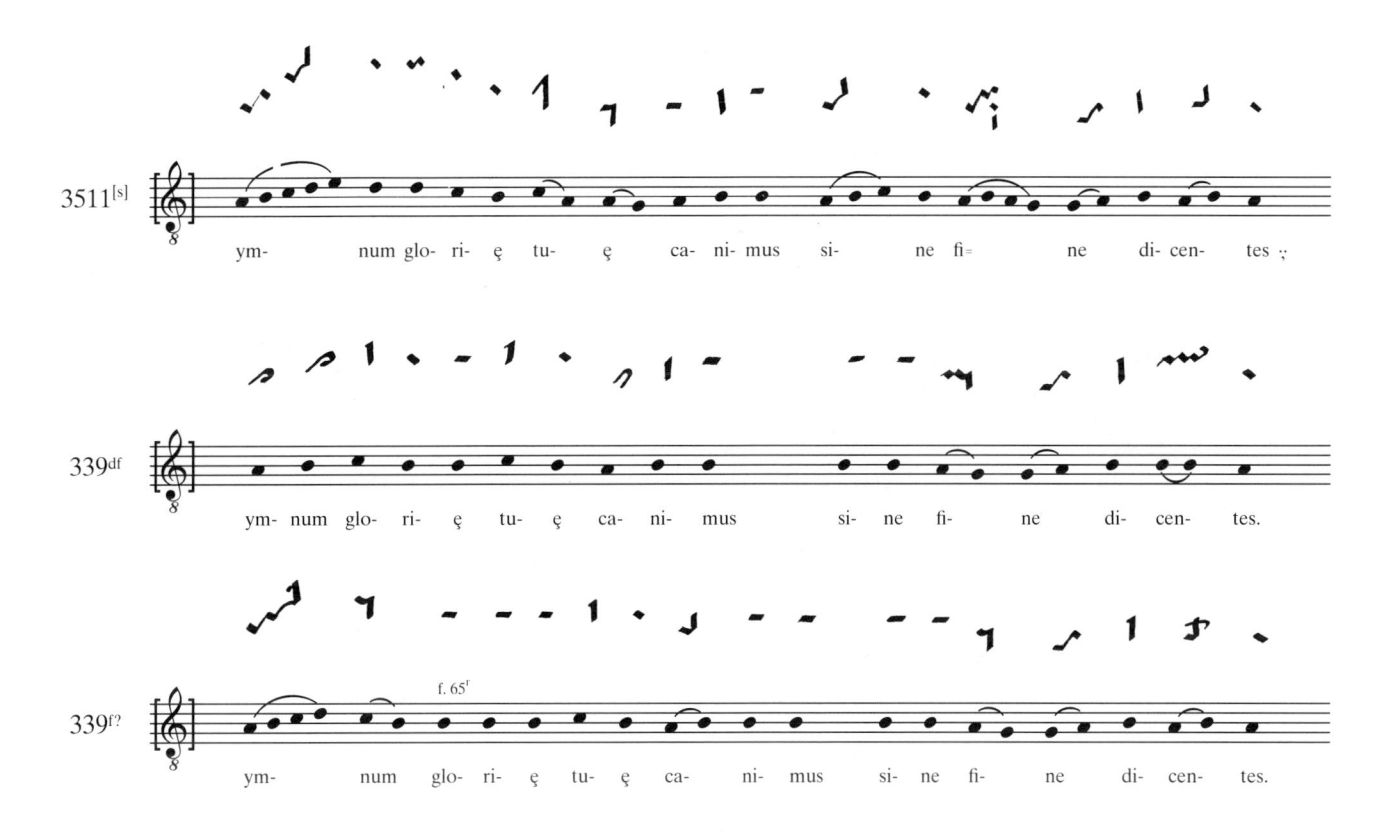

3511[s] ym- num glorię tuę canimus sine fi= ne dicentes ;

339df ym- num glorię tuę canimus sine fi- ne dicentes.

339f? ym- num glorię tuę canimus sine fi- ne dicentes.

127 Quem laudant angeli atque archangeli. cherubin quoque et seraphin non cessant clamare dicentes. S⟨an⟩c⟨tu⟩s.

II. Proper Prefaces in the Missal Lo 3511 from St. Peter's *intra muros*, Benevento

(For the original order in Lo 3511, fols. 170ᵛ–173ᵛ, editorially rearranged below according to chant category, see table 7, p. 5 above.)

With chant *In cotidianis diebus*

CP 1322: Christmas and the octave, Purification, and Annunciation, p. 27
(*Eternę deus* and *et ideo* use the chant *In festiuitatibus*.)

CP 863: Lent, p. 27

CP 879: Holy Trinity, pp. 28–29

CP 699: For the dead, p. 29
(Without notation in the MS; the version below is the editor's.)

With chant *In festiuitatibus*

CP 1294: Epiphany and the octave, p. 30

CP 366: Assumption and Nativity of St. Mary, pp. 30–31

CP 1484: Apostles, p. 31
(= 1487) (Without notation in the MS; the version below is the editor's.)

With chant *In sollemnitatibus*

CP 1524: Easter and the octave, and all Sundays until the Ascension, p. 32
(§1)

CP 1165: Ascension and the octave, p. 33

CP 813: Pentecost and the octave, pp. 33–34

CP 1200: Holy Cross, p. 35
(The first two medial cadences use the chant *In cotidianis diebus*.)

CP 203: Dedication of the Church, pp. 35–36
(All medial cadences, except those taken from the common preface, use the chant *In cotidianis diebus*.)

CP 687: Dialogue and common preface *In sollemnitatibus*, pp. 36–37
(Editorially reconstructed according to the Lo 3511 version for use with proper prefaces listed immediately above, pp. 32–36.

Prephatio de natale dñi. quę omnibus diebus usque in octauas ad oms missas de natale dicenda est.
Similit quoque et in purific et annuntiatio Sce marie eadem dic.

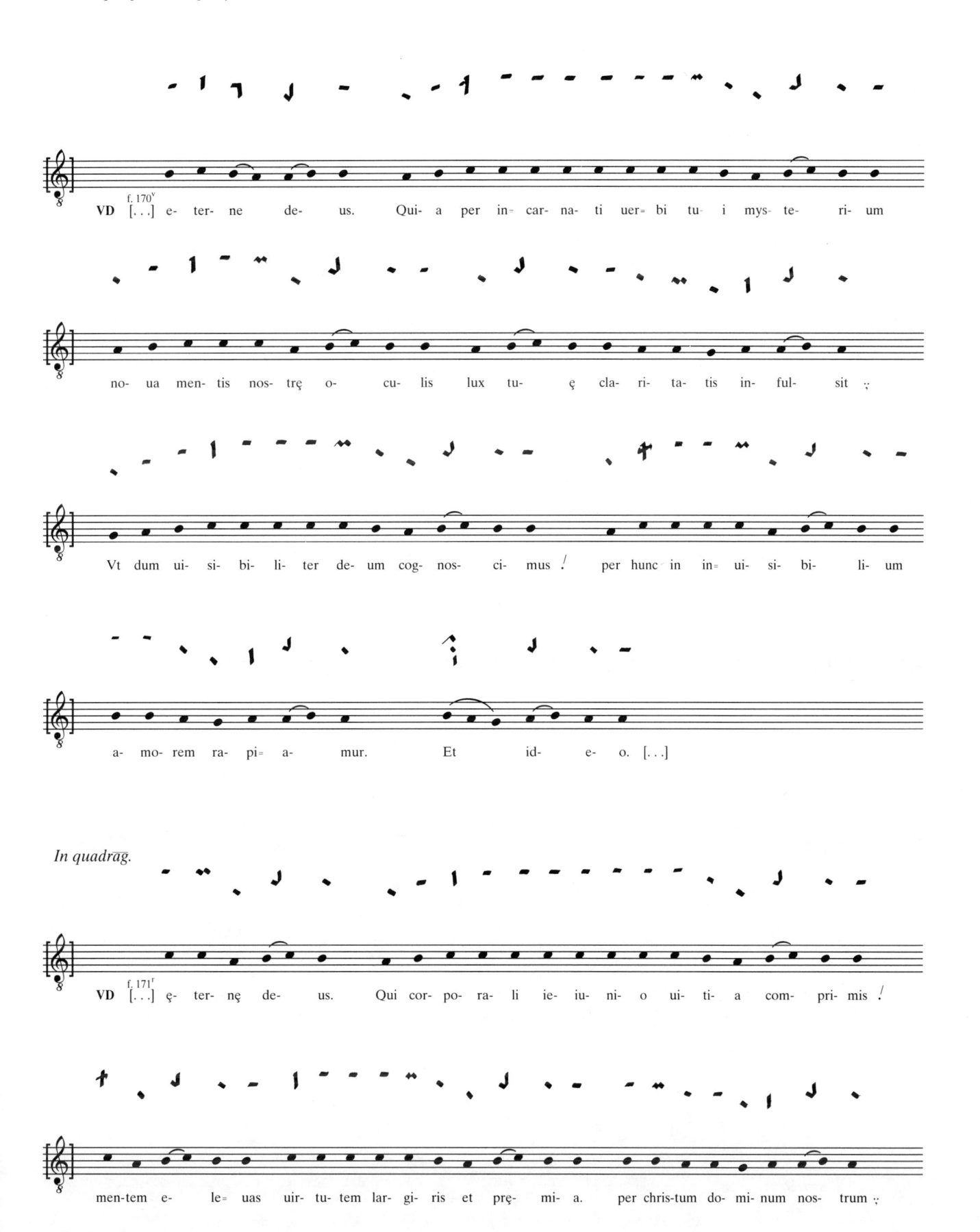

VD [...] e-ter-ne de-us. Qui-a per in-car-na-ti uer-bi tu-i mys-te-ri-um

no-ua men-tis nos-trę o-cu-lis lux tu-ę cla-ri-ta-tis in-ful-sit ;

Vt dum ui-si-bi-li-ter de-um cog-nos-ci-mus ! per hunc in in-ui-si-bi-li-um

a-mo-rem ra-pi-a-mur. Et id-e-o. [...]

In quadrāg.

VD [...] ę-ter-nę de-us. Qui cor-po-ra-li ie-iu-ni-o ui-ti-a com-pri-mis !

men-tem e-le-uas uir-tu-tem lar-gi-ris et prę-mi-a. per chris-tum do-mi-num nos-trum ;

Scę trinitatis.

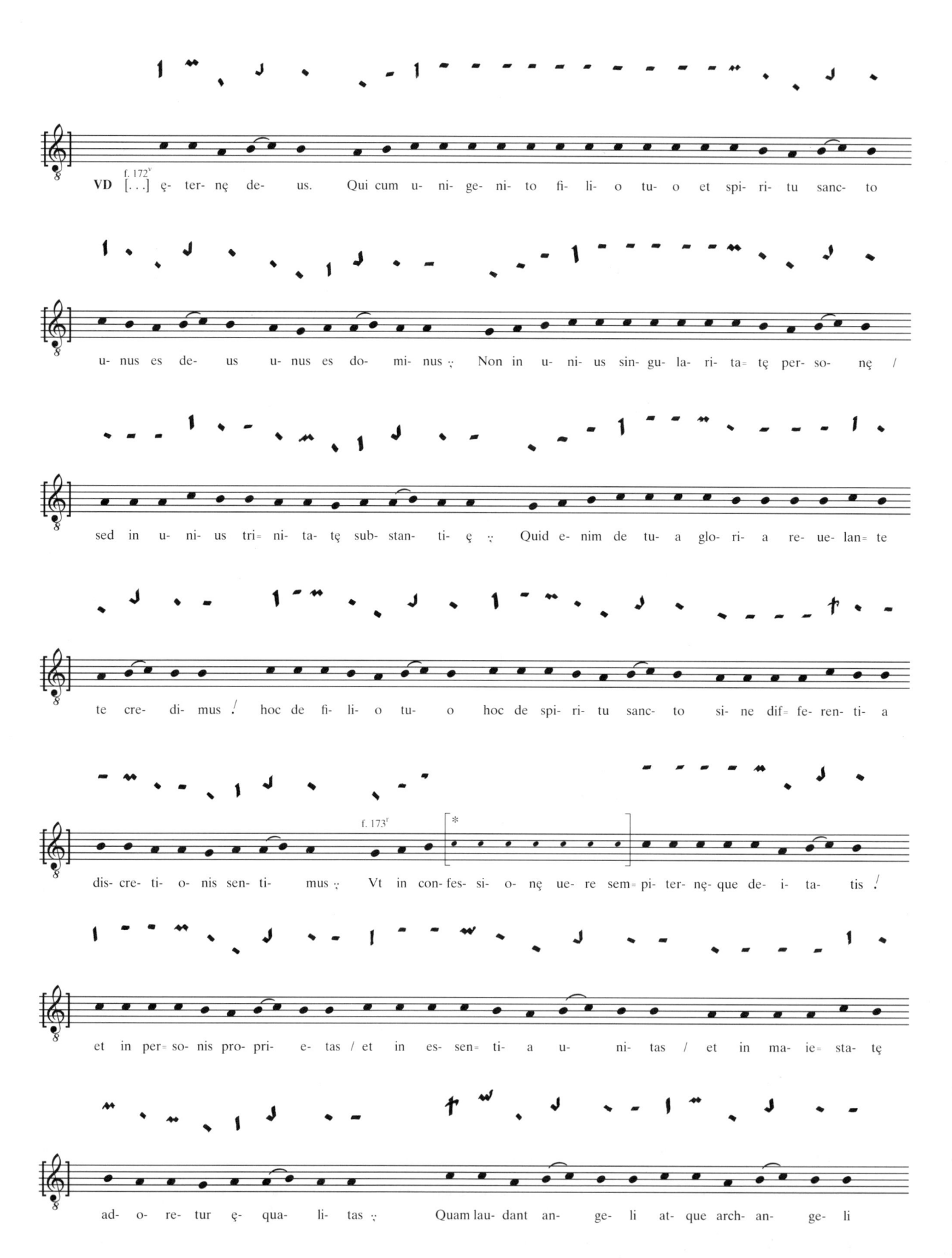

VD [...] ę-ter-nę de- us. Qui cum u- ni- ge- ni- to fi- li- o tu- o et spi- ri- tu sanc- to

u- nus es de- us u- nus es do- mi- nus ; Non in u- ni- us sin-gu- la- ri- ta= tę per- so- nę /

sed in u- ni- us tri= ni- ta- tę sub- stan- ti- ę ; Quid e- nim de tu- a glo- ri- a re- ue- lan= te

te cre- di- mus ! hoc de fi- li- o tu- o hoc de spi- ri- tu sanc- to si- ne dif= fe- ren- ti- a

dis- cre- ti- o- nis sen- ti- mus ; Vt in con- fes- si- o- nę ue- re sem- pi- ter- nę- que de- i- ta- tis !

et in per= so- nis pro- pri- e- tas / et in es- sen- ti- a u- ni- tas / et in ma- ie- sta- tę

ad- o- re- tur ę- qua- li- tas ; Quam lau- dant an- ge- li at- que arch- an- ge- li

*Notes cut off by binder's knife.

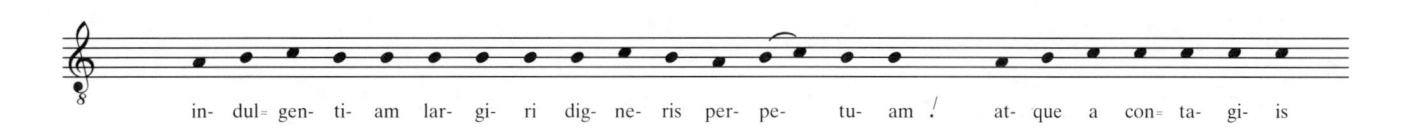

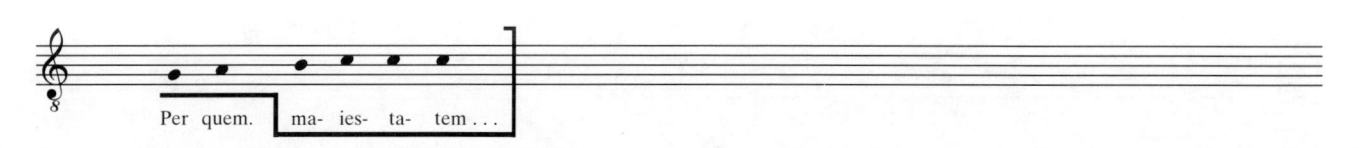

che- ru- bin quo- que et se- ra- phim ! qui non ces- sant cla- ma- re di- cen- tes.

Pro defunctis.

f. 173ᵛ Per chris-tum do- mi- num nos- trum. Per quem sa- lus mun- di ! per quem ui- ta ho- mi- num !

per quem re= sur- rec- ti- o mor- tu- o- rum. Per ip- sum te do- mi- ne sup- pli- ci- ter de- pre- ca- mur !

ut a- ni= ma- bus fa- mu= lo- rum fa- mu- la- rum- que tu- a- rum quorum memoriam a- gimus *

in- dul= gen- ti- am lar- gi- ri dig- ne- ris per- pe- tu- am ! at- que a con- ta- gi- is

mor- ta- li- ta- tis ex- u= tas ! in e- ter- nę sal- ua- ti- o- nis par- tem res- ti- tu- as ·:·

Per quem. ma- ies- ta- tem…

*Words between brackets are enclosed by lines in the MS (for possible omission?).

In ępyph usque in octauas.

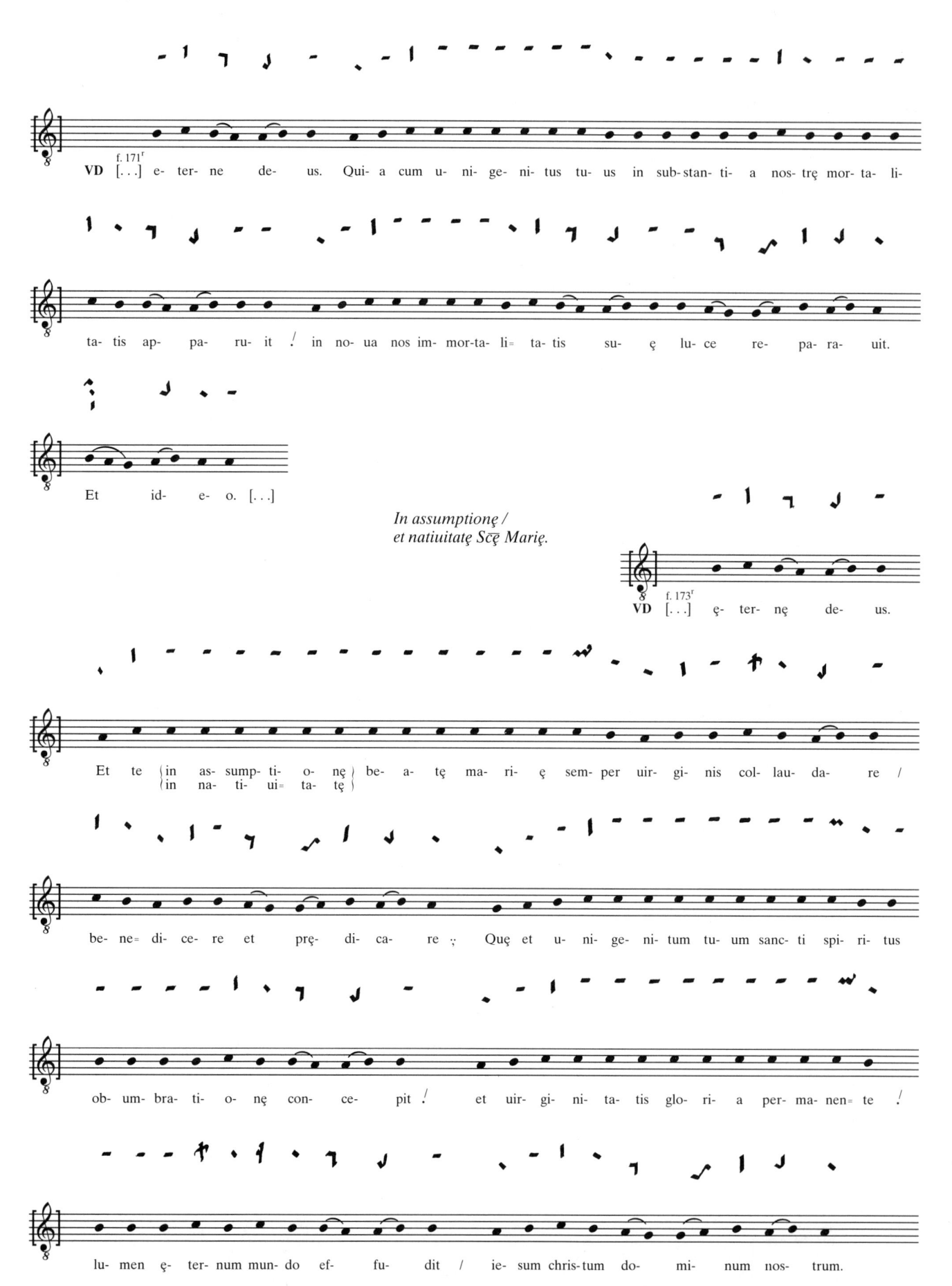

VD [...] e- ter- ne de- us. Qui- a cum u- ni- ge- ni- tus tu- us in sub- stan- ti- a nos- trę mor- ta- li- ta- tis ap- pa- ru- it / in no- ua nos im- mor- ta- li- ta- tis su- ę lu- ce re- pa- ra- uit.

Et id- e- o. [...]

In assumptionę / et natiuitatę Scę Marię.

VD [...] ę- ter- nę de- us. Et te {in as- sump- ti- o- nę} be- a- tę ma- ri- ę sem- per uir- gi- nis col- lau- da- re / {in na- ti- ui- ta- tę} be- ne- di- ce- re et prę- di- ca- re ;· Quę et u- ni- ge- ni- tum tu- um sanc- ti spi- ri- tus ob- um- bra- ti- o- nę con- ce- pit / et uir- gi- ni- ta- tis glo- ri- a per- ma- nen- te / lu- men ę- ter- num mun- do ef- fu- dit / ie- sum chris- tum do- mi- num nos- trum.

Quem lau- dant. an- ge- li at- que arch- an- ge- li . . .

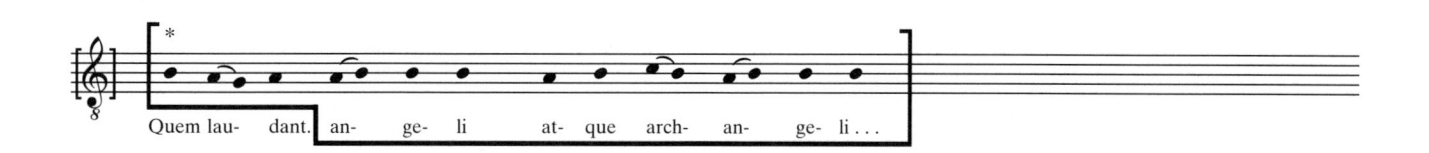

In apostolis.

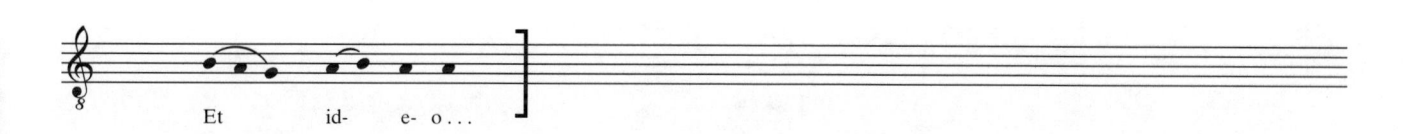

VD [...] e-quum et sa- lu- ta- re. Te do- mi- ne sup- pli- ci- ter ex- o- ra- re ! ut gre-gem tu- um pas-tor ę- ter- nę non de- se- ras ! sed per be- a- tos a- pos- to- los tu- os ! con- tí- nu- a pro-tec- ti- o- nę cus- to- di- as ; Vt is- dem rec- to- ri-bus gu- ber- ne- tur ! quos o- pe- ris tu- i ui- ca- ri- os e- i- dem con- tu- lis- ti prę= es- se pa- sto- res ;

Et id- e- o . . .

*The alternate proper-preface conclusion is cued with the words *Quem laudant* only and without notation. (The chant given here is an editorial reconstruction. Also see the Lo 3511 *cotidiana* version, pp. 28–29 above and the Cassinese *dominicalis* version of 127, p. 25 above.)

32

In pascha ⁘ usque in octauas ⁘ et omnibus diebus dnicis.   usque in ascensa.

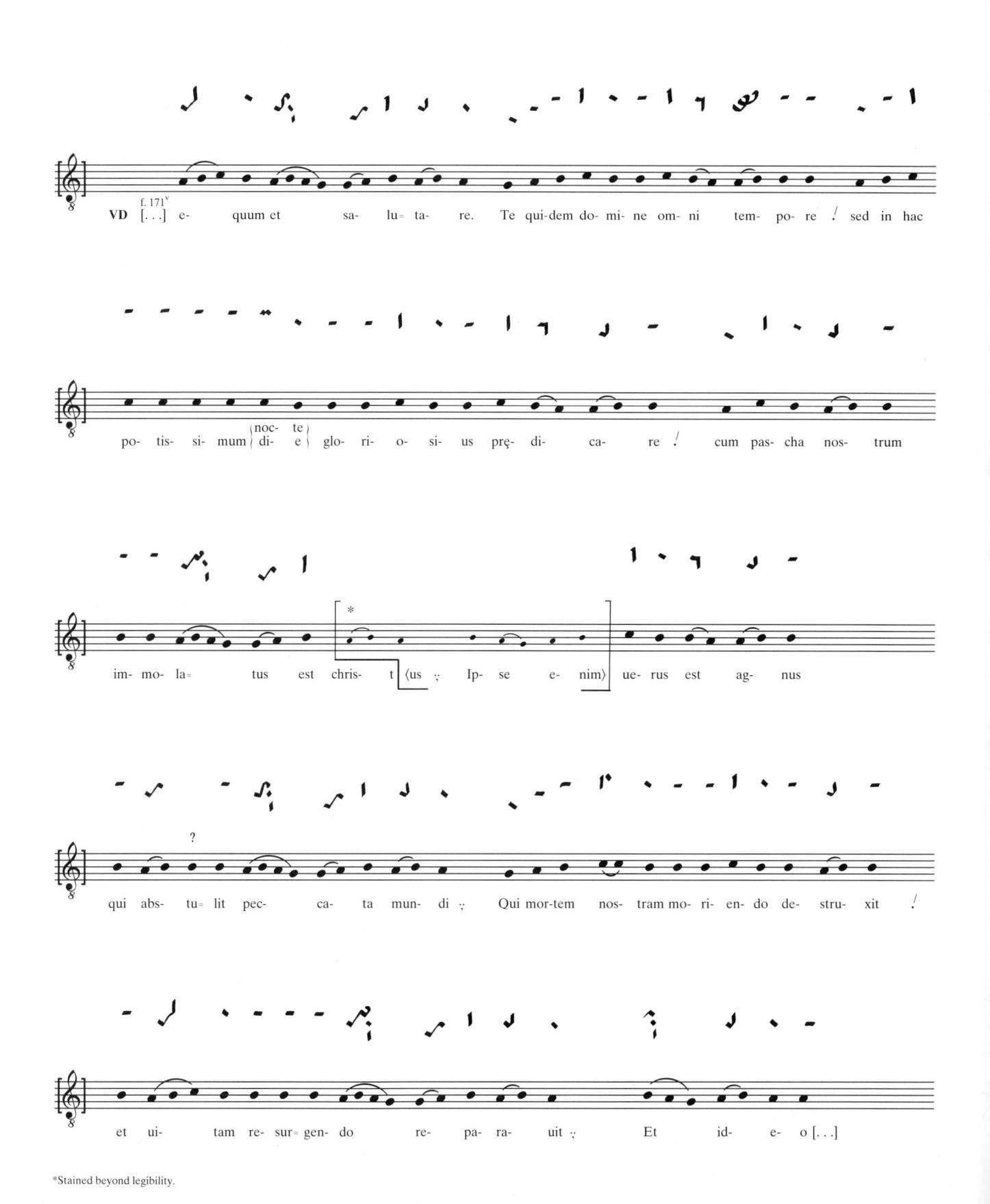

VD [...] e- quum et sa- lu=ta- re. Te qui-dem do- mi- ne om- ni tem- po- re ⁘ sed in hac po- tis- si- mum ⟨noc- te / di- e⟩ glo- ri- o- si- us prę- di- ca- re ⁘ cum pas- cha nos- trum im- mo- la= tus est chris- t⟨us ⁘ Ip- se e- nim⟩ ue- rus est ag- nus qui abs- tu= lit pec- ca- ta mun- di ⁘ Qui mor- tem nos- tram mo- ri- en- do de- stru- xit ⁘ et ui- tam re- sur= gen- do re- pa- ra- uit ⁘ Et id- e- o [...]

*Stained beyond legibility.

In ascensa usque in oct.

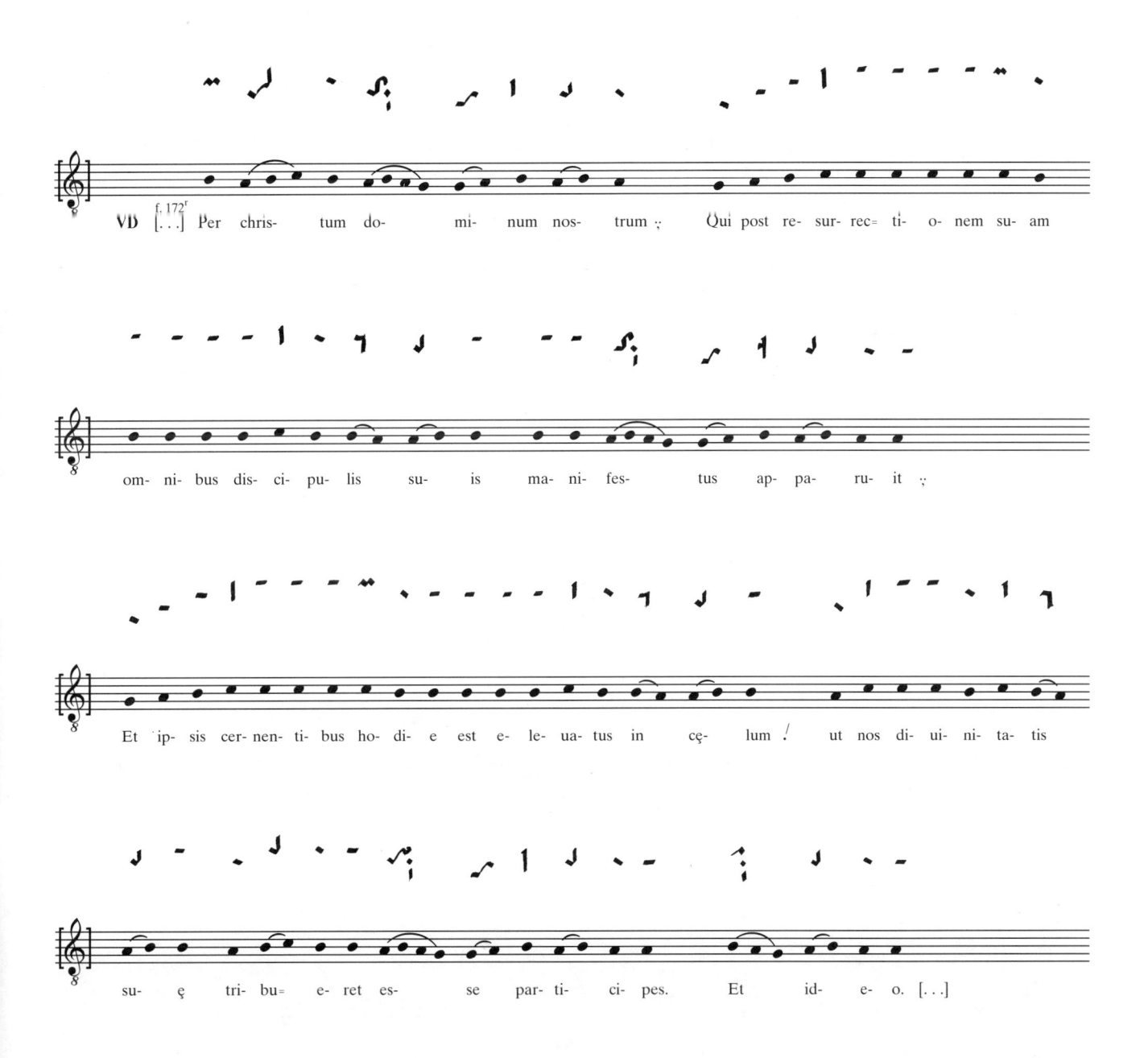

VD [...] Per chris- tum do- mi- num nos- trum ; Qui post re- sur- rec- ti- o- nem su- am

om- ni- bus dis- ci- pu- lis su- is ma- ni- fes- tus ap- pa- ru- it ;

Et ip- sis cer- nen- ti- bus ho- di- e est e- le- ua- tus in cę- lum ! ut nos di- ui- ni- ta- tis

su- ę tri- bu- e- ret es- se par- ti- ci- pes. Et id- e- o. [...]

In pent usque in octauas.

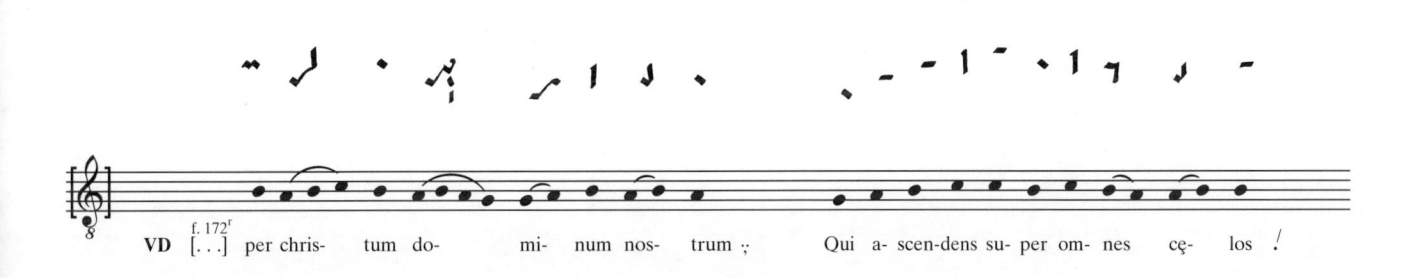

VD [...] per chris- tum do- mi- num nos- trum ; Qui a- scen-dens su- per om- nes cę- los !

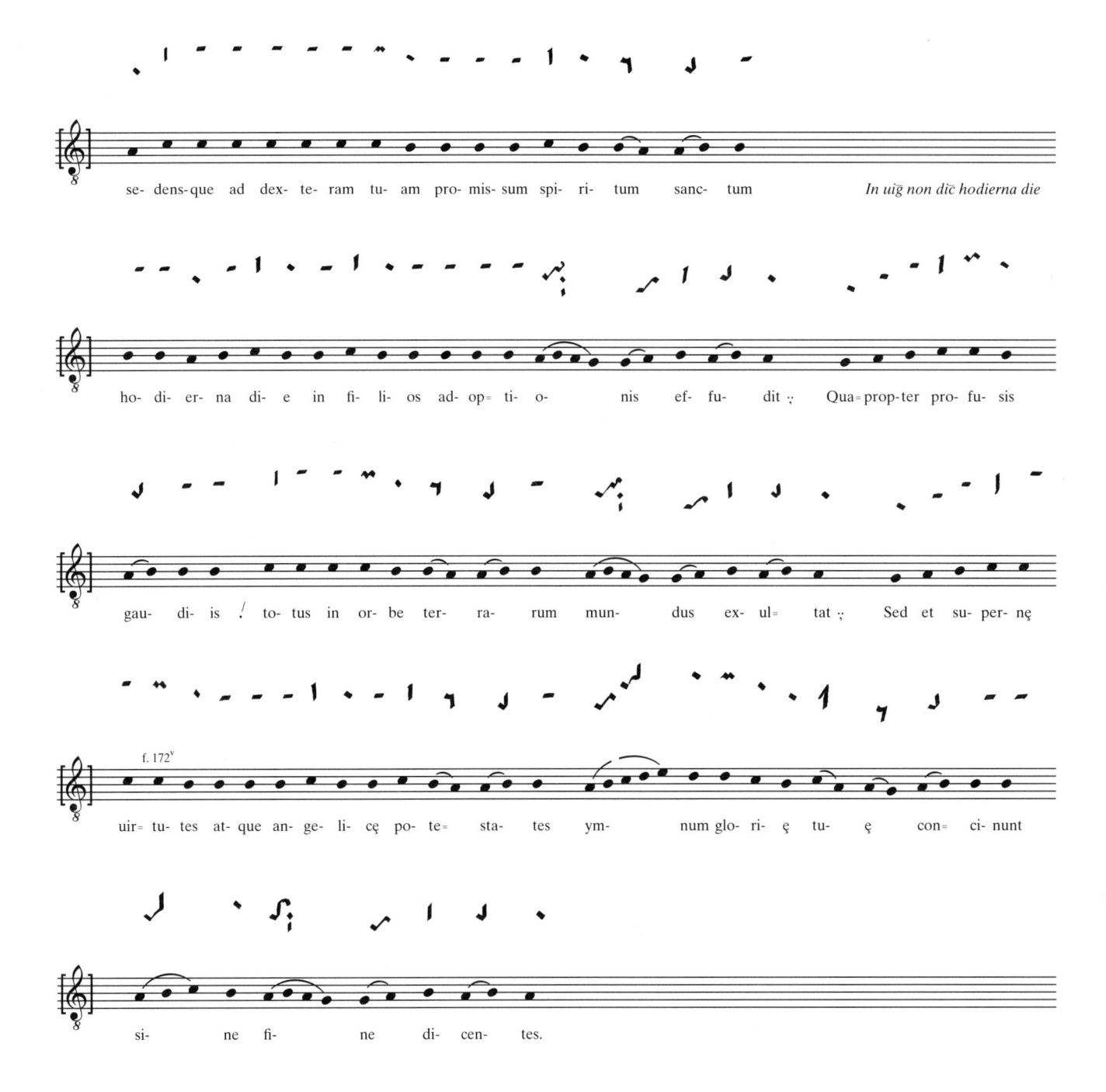

se- dens- que ad dex- te- ram tu- am pro- mis- sum spi- ri- tum sanc- tum *In uig non dic hodierna die*

ho- di- er- na di- e in fi- li- os ad- op- ti- o- nis ef- fu- dit ; Qua= prop- ter pro- fu- sis

gau- di- is ! to- tus in or- be ter- ra- rum mun- dus ex- ul= tat ; Sed et su- per- nę

f. 172ᵛ

uir= tu- tes at- que an- ge- li- cę po- te- sta- tes ym- num glo- ri- ę tu- ę con= ci- nunt

si- ne fi- ne di- cen- tes.

In S crucis.

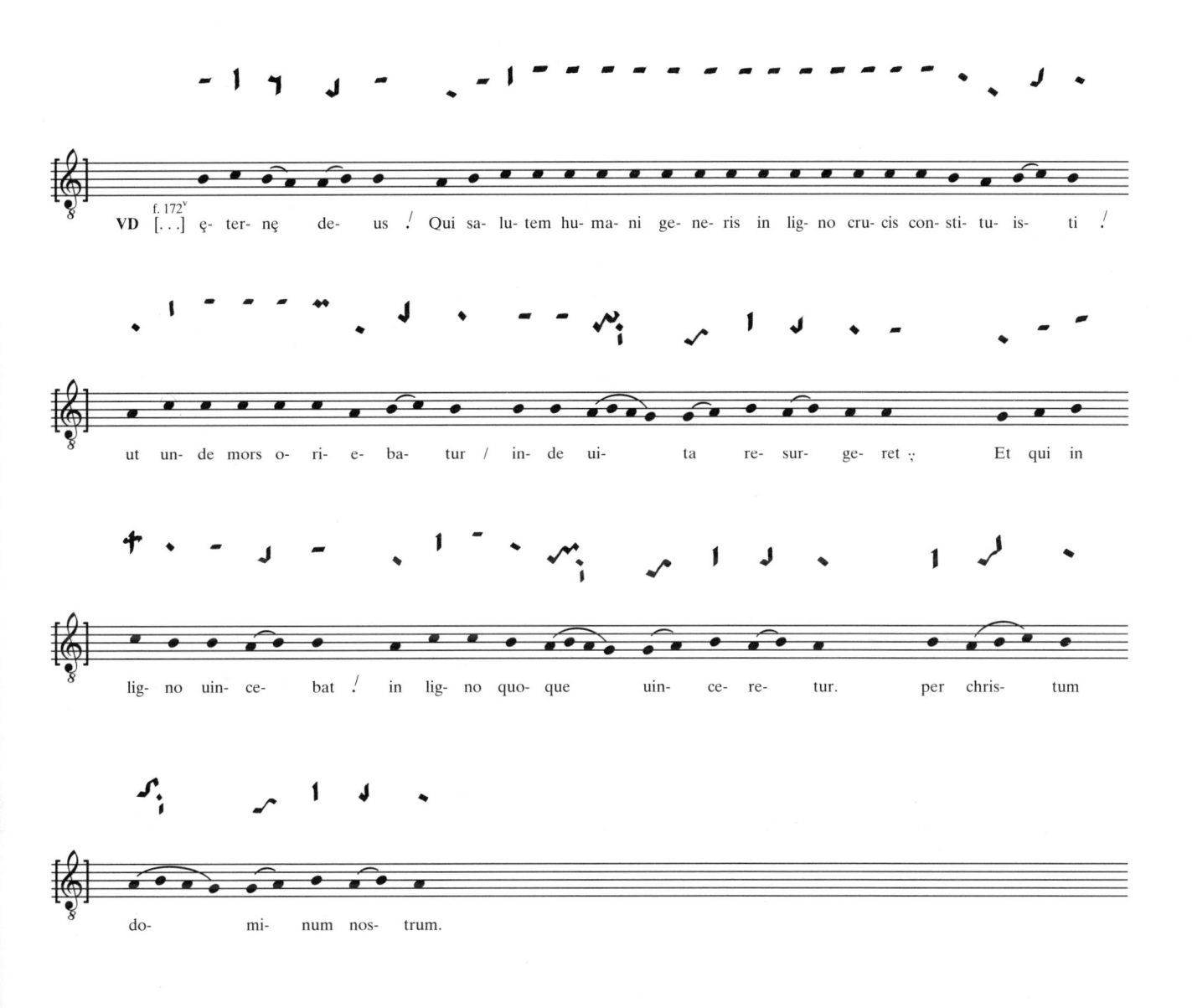

VD [...] ę- ter- nę de- us ! Qui sa- lu- tem hu- ma- ni ge- ne- ris in lig- no cru- cis con- sti- tu- is- ti ! ut un- de mors o- ri- e- ba- tur / in- de ui- ta re- sur- ge- ret ·; Et qui in lig- no uin- ce- bat ! in lig- no quo- que uin- ce- re- tur. per chris- tum do- mi- num nos- trum.

In dedicatio ęcclę.

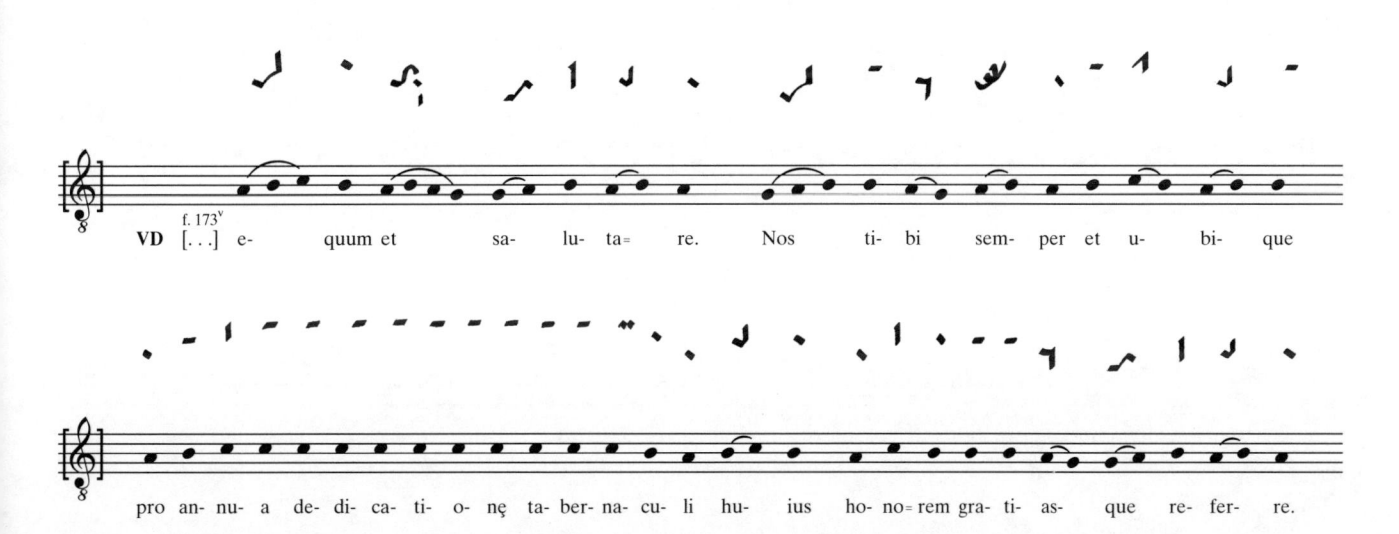

VD [...] e- quum et sa- lu- ta- re. Nos ti- bi sem- per et u- bi- que pro an- nu- a de- di- ca- ti- o- nę ta- ber- na- cu- li hu- ius ho- no- rem gra- ti- as- que re- fer- re.

36

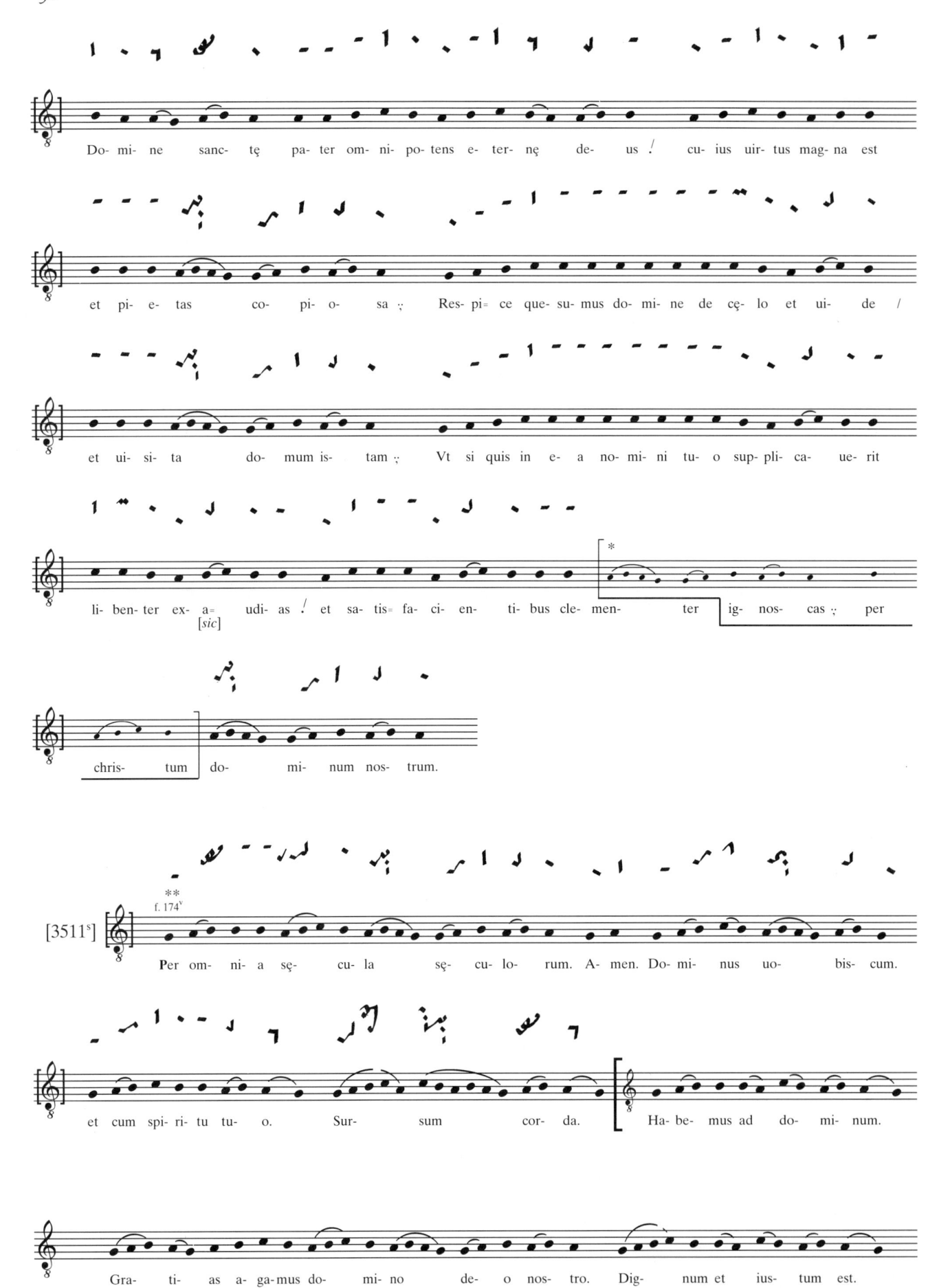

Do- mi- ne sanc- tę pa- ter om- ni- po- tens e- ter- nę de- us ! cu- ius uir- tus mag- na est

et pi- e- tas co- pi- o- sa ;. Res- pi- ce que- su- mus do- mi- ne de cę- lo et ui- de /

et ui- si- ta do- mum is- tam ;. Vt si quis in e- a no- mi- ni tu- o sup- pli- ca- ue- rit

li- ben- ter ex- a- udi- as ! et sa- tis- fa- ci- en- ti- bus cle- men- ter ig- nos- cas ;. per
[sic]

chris- tum do- mi- num nos- trum.

[3511ˢ] **
f. 174ᵛ
Per om- ni- a sę- cu- la sę- cu- lo- rum. A- men. Do- mi- nus uo- bis- cum.

et cum spi- ri- tu tu- o. Sur- sum cor- da. Ha- be- mus ad do- mi- num.

Gra- ti- as a- ga- mus do- mi- no de- o nos- tro. Dig- num et ius- tum est.

*Stained and partially cut off.
**Or "E Ga a a abc" for *Per omnia sę-*, if the custos is disregarded.

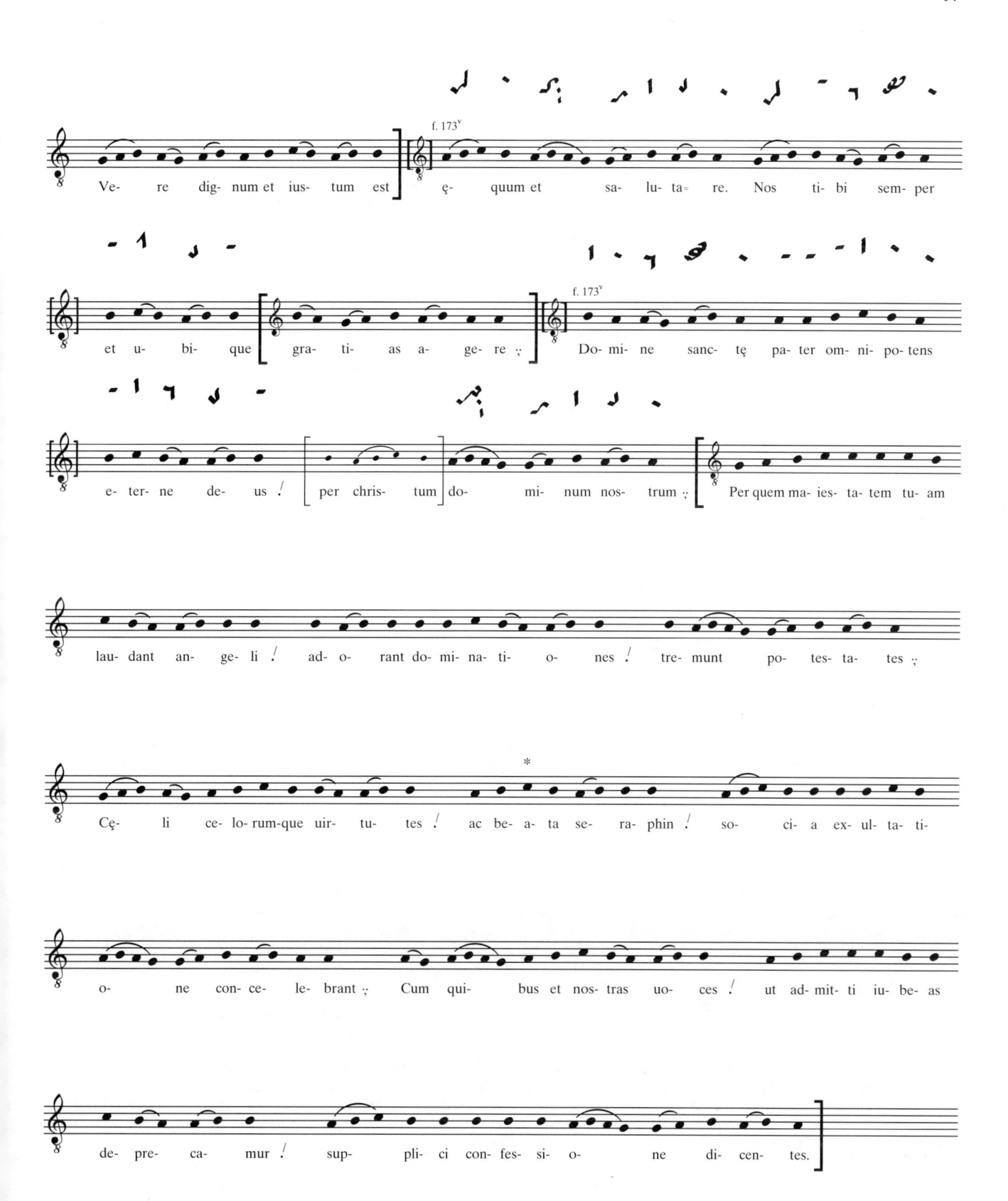

Vere dignum et iustum est ę- quum et sa- lu- ta= re. Nos ti- bi sem- per et u- bi- que gra- ti- as a- ge- re ;· Do- mi- ne sanc- tę pa- ter om- ni- po- tens e- ter- ne de- us ! per chris- tum do- mi- num nos- trum ;· Per quem ma- ies- ta- tem tu- am lau- dant an- ge- li ! ad- o- rant do- mi- na- ti- o- nes ! tre- munt po- tes- ta- tes ;· Cę- li ce- lo- rum- que uir- tu- tes ! ac be- a- ta se- ra- phin ! so- ci- a ex- ul- ta- ti- o- ne con- ce- le- brant ;· Cum qui- bus et nos- tras uo- ces ! ut ad- mit- ti iu- be- as de- pre- ca- mur ! sup- pli- ci con- fes- si- o- ne di- cen- tes.

* or be- a- ta se- ra- phin !

III. Common Prefaces of Mixed Traditions from Border Areas and the North

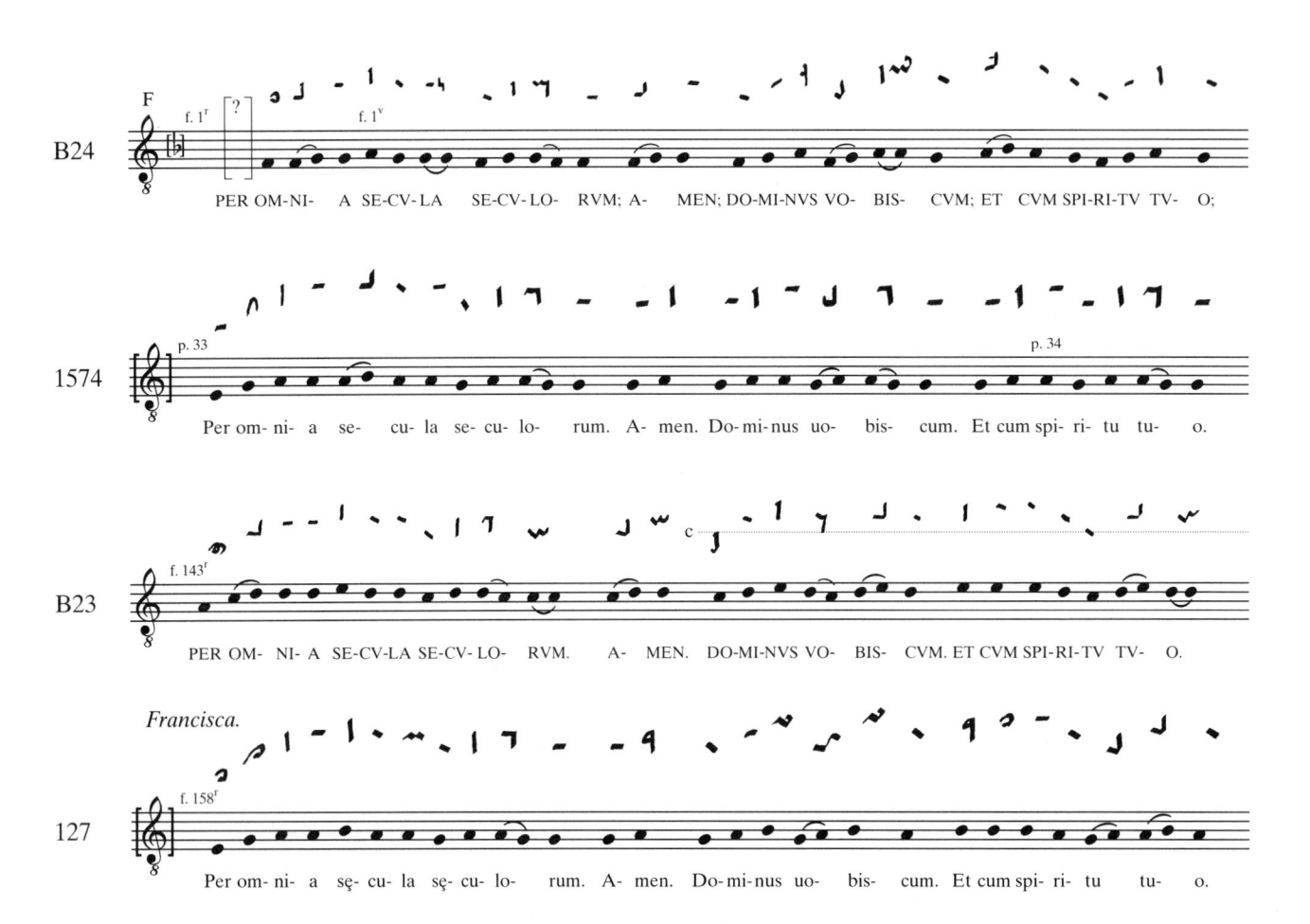

[Musical notation for B24, 1574, B23, and 127 (Francisca), with text underlay:]

B24: PER OM-NI- A SE-CV-LA SE-CV-LO- RVM; A- MEN; DO-MI-NVS VO- BIS- CVM; ET CVM SPI-RI-TV TV- O;

1574: Per om- ni- a se- cu- la se-cu- lo- rum. A- men. Do-mi-nus uo- bis- cum. Et cum spi- ri- tu tu- o.

B23: PER OM- NI- A SE-CV-LA SE-CV-LO- RVM. A- MEN. DO-MI-NVS VO- BIS- CVM. ET CVM SPI-RI-TV TV- O.

Francisca.

127: Per om- ni- a sę- cu- la sę- cu- lo- rum. A- men. Do-mi-nus uo- bis- cum. Et cum spi- ri- tu tu- o.

B24: Subiaco, early twelfth-century notation. Initial phrases in the common preface recall the Cassinese version *In dominicis seu festis diebus* (339[df] above); but elements in the opening dialogue, the frequent recitations on b-flat (= "c" if transcribed in the G-hexachord), and medial cadences of the Pentecost proper preface (p. 46 below) are reminiscent of the Cassinese formulas *In cotidianis diebus* (426 and C32 above), though here applied inconsistently. (See Sources, above.)

1574: Perhaps Gaeta, late twelfth or early thirteenth-century notation. The opening dialogue in part resembles old Beneventan forms (cf. 33 and 40, above), while the medial cadences within the common preface resemble idiosyncratic later Benevento forms seen in the version *In cotidianis diebus* of Lo 3511 (3511[c], above). The accent-pes rising a half step found in this cadence recurs in the appended Sanctus, fully notated (see below and also Thannabaur 41, Var., p. 114). The proper-preface conclusion *Et ideo . . . dicentes* (p. 44 below) seems to have been taken from a tonus sollemnior *sui generis*.

B23: San Bartolomeo, Norcia? Notation added mid-twelfth century. Elements of the older Benevento version (see 33 and 40, above) are reworked in a consistent manner, both in the common preface itself and the proper-preface conclusion *Et ideo . . . dicentes*. The middle note of the Beneventan rising initial figure "Gab" is regularly left out, so that many internal phrases begin "Gb aG" if transposed—in the MS they are cleffed to read "ce dc." The opening dialogue, *sui generis*, mixes phrases from different traditions, including bits of the *Francisca* version found in certain southern MSS (see 127 in the text below), and of the Cassinese everyday version—of which otherwise there is no trace. The appended fully notated Sanctus approaches the Vatican edition of Thannabaur 41 (see BTC II/3, pp. 116 and 114; also see Sources, above).

127: *Francisca,* the second of three common prefaces in a late eleventh-century Cassinese missal (see Sources, above). A "Frankish" version, but the time and place of borrowing or of recollected imitation remain unclear. The opening dialogue closely resembles the later Franciscan-Roman-curial form; but the strictly formulaic preface with the same tenor, "b", for the forephrase and afterphrase, with the internal initium of just one note, "a", to begin the forephrase, and with the single note "c" for important accents of the tenor recitation (especially before the very regular medial and final cadences) seems either to be early or else a scribal construction on a given formulaic model.

38

39

B24: SVR- SVM COR- DA; HA- BE- MVS AD DO- MI- NVM; GRA- TI- AS A- GA- MVS

1574: Sur- sum cor- da. Ha- be- mus ad do- mi- num. Gra- ti- as a- ga- mus

B23: SVR- SVM COR- DA HA- BE- MVS AD DO- MI- NO. GRA- TI- AS A- GA- MVS

127: Sur- sum cor- da Ha- be- mus ad do- mi- num. Gra- ti- as a- ga- mus

B24: DO- MI- NO DE- O NOS- TRO; DIG- NVM ET IVS- TUM EST;

[sic]

1574: Do- mi- no De- o nos- tro. Dig- num et ius- tum est.

B23: DO- MI- NO DE- O NOS- TRO. DIG- NVM ET IVS- TVM EST.

[sic]

127: do- mi- no de- o nos- tro. Dig-num et ius- tum est.

*Left side of present virga erased: original either ♩, "cb," or ♩, "Gb." (Leaps of a third to and from "c" found in this version adumbrate northern versions having this feature, including the Sarum preface tone.)

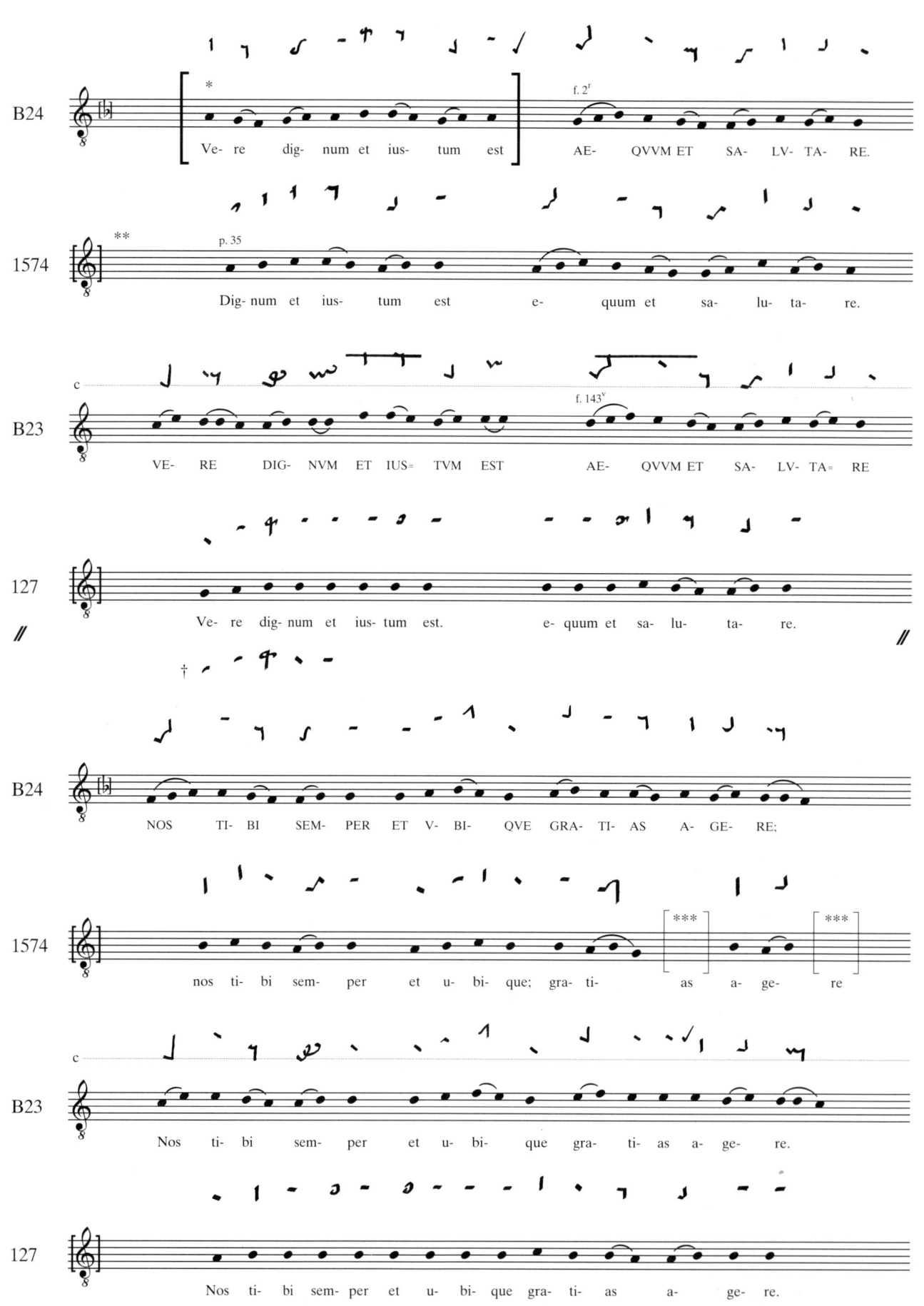

*Folio with *Vere dignum et iustum est* torn out.
**The word *Vere* is now missing: probably a leaf was removed between the present pp. 34 and 35.
***Note erased.

† The original neumes for *Vere dignum et* (given here below the text) read "a b c b b," conforming with the preceding custos. They were erased and replaced by the 127 version as found on the staff.

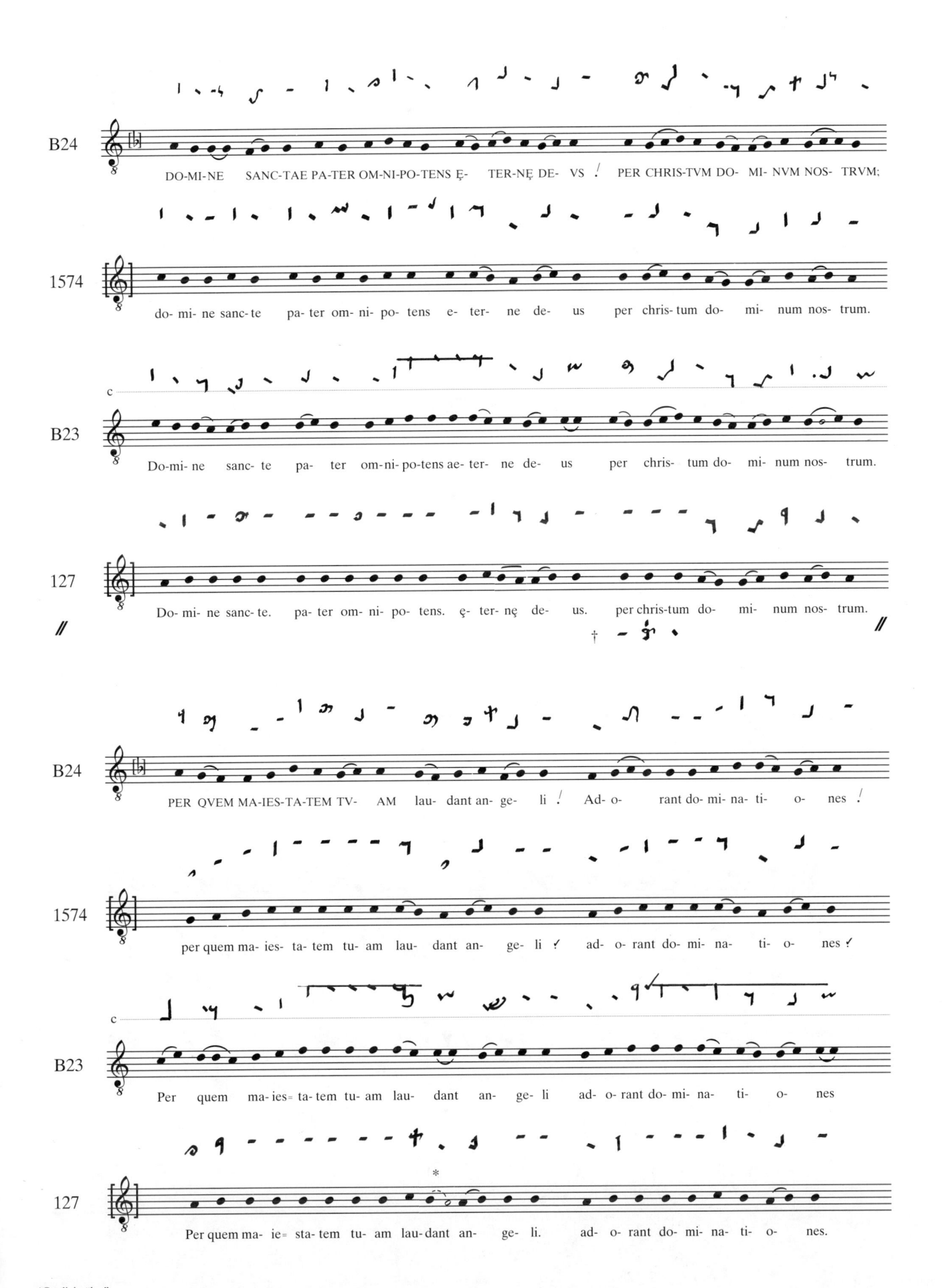

B24 DOMINE SANCTAE PATER OMNIPOTENS ETERNE DEVS! PER CHRISTVM DOMINVM NOSTRVM;

1574 domine sancte pater omnipotens e-terne deus per christum dominum nostrum.

B23 Domine sancte pater omnipotens aeterne deus per christum dominum nostrum.

127 Domine sancte. pater omnipotens. eterne deus. per christum dominum nostrum.

B24 PER QVEM MAIESTATEM TVAM laudant angeli! Adorant dominationes!

1574 per quem maiestatem tuam laudant angeli ⸱ adorant dominationes ⸱

B23 Per quem maies=tatem tuam laudant angeli adorant dominationes

127 Per quem maie=statem tuam laudant angeli. adorant dominationes.

*Or clivis, "ba."
† The replacement neumes for *per christum* (given below the text) read "b abc b."

42

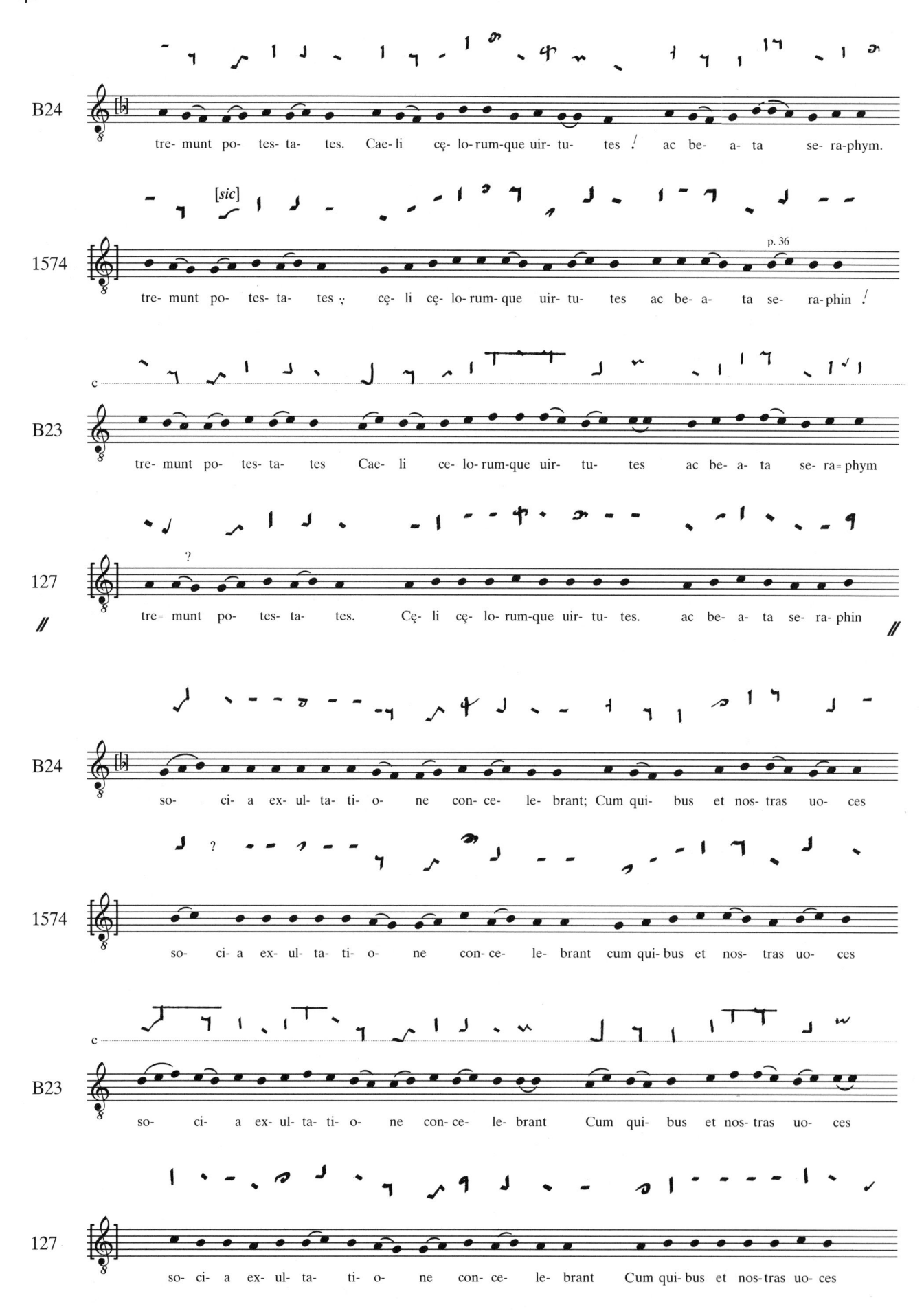

B24: tremunt potestates. Caeli cęlorumque uirtutes ! ac beata seraphym.

1574: tremunt potestates ; cęli cęlorumque uirtutes ac beata seraphin !

B23: tremunt potestates Caeli celorumque uirtutes ac beata seraphym

127: tremunt potestates. Cęli cęlorumque uirtutes. ac beata seraphin

B24: socia exultatione concelebrant; Cum quibus et nostras uoces

1574: socia exultatione concelebrant cum quibus et nostras uoces

B23: socia exultatione concelebrant Cum quibus et nostras uoces

127: socia exultatione concelebrant Cum quibus et nostras uoces

43

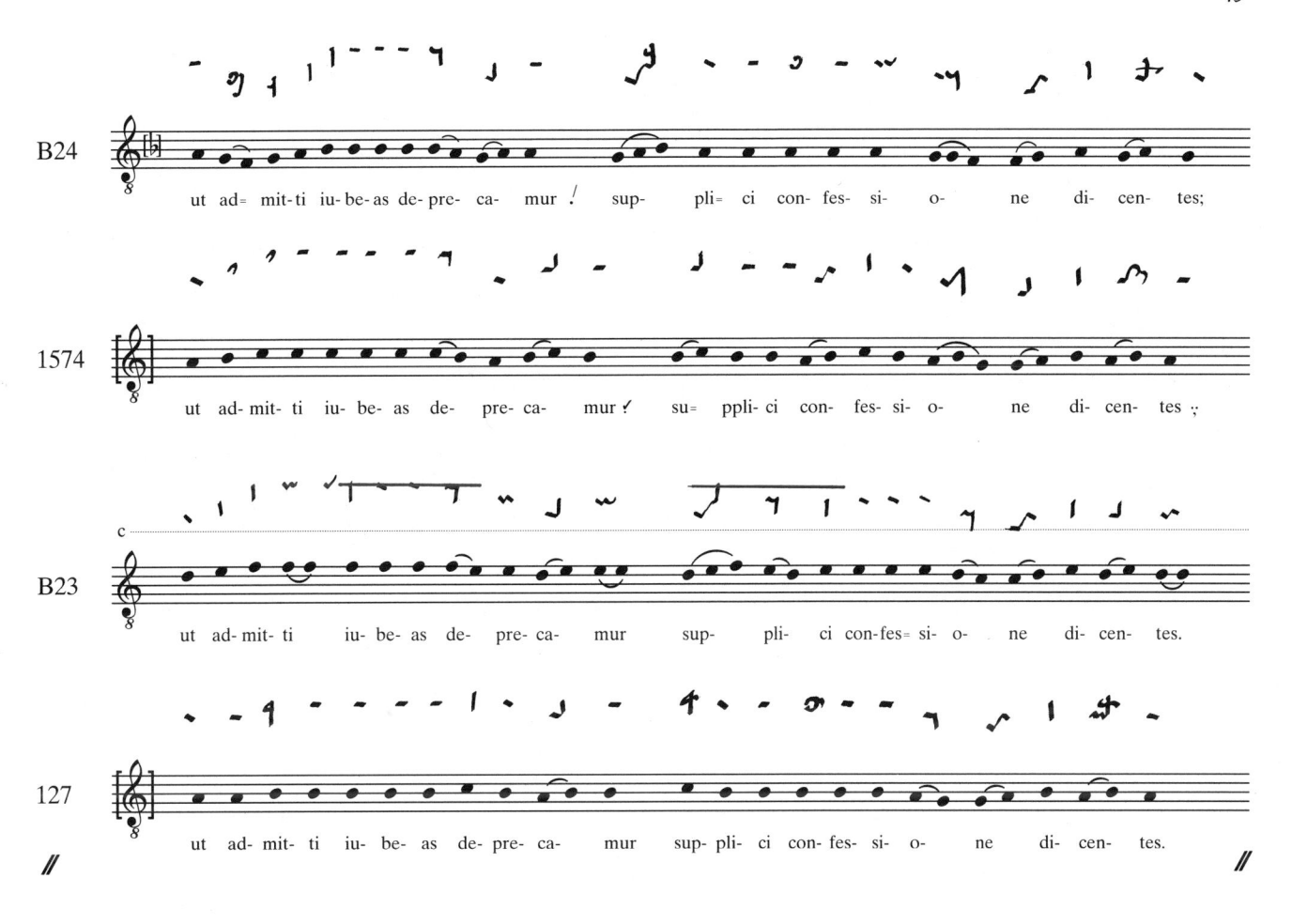

B24 ut ad-mit-ti iu-be-as de-pre-ca-mur! sup-pli-ci con-fes-si-o-ne di-cen-tes;

1574 ut ad-mit-ti iu-be-as de-pre-ca-mur! su=ppli-ci con-fes-si-o-ne di-cen-tes;

B23 ut ad-mit-ti iu-be-as de-pre-ca-mur sup-pli-ci con-fes=si-o-ne di-cen-tes.

127 ut ad-mit-ti iu-be-as de-pre-ca-mur sup-pli-ci con-fes-si-o-ne di-cen-tes.

B24 Scs. Scs. Scs. Dns ds sabaoth. Pleni sunt [etc.]

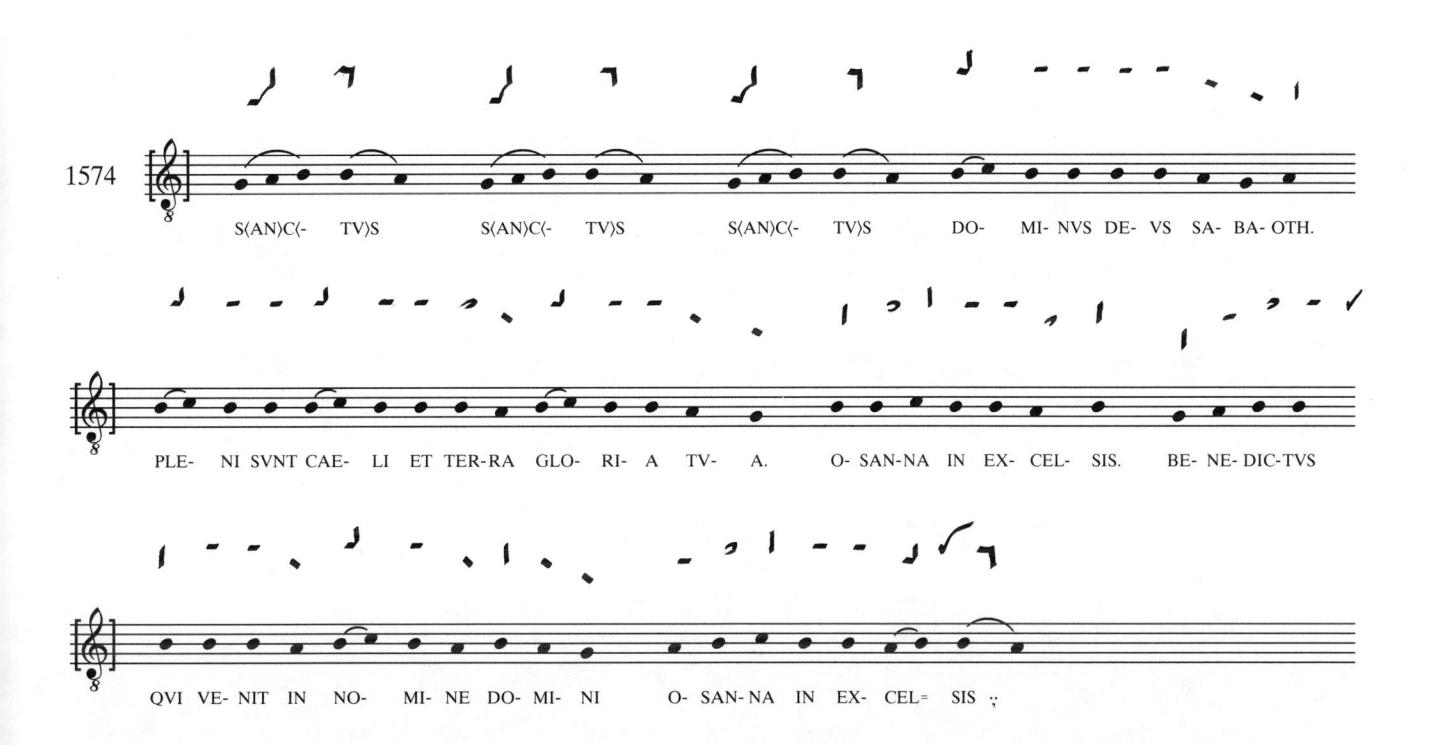

1574 S(AN)C(-TV)S S(AN)C(-TV)S S(AN)C(-TV)S DO- MI- NVS DE- VS SA- BA- OTH.

PLE- NI SVNT CAE- LI ET TER-RA GLO- RI- A TV- A. O-SAN-NA IN EX-CEL- SIS. BE-NE-DIC-TVS

QVI VE-NIT IN NO- MI-NE DO-MI-NI O-SAN-NA IN EX-CEL=SIS ;

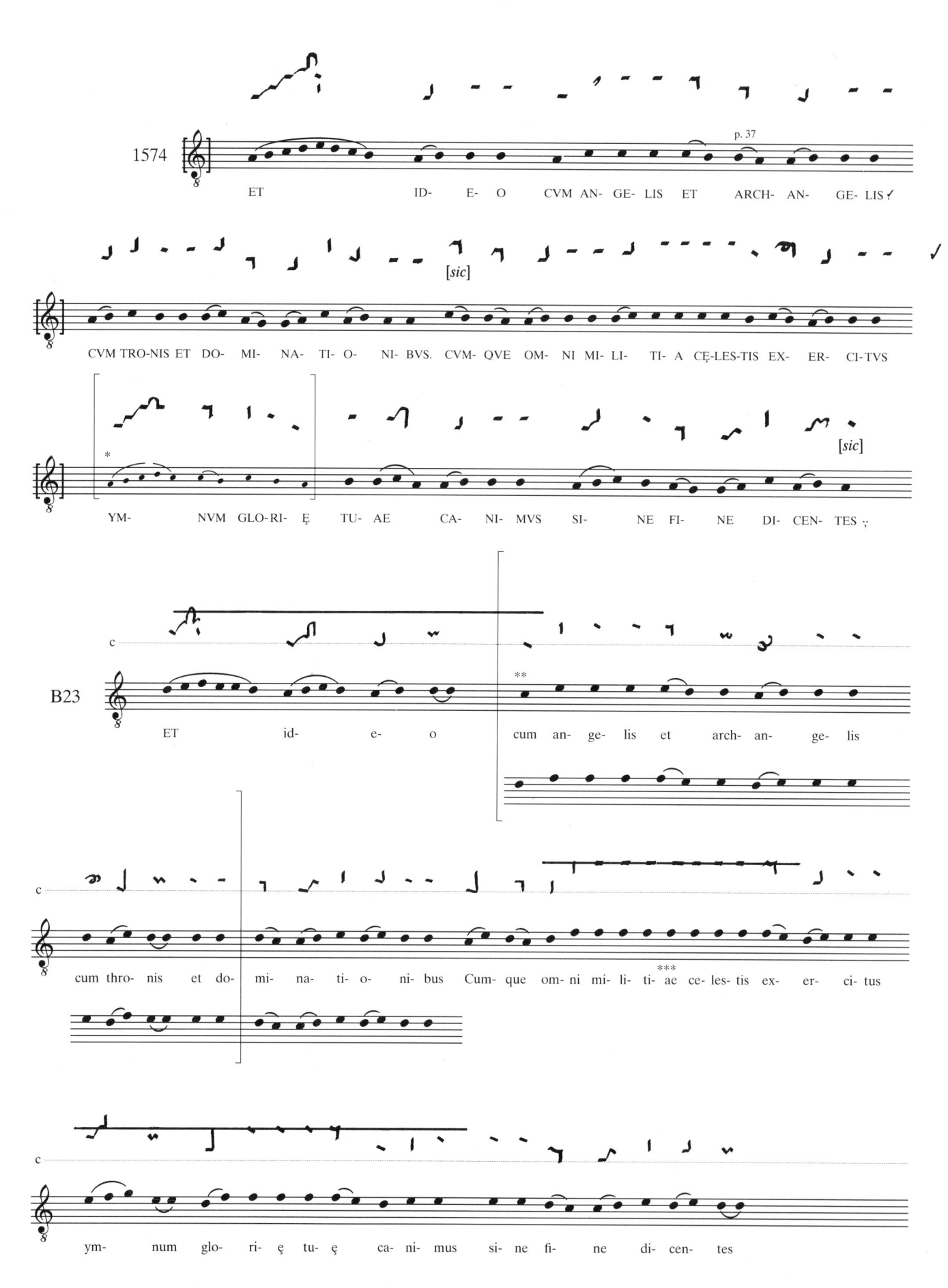

1574
ET IDEO CVM ANGELIS ET ARCHANGELIS
CVM TRONIS ET DOMINATIONIBVS. CVMQVE OMNI MILITIA CĘLESTIS EXERCITVS
[sic]
YMNVM GLORIĘ TUAE CANIMVS SINE FINE DICENTES

B23
ET ideo cum angelis et archangelis
cum thronis et dominationibus Cumque omni militiae celestis exercitus
ymnum glorię tuę canimus sine fine dicentes

*Contradicts preceding custos, but pitch levels for YMNVM GLORIĘ are uncertain.
**Sic: should read as in the corrected version given immediately beneath the text.
***e of militiae erased.

45

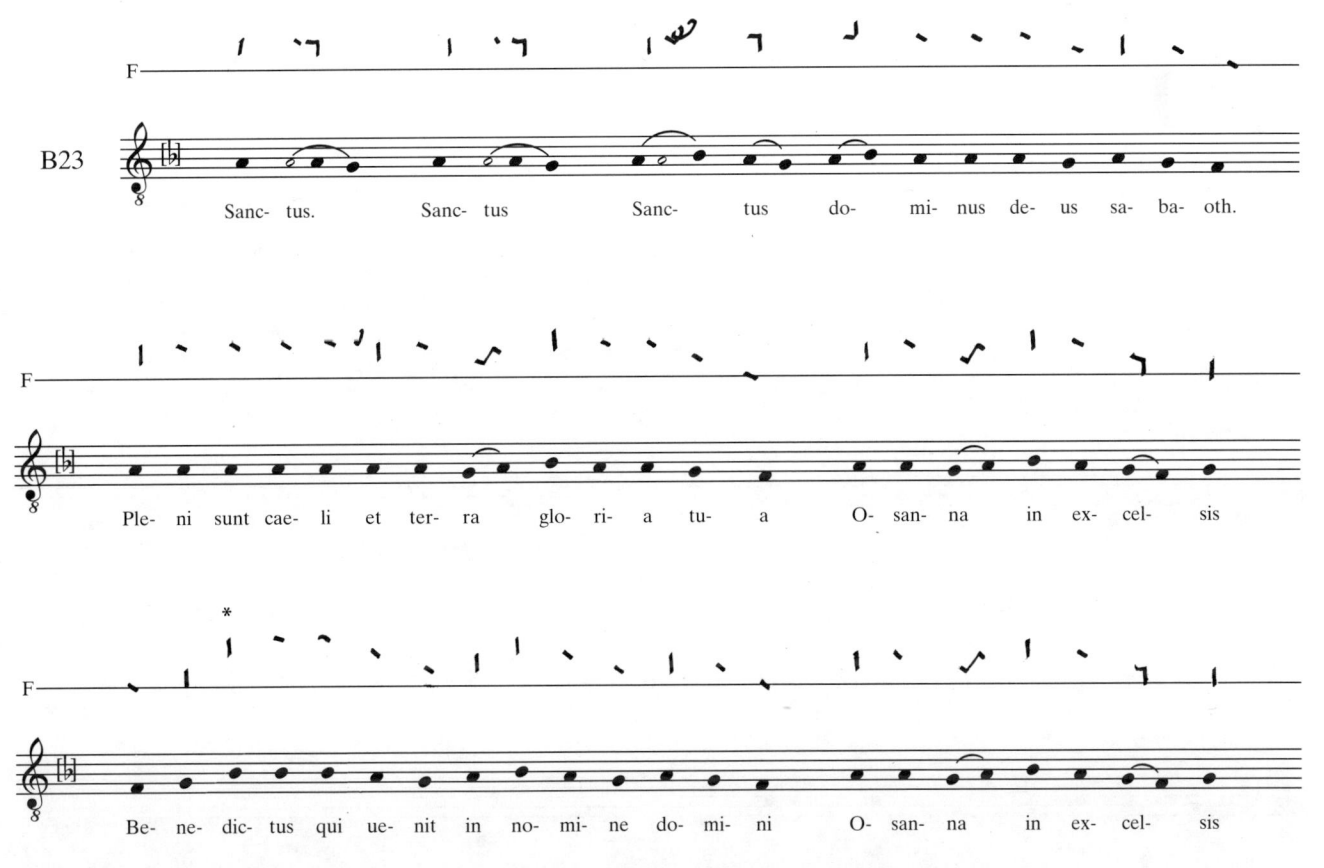

* Ambiguous diastematy: the notes for *dic-tus qui* can be read one step lower, as in the transcription of Thannabaur 41, p. 116 of the main text.

Preph.

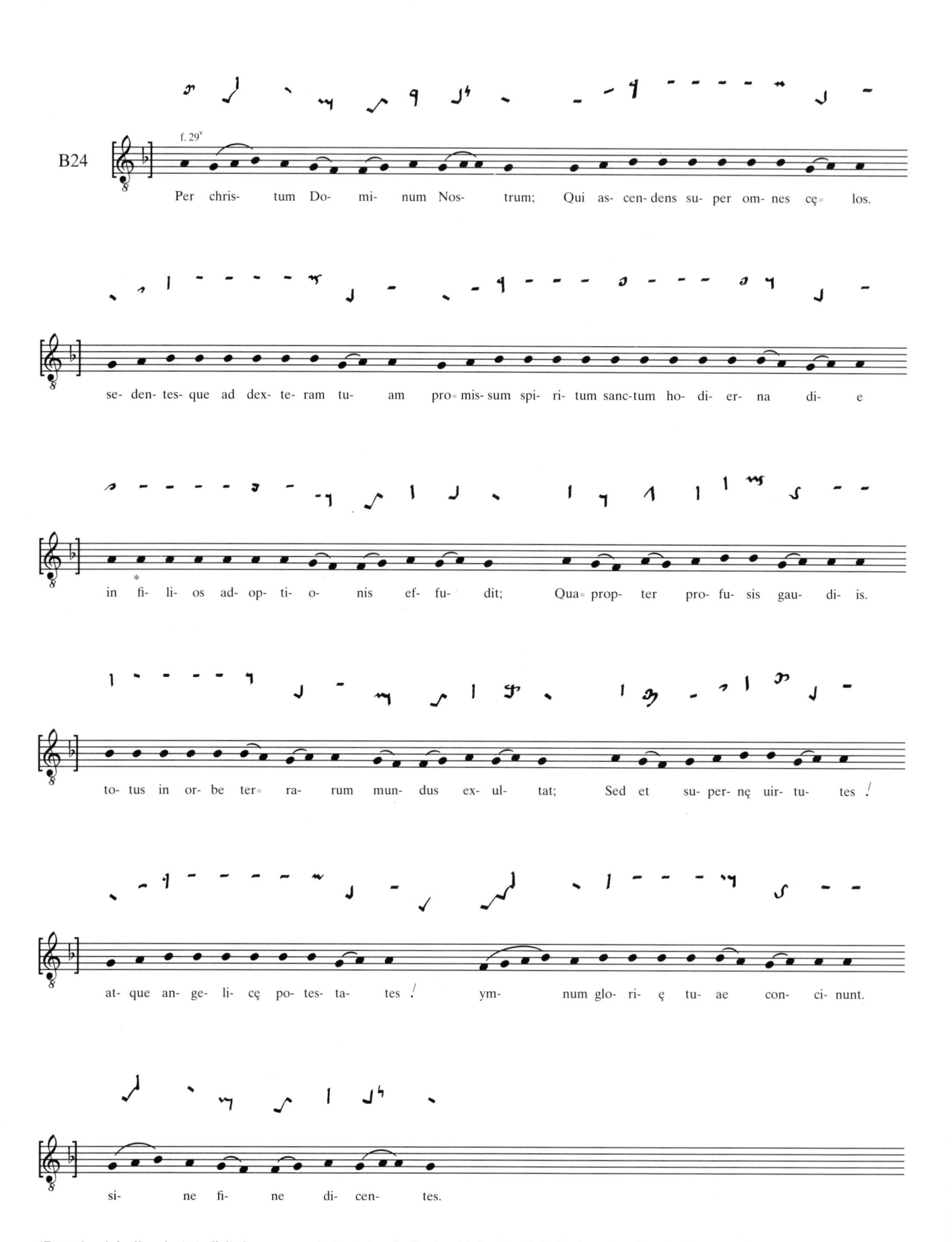

B24 Per chris- tum Do- mi- num Nos- trum; Qui as- cen- dens su- per om- nes cę- los.

se- den- tes- que ad dex- te- ram tu- am pro- mis- sum spi- ri- tum sanc- tum ho- di- er- na di- e

in fi- li- os ad- op- ti- o- nis ef- fu- dit; Qua- prop- ter pro- fu- sis gau- di- is.

to- tus in or- be ter- ra- rum mun- dus ex- ul- tat; Sed et su- per- nę uir- tu- tes

at- que an- ge- li- cę po- tes- ta- tes ym- num glo- ri- ę tu- ae con- ci- nunt.

si- ne fi- ne di- cen- tes.

*Text and music for filios adoptionis effudit; Quapropter were inadvertently omitted by the original scribe and added in tiny script and notation between the lines.

IV. Common Preface in the Canosa Missal
Baltimore W6

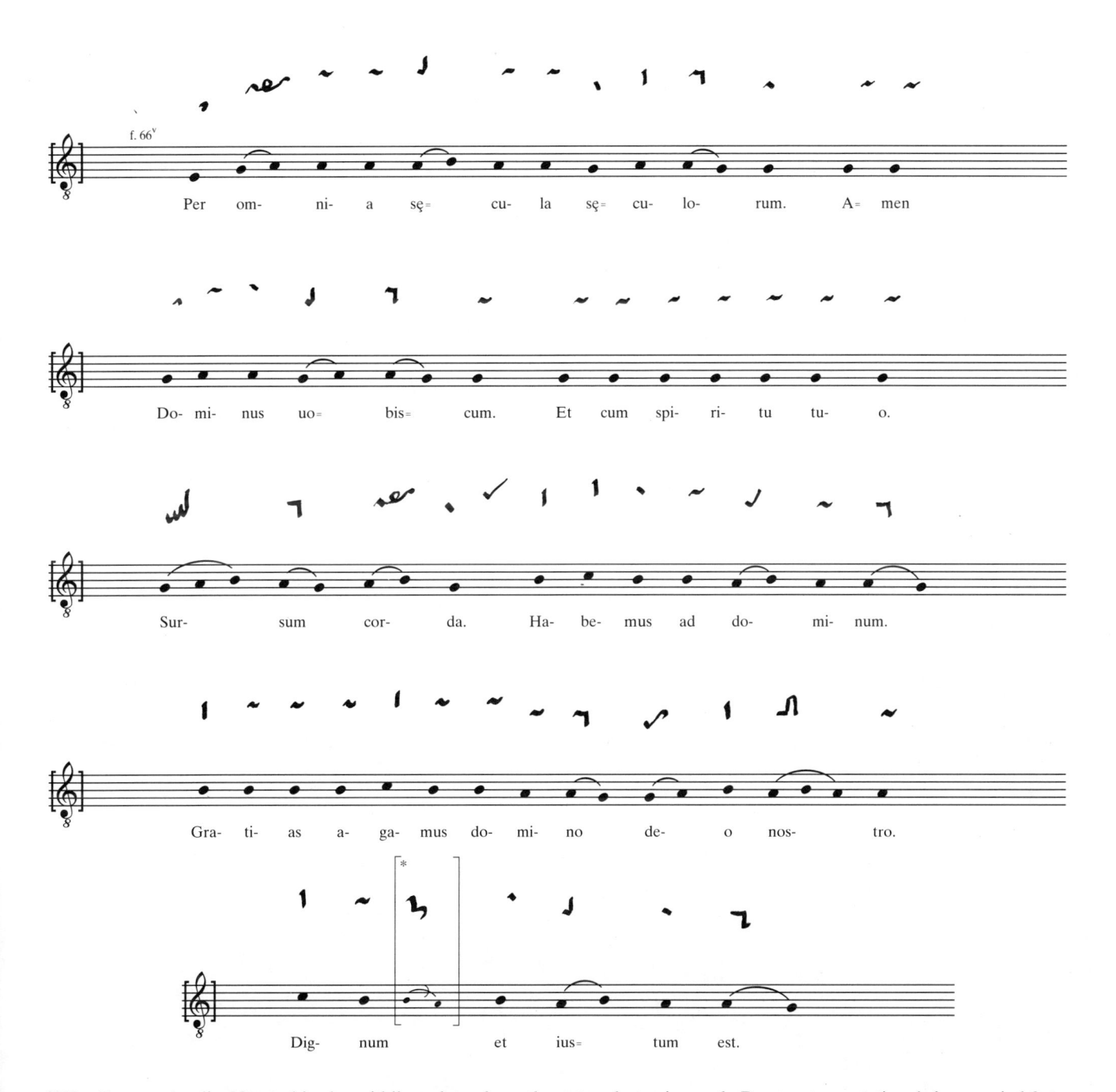

Per omnia sęcula sęculorum. Amen

Dominus uobiscum. Et cum spiritu tuo.

Sursum corda. Habemus ad dominum.

Gratias agamus domino deo nostro.

Dignum et iustum est.

W6: Canosa, Apulia. Notated in the middle or late eleventh century but using early Beneventan notational signs copied from an exemplar dating from the beginning of the century or earlier. The opening of the dialogue resembles that of 1574 (see above), but the celebrant's chant, *sui generis,* reflects a manner of singing the common preface similar in certain respects to the *Francisca* version of 127 but in other respects similar to the presumably later Cassinese version *In cotidianis diebus* of 426, C32, and 339[c] (see above). Missing custodes at the ends of certain lines and occasionally inaccurate heightening of the neumes render the choice of tenor from *Vere Dignum* through *Per christum dominum nostrum* uncertain: "b" or "c"—at the pitch employed for the transcription below? (From *Per quem maiestatem* to the end, the only tenor possible for the forephrase is one on "c"; the tenor on "c" should therefore probably also be sung throughout.)

The full text of Sanctus and the proper-preface conclusion *Et ideo ... dicentes* are appended, without notation. (See Sources, above, and the introductory essay on South Italian Preface Chant Traditions, pp. xlvi–li.)

*Almost certainly not a liquescent neume but a redundant superscript final *m* for *dignum.*

48

Ve- re Dig- num et ius- tum est. ę- quum et sa- lu- ta- re ∤

Nos ti- bi sem- per et u- bi- que gra- ti- as a- ge- re ∤

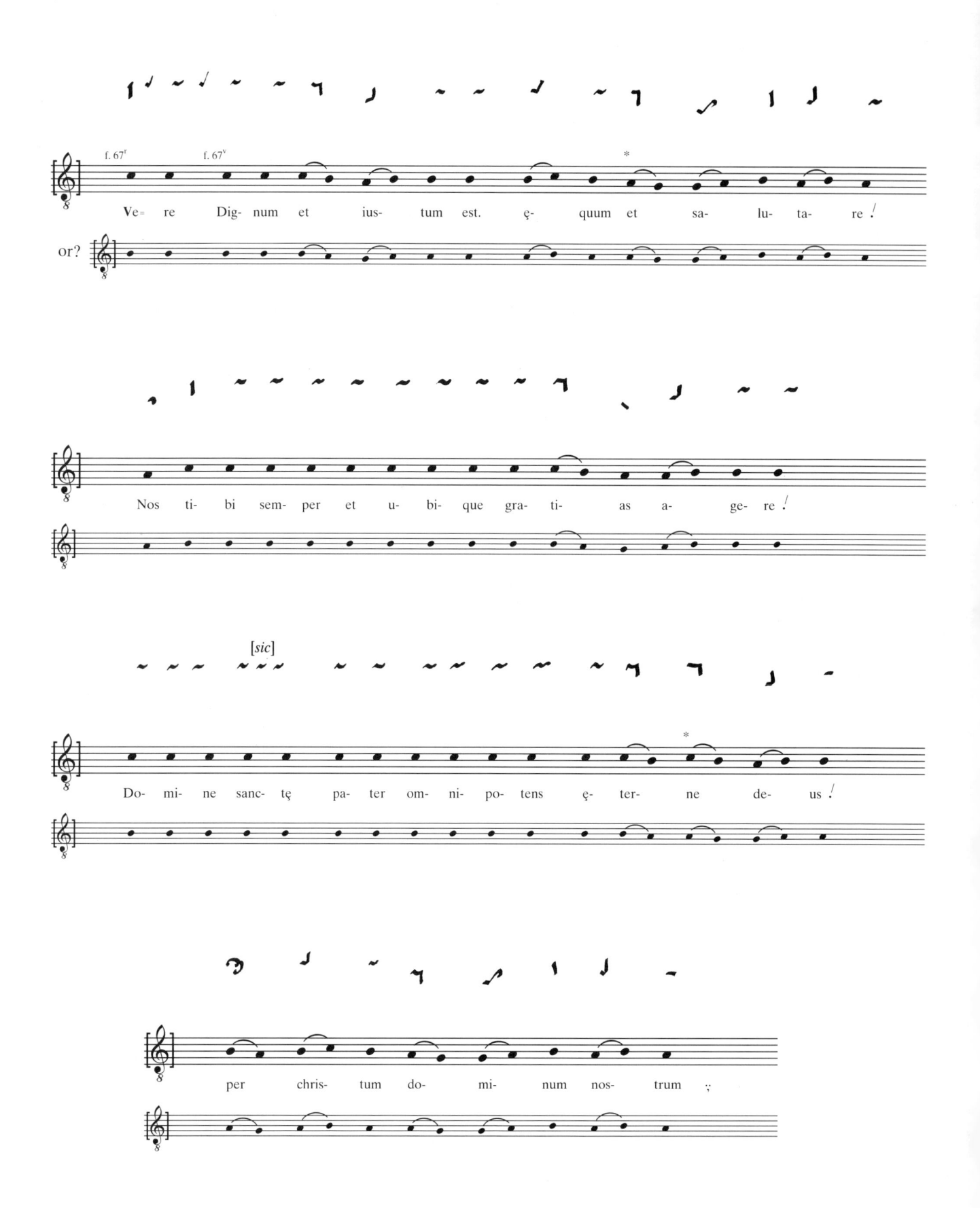

Do- mi- ne sanc- tę pa- ter om- ni- po- tens ę- ter- ne de- us ∤ [sic]

per chris- tum do- mi- num nos- trum ;

*Or "ba"

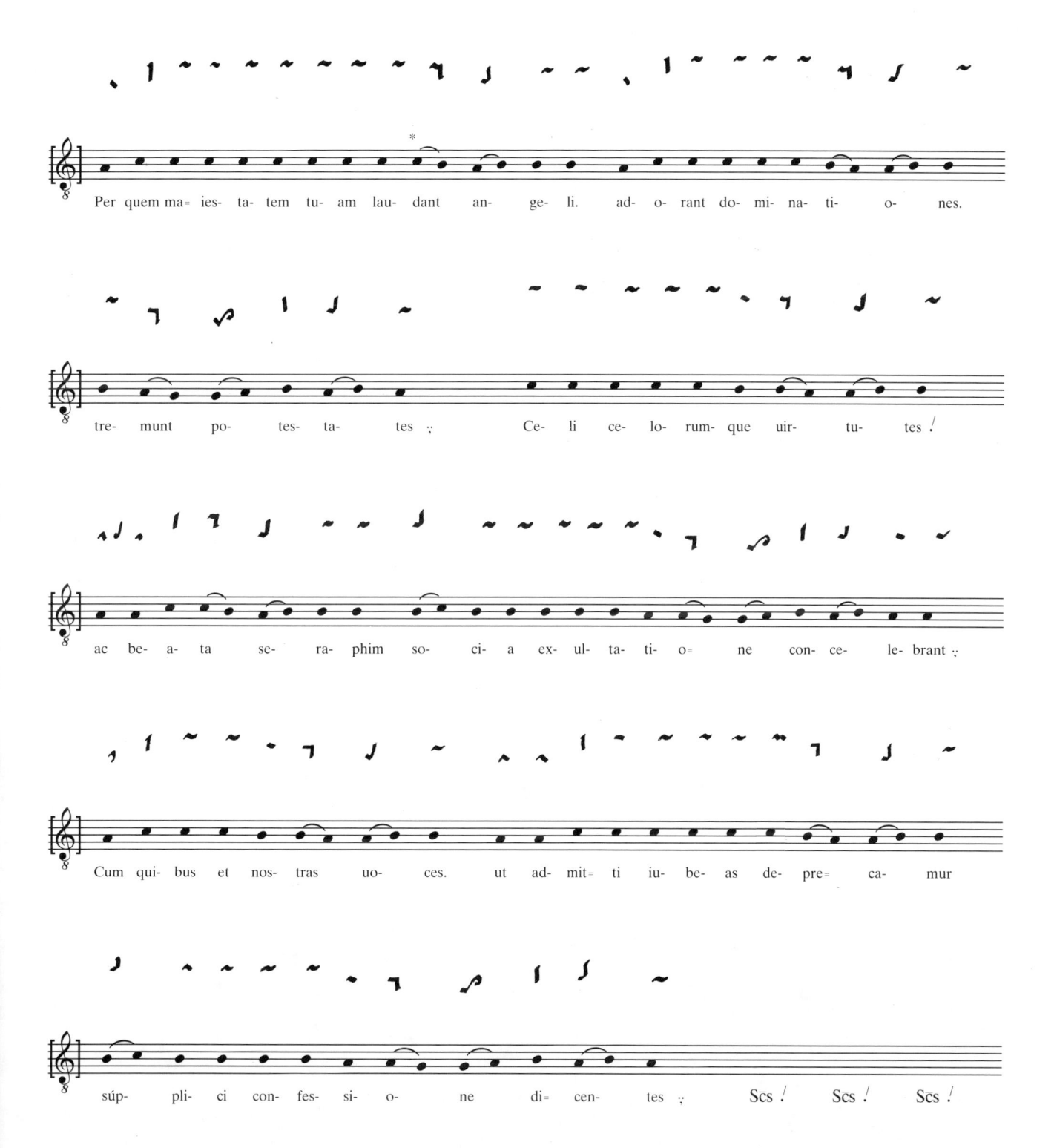

Per quem maiestatem tuam laudant angeli. adorant dominationes.

tremunt potestates ⁖ Celi celorumque uirtutes

ac beata seraphim socia exultatione concelebrant ⁖

Cum quibus et nostras uoces. ut admitti iubeas deprecamur

súpplici confessione dicentes ⁖ Scs ! Scs ! Scs !

Dns ds sabaóth ! Pleni sunt celi et terra glā tua. Osanna in excelsis !
Benedictus qui uenit in nomine dni. Osanná in excelsis ⁖

Et ideo cum anglis et archanglis cum tronis et dnationibus.
Cumque omi militia cęlestis exércitus ! hymnum glę tuę canimus
sine fine dicentes. Scs. Scs. Scs.

*Or "ba"

Sanctus Chants
Having
Tropes or Pros(ul)as
in South Italian Sources
Commentaries

A uniform title serves for all the different versions of a trope [or pros(ul)a]. Titles have been standardized . . . according to the classical rules of spelling and grammar. Internal references to these titles and to Sanctus chants usually cite both individual commentaries (the smaller page number to the left of the connective "and" or comma) as well as complete entries notated in the main text (the larger page numbers to the right of the connective).

In some cases only a selection from among the different manuscript versions could be printed in the main text. . . . These versions with music in the main text are marked with an asterisk in the list of sources in the commentaries.

A single manuscript version of each trope, [and/or pros(ul)a] is printed as a "typical text" . . . so as to show its structure (whether poetry or prose) and its relations to the surrounding Sanctus text and music. The Sanctus text is printed flush left when the trope is in prose; it is centered in the column when the trope [and/or pros(ul)a] has poetic form.

No emendations have been made in the Latin typical texts: they are printed as they stand in the sources— except that abbreviated cues for the Sanctus text have been expanded within angled brackets; the sign § has been placed in the margin to call attention to lines not in the prevailing meter or imperfectly so; and . . . "xps" has everywhere been expanded to "christus." Selected variants and conjectural emendations of the Latin text employed for the translations are printed in italics enclosed in parentheses.

Editorial Methods in BTC II

Chants Having Tropes or Pros(ul)as in South Italian Sources

Sanctus 3
Thannabaur 74

Trope: *Admirabilis splendor*
Hosanna² Prosula: *Indefessas uoces*

Sources

*Cologny-Geneva, Bodmer 74, fols. 124ᵛ–125ʳ (last of nine collected Sanctus). A tenor on c is used for the phrases *Pleni sunt cęli, qui uenit in nomine,* and for the trope phrase [2] . . . *in principio*. The only south Italian version to include the wandering verse *Indefessas uoces* as a Hosanna prosula. The first word of the trope is spelled *Ammirabilis*.

*Benevento 35, fol. 197ʳ (eleventh of sixteen collected Sanctus now surviving in the MS). A tenor on c is used at *Pleni sunt celi, qui uenit in nomine,* and at [2] . . . *in principio*. The trope begins *Ammirabilis*.

*BAV Urb. lat. 602, fol. 63ʳ⁻ᵛ (third of twelve collected Sanctus). A tenor on b is used at *Pleni sunt cęli, qui uenit in nomine,* and at [2] . . . *in principio*. The trope begins *Ammirabilis*. Rubric:

Nat̄ s̄ ioh̄is eūg Purificati. Et s̄. Ben̄.

*Montecassino 546, fol. 68ʳ⁻ᵛ (third of six collected Sanctus). A tenor on b is used at *Pleni sunt cęli, qui uenit in nomine,* and at [2] . . . *in principio*. The trope begins *Admirabilis*.

(*)Benevento 34, fol. 20ʳ⁻ᵛ (in the third mass for Christmas Day, after ℣ *Tu humiliasti sicut uulneratum superbum . . . et exaltetur dextera tua domine. iusti⟨tia⟩* of the *Of. Tui sunt celi et tua est terra* and before *Agnus dei . . . miserere nobis. Adsis placatus*). Notated with c clef only at the start through *Ammi*, and with c clef and yellow line and F clef and red line from *rabilis* to the end, except that the c line has been cut off by the binder's knife from *omne* through *Bene*. Almost identical with the version of MC 546, except for the wording *erat* (for *eras*) in [2]; the unique addition of *[+3] *Dominus deus noster* appropriate to Christmas; and the melisma ending the first *in excelsis*, which is exactly the same as the ending of the last *in excelsis* in MC 546.

Benevento 38, fols. 166ᵛ–167ʳ (first of six collected Sanctus copied after the completion of the original MS). The entire Sanctus without tropes is notated *in campo aperto* in accurately diastematic Beneventan notation dating from the third quarter of the eleventh century. The trope elements [1–3], beginning *Ammirabilis* (now cut off after the first word *Cui* of [4]), were notated successively without Sanctus cues across the bottom margins of fols. 166ᵛ and 167ʳ, in the same hand as the Sanctus above. The completion of Vs [4] and many words of [1–3] were trimmed off. (There would not have been room on the page to insert a prosula.) A tenor on b is used for *Pleni sunt celi* and *qui uenit in nomine* (as in the versions of Urb 602 and MC 546) but a tenor on c is used for the trope phrase [2] . . . *in principio* (as in the versions of Bod 74 and Ben 35). Identical melismas at the ends of the two phrases for *excelsis* differ slightly from those in other versions. These details apart, the surviving phrases resemble other versions and especially Ben 35.

Altar Book Incipit

Zagreb, MR 166, p. 203 (attached to the end of the fourth common-preface chant, rubricked *Item ī dn̄icis diebus,* and immediately preceding the rubric *Item ī festiuitatibus scōrum* for the fifth and last common-preface chant). The fourth and fifth common prefaces are notated *in campo aperto* with accurately diastematic neumes similar to those of Urb 602 or the second music scribe of Ben 35. (The first three common prefaces are notated in a slightly different, less skilled hand.) Only the first *Sanctus* acclamation is appended, with notation heightened in such a way as to begin incorrectly on the same pitch as the last note of the preface:

. . . dicentes. S.

Exactly this shortened form of the *Sanctus* acclamation appears as the second acclamation of Thannabaur 74 in Bod 74 (see p. 5 of the main text). If the preface is imagined in the hard G hexachord, ending *dicentes*ᵇ ᵃᵇ ᵃ, then the Sanctus incipit ought to begin one step lower: S⟨*anctus*⟩ᴳᵃᴳᶜᵇᵃᵃ ᴳ; or if the preface is imagined in the soft F hexachord with b-flat, ending *dicentes*ᵃ ᴳᵃ ᴳ, then the Sanctus incipit might indeed begin on G but continue with b-natural.

The first part of the missal, pp. 1–326, is thought to have been written in the area of Montecassino and later brought to Dalmatia; the second part, pp. 327–54, seems to have been written in Dalmatia but in a Beneventan hand. (See above, pp. 4–5, for further description.)

Notes on the Melodies

References: Hiley, "Ordinary of Mass Chants in English, North French and Sicilian MSS," p. 101; Levy, "Byzantine Sanctus," pp. 21–22; MMMA 17, Th 74 (STr 4, HPr 98); and Planchart 2:316–17.

See the excursus on anaphoral chant, BTC II/1, p. xvi, and the description of Za MR 166 in BTC II/3, p. xxi, and table 7 on p. 5.

Thannabaur lists twenty-one Italian sources from all over Italy for this Sanctus melody, most of them having the trope *Admirabilis splendor*. He lists only three French and Norman-Sicilian sources, none of them early and none with tropes. (In most French sources—the majority Aquitanian—the trope *Admirabilis splendor* is associated with another Sanctus melody, Thannabaur 111, which in Italy occurs rarely.) Thannabaur 74 must therefore have originated in Italy. Furthermore, south Italian sources mostly agree in their readings except for minor variants.

The melodic kernel employed for *Pleni sunt cęli* and *qui uenit in nomine* is the same as that found in a great many Sanctus and other pieces for the ordinary, based on anaphoral chant. (See References, above.) The Cassinese versions in Urb 602 and MC 546, as well as the Cassinese-based version of Ben 34, have these phrases with a tenor or reciting note on b. However, both the Roman manuscript Bod 74 and Ben 35—some of whose ordinary chants and tropes seem to have been borrowed from the Roman repertory—have c-tenors for these phrases. The melodies in the trope versions for [2] . . . *in principio* have tenors on either b or c, matching the tenors used in the Sanctus melodies. (But in the fragmentary version appended with other ordinary chants to Ben 38, the two Sanctus phrases have tenors on b while the trope phrase *in principio* has a c-tenor. This version cannot have been copied earlier than that in Bod 74.)

The Sanctus melody rises to c and in most versions extends the low range of mode 8 to D at *Deus sabaoth* and *Benedictus*. A concluding melisma for *excelsis* recapitulates the Sanctus acclamation, except in Ben 34. There, both acclamation and concluding melisma have been abbreviated, the latter as in MC 546. On the other hand, the last *excelsis* melisma in Bod 74 was expanded so as to prefigure the melody for the brief prosula *Indefessas uoces nostras exaudies in excelsis*, which in turn concludes with a longer melisma drawing upon all the melodic material of Sanctus.

The trope melody, derived from the Sanctus melody, is stable in all south Italian versions. It expands the range of the Sanctus melody upwards to d (at *immarcessibilisque*) and downwards to C (as at *sanctusque*). The Christmas verse added in Ben 34, [+3] *Dominus deus noster*, first develops the anaphoral-chant kernel with tenor on b, then touches top d three times (twice on the word *domina*) and ends with the melisma of the Sanctus acclamations.

NOTES ON *Admirabilis splendor* WITH *Indefessas uoces*
References: CT 7, pp. 67–68 (no. 1), 353–54, 356–57, and 360; Ireland, 1:173–74 and 2:152–58; and Planchart, 1:277–79 and 2:9, 19, and 316–17. For *Indefessas uoces*, see CT 7, p. 67 (no. 1 F), p. 123 (no. 62 D), and pp. 123–24 (no. 63).

CT 7 supplies references in scripture and the liturgy for *Admirabilis splendor*, of which the following are the most important: for Vs [1], Isa. 9:6 and I Tim. 6:16 (for the alternative reading *inaccessibilisque lux* of non-Italian MSS); for Vs [2], John 1:1; for Vs [3], John 14:26 and Te Deum laudamus; for Vs [4], Phil. 2:10–11 and Rom. 14:11 quoting Isa. 45:23; and for Vs [+3] (Ben 34 only) *uenit carnem ut assumeret*, Te Deum laudamus. Also see Iversen, "Pax et Sapientia," pp. 49–54.

Cf. the prosula wording **Indefessas uoces** with the ending **Tibi uoces indefessas** of the prosula *Qui uenisti carnem sumens* in Bod 74 (BTC II/3, pp. 72 and 45) and with the trope element [4] *Indefessa uoces nostras exaudi* of *Immortalis et uerus* (BTC II/3, pp. 76 and 47).

The trope is prose.

Source of text and translation below: Bod 74

Sanctus

[1]   Ammirabilis splendor
    inmarcessibilisque lux
    pater deus

Sanctus

[2]   Verbum quod erat
    in principio apud deum

Sanctus Dominus deus sabaoth

[3]   Paraclitus sanctusque spiritus

Pleni sunt cęli et terra gloria tua
Osanna in excelsis

[4]   Cui omne flectitur genu
    et omnis lingua proclamat dicens

Benedictus qui uenit in nomine domini
Osanna _____ in excelsis _____
  ℱ **Indefessas uoces
     nostras exaudies**   in excelsis _____

                        *

Holy

[1]   The wonderful Brightness,
    Light unfading,
    God the Father!

Holy

[2]   The Word, which in the beginning
    was with God!

Holy Lord, God of hosts,

[3]   The Advocate and Holy Spirit!

Heaven and earth are full of thy glory;
Hosanna on high!

[4]   To whom every knee bends
    and every tongue cries out, saying:

Blessed is he that comes in the name of the Lord;
Hosanna _____ on high! _____
  [ℱs] **Our unweariied voices
       thou shalt hear**   on high! _____

Ben 34:

S⟨an⟩c⟨tu⟩s.

[+³]   *Dominus deus noster*
         uenit carnem ut assumeret
         per beatam uirginem mariam genitricem
         regina et domina polorum et terris.

Dominus deus sabaoth.

[3⁴]   *Paraclitus sanctusque spiritus.*

*

Holy

[+³]   *The Lord our God*
         came to take flesh
         through the blessed virgin Mary, his mother,
         Queen and Lady of the heavens and on earth.

Lord God of hosts,

[3⁴]   *The Advocate and Holy Spirit!*

Trope verses [1], [2], and [3] direct each preceding Sanctus acclamation toward a single Person of the Trinity—Father, Son, and Holy Spirit. Verse [4] serves to introduce *Benedictus qui uenit in nomine domini.* These four elements, in the order of the BTC text, constitute the words of the trope in thirty-seven of the forty-four sources listed in CT 7, of which the earliest are the Winchester Tropers, CC 473 and Ox 775. Northern French, Norman-Sicilian, and Aquitanian sources for the most part join the trope with Thannabaur 111 rather than with Thannabaur 74. They tend to use the wording *inaccessibilisque* (or variants) in [1] and *utriusque* in [3], where Italian manuscripts in general use *inmarcessibilisque* and *sanctusque*.

Thannabaur 111 is never found with this trope in Italian sources, although that melody is found untroped in two Nonantolan manuscripts and in Ben 35. (See p. 121 below and p. 121 of the main text.) In Italy, *Admirabilis splendor* was always sung with Thannabaur 74, to which Sanctus the Italian melody for the trope is related. *Admirabilis splendor* does not appear in east Frankish sources, but its wide and early distribution in western Europe and Italy implies a tenth-century origin. The text abounds in quotations and near-quotations from scripture. (See the citations from CT 7 given in References, above.)

Verse [+³] is known only from Ben 34, where the piece is assigned to the propers of Christmas Day. Praise of Mary as *genitricem* and *regina et domina polorum et terris*, everywhere appropriate at Christmas, would have been especially apt in the cathedral of Benevento, dedicated to the Virgin Mother of God.

According to the concordances of CT 7, the miniature prosula **Indefessas uoces** appended to the second Hosanna is known in connection with *Admirabilis splendor* only from Bod 74 and from one other central Italian manuscript fragment, BoC 7, although it occurs alone in Pia 65. In the central Italian manuscripts Mod 7, PdC A 47, and RoV C 52—and the later Ben 34—the words are used as the last trope element of *Immortalis et uerus.* (See pp. 74 and 46 below.) This scrap of evidence strengthens the hypothesis that the Bod 74 Sanctus repertory is somehow related to a central Italian repertory, now glimpsed in the sources Mod 7 and PdC A 47 from the Ravenna area and in RoV C 52, probably from the abbey of Sant'Eutizio, Val Castoriana near Norcia (according to Huglo), or perhaps from Tuscany (according to Supino Martini).

Sanctus 12
Thannabaur 92

Altissime creator = *Altissimeque Rector*
Hosanna² Prosula: *Conditor alme Domine*

SOURCES

*BAV Urb. lat. 602, fols. 62ʳ–63ʳ (second of twelve collected Sanctus). The single elements [1^MC], [2^MC], [3^MC], and [4] of the Cassinese text, beginning *Altissime creator*, are underlaid in prosula style to each preceding segment of the Sanctus melody. Vs [5^MC], abbreviated *Repleti sumus deus noster*, is inserted before Hosanna¹; and Vs [6^MC] *Ebreorum proles* comes before rather than after *Benedictus qui uenit*. The last *Osanna in excelsis* with its entire melisma written out precedes the prosula **Conditor alme domine,** lines [7–14] of which are copied successively without the short anticipatory melisma at the end of each line found in MC 546. Cf. Thannabaur's transcription, cited in References, below, with the transcription in the BTC main text. Rubric, on fol. 61ᵛ:

S̄ stēph. F̄r ii. in ālb.
Assuti s. m. Et oium scorum.

(*)Montecassino 546, fols. 67ᵛ–68ʳ (second of six collected Sanctus). On fol. 67ᵛ, notated with an F clef and red line and with an intermittent yellow line wherever the melody touches c ; on fol. 68ʳ, beginning with [4] . . . *nobis indignis*, notated with c clef and yellow line and with F clef and red line. The elements of the Cassinese text *Altissime creator* are grouped as follows: [1^MC–4], [5] complete, [6^MC]; and the *prosula [7–14]. This version differs from the others in that it breaks the *Hosanna² melisma into sections that are attached to the final syllables of the prosula segments in succession, so that the final melisma of one prosula segment prefigures the melody of the next. The melisma for the second *Osanna in excelsis* appears only in this segmented fashion. See the typical text following and Thannabaur's transcription, cited in References, below.

*Benevento 34, fol. 283ʳ⁻ᵛ (the second of eight collected Sanctus—the second of three with tropes, which are followed by two without tropes and, after Agnus Dei and a MS lacuna, by three more troped Sanctus). The non-Cassinese text, beginning *Altissimeque rector*, with variants. Elements [1], [2], [3], and [4] are, however, interspersed in the base text of Sanctus approximately as in Urb 602. The melody for *gloria tua* differs from that of all other south Italian MSS. The words *in excelsis* to conclude element [14] of the prosula are missing.

*Cologny-Geneva, Bodmer 74, fol. 123ʳ (fifth of nine collected Sanctus). The standard non-Cassinese text and arrangement, beginning *Altissimeque rector* as in Versio I of CT 7—except [10] ***mari sustentor*** for ***maris sustentator*** (see References, below). Element [5] appears complete after the first *Osanna in excelsis*; and element [6] *Ebreorum proles* follows *Benedictus qui uenit in nomine domini*. The second *Osanna in excelsis* appears with its entire melisma before the prosula [7–14] **Conditor alme domine,** the lines of which are given successively as a single unit, without appended melismas.

(*)Benevento 35, fol. 196ʳ (seventh of sixteen collected Sanctus now surviving in the MS). The first line in the MS is notated with c clef but no yellow line and with F clef and red line; the second line of the MS, beginning *misericors nobis indigni,* with F clef and red line only; from the third line of the MS, beginning *sumus quam non meremur,* to the end, both c clef with yellow line and F clef with red line are present. A lacuna of at least one folio between the present fol. 195 and the present fol. 196 has deprived the piece of its opening acclamations and elements [1–2], so that the text now begins [3] *Parce peccata cuncta. Dominus deus sabaoth.* [4] *Domini misericors,* approximately as in Ben 34, but the verbal text is corrupt. Only **Pleni sunt . . . gloria tua,* *[5] *Repleti sumus,* the first **Osanna in excelsis,* *[6] *Hebreorum proles,* and *[+⁷] *Dona celestis*—all of which differ from the version of Ben 34—are transcribed in the main text, pp. 14–16.

NOTES ON *Altissime creator = Altissimeque rector Conditor alme Domine* AND THE MELODIES

The Sanctus melody Thannabaur 92 never occurs without *Altissime creator = Altissimeque rector* in its sources, all Italian. The Sanctus mostly depends on the "trope" melody, not the reverse. I therefore discuss Sanctus melody and "tropes" under a single heading.

References: Boe, "Hymns and Poems at Mass in Eleventh-Century Southern Italy"; CT 7, pp. 71–74 (no. 5, I and III), 353–54, 356, 358–59, 390 (pl. 2, from To 18); and 395 (pl. 31, from MC 546); CT 7, pp. 89–90 (no. 24 B) for the wandering Vs [6]; Levy, "Byzantine Sanctus," pp. 21–28; MMMA 17, Th 92 (STr 7, HPr 34a); and Thannabaur, p. 263ff., Beilagen 1 and 2 (transcriptions of the versions of Urb 602 and MC 546).

Cf. BTC II/2, pp. 10–14 and 32 (Gloria in excelsis Bosse 51 = 2, Var. 1 and 2, *Ciues superni . . . Christus surrexit*), especially the prosulas and their melismas. See BTC II/3, pp. 98, 93, and especially p. 98 (*Quem cherubim atque seraphim + Cui pueri Hebraeorum,* Thannabaur 63, Vs [+MC²]) for Vs [6] of the present piece.

Meter: Elements [1–4] of the text can be grouped as a stanza with the accentual pattern 3x· 7p + 7p(p) + 5p. In the version of Ben 35, Vs [+⁷] is organized as 2x· (5p + 5p) in the regular accentual pattern ´ ~ ~ ´ ~ . (See below.) Wandering verse [6] is prose. Elements added to Sanctus are enumerated by consecutive arabic numerals, whether they function as trope or as quasi-prosula.

Source of the non-Cassinese text and translation below: Bod 74

        Sanctus
          Sanctus
            Sanctus
        dominus deus sabaoth

[1]   Altissimeque rector
[2]   poli sede redemptor
[3]   parce peccata cuncta
[4]   domine misericors nobis indignis

   Pleni sunt cęli et terra   gloria tua
   Osanna _____ in excelsis

[5] Repleti sumus
      quam non meremur propter peccata
      quę gessimus gloriam tuam nobis dona

   Benedictus qui uenit in nomine domini
[6]   Ebręorum proles ore concrepauerunt
Osanna _____ in excelsis
[7] 𝆑 **Conditor alme domine**
[8]   **poli rector**
[9]   **telluris gubernator**
[10]   **mari sustentor**
[11]   **miserere**
                  plasmę tuę
[12]   **quem formasti de humo**
[13]   **ad tuam imaginem**
[14]   **misericors**
                          in excelsis
              *

Source of the Cassinese revised text and translation below: MC 546

        Sanctus
          Sanctus.
            Sanctus.
        Dominus deus sabaoth.

[1ᴹᶜ]   Altissime creator
[2ᴹᶜ]   Orbisque gubernator.
[3ᴹᶜ]   Laxa peccata cuncta.
[4]   domine misericors. nobis indignis.

   Pleni sunt cęli et terra   gloria tua
   Osanna _____ in excelsis.

[5] Repleti sumus
      quam non meremur propter peccata
      que gessimus gloria tua   deus noster.

   Benedictus qui uenit in nomine domini.
[6ᴹᶜ]   Hebreorum proles ore personuerunt.
   Osanna ____
[7]   **Conditor alme domine.** _____
[8]   **Poli rector.** _____
[9ᴹᶜ]   **Terre ponderator.** _____
[10ᴹᶜ]   **Maris dilatator.** _____
[11]   **Miserere plasmatum.** _____
[12]   **Quod formasti de humo.** ____
[13]   **Ad tuam ymaginem.** _____
[14]   **Misericors**
      in excelsis.
              *

Bod 74	Holy,
	  Holy,
	    Holy
	      Lord God of hosts
			Holy,
			  Holy,
			    Holy,
			      Lord God of hosts!
				MC 546

[1]	And highest Ruler,	[1MC]	O Creator most high,	
[2]	Redeemer, from the throne of heaven,	[2MC]	and Ruler of the world:	
[3]	spare all our sins,	[3MC]	relieve our sins,	
[4]	O Lord, merciful to us unworthy ones.	[4]	O Lord, merciful to us unworthy ones.	
	Heaven and earth are full of thy glory: Hosanna _____ in the highest.		Heaven and earth are full of thy glory; Hosanna _____ in the highest.	

[5]	Filled are we:
	  grant us thy glory, which we do not deserve
	  because of the sins we have committed.
		[5]	We are filled full
			  of thy glory, which we do not deserve
			  because of the sins we have committed,
			  O our God!	

	Blessed is he that comes in the name of the Lord.		Blessed is he that comes in the name of the Lord;	
[6]	The offspring of the Hebrews raised the shout: Hosanna _____ in the highest.	[6MC]	The offspring of the Hebrews cried all together: Hosanna ____	
[7]	𝄞 O kind Lord and Maker,	[7]	O kind Lord and Maker, ____	
[8]	Ruler of heaven,	[8]	Ruler of heaven, ____	
[9]	Governor of earth,	[9MC]	Upholder of the earth, ____	
[10]	Sustainer of the sea (*maris*),	[10MC]	Extender of the sea, ____	
[11]	Pity thy creation	[11]	Pity the creation ____	
[12]	thou didst form from clay	[12]	thou didst form from clay	
[13]	into thine image;	[13]	into thine image; ____	
[14]	Thou art merciful in the highest.	[14]	Thou art merciful in the highest.	

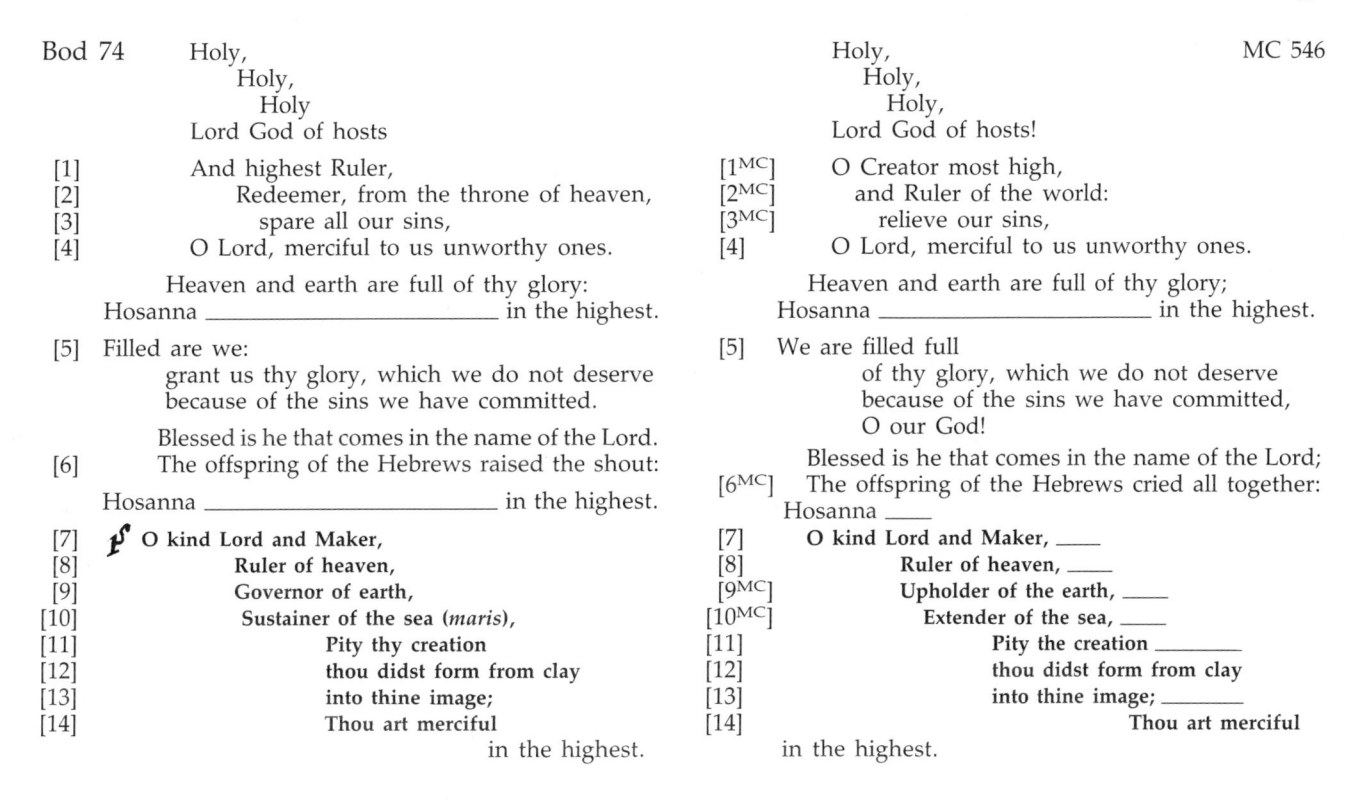

Thannabaur, in his introductory essay on this piece (see References, above), presents the inserted text elements with their mostly syllabic melodic phrases as dependent on or derived from the Sanctus melody. He notes the surprising variety of ways these insertions are positioned in different sources and concludes that the stable Sanctus melody must be independent of and earlier than the inserted text elements. He regards the first four insertions as prosulas, because the text elements have been set to the melodic phrases of the Sanctus melody that precedes them, mostly one note to a syllable.

His view is the opposite of mine. The melodies for the text elements are equally stable in whatever position they are found within the base chant. Furthermore, I regard the common definition of "prosula" Thannabaur implies—that is, the syllabic texting of a preceding or pre-existent melisma—as inadequate. In my view, prosulas, like their longer relatives the prosas or sequences, must have at least one set of paired, tripled, or otherwise repeated lines of the same or nearly the same syllable count that are set syllabically to the same or nearly the same tune. (See Editorial Methods above, under Definition of Pros[ul]a in BTC II/3, p. xii.) Such repetition does not occur until the two text segments following the Hosanna melismas, namely elements [5] and [7–14], and there only imperfectly. Elements [7–14] indeed form a prosula of sorts in all versions, but for element [5] the case is not so clear. This element and the preceding *Osanna __ in excelsis* produce a correct but miniature Hosanna[1] prosula in the versions of Ben 34 and Bod 74 but less clearly so in MC 546 and Ben 35, and not at all in Urb 602, as we shall see.

Verse [6] *Hebreorum proles* does not even show syllabic underlay of a pre-existent melisma: rather, it is a contrafactum. Its text and *Benedictus qui uenit in nomine domini* are underlaid to the same music almost note for note in the same neumatic—not syllabic—style. Moreover, the phrase for Vs [6] begins F G a (except in Urb 602), whereas other phrases in this Sanctus begin on G, or sometimes on b or a (though returning to G as final). These features suggest a different origin for Vs [6] than for the rest of the piece. Indeed, it occurs in another Sanctus trope but borrowed from the present piece. (See References, above, for *Quem cherubim atque seraphim + Cui pueri Hebraeorum*.) The element probably originated as an office or processional antiphon for Palm Sunday.

The two elements [5] and [+7] in the now incomplete version of Ben 35 deserve attention. In MC 546, Ben 34, and Bod 74, element [5] functions more or less as a Hosanna[1] prosula, placed in the normal position after its related Hosanna[1] melisma. In Ben 35, element [5], worded *Repleti sumus quam non meremur propter peccata que gessimus nos indignis*, precedes the first Hosanna, a highly unusual position for a Hosanna prosula. (In Urb 602, [5^(MC)] also precedes the first Hosanna but in such curtailed form—four words only—that it cannot be regarded as a Hosanna prosula. In fact, there is no melisma in the version of Urb 602 that corresponds to the notes of [5^(MC)].)

Element [5] in the version of Ben 35 is similar to [5] in the later manuscript Ben 34. In this later version, element [5] continues with different words:

[5] Repleti sumus
    dona celestes   quesumus christe   5p + 5p
    parce peccata   nobis indignis.   5p + 5p

Strange to say, exactly these lines and their simple tune had been copied in Ben 35, not as part of [5] *Repleti sumus* but as the separate Vs [+⁷]. This verse may come from a popular hymn or the refrain of a metrical litany. The neuter plural *dona* treated as a feminine plural, *dona celestes* (cf. modern Italian *le mura*, etc.), and *parce* used with the accusative suggest popular usage. I have edited these lines and their melody in modern notation below, with two possible rhythms that seem to suit some texts in rhythmical verse. Here, each unit of five syllables is accented:

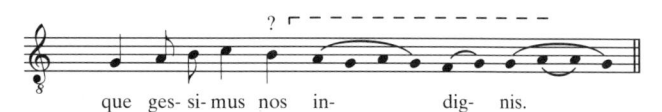

[musical notation: 35:[+⁷] Do- na ce- les- tis que- su- mus chris- te]

[musical notation: par- ce pec- ca- ta no- bis in- dig- nis.]

[musical notation: 35:[5] quam non me- re- mur prop- ter pec- ca- ta]

[musical notation: que ges- si- mus nos in- dig- nis.]

or

[musical notation: 35:[+⁷] Do- na ce- les- tis que- su- mus chris- te]

[musical notation: par- ce pec- ca- ta no- bis in- dig- nis.]

In MC 546 and Bod 74, element [5] *. . . quam non meremur* has the same melody as the text that begins *Dona celestes* in Ben 34 and Ben 35. The opening words *Repleti sumus* were doubtless added in MC 546 and Bod 74 with the intention of embroidering the base text *Pleni sunt*. In Ben 35 this reference to the Sanctus text was not made.

In all manuscripts the first *Osanna in excelsis* employs a melismatic version of the melody used for *Dona celestes*. Thannabaur supposed the Hosanna melody came first, but its awkward repeated notes and confined range make it a poor specimen of a melisma. On the other hand, its repeated notes make sense as a hymn melody for rhythmical verse. (See Boe, "Hymns and poems at Mass in Southern Italy," cited in References above.)

I now turn to the text elements [1–4], which in Urb 602 and Ben 34 separately expand the individual Sanctus acclamations. Together, these elements constitute a self-contained stanza with four regular lines of seven syllables each, plus an added line, *nobis indignis*, of five syllables.

[1]   Altissimeque rector   7p
[2]   Poli sede redemptor   7p
[3]   Parce peccata cuncta   7p
[4]   Domine misericors   7pp
       (or 602, 34: *miserere*   7p)
           nobis indignis.   5p

When elements [3–4] above are compared with the last part of [+⁷] *Dona celestes*—the same text as [5] of Ben 34—their similarity is evident. *Parce peccata* in [+⁷] corresponds to [3] *Parce peccata cuncta*, and *nobis indignis* corresponds to [4] *Domine misericors* (or *miserere*) *nobis indignis*. It seems that an expanded alternative to *Dona celestes* was interpolated into the Sanctus acclamations as elements [1–4]. Each of these self-contained stanzas petitioning for pardon is strange stuff for troping Sanctus; their effect combined (in Ben 34 and Ben 35) is stranger still. Not even an ill-lettered Benevento scribe would have composed afresh the same prayer for pardon, once in lines of seven syllables and then again in lines of five syllables. I think that two pieces of popular liturgical verse that had been independently attached to Sanctus (like the Easter verses *Hodie Dominus Iesus Christus resurrexit a mortuis* attached to Thannabaur ?64 [cf. 60, 66, 67] in Bod 74—see Appendix II, pp. 124 and 131) were copied successively and thus fused, either through inadvertence or because of their common ending *nobis indignis*. As stated before, I think that the music of the hymn melody once associated with these textual elements was transferred to the Sanctus melody, rather than the reverse. The unusual notation for the three repeated opening notes of the first *Sanctus* confirms the process. (See main text, p. 12, as notated in the Urb 602 version.)

If indeed the first four elements existed as an independent hymn, one wonders why the first line of the non-Cassinese and certainly older version of them should begin *Altissimeque rector* with the enclitic *-que*, "and." Possibly the stanza once read

> Poli sede redemptor
> Altissimeque rector
> Parce peccata cuncta
> ....

and the first two lines were transposed when adapted for use as a Sanctus trope. "Holy and most high Ruler" can be understood as referring to the Father; "Holy Redeemer . . ." must refer to the Son. The invariable liturgical habit of naming the Father before the Son, rigorously observed when Sanctus acclamations were interpolated with tropes, may have provoked the transposition of lines, if indeed *Poli sede redemptor* was the original first line.

A hypothetical reconstruction of such a four-line hymn, using elements [1–4] independently of Sanctus, is given below. Exactly what shape the end of the line *Domine miserere* and the final *nobis indignis* might have taken is uncertain: Bod 74 gives *Domine misericors* before *nobis indignis*. The general melodic similarity to the putative hymnic reconstruction of *Dona celestes* given earlier is striking.

It remains to compare the revised Cassinese text with the non-Cassinese text of Bod 74, where *Dona celestes*, found in Ben 35 and Ben 34, had disappeared. (See the typical texts above.) The two elements [9] *tellus gubernator* and [10] *mari susten⟨ta⟩tor* became, in more apt Cassinese figures, [9MC] *Terre ponderator* and [10MC] *Maris dilatator*: "Upholder of the land" and "Extender of the sea." These corrections also avoided repetition of the word *gubernator* used earlier in the revised [2MC] *Orbisque gubernator*. (In Bod 74, the incorrect genitive *tellus*, also found in Ben 34, was corrected by an erasure to *telluris*, entailing the addition of a repeated note.) A not-uncommon use of *plasma* as feminine noun in element [11] *Miserere plasmę tuę*, also found even in Urb 602, was corrected in MC 546 first to *Miserere plasma tuum*—a neuter accusative after *miserere*—as the notation and the relative *quod* of the following line show, and then to the stilted plural *plasmatum*—which I take to be the correct genitive after *miserere* but which lacks one syllable for the melody and is still followed by the singular neuter relative *quod*. (Iversen reads *plasmātum*, the perfect participle of *plasmo, plasmare*, which agrees with the neuter relative *quod* but contradicts the musical phrase, meant for the accentuation *plásmătum*.) *Concrepauerunt* in Vs [6] became *personuerunt* in the Cassinese version: the two words may have long existed as variants in Palm-Sunday antiphons.

These successive editorial interventions—element [11] excepted—yielded the Cassinese version of the text used in Urb 602, a text intended to furnish Sanctus trope elements combined with a Hosanna[2] prosula. In Urb 602 (and in the much later Ben 34, copied by a Cassinese-trained scribe, who however used the non-Cassinese text), elements [1–4] are inserted like trope verses after each *Sanctus* and after *Dominus deus sabaoth*. Because each *Sanctus* has the same melody as the inserted text following, the Urb 602 complex resembles early east Frankish melodic tropes, which were attached to the last syllables of their preceding base text and were sometimes followed by texted versions of the added melodies. But, in the Urb 602 version, the Holy Ghost is not invoked after the third Sanctus, and the syntactic unity of elements [1–4] is disturbed by the intruded Sanctus acclamations. The literate and liturgically perceptive editor of the late Cassinese collection MC 546 rejoined these elements into one stanza, placing them after *Dominus deus sabaoth* and before *Pleni sunt celi*, just as in the arrangement of the non-Cassinese text in Bod 74.

In compensation, the editor of MC 546 arranged the Hosanna[2] melisma and its prosula elements [7–14], beginning **Conditor alme domine**, in roughly the same manner that elements [1–4] had been arranged in Urb 602. Short melismatic phrases seemingly drawn from the Hosanna[2] melody were attached to the last syllables of each segment of prosula text, prefiguring the melody for the next segment. In MC 546, the full melisma for *Osanna in excelsis* was never written out entire. A model for this treatment, other than east Frankish manuscripts, might have been found in the versions of this Sanctus in Bod 74 and Ben 35, where conventional brief "punctuation melismas," usually having the notes GabaaG, were added to the last syllables of *excelsis*, to [5] in Bod 74, to *gloria tua*, and, shortened, to [4]. (Such melismas are found in other Roman ordinary chants.)

The opening melisma of twelve notes for the first syllable of *Dominus deus sabaoth* is not completely texted in element [4], which follows in Urb 602 and Ben 34; its last six notes, Gab abc, correspond to the notes for the first syllable of *nobis indignis*. I do not believe that these notes were grouped into a melisma because sufficient syllables to underlay them were lacking; rather, they marked the beginning of the last line of five syllables in a stanza whose other lines had seven syllables. This melisma at the beginning of *nobis indignis* has, in my view, also generated the beginning of the *Pleni sunt celi et terra* section of the base chant, with its opening melisma consisting of the same six notes. This section of the base chant never appears in syllabic, texted form.

Sanctus melody Thannabaur 92 lacks pith, when divorced from its textual origins in the "trope" text. The unmotivated melismas for the first syllables of *Dominus deus sabaoth* and *Pleni sunt celi* sound extravagant. The view that this Sanctus melody was agglomerated from melodies original to its accompanying "trope" texts—the forms of which we can grasp only dimly—is to some extent confirmed by the sources, which never present the Sanctus melody by itself.

The piece is Italian, but the non-Cassinese version might just as well stem from central Italy as from the south. The meager concordances from north of Rome given by Thannabaur and Iversen—Mod 7, To 18, Vce 161, and BoC 7—all have for element [2] the wording *Clemens atque redemptor* instead of *Poli sede redemptor*. The version of Bod 74, which is as old as any, owes nothing to the Cassinese version as later transmitted.

Sanctus 20
Thannabaur 178
Hosanna² Prosula: *Ante thronum Domini*

Source

*Benevento 35, fol. 197^(r-v) (twelfth of sixteen collected Sanctus now surviving in the MS). Notated at the start with an a clef without line, and with an F clef with red line; but fol. 197^v has an F clef and red line only to the end, except that the F clef for the first line at the top of the verso has been torn off. The only known source for the Sanctus melody and the prosula.

Notes on the Melody

References: MMMA 17, Th 178 (HPr 10); Thannabaur, pp. 79–81 (transcription of the Sanctus melody).

Two motives and a freely treated cadence figure supply the substance of this mode-2 Sanctus and prosula. The two motives (A and B, next), followed by some form of cadence (c or C, next) alternate throughout the piece in a style typical of old Beneventan compositions. This alternation can be sketched:

A + c, C, A + c	(*Sanctus* . . .)
B + c', A + c'	(*Dominus deus* . . .)
B + c' +c', (A + c') + c'	(*Pleni sunt* . . .)
(B + c) + C'	(*Osanna* . . .)
A' + c' + B' + c''	(*Benedictus* . . .)
7x (A'' + c')	(*Osanna* and prosula)
C''	(*in excelsis.*)

Every phrase but that for *Benedictus . . . domini* ends on the modal final, D. The first motive, A, rises in a scalar melisma from D to a and descends, with a doubled note on GG, to some form of the cadence figure. The second motive, B, drops into the plagal range from D to low A, returning to the final D by way of a stressed C. The cadence figure touches F, often doubling it, and usually C, often ending with an approach to the final from below, CD D. These formulas are varied only at *Benedictus qui uenit in nomine domini*. Here motive A rises only to G, not to a, and the last note of the phrase descends to C, thus lending a touch of variety before the sevenfold repetition of altered forms of motive A and cadence c in the Hosanna² melisma and prosula, where the phrases all end on D.

Notes on *Ante thronum Domini*

References: CT 7, pp. 75 (no. 7) and 359. Rev. 5:1, 7:9–15, and AH 7, no. 136, 71, and no. 138, 5b, are cited as sources for the text in CT 7. Also see Iversen, "Sur la géographie des tropes du Sanctus," p. 56.

Meter: Each line of the prosula is sung to the same melody, but the accentuation within each line varies and the first line has an extra syllable.

[Ps¹]   7pp + 7p
[II–IV]   3x· (7p + 6p)

Source of text and translation below: Ben 35

Sanctus. Sanctus. Sanctus.
Dominus deus sabaoth.
Pleni sunt celi et terra gloria tua.
Osanna in excelsis.
Benedictus qui uenit in nomine domini.
O _____ sanna

[Ps¹]   Ante thronum domini omnes angeli tremunt
[II]   ante conspectu dei omnes sancti clamant.
[III]   Laudes patresque regem tibi laudes deo.
[IV]   Voce magna proclamant dicuntque osanna
          in excelsis.
                    *
Blessed is he that comes in the name of the Lord.
Ho- _____ sanna

[Ps¹]   Before the Lord's throne, all angels tremble;
[II]   Before the face (*conspectum*) of God,
          all saints do shout.
[III]   And the fathers [shout] praises to the King (*regi*),
          praises to thee, O God;
[IV]   With a loud voice they cry out and say Hosanna
          in the highest!

In the lines of the prosula, the first motive A of the Sanctus melody, lightly varied, is closed four times with a variant of cadence c, and no other melodic material appears. It might therefore seem that this text came from a preexisting hymn and furnished motive A for the Sanctus, like [+7] *Dona celestes* of the preceding Sanctus in this edition, *Altissime creator = Altissimeque rector* (see p. 55 and p. 12). Not so—the Sanctus melody stands well enough by itself. Its swinging, regular alternation of high and low motives is characteristic of the local Beneventan melodic style, whereas the prosula text uses only the first of the two motives. Motive B is not used. In this case, the prosula is derivative—a local attempt to create a prosula for an indigenous Sanctus melody, relying on what Iversen calls "versus technique" and Levy calls "variation versus." My argument rests in part on the rhythmical irregularity of the first line. Occasional irregularities in rhythm and syllable count occur in the Italian variation versus, but not in the first lines, which set the pattern for the rest. [dPs¹] *Ante thronum domini omnes angeli tremunt* is structured 7pp + 7p instead of 7p + 6p, as are other lines and as fits the tune. Furthermore, in this first line, the extra syllable is accommodated to the tune in a clumsy way. Consequently, the text can hardly be a venerable survivor from the Italian past but must represent a Beneventan *tropista's* attempt to imitate Hosanna prosulas from the north. The piece bears interesting witness to the incorporation of a new genre into local Sanctus composition.

Line [III] *Laudes patresque regem tibi laudes deo* is unintelligible as it stands. In the translation above, I suggest changing the accusative *regem* to the dative *regi;* or the first *Laudes* might be changed to *Laudant*.

The text makes no allusion to the meaning of *Hosanna,* "save now." Line [IV] reverts to the introductory theme of the celebrant's preface chant that leads into Sanctus: ". . . with angels and archangels and all the company of heaven, evermore praising thee and saying: Holy Holy, Holy . . . ," though it here leads into *osanna* in excelsis.

Sanctus 22
Thannabaur 45

Antra modicis deserti

Source

*Benevento 35, fol. 195ʳ (first of sixteen collected Sanctus now surviving in the MS). Intended for the Nativity or the Beheading of St. John Baptist, but without rubric.

Notes on the Melody

Reference: MMMA 17, Th 45 (STr 11).

The typically south Italian melody serves for both Sanctus and added text. Although it never goes below the final, it is in mode 8, for its tenor is clearly c, not d. The melody consists of two phrases only, repeated with slight variations, expansions, and contractions. The first phrase begins with a rising fourth, Gc, then falls by undulating stepwise motion after touching d to the final, G. The second phrase derives from anaphoral chant (see Levy, "Byzantine Sanctus," and BTC II/1, p. xvi). It begins G ab and uses a b-tenor, rising to c. It first appears at *Pleni sunt celi et terra gloria tua* and returns for *Benedictus qui uenit* and *in nomine domini*. These two musical phrases alternate to the end of the piece. (Here the added text elements are left out of consideration.)

Sanctus . . .	A', A', A'; A
Pleni sunt . . .	B
Osanna¹ . . .	A
Benedictus . . .	B
Osanna² . . .	A'

The first phrase A', slightly expanded from the form A appearing at *Dominus deus sabaoh*, is sung thrice for the Sanctus acclamations. (I am supposing that the full melody of the first acclamation was intended as well for the second and third *Sanctus,* which are only cued with the first notes of the phrase. Abbreviated cues for repeated melodies are often found in this manuscript.) In these first statements of A' and A, the melodic arch reaches d : Gcb dcbaG . . . The Hosannas, however, remain within the range of a fourth, G–c, even though the second Hosanna is much extended. The latter begins on c, implying a rising fourth from the G final of the preceding phrase. Every phrase of the piece ends on G.

The elements of added text are set to the melodies used for the preceding phrases of the base text. Neumatic groups in the base text are sometimes dissolved and sometimes not; accented syllables are placed inconsistently in relation to the tune. Elements [1–3] and part of [4] are underlaid syllabically, approximately as in a prosula, but [5] and [6] have neumatic, not syllabic, word underlay. The model for setting the added text elements seems to have been the Roman and south Italian Kyrie verse, where the melody sung in melismatic form with the base text is repeated syllabically for the verses, and where sense and syntax of the verses are often independent of the base text. (See BTC II/1, pp. xxv–xxvi and xxxv.) Certainly this model serves for elements [1–4]. Elements [5–6] can be compared with more elaborate south Italian Kyries where the verse retains the neumatic style of the base text (see BTC II/1, pp. 15 and 28, *Auctor caelorum*.)

Notes on *Antra modicis deserti*

References: CT 7, pp. 75–76 (no. 8), 359, and 396 (pl. 32, Ben 35). Iversen shows how the text was cobbled together from two hymns to St. John Baptist: the famous *Vt queant laxis*, AH 50, no. 96 (ascribed to the Lombard Paul the Deacon, 730–99), and *Almi prophetae progenies*, AH 27, no. 137. Both texts were edited earlier in AH 2, nos. 52–53 and 54. Iversen cites the New Testament sources for John the Baptist's birth and martyrdom, to both of which the hymns refer.

Meter: The sapphic and alcaic meters of the text sources have been destroyed.

Source of text below: Ben 35

Santus.
[1] Antra modicis deserti nati abdita pendit.
S⟨an⟩c⟨tu⟩s.
[2] Abstruso uentris cubili regem manentem recubans.
S⟨an⟩c⟨tu⟩s.
[3] Genitus peremte loquele modulos organa uocis.
Dominus deus sabaoh.
[4] Per orbis uastis non fuit limphis iohannes genitus.
Pleni sunt celi et terra gloria tua.
[5] Celsi meritisque laue pudoris niuei martyr.
Osanna ___ in excelsis.
[6] Tramite lingue redura adultera fratris habere uxorem.
Benedictus qui uenit in nomine domini.
Osanna ___ in excelsis. ___

Iversen writes (my translation):

> This confused text . . . is placed at the head of the collection of Sanctus tropes in Ben 35, which is our only source. It is clear that the text, which relates to St. John Baptist, was composed of phrases taken from two hymns to St. John Baptist. . . . [See References, above.] But the order of the words and the meaning of the phrases—as well as their versification—have been disregarded in the Beneventan trope. With the help of the sources for the text, one can guess its general meaning.

I give no translation because no translation is possible. Whoever put the text together did not know what the words meant, except for their general drift. (There is no connection whatever between the base text of Sanctus and the added elements.) Iversen summarizes the drift of the verses as follows:

> [1–2] The text seems to refer to Elizabeth's conception and John's reaction in his mother's womb to Mary's voice when she visited Elizabeth. (Luke 1:7, 13, 15, 41)
>
> [3] . . . deals with the gift of speech that returns to Zacharias after John's birth, with an allusion at the same time to John as "the voice crying in the wilderness." (Luke 1:20, 22, 57–64; Matt. 3:1–3; Mark 1:2–8; John 1:23)
>
> [4] Here the text seems to speak of the greatness of John the Baptist. (Luke 1:76; Matt. 11:11–15; Luke 7:28)
>
> [5–6] On the martyrdom of John (Mark 6:16–29; Matt. 14:3–11).

Iversen locates the Beneventan trope text in the various stanzas of the two hymns cited. Based on her identification, the format below shows the derivation of every word from the trope in those hymns. (The AH text of the hymns is given, except where contemporary south Italian versions—those of MC 506 and Ott 145—present the variants used in the trope.)

[1] Antra[1] modicis[2] deserti[3] nati[4] abdita[5] pendit.[6]
[2] Abstruso[1] uentris[2] cubili[3] regem[4] manentem[5] recubans.[6]
[3] Genitus[1] perempte[2] loquele[3] modulos[4] organa[5] uocis.[6]
[4] Per[1] orbis[2] uastis[3] non[4] fuit[5] limphis[6] iohannes[7] genitus.[8]
[5] Celsi[1] meritisque[2] laue[3] pudoris[4] niuei[5] martyr.[6]
[6] Tramite[1] lingue[2] redura[3] adultera[4] fratris[5] habere[6] uxorem.[7]

*

AH 50, no. 96:

I.   Vt queant laxis resonare fibris
     Mira gestorum famuli tuorum
     Solue polluti labii reatum,
         Sancte Iohannes.

II. Nuntius celso ueniens Olympo
     Te patri magno fore nasciturum
     Nomen et uitae seriem gerendae
         Ordine promit.

III. Ille promissi dubius superni
     Perdidit promptae **modulos**[4] **loquelae**[3]
  [3] Sed reformasti **genitus**[1] **peremptae**[2]
         Organa[5] **uocis.**[6]

IV. [2] **Ventris**[2] **abstruso**[1] (*MC 506*) **recubans**[6] **cubili**[3] (*Ott 145*)
         Senseras **regem**[4] thalamo **manentem**[5]
         Hinc parens **nati**[4] mentis uterque
            Abdita[5] **pandit.**[6]
  [1]
V.   **Antra**[1] **deserti**[3] **modicis**[2] ab (*Ott 145*) annis
         Ciuium turmas fugiens petisti
         Ne leui saltem maculare uitam
            Famine posses.

VI. Praebuit . . .
VII. Ceteri tantum . . .

VIII. Non[4] fuit[5] uasti[3] spatium per[1] orbis[2]
      Sanctior quisquam genitus[8] Ioanne[7]
  [4] Qui nefas saecli meruit lauantem
         Fingere **lymphis.**[6]

IX.   O nimis felix **meritique**[2] **celsi**[1]
  [5] Nesciens **labem**[3] **niuei**[5] **pudoris**[4]
      Praepotens **martyr**[6] eremique cultor
         Maxime uatum.

X–XII. ....
AH 27, no. 137:
I.   Almi prophetae progenies pia
      Clarus parente et nobilior patre
      Quem matris aluus claudere nescia
      Ortus erilis prodidit indice

II–V. ....

VI.   Assertor aequi non ope regia
      Nec morte **dura**[3] **linquere**[2] **tramitem**[1]
  [6] Veni coactus, non licet, ait, tibi
         Vxorem[7] **habere**[6] **fratris**[5] **adulteram.**[4]

VII–VIII. ....

The compiler's method is beneath contempt, and the wider implications to be drawn from Iversen's brilliant detective work are depressing. Wherever in Benevento this piece was compiled, Latin texts for the liturgy—other than those of the ordinary itself—can have served for little more than sanctimonious gabble. Other cases of destructive borrowing have been discovered, but this is the worst. (Cf. the *Kyrie Rex Deus immense*, also found only in Ben 35, BTC II/1, pp. 71 and 186, and the first item in the ordinary collection of Bod 74, the Kyrie *Incarnatum quoque* [recte *Incarnate quoque*], BTC II/1, pp. 44 and 110.) At least these pieces were never copied, so far as we know; and perhaps they were seldom sung.

Sanctus 24
Thannabaur 197

Trope: *Caelestia sidera*

Hosanna¹ **Prosa:** *Plasmatum populum*
Hosanna² **Prosa:** *Dulcis est cantica*

SOURCES

*Benevento 35, fol. 196^{r-v} (eighth of sixteen collected Sanctus now surviving in the MS). *Caelestia sidera* is not included. Both prosas are copied without separate melismatic *Osanna in excelsis*.

*Benevento 34, fol. 176^{r-v} (after V. *Maiestas domini edificauit templum . . . et collaudauerunt dominum dicentes deus israhel. custodi.* of the off *Domine deus in simplicitate* and before *Agnus Dei . . . miserere nobis. Salus et uita* of the Dedication mass). The MS is not included in Thannabaur's list of sources for the Sanctus melody. As in Ben 35, both prosas are copied without separate melismatic *Osanna in excelsis*.

*Benevento 40, fol. 104^{r-v} (in the second set of propers for the Milanese saints Nazarius and Celsus—see commentary to Appendix I, p. 123, for full description). Truncated prosas are attached to a seemingly unique Sanctus melody, BTC-Scs 3 (? = Thannabaur 111, Var., pp. 129 and 149). The version is transcribed in Appendix I, p. 128.

NOTES ON THE MELODIES

References: Charles M. Atkinson, "Text and Music, and the Persistence of Memory in *Dulcis Est Cantica*," in *Recherches nouvelles sur les tropes liturgiques*, ed. Wulf Arlt and Gunilla Björkvall, Studia Latina Stockholmiensia 36, (Stockholm, 1993), pp. 96–117; CT 5, pp. 406–07, pls. 2 and 3; and MMMA 17, Th 197 (STr 24b, HPr 158, HPr 63). Cf. Thannabaur 89 and 111, especially the Nonantolan variants of Thannabaur 111 after melody 38, p. 129, and after melody 71, p. 149.

See BTC II/3, Thannabaur 111, Var., pp. 121 and 121, and Appendix I, pp. 123 and 128.

The Sanctus melody Thannabaur 197 is known from three sources only: Ben 35, Ben 34, and Mod 7—the last from the Ravenna-Forlimpopoli region. In all three, it is associated with the paired prosas *Hosanna Plasmatum populum* and *Hosanna Dulcis est cantica*. The neumes for the Sanctus melody in Ben 34 closely resemble those in Ben 35 and must have been copied from Ben 35 or a local source like it, although the somewhat altered prosa melody might have been copied from another exemplar. Further concordances between the ordinary chants of Ben 35 and Mod 7 exist. Probably the Sanctus melody with its prosas was borrowed from a central Italian source, like Mod 7, by the omnivorous editor of Ben 35.

In the earlier manuscript Ben 40, truncated prosas and some of the melismas for them were copied in an inconsistent manner and joined to BTC-Scs 3—which Sanctus melody, however, is related to the Nonantolan version of Thannabaur 111 in certain passages. (See References, above.) For technical reasons this version could not be laid out together with the versions of Ben 35 and Ben 34 and is therefore transcribed separately in Appendix I. In BTC II/3, the much altered version of Thannabaur 111 associated with *Hosanna Dulcis est cantica* in Ben 40 is referred to as "BTC-Scs 3 (? = Thannabaur 111, Var., pp. 129 and 149)." Atkinson has determined that a variant of Thannabaur 111 very different from that in Ben 40 but close to that in Ben 35 (q.v., p. 121) accompanies the second occurrence of *Dulcis est cantica* in the manuscript Apt 18, fol. 77^{r-v}, for the feast of the Dedication. (See "Text, Music," pp. 101–03, and CT 5, pls. 2 and 3.) Both *[Hosanna] Dulcis est cantica* and *[Hosanna] Plasmatum populum* were however associated with another Sanctus melody, Thannabaur 89, in almost all the many Aquitanian and Catalonian sources where they appear. Both share the same prosa tune, which Atkinson has demonstrated derives from the second Hosanna melisma of Thannabaur 89—which tune persisted even when the prosas were attached to Thannabaur 111 or 197. Thannabaur 197, the present Sanctus, must have originated in Italy and was almost certainly composed after the prosas were imported.

Neither of the two Benevento manuscripts supplies melismatic versions without prosa words for *Osanna in excelsis*. Only texted versions are given, wherein the opening *Osanna* is actually part of the prosa. While a singer prepared in advance might have omitted the prosa by jumping from the opening *Osanna* to the brief melisma that closes the text just before *in excelsis*, surely the scribes of Ben 35 and Ben 34 intended that only the texted Hosannas should be sung. (In other pieces found in both manuscripts, complete melismatic Hosannas *were* copied in addition to the texted prosas or prosulas that follow.)

The prosa melody as it stands in Ben 35 and 34 employs a well-defined sequence structure using paired lines. Indeed, pairing occurs at two levels, as in many sequences: *macro-pairing* (marked [⊕s1.¹] and [1.¹¹] in the typical text below) and *micro-pairing* (marked b and b' within the a b b' structure sketched under Meter, below). The latter might instead have been indicated as [1] [2].¹ [2].¹¹, but then the larger pairs could not have been shown. The structure of [⊕s1.¹] recurs as the first section of the second prosa and is therefore designated [1.¹¹]. The second prosa is rounded off by an *Abgesang* following the two preceding *Stollen*, [2] *Suscipe cum agmina:* [⊕s1.¹] [1.¹¹] [2]. The short, balanced melody, which perfectly matches the text, doubtless helped spread the prosas throughout southern France and into Italy. Its plagal range of a seventh, from A up to G (when the melody is notated with a D-final) avoids upper a, which might have suggested mode 1. Lesser cadences use the franculus idiom, C D D, in Ben 35 notated with the apostrophus ♪ ⁻ ⁻ (see Boe, "Beneventan Apostrophus"). The more important cadences at *excelsis* and *in hac aula* descend instead from F to D.

The Sanctus melody Thannabaur 197 incorporates motives from the prosa. The franculus cadence in neumatic form is present everywhere. Yet the Sanctus is not merely a stringing together of notes drawn from the prosa: it employs them in new ways. Although the Sanctus, whose range is just that of the prosa, lacks an extensive melisma for *Osanna in excelsis*, the prosas (especially the second) satisfy the need for climax in their own "prosaic" way.

The first half of the melody for the unique trope verse [+] *Cęlestia sydera* (which appears only in Ben 34) is borrowed from the half-line [2] . . . *angelorum carmina* in the second prosa. The trope verse was probably first meant as an addition to the second prosa, *Osanna dulcis est cantica*, as is suggested by the assonance, *Cęlestia sydera magna et infima*. Wherever inserted, the line makes little sense, especially as it appears here, isolated after *Dominus deus sabaoth* and before *Pleni sunt cęli*—however true it is that the heavens are full of celestial stars!

NOTES ON *Osanna plasmatum populum*
Osanna dulcis est cantica

References: AH 47, p. 343; Atkinson, "Text, Music"; CT 5, pp. 257–58, 373–74 and pls. 2 and 3 (from the MSS Apt 17 and Apt 18); CT 7, pp. 29–31, 109–11 (no. 48, I and IV), 159–60 (no. 111), 377 (pl. 13, PaN 1137), 380 (pl. 16, PaN 903), 381 (pl. 17, Apt 17), 387 (pl. 23, Hu 4), 391 (pl. 27, Mod 7), 357, 360, and 362; and Gunilla Iversen, "Osanna Dulcis Est Cantica. On a Group of Compositions Added to the Osanna in excelsis," in *Cantus planus: IMS Study Session à Tihany 1987*, ed. by Laszlo Dobszay (Budapest, 1990), pp. 275–96.

Meter:	Words	Music
[⊕s1.¹]	9pp	a
	4p + 8p	b
	4p + 7p	b'
[1.¹¹]	9pp	a
	4pp + 8pp	b"
	4pp + 8p	b(')
	6p	c
[2]	7pp + 7pp	d
	7p	b' (last part)

Source of text and translation below: Ben 35

Sanctus. Sanctus. Sanctus.
Dominus deus sabaoth.
Pleni sunt celi et terra gloria tua.

[⊕s1.¹] Osanna plasmatum populum
et qui uerum   fore promit ore christum
et qui cosmi   satorem permanentem ___
in excelsis.
Benedictus qui uenit in nomine domini.

[1.¹¹] Osanna dulcis est cantica
melliflua   nimisque laudabilia
organica   trinum et unum laudemus
omnes in hac aula.

[2.] Suscipe cum agmina angelorum carmina.
Sit dicat nunc osanna ___
in excelsis.

*

Holy, Holy, Holy,
Lord God of hosts.

34:([+]) *Celestia sydera magna et infima.*
Stars of heaven, great and very low—)
Heaven and earth are full of thy glory.

[⊕s1.¹] SAVE NOW the people thou hast formed,
Who declare thee to be the true Christ, (40: *Te qui*)
ever the lasting Creator of the world ___
in the highest.

[1.¹¹] HOSANNA is a sweet song,
Mellifluous, very praiseworthy,
sung with organa; let us all
in this hall, praise the Three and One!

[2] Receive [our] songs with [those] of the throngs
of angels,
that (34: *ut*) they may now sing (*dicant*) ___
in the highest.

Atkinson and CT 7 lists five non-Italian sources for *Hosanna Plasmatum populum*, three of which (PaN 1120, PaN 1118, and PaN 778) are Aquitanian, the first belonging to the late tenth or earlier part of the eleventh century. The others, Vich 105 and PaN 495, are Catalonian. All but one of these sources link it to *Hosanna Dulcis est cantica* within the same Sanctus melody. But *Hosanna Dulcis est cantica*, again according to Atkinson and CT 7, is found without *Hosanna Plasmatum populum* in eight other manuscripts, including the Aquitanian sources PaN 887, PaN 909, and PaN 903. It therefore seems likely that *Hosanna*

Dulcis est cantica, the prosa for the second Hosanna, was written first. At least it was copied by itself in PaN 887, a manuscript dated not later than 1032. If this date is indeed the *terminus ante quem* for the second prosa, then *Hosanna Plasmatum populum* might have been written a little later for the first Hosanna but using the same melody as *Hosanna Dulcis est cantica*. (Atkinson has confirmed this supposition by manuscript evidence: see "Text, Music," p. 97.) Whatever the precise origin of *Hosanna Plasmatum populum*, the pair are among the earliest Hosanna prosas or prosulas known, as Iversen remarks.

Hosanna Plasmatum populum employs *o* assonance. (In Romance-speaking countries, the pronunciation of Latin -*um* often approximated *o* or nasalized *o*.) *Hosanna Dulcis est cantica* employs *a* assonance, achieving it at the cost of conventional grammar: *cantica* is used as a feminine singular, but modified by the neuter plural adjective *laudabilia*, and *cum* is used with the accusative in the phrase *cum agmina*. In the first prosa, *ore* is rhymed internally with *fore*, the unusual future infinitive chosen for rhyme's sake in preference to *esse*.

Hosanna Plasmatum populum returns the word *Hosanna* to its literal Hebrew sense: "save now." On the other hand, *Hosanna Dulcis est cantica* treats *Hosanna* as the name for the song, a "sweet song," possibly made even sweeter and more praiseworthy as *cantica organica* by being sung in organum (or with the organ?). Iversen's work has greatly clarified how *Hosanna* was interpreted. She lists many later pieces deriving from these two types of interpretation.

In Ben 35, Ben 34, and Mod 7, the letters of *Te* are reversed, so that the second and third lines of [1].[I] now begin *Et* instead of *Te*. This reading violates the sense, removing the accusative subject of the infinitive *fore*, but points toward a possible source for the version of Ben 35. The scribe of the earlier manuscript Ben 40 wrote *Te* in his truncated version. The editor of Ben 35 therefore did not use Ben 40 as his exemplar in this case but must have used a central Italian version resembling that of the Ravennese manuscript Mod 7. Where the scribe of Ben 40 got his strange version—tucked among the partly Ambrosian propers for the Milanese saints Nazarius and Celsus, with its uniquely repeated *Pleni sunt celi* phrase and its unique variants of Thannabaur 111—cannot now be determined. That the only other known pairing of the prosa *Hosanna Dulcis est cantica* with Thannabaur 111 should be found in Apt 18—a manuscript which is thought to date from around the year 1000—is however suggestive.

Under Notes on the Melody, above, the isolated trope element [+] *Cęlestia sydera magna et infima* was mentioned as occurring only in Ben 34. Coming after *Dominus deus sabaoth* and before *Pleni sunt celi et terra gloria tua*, it seems out of place, all the more so because preceding trope elements for the Sanctus acclamations are absent. As stated above, the line was probably composed for insertion within the second Hosanna prosa, part of whose tune and whose assonance it borrows.

Conditor alme Domine, Hosanna[2] Prosula,   12
   See p. 55, *Altissime creator* = *Altissimeque rector*, Thannabaur 92.

Sanctus   29
Thannabaur 152 (=154, Vatican I)

Trope: *Corona iustitiae*

Hosanna[2] Prosula:
Gloria Christe omnes resurgamus

SOURCES

*Benevento 35, fol. 198[v] (fifteenth of sixteen collected Sanctus now surviving in the MS).

(*)Benevento 34, fols. 285[v]–286[r] (last of eight collected Sanctus: three with tropes, followed by two without tropes and—after Agnus Dei and a MS lacuna—by three more troped Sanctus of which this is the last). Clefs and colored lines were never added to the last group of three Sanctus, their notation remaining *in campo aperto*. In relation to three scarcely visible dry-point lines, the first note seems to have been intended as b :

So read, the melody is a fifth higher than in Ben 35. (In the facsimile edition of PM 15, the mark resembling a c clef, just after the first note, is in fact a hole in the MS.)

The music is almost the same as in Ben 35. Only the differing arrangement of the second *Osanna* with the beginning of the prosula *Gloria christe* and its end *sancta tibi in templo sancto in excelsis* are transcribed, pp. 30–31. The words of the version of Ben 34 are given as typical text in the commentary below, along with two melodic variants in letter notation for passages not included in the main text. (All variants are transcribed at the same pitch as the cleffed version of Ben 35, for ease of comparison.)

NOTES ON THE MELODIES

References: Levy, "Byzantine Sanctus," p. 24; MMMA 17, Th 152 (STr 40).

In BTC II/3, cf. Thannabaur 154 (=152) troped with *Deus fortis*, pp. 68 and 32, and troped with *Deus pater ingenitus*, pp. 71 and 38. Cf. the trope melody for *Corona iustitiae* with that for *Deus pater ingenitus*. For the melody used in the prosula *Gloria Christe omnes resurgamus*, see the Hosanna[2] melisma that follows *Deus fortis* on p. 37, where the words *Qui uenisti* are cued with the first notes of the melisma. The prosula *Qui uenisti carnem sumens*, complete, is printed with Thannabaur 154 (=152), *Deus pater ingenitus*, pp. 72 and 42–45.

Sanctus melody Thannabaur 152 differs from Thannabaur 154—the well-known Sanctus I of the Vatican edition—only in the opening acclamations, *Sanctus, Sanctus, Sanctus Dominus,* and in the first Hosanna. The rest of Thannabaur 152 is the same as Thannabaur 154 in its Beneventan version. It was clearly adapted from Thannabaur 154 and appears only in the two Beneventan sources, with the trope *Corona iustitiae* and the Hosanna² prosula *Gloria Christe omnes resurgamus.*

Sanctus Thannabaur 154 was sung at the highest feasts and often at Easter, as it still is today. When troped with *Deus pater ingenitus,* it was assigned to Christmas, Epiphany, and the Nativity of St. John Baptist in Urb 602, and it was entered among the propers of the Gregorian Easter-Day mass in Ben 40. Troped with *Deus fortis,* it was assigned to Easter and St. Peter's Day in Urb 602. These paschal associations of the Sanctus melody account for and clarify the intended paschal references of the new Sanctus trope and Hosanna prosula. The reference to Easter is obvious in the prosula but in the trope it is obscured by confused imagery.

The music for the trope verses beginning *Corona iustitiae* was adapted from *Deus pater ingenitus,* which in turn developed and expanded anaphoral-chant material in Thannabaur 154 (=152). (See References, above.) From the standpoint of the music, what was borrowed was satisfactorily integrated with the new text.

The Hosanna² prosula borrows the melody of another, *Qui uenisti carnem sumens,* which is attached only to Thannabaur 154 (=152). (See References, above.) In the present piece, however, the melismatic form of the prosula melody is not given intact as part of the last *Osanna in excelsis,* but only in its syllabic form with the text *Gloria Christe omnes resurgamus.* The scribe of Ben 34 placed the prosula in the middle of the last Hosanna, where a melisma might have been expected. The scribe of Ben 35, however, placed it after *Benedictus qui uenit in nomine domini* and before the last *Osanna in excelsis,* which is given its standard short form, as in the Vatican edition.

Ben 35 is an earlier manuscript than Ben 34. (Styles of notation and versions of tropes in the two manuscripts and their concordances amply support this conclusion.) In the present instance, it is easy to see that the Ben 35 version must be earlier than that of Ben 34. Twice, the scribe of Ben 35 supplied more notes than were needed for the syllables of his text: at [4] *Ebreorum proles procla**mant** dicentes* and at the end of the prosula, *in **tem**plo sancto.* (See the main text, pp. 30–31.) The first mistake was corrected in Ben 35 by addition of a superscript *ba,* yielding *proclamabant;* the second was corrected in Ben 34 by the omission of the unneeded repeated note. The latter mistake is the more interesting, because it strengthens the supposition that *Qui uenisti carnem sumens* was the model for *Gloria Christe omnes resurgamus.* In the presumed model, as notated in Urb 602, there are two repeated notes, D D , in the last phrase, just before the end:

C DF E F E DD C
tibi uoce indefessa

At the corresponding phrase in Ben 35, *in templo,* the syllable *tem-* has two distinct D's, the second of which is a liquescent, instead of the expected doubled note with liquescence: ⁓ . The two mistakes in Ben 35 were not the sort to have been made while copying from a correct exemplar, complete with new text, but rather while copying the melody alone, from a source having different words, and then adding new words beneath the borrowed melody as copied. From these mistakes it is clear that the version of Ben 35 is earlier than that of Ben 34. It is also clear that the arrangement of new text and borrowed music found in Ben 35 was almost certainly made fresh for that manuscript.

NOTES ON *Corona iustitiae*
Gloria Christe omnes resurgamus

References: AH 47, no. 360 (for the related prosula **Qui uenisti carnem sumens**); Terence Bailey, *Antiphon and Psalm in the Ambrosian Office,* Musicological Studies, 50/3 (Ottawa, 1994), pp. 313, 339, and 349; Terence Bailey and Paul Merkley, *The Antiphons of the Ambrosian Office,* Musicological Studies, 50/1 (Ottawa, 1989), pp. 57, 68, and 172 (no. 280); CAO #1934; CT 7, pp. 88–89 (no. 23, citing II Tim. 4:8 for the phrase *Corona iustitiae*), 172–73 (no. 129, for **Qui uenisti carnem sumens**), and 359.

In BTC II/3, see the prosula **Qui uenisti carnem sumens** with *Deus ingenitus,* Thannabaur 154 (=152), pp. 71 and 42–45. Also see pp. 55, 12, and 16 (*Altissime creator = Altissimeque rector,* Thannabaur 92), and pp. 98, 93, and 98 (*Quem cherubim atque seraphim + Cui pueri Hebraeorum,* Thannabaur 63) for the phrase *Hebraeorum proles* of Vs [4].

Meter: The trope is prose. The Hosanna² prosula has the pattern

| [Ps¹] | 11p | + | 9p | + | 11p |
| [II] | 11pp | + | 9pp | + | 9p |

Source of text and translation: Ben 34. Except for the passages given in the main text and the two variants transcribed below in letter notation at the pitch of the Ben 35 version, the melody of Ben 34 is the same as that of Ben 35.

In order to provide the liturgical context in which the trope is to be understood, the Easter proper preface from the Beneventan missal Lo 3511 (*olim* Ben 29), fols. 173ᵛ, 171ᵛ, and 174ᵛ, is given before the Sanctus text below. (See above, pp. xxx, 32, and 36–37.)

Vere dignum et iustum est equum et salutare.
Te quidem domine omni tempore ;
   sed in hac potissimum die gloriosius prędicare ;
   cum pascha nostrum immolatus est christus ;
   ipse uerus est agnus qui abstulit peccata mundi ;
Qui mortem nostram moriendo destruxit ;
   et uitam resurgendo reparauit ;
Et ideo cum angelis et archangelis
   cum thronis et dominationibus ;
Cumque omni militia cęlestis exercitus
   ymnum glorię tuę canimus
   sine fine dicentes ;

Sanctus. Sanctus. Sanctus Dominus.
[1] Corona iustitię angelica uoce proclamant.
Deus sabaoth.

[2] Qui sanctis tuis adorando dicebat.
Pleni sunt cęli et terra gloria tua.

[3] Rutilans ac benigna nostra forma pręcando dicebat.
Osanna in excelsis.

[4] Hebreorum proles proclamabant dicentes.
Benedictus qui uenit in nomine domini.

Osanna

[Ps^I]   **Gloria christe omnes resurgamus**
        mundi carmina proferamus
        tuam laudabilem crucem uenire.

[II]   **et ut agnoscamus mirabilia**
        ut saluet nos tua dextera
        sancta tibi in templo sancto

in excelsis.

        *

It is truly meet, right, and our bounden duty
at all times to proclaim thee, O Lord,
  but yet more gloriously on this day as Most Mighty:
    because Christ our Passover was sacrificed;
  For he is the very Lamb who has taken away
    the sins of the world;
Who by dying has destroyed our death,
    and by rising again has restored life;
Therefore, with angels and archangels,
    with thrones and dominions
    and with all the company of the heavenly army,
    we sing the hymn of thy glory,
      evermore saying:

"Holy, Holy, Holy Lord,
[1] The Crown of Righteousness!"
    With angelic voice they proclaim:

"God of hosts!"

[2] To whom (CT: *Cui*) by thy saints adored,
    they said (CT: *dicebant*):

"Heaven and earth are full of thy glory!"

[3] ? . . . . was saying:
"Hosanna in the highest!"

[4] The offspring of the Hebrews shouted, saying:
    "Blessed is he who comes in the name of the Lord.

Hosanna"

[Ps^I]   **Let us all arise in glory, O Christ,**
      let us offer the songs of the world,
      coming to thy precious cross:

[II]   **And so that we may acknowledge**
      thy wondrous works;
    so that thy right hand may save us—
  ? **[let there be] holy things to thee**
      in [thy] holy temple!

    (OR: **so that thy holy right hand**
    may save us in the temple hallowed to thee.)

"in the highest!"

Corona iustitie, "the crown of righteousness" (II Tim. 4:8), is the reward the faithful, persevering Christian will receive.

> The time of my departure is at hand. I have fought a good fight, I have finished my course, I have kept the faith: Henceforth there is laid up for me a crown of righteousness, which the Lord, the righteous judge, shall give me at that day: and not to me only, but unto all them also that love his appearing.

But in the trope, "Crown of Righteousness" is either a name for the victorious Christ or it refers to the diadem placed on his triumphant head. Isaiah 28:5 provides the model for the expression as a divine epithet, but with *corona gloriae* instead of *corona iustitiae*.

> In die illa erit Dominus exercituum [Dominus Deus Sabaoth!] corona gloriae et sertum exsultationis residuo populi sui . . .

The model is apt because "Crown of glory" as a name for God is associated with the epithet "Lord of hosts" found in Sanctus. There are still other biblical uses of the term "crown of glory": Isa. 62:3, "Et eris corona gloriae in manu Domini, et diadema regni in manu Dei tui"; Ps. 8:5–10, "gloria et honore coronasti eum," quoted in Heb. 2:7–8 and summarized in 2:9, "Videmus Iesum propter passionem mortis gloria et honore coronatum . . ."; also I Peter 5:4, "Et cum apparuerit princeps pastorum, percipietis immarcescibilem gloriae coronam."

The author of the trope, then, seems to have substituted *Corona iustitiae*, "Crown of Righteousness," recalled from the passage in II Timothy, for *Corona gloriae* from Isaiah 28:5, where the Lord of hosts is called the "Crown of glory" of his people. By transference, "Crown of Righteousness" becomes one of the name of God, an acclamation of the Savior.

Iversen's correction of Vs [2], *Cui sancti tui adorando dicebant*, probably shows how the line was in fact understood by the author, where *adorando* and the deponent *precando* in the next line function as Italian gerundive semi-participles: "To whom the saints, adoring, said." The dative *Cui* is needed for sense.

(*Qui* was certainly sometimes used as a "caseless" relative pronoun, even though *cui* has returned as a dative and genitive in modern Italian.) I have preferred to translate the rest of the line literally, treating *adorando* as a gerundive with *cui* and *sanctis tuis* as dative of agent.

I cannot translate Vs [3]. "Red"—*rutilum* in Ben 35, corrected to *rutilans*, "reddening," in Ben 34—refers somehow to the Easter office hymn *Aurora lucis rutilat*. (But cf. Isa. 63:2, *rubrum est indumentum tuum*, a passage sometimes read on Good Friday.) Further, it is uncertain whether *nostra forma*—that is, humankind—is the subject of *dicebat* or is meant as an ablative, referring to Christ "in our form." In this verse, the semi-literate tropist failed to make clear what he wanted to say.

Vs [4] is a standard "wandering verse" often found as an introduction to *Benedictus qui uenit*. (See the Scripture references describing the entrance into Jerusalem on Palm Sunday, as given in CT 7.)

Each of the four trope lines ends with a verb of saying: *proclamant, diceba(n)t, dicentes*. That is, the trope extends the celebrant's preface into the Sanctus itself. Within the context of the Easter Sanctus in which they are imbedded (see above), the enigmatic verses of this trope can be understood as anticipating the paschal summons of the prosula: "Let us all arise in glory, O Christ, to come to thy cross!" The lines following this in the prosula refer to texts connected with Easter: "Let us acknowledge thy wondrous works, that thy right hand may save us" derives from Ps. 97:1–2 (Ps. 98), *Cantate Domino canticum nouum, quia mirabilia fecit: saluabit sibi dextera eius*, and also from Ps. 117:16 (Ps. 118), *Dextera Domini fecit uirtutem, dextera Domini exaltauit me: non moriar, sed uiuam . . .* , the great Passover psalm. The last line, **sancta tibi in templo sancto**, perhaps alludes to the ancient admonition to communicants, *Sancta sanctis*; but see also I Cor. 3:17 and Eph. 2:21. (In [II] of the prosula, the musical phrase does not easily allow a break after the word *sancta* and before *tibi*; the music rather demands the division *ut saluet nos tua dextera / sancta tibi in templo sancto*.)

The paschal associations of the Sanctus melody, Thannabaur 152 (= 154), reinforce the Eastertide references in the prosula *Gloria Christe omnes resurgamus*. But it is by no means clear that the trope *Corona iustitiae* also refers to Easter—in spite of my attempts to read it in this sense. Another interpretation of the trope is possible.

In Ambrosian vespers of St. Stephen (26 December), the antiphon on the psalms reads *Coronavit te Dominus corona iustitiae: et dedit tibi nomen sanctum gloriae* (thus in Suñol's edition of the Milanese evening office, *Liber Vesperalis Mediolanensis*, p. 101; the text was also used at vigils and matins of St. Stephen—see the citations of Bailey and Merkley in References, above). No text survives for an old Beneventan office of St. Stephen. (See Kelly, *The Beneventan Chant*, pp. 61–62 and 94, for what little is known of the old Beneventan office.) It is however possible and even likely that such a prominent Ambrosian text found employment in the southern Lombard "Ambrosian" rite, if not for Stephen or Vincent (another Milanese assignment of the text), then for a pool of texts for any martyr saint. The text appears inconspicuously as one of several psalm antiphons at lauds of the common of one martyr in Hartker's and the Rheinau antiphoners, CAO #1934, where it is given the more closely scriptural third-person form, *Coronauit eum Dominus corona iustitiae et dedit illi nomen sanctum gloriae* (II Tim. 4:8 and Phil. 2:10). It does not, however, appear in Ben 21, the (Gregorian) Benevento antiphoner also catalogued in CAO.

It is easier to imagine that the Benevento tropist lifted the phrase *corona iustitiae* from a remembered and familiar liturgical text associated with the occasion his trope was destined for—a martyr saint or the protomartyr Stephen—than that he should have discovered or remembered the phrase directly from scripture. The opaque second trope verse, *Qui sanctis tuis adorando dicebat*, mentions the saints and in this interpretation acquires a veneer of suitability. *Rutilans* (or *rutilum* in Ben 35) in the third verse might refer to the martyr's blood. If we suppose the text destined for the feast of a martyr in Eastertide, both prosula and trope take on emblematic relevance.

Cui pueri Hebraeorum, 93
  See p. 98, *Quem cherubim atque seraphim*,
  Thannabaur 63.

Sanctus
Thannabaur 154 (=152); Vatican I 32

Trope: *Deus fortis*

Hosanna² prosula cued in Urb 602:
Qui uenisti ⟨carnem sumens⟩

Sources

*BAV Urb. lat. 602, fols. 65ᵛ–66ᵛ (sixth of twelve collected Sanctus). Rubric:
  In resurrectione domini. Et s̄ci petri.

*Cologny-Geneva, Bodmer 74, fols. 121ᵛ–122ʳ (second of nine collected Sanctus). Rubric: A̅L̅.

Altar Book Incipit

Montecassino Compactiones, a single loose folio formerly in Compactio VI (the sole Sanctus incipit, after Sursum corda and the standard Cassinese Sunday and festival chant for the common preface, and before the exordium and Lord's Prayer). Precisely diastematic notation *in campo aperto* with many liquescents, suggesting a Cassinese origin between 1060 and 1090. The leaf may not be from a missal: the preface and Sanctus incipit are immediately followed by the complex introducing the Lord's Prayer, without intervening canon. See pl. 1, p. lxxvii, and Cassinese Sources, p. 3, above; also see Brown, *Hand List,* p. 92.

The apparent whole step between the last note of the first *Sanctus* and the first note of the second *Sanctus* (properly on the same pitch in this melody) enabled the scribe to render the triad outline of the third *Sanctus* with correct diastematy in the limited space available and still show the proper relationship between the first *Sanctus* and the end of the preface. At the pitch level employed in the main text for Thannabaur 154, pp. 32 and 38, the end of the preface and Sanctus incipit, with its "mistake" corrected, read:

```
     ℓ           ℓ                          ↗
  C  ED E    F  D   D C E  DC DE D  F EE E    E DE E
Cum quibus et nostras uoces ut admitti iubeas deprecamur

     ℓ         ℓ
  F  ED E    F EDC CD   E DE D
supplici confessi o   ne dicentes.

   ℓ                         ↗            ℓ      ℓ
  E   DEDC     CDE   DEDDC  C    E            G FG G
S⟨an⟩c⟨tu⟩S.  S⟨an⟩c⟨tu⟩S. S⟨an⟩c⟨tu⟩S · · · ⟨dominus⟩
```

Fragment of rubric in top left margin: ⟨dom⟩inicā [?]

NOTES ON THE MELODY

References: Boe, "Ordinary in English," 1:418–29 and 3:106–15; Hiley, "Ordinary of Mass Chants in English, Northern French and Sicilian MSS," p. 104; Ireland 1:118–20 and 2:23–27; MMMA 17, Th 154 (STr 52 and 222, HPr 180); and Planchart 1:277–81 and 2:319–24.

In BTC II/3, cf. this Sanctus melody joined with the trope *Deus pater ingenitus,* pp. 71 and 38; also cf. Thannabaur 152, a variant of the present Sanctus with the trope *Corona iustitiae* and the Hosanna² prosula *Gloria Christe omnes resurgamus,* pp. 65 and 29. Cf. BTC II/3, pp. 121 and 122 (Thannabaur 216, Var.), for a melody similarly expanded from anaphoral chant. Also see pl. 1, p. lxxvii. In BTC II/1, see the excursus on anaphoral chant and the references to Levy, "Byzantine Sanctus," p. xvi; in BTC II/3, see p. xxxvii.

The Sanctus melody was sung everywhere in France, Norman Sicily, and Italy. It is found in many of the earliest manuscripts having ordinary melodies. According to Thannabaur's index, it was rare in east Francia: he lists only one early east Frankish manuscript dated 1001, Ba 5 from Reichenau. (The impression he gives is not entirely correct, since Thannabaur omits several important early adiastematic manuscripts from his index.) In Italy, the melody was sung on Easter, Christmas, and other high feasts, and was associated especially with the trope *Deus fortis* (eighteen Italian sources in Thannabaur) and *Deus pater ingenitus* (ten Italian sources). The Sanctus incipit, without trope, is given as the continuation of the Sunday chant for the common preface in a Cassinese fragment dating from the years 1060–90 (see Altar Book Incipit and References, above). The later popularity of this Sanctus melody at Montecassino is attested by its inclusion as the first and sixth Sanctus of the twelve in Urb 602 and as the first of six in MC 546.

In only two of the thirty-four Italian occurrences cited by Thannabaur is the Sanctus not troped. On the other hand, Thannabaur lists twelve French and Norman-Sicilian sources for *Deus pater ingenitus* and only three French sources for *Deus fortis.*

The Sanctus melody undoubtedly grew from anaphoral-chant formulas. It expands their tonal regions upward from the kernel G a b (or C D E, as pitched in Bod 74) to top e and even f (or to a and even b or b-flat in Bod 74). In the Vatican edition, where the final is b (equivalent to E in Bod 74), the melody is assigned to mode 4, transposed, but the final is of little importance for the melody. Its patterns are not typical of mode 4, even though the note a functions as reciting note (in the untransposed mode with final of E, as in Bod 74).

Trope elements [1], [2], and [3], attached to successive acclamations, restate the melodic substance of Sanctus in balanced and contrasting ways characteristic of the best tropes. But element [4] uses different material, is longer, and has a wider range than elements [1–3]. It is true that the melodies for trope elements [4–9] develop motifs from *Pleni sunt cęli et terra gloria tua* and *Benedictus qui uenit in nomine domini.* But the entire complex of base text and trope employs the melodic field for singing Te Deum laudamus, in its turn derived from anaphoral chant. The relationship is a significant one. Te Deum laudamus is thought to be related to prefatory and post-Sanctus texts of early eucharistic anaphora, especially paschal anaphora. (See the references to Kähler, below.) Thannabaur lists verses [4–9] as a separate trope, his Tr. 222, although all his Italian instances link these verses with *Deus fortis.* (And in all Italian instances, elements [4–9] are associated with Thannabaur 154.) Neither text nor music of verses [4–9] are typical of Sanctus tropes; they undoubtedly belong to an earlier stage of the liturgy than most tropes and may be pre-Gregorian. They need further study.

Although the Sanctus melodies in Bod 74 and Urb 602 are nearly identical, their trope melodies sometimes diverge, so that neither version could have been copied from the other or even from a common exemplar. Such divergence can be seen in Vs [2]: *Filius excelsus dei patris* ends on D in Urb 602, but [2] *filius excelsis* ends on C in Bod 74.

NOTES ON *Deus fortis*

References: CP 1:xxx and no. 1261; CT 7, pp. 38, 95–97 (no. 34, showing the partial and intermingled distribution of trope elements in the different MSS, and citing II Sam. 22:3, *Deus fortis meus* in the Vulgate, as a source for Vs [1]), 172–73 (no. 129, **Qui uenisti carnem sumens**), 351–54, 365 (pl. 1, SG 484), 373 (pl. 9, Lo 13), and 393 (pl. 29, RoC 1741); Ireland, 1:118–20 and 2:23–27; Kähler, *Studien zum Te Deum,* especially p. 37; Levy, "Byzantine Sanctus," pp. 23–24; and PL 85:484.

For related liturgical texts, cf. *Hagios o Theos, Sanctus Deus. Hagios Ischyros. Sanctus Fortis* . . . of the Good Friday liturgy and Te Deum laudamus. See BTC II/3, pp. 72–74 and 42–45, for the prosula cued in Urb 602, **Qui uenisti carnem sumens,** with complete text from Urb 602, fol. 61ᵛ.

The trope is prose.

Source of text and translation below: Urb 602

Sanctus.
[1]   Deus fortis.
Sanctus.
[2]   Filius excelsus dei patris.
Sanctus dominus.
[3]   Spiritus sanctus qui regnas in trinitate.
Deus sabaoth.
[4]   Te laudat /
       Te adorat /
       Te glorificat
       Omnis creatura tua.
Pleni sunt cęli et terra gloria tua.
[5]   Tu ergo salua nos domine
       qui redemisti nos.
Osanna in excelsis.
[6]   Tuum est domine regnum tua potestas.
[7]   Tibi omnes angeli Et archangeli.
[8]   Tibi omnis tua sancta proclamat ecclesia.
Benedictus qui uenit in nomine domini.
[9]   Tibi honor et imperium per cuncta secula.
Osanna _____ in excelsis.
   [⊕s] **Qui uenisti** . . . .

*

Holy,
[1]   Mighty God;
Holy,
[2]   Exalted Son of God the Father;
Holy Lord,
[3]   Spirit holy, who reignest in the Trinity:
God of hosts!
[4]   All thy creatures
       praise thee,
       worship thee,
       glorify thee:
Heaven and earth are full of thy glory.
[5]   Save us therefore, O Lord,
       thou who hast redeemed us.
Hosanna in the highest!
[6]   Thine, O Lord, is the kingdom,
       thine the power!
[7]   To thee all angels and archangels,
[8]   To thee all thy holy church proclaims:
Blessed is he that comes in the name of the Lord!
[9]   To thee be honor and dominion
       throughout all ages;
Hosanna _____ in the highest!
   [⊕s] **Thou who didst come** . . .

The trope *Deus fortis* is not found in any manuscript from the city of Benevento, although Sanctus Thannabaur 154 with its other famous trope *Deus pater ingenitus* was introduced there early. The editor of Ben 35 probably omitted Thannabaur 154 with one or the other trope in favor of his own arrangement of Thannabaur 154 for Eastertide, namely Thannabaur 152 with *Corona iustitiae* (see pp. 65 and 29), although he might just have included Thannabaur 154 with either trope (or possibly both of them) on one or more of the folios now missing from the Ben 35 Sanctus collection. Moreover, the editor of Ben 34, who included much other material that was sung at Montecassino, likewise omitted *Deus fortis* in favor of Thannabaur 152 with *Corona iustitiae,* in this respect presumably following Ben 35.

In central and southern Italy, the first three lines of *Deus fortis* were usually joined to lines [4–9], beginning *Te laudat / Te adorat,* whereas in east Frankish, west Frankish, Norman-Sicilian, and a few north Italian sources, *Deus fortis* is found alone or linked to other texts but not to *Te laudat / Te adorat,* which is found only in Italy. The complicated distribution in different regions of these trope elements and of others not found in south Italian manuscripts is shown by Iversen in CT 7 (see References, above). Her study corrects the skewed impression given by Thannabaur's index—which omits many early adiastematic sources—that the trope was almost unknown in east Francia.

Although each of the first three verses acclaims one of the Persons of the Trinity, after the fashion of most Sanctus tropes, the opening concise reference to the western Good Friday liturgy—*[H]Agios o Theos* ("Holy God, Holy Mighty, Holy Immortal"), an acclamation used more generally in the East and in non-Roman western liturgies—is unusual. Yet in a trope for Easter it is extraordinarily apt. The Easter *laudes* of Christ the Victor begin in Vs [4] with acclamations related to the "we praise thee, we worship thee, we glorify thee" phrases of Gloria in excelsis. But here the "we" forms are changed to third-person declarations of praise, modeled in syntax on that section of Te Deum laudamus following the internal triple Sanctus within Te Deum:

GLORIA IN EXCELSIS	TROPE, Vs [4]
Laudamus te.	Te laudat /
Benedicimus te.	
Adoramus te.	Te adorat /
Glorificamus te	Te glorificat omnis creatura.

TE DEUM LAUDAMUS
Te gloriosus Apostolorum chorus:
Te Prophetarum laudabilis numerus:
Te Martyrum candidatus laudat exercitus.

There is no *Te benedicit* to match *Benedicimus te* of Gloria in excelsis, perhaps in order not to anticipate *Benedictus qui uenit* of the base Sanctus text.

Vs [5] *Tu ergo salua nos domine qui redemisti nos* appropriately precedes the first Hosanna, in Hebrew meaning "salua, saluifica." This verse also resembles certain other verses of Te Deum laudamus:

> Tu ad liberandum suscepturus hominem
>   non horruisti Virginis uterum.
> ....
> Te ergo quaesumus, tuis famulis subueni,
>   quos pretioso sanguine redemisti.
> Aeterna fac cum sanctis tuis in gloria numerari (munerari).
> Saluum fac populum tuum Domine,
>   et benedic hereditati tuae.

Vs [6] quotes part of the doxological addition to the Lord's Prayer, *Tuum est domine regnum, tua potestas*, and is followed by two verses that are very like these verses of Te Deum laudamus:

> Tibi cherubim et Seraphim incessabili uoce proclamant:
> ....
> Te per orbem terrarum sancta confitetur Ecclesia.
>
> *
>
> [7] Tibi omnes angeli Et archangeli.
> [8] Tibi omnis tua sancta proclamat ecclesia.

Vs [9] is a final doxology preceding the second *Osanna in excelsis*.

These verses constitute an independent hymn, a miniature Te Deum laudamus, inserted into Sanctus so as to reinforce the base text in an Easter context. As suggested earlier, the text of [4–9] may once have functioned as a post-Sanctus in a pre-Gregorian or non-Gregorian Italian liturgy, a text preserved in the guise of an Easter trope. Kähler (p. 37; see References, above), following Dom Cagin, quotes an Easter *illatio* or preface from the Mozarabic rite (PL 85, p. 484; CP 1261, but see CP 1:xxx).

> Unde merito illi omnes angeli
>   omnesque sancti non cessant clamare quotidie ita dicentes
> Te celi celorum,
> Te potestates,
> Te throni et virtute laudant.
> Tibi cetus angelorum in excelsis concinunt hymnum.
> Tibi Cherubin ac Seraphin incessabili voce proclamant dicentes
> Agyos Agyos Agyos Kyrie Otheos.
> Sanctus Sanctus Sanctus, Dominus Deus Sabaoth.
> Pleni sunt celi et terrae gloria majestatis tue.
> osanna filio David.
> Benedictus qui venit in nomine Domini,
> osanna in excelsis.
> Agyos Agyos Agyos.
> Te Domine laudat omnis virtus celorum et exercitus angelorum.
> Tibi hymnum depromunt melliflua carmina sanctorum.
> Tibi psalant choree Virginum et cetus confessorum.
> Tibi genua curvant celestia, terrestria, Et inferna.
> Laudant te Regem omnium seculorum.
> Osanna in excelsis.

The resemblance to verses [4–9] of *Deus fortis* is striking. Yet this Spanish *illatio*, known to us only from a sixteenth-century edition, can hardly have supplied their direct source. Some Gallican, north Italian, or Ravennate *immolatio* must lie behind them.

Sanctus 38
Thannabaur 154 (=152); Vatican I

Trope: *Deus pater ingenitus*

Hosanna[2] Prosula: *Qui uenisti carnem sumens*

SOURCES

*Benevento 40, fol. 26[r] (following the verse *Ibi confregit . . . illuminans tu mirabiliter a montibus eternis. Alleluia* of the *of Terra tremuit* and before *Agnus dei . . . miserere nobis. ū Rex regum* of the Gregorian mass for Easter Day). Diastematy of large intervals is compressed for lack of space *in campo aperto*. Perhaps a feigned low B-flat should be sung at [2] *Filius eius unigenitus*: the note B occurs nowhere else in the piece nor in any other version.

*Cologny-Geneva, Bodmer 74, fol. 121[r-v] (first of nine collected Sanctus). Rubric:

> INCIPIUNT $\overline{SCS}$. $\overline{SCS}$. $\overline{CU}$ $\overline{VR}$.

*Montecassino 546, fol. 67[v] (first of six collected Sanctus). This version differs from all other south Italian versions in that it breaks up the Hosanna[2] melisma into sections, each of which is attached to the last syllable of the preceding prosula segment, prefiguring the melody of the next segment of text.

BAV Urb. lat. 602, fol. 61[r-v] (first of twelve collected Sanctus). The words of this version are given as the typical text, below. The shorter alternative second *Osanna in excelsis* (as found in Ben 40 and Bod 74 for use without the prosula) does not appear, but the extended Hosanna[2] melisma is given before **Qui uenisti carnem sumens**. Rubric:

> In $\overline{nat}$. In $\overline{epipha}$
> Natiū $\overline{s}$. iohis $\overline{bap}$.

Melodic variants in Urb 602 from the version of Ben 40 (printed in the main text) are given immediately below, except for mere variant neume forms and indications for liquescence.

>   DEDD C
> [2] Filius dei   unigenitus.
>
>   DG   aaG
> [3] Spiritus paraclitus
>   GF G GaG
> Pleni sunt cęli et
>   EDE E   GF
> Osanna in excelsis. in nomine

In the second Hosanna, the twenty-third and fifty-sixth notes, counted as they occur in the Ben 40 version, read D, not E; similarly in the prosula:

>   D   D
> pro totius Vt possimus

Benevento 34, fol. 285[r-v] (seventh of eight collected Sanctus—three with tropes followed by two without tropes and, after Agnus Dei and a MS lacuna, by three more troped Sanctus of which this is the second). Clefs and colored lines for pitch were never added to the last group of three Sanctus, the notation remaining *in campo aperto*. The musical text is almost exactly the same as in Urb 602, but the wording [2] *Filius eius* found in Ben 40 and Bod 74 is used instead of the Cassinese wording *Filius dei*, as in Urb 602 and MC 546. The words *in excelsis* have been clumsily intruded at the beginning of the Hosanna² melisma (which has the same notes as in Urb 602, except for the omission of the last three, DEE, the twenty-third and fifty-sixth notes reading D̪. But the prosula has *pro totius* and *ut possimus* as in Ben 40 and MC 546, suggesting that the scribe copied the Hosanna² melisma from a version like Urb 602 and the prosula text from another, like Ben 40 or MC 546. The final word to complete the prosula text, *osanna*, is also omitted, so that the concluding prosula lines read *ut possimus laudes promere tibi uoce indefessa in excelsis*.

ALTAR BOOK INCIPIT

Montecassino Compactiones, a single loose folio formerly in Compactio VI (the sole Sanctus incipit). See the description of the source in the immediately preceding commentary for *Deus fortis*, pp. 68–69.

NOTES ON THE MELODY

References: MMMA 17, Th 154 (STr 55, HPr 180). See the references for the Sanctus melody in the immediately preceding commentary for *Deus fortis*, p. 69.

The melody for Sanctus Thannabaur 154, whether troped with *Deus fortis* (q.v., pp. 32–37) or with *Deus pater ingenitus*, reads almost exactly the same in all the sources used in this edition. The agreement between them is astonishing.

The melodies for trope verses [1–3] of *Deus pater ingenitus* use the same anaphoral-chant derived material as the Sanctus melody and the three opening verses of *Deus fortis*. The association of *Deus pater ingenitus* with Thannabaur 154 is nearly universal: the five instances with Thannabaur 216 (see BTC II/3, pp. 121 and 122) are all Aquitanian and mostly from Limoges. A single instance of its association with Thannabaur 103 is late.

NOTES ON *Deus pater ingenitus*

Qui uenisti carnem sumens

References for *Deus pater ingenitus*: Boe, "Ordinary in English," 2:418–22 and 3:106–14; CT 7, pp. 38, 101–03 (no. 40, with citations of trinitarian formulations in the creeds, the writings of the Fathers, and the liturgy), 351, 353, 356, 358, 362, 365 (pl. 1, SG 484), 370 (pl. 6, Ox 775), and 395 (pl. 31, MC 546); Hiley, "Ordinary of Mass Chants in English, North French and Sicilian MSS," p. 104; Ireland, 1:132 and 2:48–50; *New Grove* 16:464–65; and Planchart, 1:277–79, 281, and 2:9, 19, 319–20. See BTC II/3, pp. 121 and 122 (Thannabaur 216, Var.), with which Sanctus melody *Deus pater ingenitus* was sometimes associated.

References for *Qui uenisti carnem sumens*: AH 47, no. 360; Boe, "Ordinary in English," 1:445–50 and 3:109, 121; CT 7, pp. 172–73 (no. 129) and 395 (pl. 31, MC 546); Iversen, "Pax et Sapientia," p. 49, ff.; and Planchart 2:320, 324.

See BTC II/3, pp. 68 and 32 (*Deus fortis*, Thannabaur 154 [=152]), with **Qui uenisti carnem sumens** cued in Urb. 602, and pp. 65 and 29 (*Corona iustitiae*, Thannabaur 154 [=152]), where **Gloria Christe omnes resurgamus** is set to the melody of **Qui uenisti carnem sumens**. Also see BTC II/3, pp. 82 and 64 (*Quem cherubim et seraphim non cessant*, Thannabaur 223), where the prosula **Pie Christe descendisti** is set to an altered version of the same melody.

The trope *Deus pater ingenitus* is prose.
Meter of the prosula *Qui uenisti carnem sumens*:

	Words	Melody
[♂Ps¹]	(11p + 9p + 11pp)	a a' b
[II]	(11p + 9pp + 11p)	a a' b

Source of text and translation below: Urb 602

Sanctus.
[1]   Deus pater ingenitus.

Sanctus.
[2]   Filius dei unigenitus.

Sanctus dominus.
[3]   Spiritus paraclitus ex utroque procedens.
Deus sabaoth.

Pleni sunt cęli et terra gloria tua.
Osanna in excelsis.
Benedictus qui uenit in nomine domini.

Osanna ———————————————
[♂Ps¹]   Qui uenisti carnem sumens ex matre./
              pro totius mundi salute./
              Tu nos ab hoste potenter libera./

[II]   Et exaudi cunctos famulos tuos./
              Vt possimus laudes promere
              tibi uoce indefessa. Osanna.

In excelsis.

                              *

Holy
[1]   God, the Father unbegotten;

Holy
[2]   Son of God, the only-begotten;

Holy Lord,
[3]   Paraclete—Breath proceeding from Both:
God of hosts!
....

Blessed is he that comes in the name of the Lord.

Hosanna ———————————————

[♂Ps¹] Thou who cam'st, taking flesh from [thy] mother,
           for the salvation of the whole world;
           mightily deliver us from the enemy!

[II]   And give ear to all thy servants,
             that we may be able to utter praises
             to thee with unwearied voice. Hosanna

in the highest!

Each of the trinitarian verses [1–3] of *Deus pater ingenitus* is attached to a Sanctus acclamation, these verses themselves grouped "three in one." If not indeed the earliest Sanctus trope, this is among the earliest. Certainly it was among those most copied and everywhere distributed. Iversen lists thirty-eight sources having the three elements [1], [2], and [3] only. Their origin must surely be north of the Alps.

To these core verses various additions were made, as can be seen in the CT 7 concordances. Some of the added verses were acclamatory. But only two texts for Hosanna seem to have been attached to *Deus pater ingenitus*: *[Hosanna] Omnes tua gratia* (see pp. 110 and 106) and (in south Italian sources that have *Deus pater ingenitus*) *Qui uenisti carnem sumens*, a prosula for Christmastide. *Deus pater ingenitus* and *Qui uenisti carnem sumens* were entered among the Gregorian propers for Easter Day in Ben 40, the earliest gradual surviving from Benevento. The two texts were also copied in the Roman gradual Bod 74 (completed in 1071) and as the first Sanctus in the Cassinese collections Urb 602 and MC 546. If the scribe of Ben 35 omitted it—folios have been lost from his collection—he left it out in order to advance his own Easter version of the same Sanctus melody, namely, Thannabaur 152 with *Corona iustitiae* and the prosula *Gloria Christe omnes resurgamus*, the latter using the melody of *Qui uenisti carnem sumens* (see References, above). The scribe of Ben 34 seems to have copied *Deus pater ingenitus* and *Qui uenisti carnem sumens* partly from a Cassinese source and partly from a local source at Benevento, perhaps Ben 35.

While the three core verses of *Deus pater ingenitus* must have entered Italy from north of the Alps, the prosula *Qui uenisti carnem sumens* must be Italian. It is known from only two other manuscripts besides the five south Italian sources listed: Mod 7, from the Forlimpopoli-Ravenna area, and RoV C 52. In both these sources it comes after the trope *Cuius in laude* (not used in south Italy) and attached to Thannabaur 223 (see pp. 82 and 64).

The prosula *Qui uenisti carnem sumens* is Italian then, but from where in Italy? The music for the third lines of both tercets of the similarly constructed south Italian prosula *Pie Christe descendisti* is exactly the same as for the corresponding lines of *Qui uenisti carnem sumens*, namely [₵Ps¹] . . . *tu nos ab hoste potenter libera* and [ᴵᴵ] . . . *tibi uoce indefessa Osanna*. (The music for the other lines is not quite so similar.) *Pie Christe descendisti* must be south Italian in origin, seeing that it appears only in Urb 602, Ben 35, and Ben 34. All these manuscripts are later than Ben 40 and Bod 74. *Pie Christe descendisti* must therefore be the later of the two prosulas. Music for its last line must have been borrowed from *Qui uenisti carnem sumens*, not vice versa. Hence, *Qui uenisti carnem sumens* must have been sufficiently liked in southern Italy to have served as a model for a new piece. Still, the ultimate source of *Qui uenisti carnem sumens* remains in doubt; it might have been a borrowed favorite.

It is unlikely that *Qui uenisti carnem sumens* could have been written near Ravenna or at the Abbey of Sant'Eutizio or elsewhere in central Italy, and thence exported south. First, the Roman manuscript Bod 74 has several other ordinary-trope concordances with Mod 7 and RoV C 52. But Bod 74 here squarely follows south Italian custom in linking the prosula to *Deus pater ingenitus* and Thannabaur 154, rather than to *Cuius in laude* and Thannabaur 223, as in those central Italian sources. Second, both music and words of this prosula are remarkably alike in all five south Italian sources. Ben 40, Bod 74, and Urb 602 cannot be far removed from their ultimate source. On the other hand, mistakes have crept into Mod 7 and RoV C 52 (see CT 7), which manuscripts must be a step further removed from their original.

A Roman origin for *Qui uenisti carnem sumens* is equally unlikely. All other Sanctus tropes in Bod 74—with perhaps the exception of the Easter verses *Hodie Dominus Iesus Christus resurrexit a mortuis* appended to Thannabaur ?64 (cf. 60,66,67)—were imported. (See Appendix II, pp. 124 and 131.) Ordinary tropes are not found at all in other old Roman manuscripts, except for Kyrie verses. Since it appears in Ben 40, the prosula must have been written before about 1050, and such an early origin for a Hosanna prosula at Rome is almost out of the question.

Benevento and Montecassino seem to remain as possible sources. At Santa Sofia in Benevento, an eclectic repertory of tropes and prosulas attached to the Gregorian tradition was being explored, while at the same time an attempt was made to preserve something of the old Beneventan chant, as the repertory of Ben 40 shows. But the scribe of Ben 40 did not understand how to copy the prosas *Osanna plasmatum populum / Osanna dulcis est cantica* (see Appendix I, pp. 123 and 128). A scriptorium so inexperienced in the technique of Hosanna prosulas as to allow these famous pieces to be mangled could hardly have been capable of creating the polished and effortless *Qui uenisti carnem sumens*. Moreover, this prosula is assigned to Easter in Ben 40, although it was obviously meant for Christmas. (The rubrics of Urb 602 assign it to Christmas, the Epiphany, and the Nativity of St. John Baptist.) Montecassino, then, must be the source for *Qui uenisti carnem sumens*—imperial, pre-Desiderian Montecassino from 1025 to 1050, from which so few liturgical documents survive, but where knowledge of northern techniques of sequence and prosula composition might be expected.

The sense and wording of the lines follow the spare, elegant structure of the Roman collect: address, petition, and result clause. (See BTC II/1, pp. xxxi, 17, 37, and 69). The address consists of the first two lines, *Qui uenisti carnem sumens ex matre / pro totius mundi salute !* ; the petition, of the third and fourth lines, *Tu nos ab hoste potenter libera / Et exaudi cunctos famulos tuos !* ; and the result clause, of the fifth and sixth lines, *Vt possimus laudes promere tibi uoce indefessa. Osanna*. Lastly, the third line of each tercet begins with the second-person pronoun, *tu* or *tibi*, and ends with *a* assonance.

This prosula can justly be called a miniature masterpiece. Each of the two tercets has the same number of syllables, respectively, in the corresponding lines.

[♪Ps^I] (11p + 9p + 11pp)
            +
[II]   (11p + 9pp + 11p)

             a   a'   b

The accentuation of the words of the first lines (11p) of each tercet corresponds exactly.

   Qui uenísti cárnem súmens ex mátre
   Et exaúdi cúnctos fámu- los túos

   (Pí-e Chríste descen-dísti ad térram
   Dý-ra iúra íp- sa déxtra con-cúlcans)

One of the second lines of the tercets ends with a paroxytone, *salúte*, and the other with a proparoxytone, *prómere*—a difference easily accommodated by the descending melodic cadence, F E D. The melody for the third lines of the tercets is skillfully adjusted by the insertion of a two-note neume for the varying accentuation of the first four syllables:

Tu	nos	ab	hos-	te	po-	tén-	ter	li-	be-	ra
Ti-	bi	uo-	ce	in-	de-	fés-	sa	o-	san-	na
(in-	fer-	ni	por-	tas	con-	frín-	ges	for-	ti-	ter
ut-	ti-	bi	sem-	per	de-	cán-	tent	o-	san-	na)

The refined melodic technique developed for the Frankish prosa has been brilliantly transferred to a miniature of six lines whose verbal content, in Italian fashion, follows the paradigm of the Roman collect. Melody and meter group the lines 3 + 3; collect structure and meaning group them 2 + 2 + 2; the conjunction *Et* is located precisely where the two conflict, like the barline between two ¾ measures that are to be understood as one measure of 3/2. This *Et* is not superfluous: it is the keystone linking meter and meaning.

Dulcis est cantica, **Hosanna² Prosa**   24, 128
   See p. 63, *Caelestia sidera*, Thannabaur 197
   and p. 123, BTC-Scs 3 (? = Thannabaur 111).

Gloria Christe omnes resurgamus,   29
Hosanna² Prosula
   See p. 65, *Corona iustitiae*,
   Thannabaur 152 (=154).

Hebraeorum pueri ramos, **Hosanna² Prosula**   93
   See p. 98, *Quem cherubim atque seraphim*,
   Thannabaur 63.

Hodie Dominus Iesus Christus resurrexit   48, 131
Easter Verses
   See p. 77, Thannabaur ?64 (cf. 60, 66, 67)
   and p. 124, Appendix II.

Hosanna cuncta procedens, **Hosanna² Prosula**   48
   See p. 77, *Inuisibiliter penetrauit rex*,
   Thannabaur ?64 (cf. 60, 66, 67).

Hosanna Dulcis est cantica   24, 128
Hosanna² Prosa
   See p. 63, *Caelestia sidera*, Thannabaur 197,
   and p. 123, BTC-Scs 3 (?Thannabaur 111).

[Hosanna] Omnes tua gratia   106
Hosanna² Prosa,
   See p. 110, *Summe pater de quo*,
   Thannabaur 56.

Hosanna Plasmatum populum   24, 128
Hosanna¹ Prosa
   See p. 63, *Caelestia sidera*, Thannabaur 197,
   and p. 123, BTC-Scs 3 (?Thannabaur 111).

Hosanna Saluifica tuum plasma,   104
Hosanna² Prosa
   See p. 104, *Saluifica tuum plasma*,
   Thannabaur 226, Var.

Sanctus   46
Thannabaur 46, Var. 2 (p. 135)

Trope: *Immortalis et uerus*

SOURCE

   *Benevento 34, fol. 35^(r-v) (placed irregularly after the *co.* Vidimus stellam . . . adorate dominum. and before *Agnus dei . . . mundi. Rex regum* of the Epiphany mass). Notated at the start with c clef only, although on fol. 35^r three drypoint lines, corresponding to F, a, and c, are clearly visible. No trace of a yellow line can now be seen. From [1] . . . *et uerus* through [3] *Custos*, F clef and red line were added; these disappear from [3] . . . *atque defensor* through *qui uenit* and return at *in nomine domini*, remaining to the end. The only known south Italian source for the Sanctus melody and trope; but see below for concordances from north and central Italy.

NOTES ON THE MELODY

References: Levy, "Byzantine Sanctus," pp. 21–22; MMMA 17, Th 46, Var. 2 (STr 95); and Thannabaur 37 (a related Sanctus melody associated with *Immortalis et uerus* in RoV C 52).

For a family of south Italian Kyrie melodies beginning with a rising fourth and touching e , see BTC II/1, p. 68 (Melnicki 27, *Pater excelse summeque immense*), and references under Notes on the Melody; also see BTC II/3, p. 87 (Thannabaur 128, *Pater Deus qui caret initio*), and references under Notes on the Melodies.

In its Ben 34 version, the mode-8 Sanctus melody is made up of three recurring elements: x, y, and z.

Although each element is treated somewhat freely, the basic contour of each (described below) remains distinct. Element z is several times complemented, or even replaced, with an additional, freely treated cadence figure (marked "low cadence" in the diagram below), which approaches the final, G , from below. The elements thus repeat in the order x, y, z; x, y, (+ low cadence); x + (z + low cadence); y, z' (+ low cadence); x, y, (z) + low cadence. The trope as it occurs in Ben 34 employs two of these same melodic elements, but mostly z, as can be seen in the diagram of trope and Sanctus melodies on the next page.

Sanctus.	x (rises a fourth and descends a third, G c a . . .)
Sanctus.	y (rises to e and falls to G)
Sanctus. Dominus deus.	z (fall from c—often c b c b—through baG G figure)
Sabaoth.	x
Pleni sunt cęli et terra	y
gloria tua.	low cadence
Osanna in excelsis.	x + z + low cadence
Benedictus qui uenit	y
in nomine domini.	z' + low cadence
Osanna	x
in	y
excelsis	(z) + low cadence

Thannabaur lists a single source without trope for this melody, namely Mod 16—an Italian collection of miscellaneous ordinary chants, sequences, and processional chants from the late twelfth and the thirteenth centuries. In Mod 7, from the Ravenna area, Sanctus and trope have the same basic melodic elements as in the Beneventan version, although each figure varies from its Beneventan counterpart, and [3] *Custos atque defensor* is absent. The versions stem from differing realizations of adiastematic notation or from differing recollections of the melody as heard.

The melodic material—an opening rising fourth, an ascent to high e , and a fall to the final of G— occurs often in south Italian chant (see References, above). Sequential repetition of a few melodic elements in a given order is also typical. But the fact that the Sanctus tune is absent from other south Italian collections while it is present in two manuscripts from the Ravenna area, and the presence of the related melody Thannabaur 37 in RoV C 52 (formerly thought to be from Sant'Eutizio, near Norcia, but perhaps instead from Tuscany) suggest that the editor of Ben 34 got the melody from a north or central Italian collection—unless, of course, the piece was already entered on one of the now missing folios of the Ben 35 Sanctus collection. The Sanctus melody is in any case Italian, and the trope melody as found in Ben 34 is entirely derived from it.

Thannabaur 37 is known only from RoV C 52, where it, too, is troped with *Immortalis et uerus*. The Sanctus melody somewhat resembles Thannabaur 46, Var. 2. The abruptly melismatic second *Sanctus* likewise rises to e , and similar mode-8 patterns occur, though in different places. The beginning of the last *Osanna* is also similar. But the trope melody in RoV C 52 is entirely different from the trope melody in Ben 34: it seems to have been composed anew from material of its Sanctus—in this case, Thannabaur 37. Element y, rising to e , is prominent from the start; and the initial notes of element z—when z appears at all— read c a b c , rather than c b c b .

NOTES ON *Immortalis et uerus*

References: AH 47, no. 288; CT 7, pp. 123 (no. 62), 123–24 (no. 63, the wandering verse *Indefessa[s] uoces*), and 357.

For [1] *Immortalis et uerus*, see I Tim. 1:17; for the following line *Pius et seuerus*, see BTC II/2, pp. 10 and 32, Vs [10] *Pius ac benignus serenus et seuerus* of the Gloria trope *Ciues superni . . . Christus surrexit*. For [2] *Qui . . . gubernas machina solus*, see verse [8] *Qui machinam gubernas rerum* of the Kyrie *Lux et origo*, AH 47, no. 12a. For [4] *Indefessa uoces nostras exaudi* (here troping the second *Osanna in excelsis* but elsewhere a Hosanna[2] prosula), see BTC II/3, pp. 53 and 3, and CT 7, no. 63; see also BTC II/3, pp. 72 and 45, and CT 7, no. 129, within the prosula ***Qui uenisti carnem sumens***.

SANCTUS MELODY   TROPE MELODY
    x
    y
    z
                                [1] Immortalis et uerus.   z
                                    Pius et seuerus.   z
                                    Trinus atque unus.   low cadence

    x
                                [2] Qui regis alta cęlorum   y
                                    gubernas machina solus.   low cadence

    y (+ low cadence)
    x + (z + low cadence)
                                [3] Custos atque defensor   z
                                    ęterne rex.   y'

    y
    z (+ low cadence)
    x
                                [4] Indefessa uoces nostras exaudi.   z
    y
    z (+ low cadence)

Meter:
[1] 7p + 6p + 6p, shows two accents in each member;
[2] can be grouped accentually 8p + 8p, with three accents in each half, but these are borrowed lines. The alternate wording [2] *Qui regis alta polorum* in Mod 7, PdC A 47 and RoV C 52 forms the first part of a hexameter, while
[3] and [4] are prose.

Source of text and translation below: Ben 34

Sanctus. Sanctus. Sanctus. Dominus deus.
[1]   Inmortalis et uerus.
            Pius et seuerus.
                Trinus atque unus.
Sabaoth.
[2]   Qui regis alta cęlorum
            gubernas machina solus.
Pleni sunt cęli et terra gloria tua.
Osanna in excelsis.
[3]   Custos atque defensor
            ęternę rex.
Benedictus qui uenit in nomine domini.
Osanna.
[4]   Indefessa uoces nostras exaudi.
In excelsis.
                        *
Holy, Holy, Holy, Lord God—
[1]   Immortal and true,
            Faithful and stern,
                Three and One—
of hosts.
[2]   Who rulest the heights of heaven,
            Thou alone dost direct
                thy created world *(machinam)*:
Heaven and earth are full of thy glory.

Hosanna in the highest.
[3]   Guardian and Defender,
            King eternal:
Blessed is he that comes in the name of the Lord.
Hosanna—
[4]   Hear our unwearied *(indefessas)* voices—
in the highest places.

Thannabaur and Iversen (see References, above) list four manuscript sources for the trope texts: Ben 34; PdC A 47 and Mod 7 (both from the Ravenna area and without Vs [3]); and RoV C 52, with Vs [3] and a different trope melody and a different though related Sanctus, Thannabaur 37 (see above). The phrase *Pius et seuerus* is inserted into Vs [1] only in Ben 34. In all sources, Vs [4] functions as a trope, not a prosula, between the last *Osanna* and *in excelsis*.

The text was perhaps first patched together in the Ravenna area, seeing that two of the four manuscripts came from there. The words of the later Beneventan edition—although not the melodies—most closely resemble those of RoV C 52. Nevertheless, the Beneventan version must have been copied from an exemplar unlike the others, perhaps from a now-missing folio of Ben 35. In Ben 34, the piece is assigned to the propers of the Epiphany, for which feast only the ending of Vs [1] . . . *Trinus atque unus* is appropriate—when taken as referring to the manifestation of the Trinity at Christ's baptism.

Indefessas uoces, **Hosanna[2] Prosula**   3
    See p. 53, *Admirabilis splendor*, Thannabaur 74.

Sanctus
Thannabaur ?64 (cf. 60, 66, 67)

48

Trope: *Inuisibiliter penetrauit rex*

Hosanna² Prosula
Hosanna cuncta procedens

Easter Verses: *Hodie Dominus Iesus Christus resurrexit a mortuis,* (see pp. 124 and 131)

Sources

*Cologny-Geneva, Bodmer 74, fol. 122ᵛ (fourth of nine collected Sanctus). Without tropes or prosula but followed by the eight Easter verses beginning $\overline{V}$ *Hodie dominus iesus christus resurrexit a mortuis* on fol. 122ᵛ and continuing on fol. 123ʳ, of which only the first is given here. See Appendix II for the entire text. Rubric:

$$IN\ RES\overline{UR}\cdot$$

*Cologny-Geneva, Bodmer 74, fols. 123ᵛ–124ʳ (sixth of nine collected Sanctus). With trope and Hosanna² prosula. Rubric at the bottom of fol. 123ʳ: $\overline{AL}$

*Benevento 34, fol. 181ʳ⁻ᵛ (after *Cum intuerentur in cęlum . . . sic ueniet. quem⟨admodum⟩.* of the $\overline{off}$ *Viri galilei* and before *Agnus dei . . . Ad dexteram patris residens* of the mass for Ascension Day). Surviving traces show that a yellow c line, as well as c clef, was used throughout; whereas F clef and red line appear only from -*ne domini* to the end. This version is remarkably similar to the Bod 76⁶ version, except for certain altered words, the omission of line [2 .ᴵ] of the Hosanna prosula—possibly through inadvertence—and the addition of a melodic refrain after *gloria tua.*

Notes on the Melodies

References: Hiley, *Western Plainchant,* p. 163; Levy, "Byzantine Sanctus," pp. 21–22 and passim; MGG 11, ex. 2 facing col. 1360; and MMMA 17, Th 63b (STr 100[?], HPr 46a). For related melodies, see BTC II/3, pp. 90 and 76 (Thannabaur 60 [? = 66,67], *Pax in caelo* [= *Laudatur trina maiestas*]).

These two chants—that is, the fourth Sanctus of the Bod 74 collection (hence Bod 74⁴ in the main text) and the sixth Sanctus of the same collection (Bod 74⁶, which is similar to the version for Ascension Day in Ben 34)—are classified in BTC II/3 as variants of Thannabaur 64. Alternatively, each could be regarded as a distinct melody, though closely related to Thannabaur 64 and anaphoral chant. (See Levy, "Byzantine Sanctus," and BTC II/1, p. xvi.) Parallel phrases in the two chants usually begin in the same way. In Bod 74⁶, the initial rising figure, Gc cb at *Dominus deus,* matches the initial rising figure, Gb cb found at the same place in Bod 74⁴, presumably an earlier version; but the versions of *Pleni sunt . . . tua* and *Benedictus . . . domini*—phrases usually less subject to local scribal variation—are quite unlike one another.

Thannabaur could not include the Bod 74 variants of melody 64 in his index, the manuscript being then inaccessible. But he also did not include the Ascension Day Sanctus from Ben 34 (the one similar to Bod 74⁶), even though its trope, *Inuisibiliter penetrauit rex,* had already been listed in the index to PM 15. A version of the Sanctus as sung at Piacenza is entered in Thannabaur's index at melody 64. The Piacenza version, in which *Dominus deus* begins with the notes Gc , is as close as any to Bod 74⁶, whereas Thannabaur 60, where *Dominus deus* begins Gb , somewhat resembles the version of Bod 74⁴. (Also see Levy, "Byzantine Sanctus," ex. 5, and other references in his text to these melodies, and Hiley's transcription of the Mod 7 version in *Western Plainchant,* ex. II.19.1.)

Each Sanctus phrase in Bod 74⁴ ends with the same refrain melisma, abccbaG abGaaG , except the final *Osanna in excelsis.* A not dissimilar melodic refrain, G abaG (too short to be called a melisma), is attached to the ends of most phrases in the Bod 74⁶ Sanctus. (It does not appear after *gloria tua.*) In Bod 74⁴ the melody for the final *Osanna in excelsis* rises to d and descends to D for the first time. Bod 74⁶ provides two versions of the last *Osanna in excelsis,* presumably as alternatives. The first of these is simpler than the melody for the *Osanna in excelsis* preceding *Benedictus.* The second is much more elaborate. Both enlarge the range of the melody for Sanctus and its trope— up until then only a fourth—by one note, the subfinal F .

The Bod 74⁴ Sanctus has no trope or prosula but is instead followed by the Easter verses that begin *Hodie dominus iesus christus resurrexit a mortuis.* Neither of the two melismas for *Osanna in excelsis* in Bod 74⁴ exactly reproduces the mode-8 tune of the Easter verses.

The Bod 74⁶ Sanctus has six trope verses, all using the same melody. Bits of this melody are adjusted or repeated to accommodate extra syllables and changing accentuations of the text. On first glance, it might seem that the Sanctus melismas had been underlaid with the words of the trope. Yet the Sanctus phrases diverge after the opening acclamations, while the same trope melody persists (with the slight variations mentioned).

The prosula melody of Bod 74⁶ is independent of its neighboring Hosanna melismas. It shows a certain relationship to the final *Osanna in excelsis* of the Bod 74⁴ Sanctus, but even that relationship is not exact. For example, the prosula reaches top e and descends to low D , whereas the range of the Bod 74⁴ *Osanna in excelsis* is only an octave. The prosula employs a single opening tune, not repeated, for [1] *Osanna cuncta procedens subueniens in ęthera.* A second tune is used three times (not just twice) for the succeeding pairs of lines, labeled [2 .ᴵ], [2 .ᴵᴵ], and [2 .ᴵᴵᴵ].

In Ben 34, [2 .¹] does not appear, but the last words of [2 .¹] *modulatis uocibus* (as in Bod 74⁶) replace the end [1] . . . *subueniens in ęthera* (again as in Bod 74⁶). The resulting conflation may have been due to oversight, or it may reflect a conscious intent to normalize the prosula by eliminating a repetition of phrase [2], along with the clumsy repetition of the verb form *subueniens* by the form *subueniat*.

The scribe of Ben 34 wrote four rising virgas in succession for [2 .¹¹] *Angelicis armis*, quite against the rules of Beneventan notation, which reserve the virga for the top note of a phrase like this. Just such a series of four rising virgas appears for this text in Bod 74⁶, a manuscript written according to the different rules of Roman (that is, central Italian) notation. The Ben 34 scribe adjusted the notation to the Beneventan norm at the repetition of the phrase [2 .¹¹¹¹] *Suppliciter deum*. It therefore seems that Sanctus, trope, and prosula were copied into Ben 34 from a non-Beneventan exemplar whose notation resembled that of Bod 74⁶. Bearing in mind that the texts of the trope and prosula appear nowhere except in Bod 74 (completed in 1071) and in Ben 34 (copied in the twelfth century) and not at all in earlier Beneventan or Cassinese manuscripts, we may suppose that the exemplar in central Italian notation used by the scribe of Ben 34 was Roman.

Notes on *Inuisibiliter penetrauit rex*

References: CT 7, pp. 124–25 (no. 65), 352, and 357; Iversen, "Sur la géographie des tropes du Sanctus," p. 56. For the word *penetrauit*, cf. CT 7 and also Cicero, *Timaeus* 34, . . . *astra per caelum penetrantia*, and *De natura deorum* 2.153, *Quid uero hominum ratio non in caelum usque penetrauit*—occurrences of the word hardly likely to have been known to the compiler of the Sanctus trope.

See BTC II/2, pp. 19 and 72, for the source of [4] . . . *cęlum terramque regentem*, namely the hexameter of the well-known Gloria trope distich:

[1]   Laudat in excelsis cęlum terramque regentem
            angelicus cetus   laudat et omnis homo.

For the source of the phrase *cuncta caterua polorum*, see the third distich of the same Gloria trope:

[3]   Te ueneranter adorant cuncta caterua polorum
            te tellus pelagus   laudat adorat amat.

Also see the fifth verse (as cited in Planchart 2:284), *Laudat te cuncta caterva polorum, alme redemptor* of the version of the Gloria trope *O gloria sanctorum* found in PaN 887. For a parallel to the invocative *O bone rex* that begins Vs [3] of the Sanctus trope, see BTC II/2, pp. 45 and 188, the ancient Gloria trope *Vt possimus consequi*.

[5]   O bone rex et pie domine
                clementiam ineffabiliter
                tuam magnificantes deuote.

Meter: In the trope, the meters of the sources (as far as these can be identified) have been destroyed. In the prosula, the syllables are distributed somewhat irregularly.

𝄞[1]   16 pp
[2 .¹]   11pp + 3 pp
                                12p + 3pp
[2 .¹¹]   13pp + 3pp
                                12p + 3p
[2 .¹¹¹]   12p + 3p
                                14p + 3p

Source of text and translation below: Bod 74, fols. 123ᵛ–124ʳ

Sanctus

[1]   V̄   Inuisibiliter penetrauit rex

Sanctus

[2]   V̄   Te deus trinus
                in unitate permanebis

Sanctus

[3]   V̄   O bone rex cuncta caterua polorum
Dominus deus sabaoth

[4]   V̄   Qui cęlum terramque regentem domine
Pleni sunt cęli et terra gloria tua

[5]   Te laudant cuncta perpetua regna
Osanna in excelsis

[6]   V̄   Hodie lux clara regentem domine
Benedictus qui uenit in nomine domini

𝄞[1]   Osanna cuncta procedens subueniens in ęthera
[2 .¹]   Piis in alta pneuma subueniat inclita
                Accedens turba procedens modulatis uocibus
[2 .¹¹]   Angelicis thronis nunc canunt dulciflua carmina
            Nos quoque cuncta caterua modulantur in arua
[2 .¹¹¹]   Suppliciter deum poscamus osanna in alta
            Cum choris angelorum sociis concinamus dicentes
Osanna in excelsis
Osanna in excelsis

*

Holy,
[1]   The King entered, beyond our sight!

Holy,
[2]   Thou (*tu*), the threefold God,
            shalt abide in Unity.

Holy,
[3]   O good King [of] all the host of heaven,
                    (CT: *cunctę cateruę*)
Lord God of hosts;

[4]   Who rulest (34: *gubernas*) heaven and earth:
Heaven and earth are full of thy glory.

[5]   All the everlasting kingdoms praise thee:
Hosanna in the highest!

[6]   Today a bright light shines (34: *refulget*), O Lord.
Blessed is he that comes in the name of the Lord.

𝄞 [1] Now save all things, giving help,
       going forth into heaven;

[2 .I] As he approaches the illustrious heights,
        may the Spirit give help to the faithful,
        As the crowd goes forth (*turba procedente*)
        [singing] with measured voice.

[2 .II] The angel-thrones (*angelici throni*)
         now sing sweet-flowing songs;
         Let us, the whole throng, make music too,
         on the ground. (34: *modulemur*)

[2 .III] We humbly beseech God that we may sing
          Hosanna on high
          With the united choirs of angels, saying:

Hosanna in the highest!

This trope and companion prosula for Ascension Day are known only from the two manuscripts Bod 74 and Ben 34. In Ben 34, they were included among the Ascension propers but were placed without rubric among the collected Sanctus in Bod 74. The version of Ben 34 was emended from an exemplar that must have closely resembled the version in Bod 74 (see Notes on the Melody, above). Perhaps the verbal texts were garnered for Bod 74 by that same editor who compiled the opening set of Kyrie verses beginning *Incarnatum quoque* (recte *Incarnate quoque*: see BTC II/1, pp. 44 and 110) from various preexistent texts. As sources for *Inuisibiliter penetrauit rex*, the compiler used elements from the Gloria tropes *Laudat in excelsis, Vt possimus consequi,* and perhaps *O gloria sanctorum* (see References, above). *Laudat in excelsis* is not often found before 1100 in southern Italian manuscripts, and *O gloria sanctorum* never. (The texts drawn upon for Kyrie *Incarnatum quoque* were likewise unfamiliar in southern Italy.) Furthermore, the word *permanebis* in [2] *Te deus trinus in unitate permanebis* immediately calls to mind [9] *Regnum tuum solidum permanebit* of the most famous Gloria trope of all, *Laus tua Deus* (see BTC II/2, pp. 22–28 and 110).

The Hosanna prosula may have been composed by the same editor. It lacks polish. Parallelism in syllable count and accentuation among the three members [2 .I], [2 .II], and [2 .III] is only loosely maintained. Moreover, as shown below, certain words are weakly repeated.

[1]	cuncta:	cf. [3] and [5]
[2] .I]	subueniat:	cf. *subueniens* in [1]
	accedens . . . procedens:	cf. *procedens* in [1]
[2 .II]	modulantur:	cf. *modulatis* in [2 .I]
[2 .III]	in alta:	cf. *in alta* in [2 .I]

Some, but not all, of these infelicitous repetitions were removed in the version of Ben 34, and some, but not all, of the mistakes in grammar that appear in the Bod 74 version were corrected. (The version of Ben 34 is given in the main text.)

Laudatur trina maiestas   **76**
See p. 90, *Pax in caelo*, Thannabaur 60 (? = 66, 67)

Sanctus   57
Thannabaur 213, Var. (p. 200)
Hosanna² Prosa: *Laudes Deo ore pio*
(In Urb 602, a trope for Sanctus)

SOURCES

*Montecassino 546, fol. 68ᵛ (fourth of six collected Sanctus). Notated with F clef and red line and an intermittent yellow line for low C where needed. The last eleven notes of the melisma following [1 .II] . . . *organo* were copied one step too high. The red F line was omitted here, but the yellow line for low C was incorrectly entered for these eleven notes. When viewed retrospectively, the custos after the melisma corrects the mistake. Without tropes. The prosa is inserted *en bloc* between *Benedictus . . . domini* and the final *Osanna in excelsis*. Melismas are attached to the last syllables of prosa lines (see below). The standard element [2 .II] *Alfa et o* is replaced by the special Cassinese element [2 .MCᴵ] *Celi regi terre marium rerum omnium*, which here precedes [2 .III] *Patri almo*.

*Benevento 34, fols. 240ᵛ–241ʳ (after a cue for the offertory, *off Exultabunt s⟨an⟩c⟨t⟩i*, and before *Agnus dei . . . nobis. Fulgida qui regnas* of the mass for All Saints' Day). The F clef and red line were inserted a third too low, so that the notes read a third too high from [2 .II] . . . *necne dicito* to the end, although the custos after **puro carmine** and before **necne dicito** is correct. Without tropes. Four prosa elements, each preceded by its exactly corresponding melisma, are inserted after *Benedictus . . . domini* and the following melisma on the vowel O. A fifth element, [1 .III] **Trino deo omnes proclamant**, is inserted between the final *Osanna* and *in excelsis*. [2.I] **Patri almo** is followed by [2.II] *Alfa et o*; the substitute Cassinese line [2 .MC] *Celi regi* is not used. The version of this MS was not entered in Thannabaur's index under melody 213 or its variants.

(*)Benevento 38, fol. 99ᵛ (entered in an early twelfth-century hand over the erased old Beneventan mass for Pentecost—see Kelly, *The Beneventan Chant*, p. 302). Lines or clefs were never added; the notation remains *in campo aperto*. *Five prosa elements, without corresponding melisma, are appended to the final *Osanna in excelsis* of Thannabaur 223, a different Sanctus melody than is found in other south Italian versions of **Laudes Deo ore pio**. (See References, below, and References for the next Sanctus in the edition.)

Benevento 35, fol. 195ᵛ (sixth of sixteen collected Sanctus now surviving in the MS). Notated with a red F line and an a clef at the start; thereafter with F clef and red line. The Sanctus melody, exactly like that of MC 546 (except for the first syllable of the third Sanctus, which has two notes, Ga, instead of three, FGa) is broken off after *gloria tua. Osan* by a lacuna of one or more folios between the present folios 195 and 196. **Laudes Deo ore pio** may have been included, but it is impossible to say.

*BAV Urb. Lat. 602, fols. 69^r–70^r (ninth of twelve collected Sanctus). Diastematy is less precise than usual in this MS: see the notes accompanying the main text of this version. The phrases of Sanctus are troped with four separate prosa elements, including the added line *Cęli regi terrę marium rerum omnium*, here enumerated [2 .^MC]3, which precedes *Pleni sunt . . . excelsis* and [2 .^I]4 *Patri almo*. The prosa elements [2 .^II]5 *Alfa et o* and [1 .^III]6 *Trino deo omnes proclamant* are inserted in succession between *Benedictus . . . domini* and the final *Osanna in excelsis*. Rubric:

In ascen domini.

Altar Book Incipit

BAV Ottob. lat. 576, fol. 226^r (last of three Sanctus incipits respectively following two chants for the common preface and the proper-preface conclusion *Et ideo . . . dicentes*, only the second and last incipits having notation). Prefaces and incipits are neumed *in campo aperto* with many liquescents. (For a more detailed description of this twelfth and thirteenth-century missal based on a Cassinese exemplar, see p. 5 above.) If transcribed in the C hexachord to match the Sanctus versions in the main text, the proper-preface conclusion and its incipit would read

```
     ℓ          ℓ        ℓ ℓ    ℓ
 [D  E F    F    F EE   F E    D  EE
 Et ideo cum angelis et archangelis

     ℓ
 D       EF E   E   E DCCDE DE  D D
 cum thronis et dominati o   nibus.

     ℓ                     ℓ
 C    D  E   F   FFEE  EFE E D EE
 Cumque omni militia celestis exercitus

     ℓ
 D    E     F EE  FE DE E  E
 ymnum glorie tue canimus

      E E   DCCD    E DE D
       sine fi ne  dicentes.

  CD D    EFG  G   Ga?  DEFEDEDC ]
 Sanctus Sanctus Sanctus . . .
```

Rubric preceding the second Sursum corda dialogue and common-preface chant, proper-preface conclusion, and attached Sanctus incipits:

In dominicis et in sollemnitatibus.

Notes on the Melody

References: Atkinson, "Music as 'Mistress of the Words' "; see also Iversen, "Music as *Ancilla Verbi* and Words as *Ancilla Musicae*," and the facsimiles accompanying both articles; Hiley, "Ordinary of Mass Chants in English, North French and Sicilian MSS," p. 108; Ireland 1:121–23 and 2:28–34; and MMMA 17, Th 213, Var. p. 200 (HPr 102).

For another Sanctus melody with this prosa in Ben 38 and five other European MSS, see BTC II/3, pp. 82 and 64 (Thannabaur 223, *Mundi fabricator* and *Quem cherubim et seraphim non cessant*). For the entry in Ben 38, see Kelly, *The Beneventan Chant*, pp. 254 and 302.

According to Atkinson's concordances, **Laudes Deo ore pio** is associated with Thannabaur 213 in twenty surviving manuscripts; with Thannabaur 223, in six; and with Thannabaur 200 and Thannabaur 211, once each. (See Atkinson's article listed in References, above. The association with Thannabaur 223 in south Italy is, however, not "early": Sanctus with **Laudes deo ore pio** was entered only in the twelfth century as an addition to Ben 38. See Sources, above.) The structure of this prosa, a a b b a (or 1 1 2 2 1), and its variants in the different manuscripts are discussed in Atkinson's article.

In a Nevers troper from about 1060, PaN 9449, the prosa melody appears without text as a sequential melisma for the final *o ——— sanna in excelsis* (fol. 72^v, for All Saints') and with the text **Laudes deo ore pio** as well, each line of which is separately preceded by a short corresponding melisma. Atkinson (who gives facsimiles and transcriptions from PaN 9449) thinks this is the earliest appearance of the prosa melody and text. In PaN 9449, they are already joined to Thannabaur 213, which is never found with other tropes or pros(ul)as. Moreover, in southern Italy Thannabaur 213 is found only in the company of **Laudes Deo ore pio** and not by itself, so it appears that the Sanctus melody was imported for the sake of the popular **Laudes Deo ore pio**.

The Sanctus melody is in fact foreign to native Italian Sanctus style, which is always based in some manner on anaphoral chant. The melody is settled in the D mode, whether sung at the pitch of our manuscripts with a final of D, or transposed up a fifth so that the chant begins on G and ends on a. Repeated franculus cadences—CD D or Ga a—anchor the final. The Sanctus melody suggests protus authenticus, mode 1, when taken by itself or together with prosa element [1]; but prosa element [2], which descends to G of the gamut and emphasizes the note F (the dominant of mode 2) instead suggests protus plagalis.

Notes on *Laudes Deo ore pio*

References: AH 7, no. 174 (see lines 2a and 2b of the sequence *O Martine sacer* having the words *in aula, concio,* and *ore*); AH 47, no. 340; Atkinson, "Music as 'Mistress of the Words' "; Boe, "Ordinary in English," 2:1074; CT 7, pp. 127–29 (no. 68, I and III), 355–56, 361, and 371 (pl. 7, Du 6); Ireland 1:121–23 and 2:28–34; Iversen, "Music as *Ancilla Verbi* and Words as *Ancilla Musicae*"; Iversen, "Pax et Sapientia," pp. 44–45; and MMMA 17, Th 213 Var. (HPr 102).

Meter:	Words	Melody
[Ps1 .I]	(4p + 4p) + 5p + (3pp + 5pp)	a
[1 .II]	(4p + 4pp) + 5p + (3pp + 5pp)	a
[2 .I]	4p + 5p(p) + 5p	b
[2 .II]	4(p) + 5pp + 5pp	b
[1 .III]	4p + 5p	a

All lines of the prosa end with the vowel *o*, assonating with the *O* of *Osanna*, except for the last line and the Cassinese substitute line [2 . MC-]³ or [2 .MC^I], **Cęli regi terrę marium rerum omnium.**

Source of text and translation below: Ben 34

Sanctus. Sanctus. Sanctus.
Dominus deus sabaoth.
Pleni sunt cęli et terra gloria tua.
Osanna in excelsis.
Benedictus qui uenit in nomine domini.
O _____

[Ps1 .I]   Laudes deo ore pio
         corde sereno
         contio melos tinnulo._____

[1 .Ii]   In iubilo cum cantico
         simul ad alto
         resonet uox cum organo._____

[2 .I]   Patri almo_____
         genito quoque flamini sancto._____

[2 .Ii]   Alfa et o_____
         puro carmine necne dicito.

O _____ sanna. _____

[1 .III]   Trino deo omnes proclamant _____
         in excelsis.

*

....

Blessed is he that comes in the name of the Lord.
O _____

[Ps1 .I]   Praises to God! with faithful mouth
         and cheerful heart,
         O assembled choir, let ringing melody (*tinnulum*),

[1 .II]   Let voice with organ(um)
         in joy with song
         on high (602: *in alto*) resound together

[2 .I]   To the Father kind,
         to the Son and Holy Spirit, too,

[2 .II]   To Alpha and Omega
         with pure song, sing

Ho _____ sanna _____

[1 .III]   To God triune;   all cry out

         in the highest!

Source of text below: Urb 602

Sanctus.

[1 .I]¹   Laudes deo ore pio
         corde sereno
         carmine demus tinnulo.

Sanctus.

[1 .II]²   In iubilo cum cantico
         simul in alto
         resonet uox cum organo.

Sanctus.
Dominus deus sabaoth.

[2 .MC]³   Cęli regi
         terrę marium
         rerum omnium._____

Pleni sunt cęli et terra ___ gloria tua.
Osanna in excelsis._____

[2 .I]⁴   Patri almo
         genito quoque flamini sancto._____

Benedictus qui uenit in nomine domini.

[2 .II]⁵   Alfa et o_____
         puro carmine necne dicitur.

[1 .III]⁶   Trino deo omnes proclamant._____

O _____ sanna _____ in excelsis.

Iversen treats every aspect of the text in conjunction with Atkinson's discussion of the music in her essay cited in References, above; what follows here summarizes her conclusions. The text seems to have been written in the early or middle eleventh century and probably came from northern France or possibly from northern Italy. The earliest source for the text known to Iversen is the Nevers troper, PaN 9449, dated 1059–60. The text regularly appears in Norman and Norman-Sicilian collections and also sometimes in England. It was imported into southern Italy, arriving during the last quarter of the eleventh century. It was never included in east Frankish collections.

In some manuscripts, elements [2 .I] and [2 .II] are found in reversed order. The text is everywhere connected with the final Hosanna, excepting only Urb 602, where words and music of each prosa element are inserted as tropes to the base Sanctus text. (See the second text above.) In Urb 602, the Cassinese element [2 .MC]³ *Cęli regi terrę marium omnium* precedes *Pleni sunt cęli et terra gloria tua* and indeed may have been composed precisely to introduce it. The later Cassinese editor of MC 546 restored the entire piece to its original function as a Hosanna² prosa but retained the added Cassinese element [2 .MC^I] *Cęli regi terrę marium rerum omnium* at the expense of [2 .II] *Alfa et O*, which he dropped to make room for it. Iversen calls attention to the typical replacement of the obscure phrase in [1 .I] *contio melos tinnulo* with the clearer Cassinese version *carmine demus tinnulo*.

Excellent facsimiles of this piece from Ma 289, Bo 2748, Vce 161, Urb 602, PaN 9449, and W¹ are supplied by Iversen and Atkinson in the articles cited.

Sanctus
Thannabaur 223; Vatican XV

64

Tropes: *Mundi fabricator*
Quem cherubim et seraphim
non cessant
Hosanna² Prosula: *Pie Christe Descendisti*

(*Laudes Deo ore pio*, see pp. 79 and 63)

SOURCES WITHOUT HOSANNA PROSULA

*Benevento 35, fols. 196ᵛ–197ʳ (tenth of sixteen collected Sanctus now surviving in the MS). The only south Italian source having the trope *Mundi fabricator*. (For north Italian and Norman-Sicilian concordances, see below.)

*Benevento 35, fol. 195ᵛ (fourth of sixteen collected Sanctus now surviving in the MS). Without trope.

*Benevento 38, fol. 167ʳ (fifth of six collected Sanctus copied some time after the original MS was completed). Clefs or lines were never added; the notation remains *in campo aperto*. Without trope.

SOURCES WITH HOSANNA PROS(UL)A

Benevento 38, fol. 99ᵛ (copied in a twelfth-century hand over the erased old Beneventan mass for Pentecost). Clefs or lines were never added; the notation remains *in campo aperto*. Without trope but with the Hosanna² prosa ***Laudes deo ore pio***. (See pp. 79 and 63, where this prosa is printed together with other south Italian versions and where all the rest are joined to a different Sanctus, Thannabaur 213, Var.) The Sanctus melody on fol. 99ᵛ—which is not printed in the main text—closely resembles the other version of the same Sanctus melody also in Ben 38 (at fol. 167ʳ, described immediately above) but begins syllabically:

$$\text{Sanctus.}^{C} \quad \text{Sanctus.}^{D} \quad \text{Sanctus.}^{F \quad D \quad E}$$

*BAV Urb. 602, fols. 73ʳ–74ʳ (last of twelve collected Sanctus). Without trope but with the Hosanna² prosula *Pie Christe descendisti*. Rubric:

In dominicis diebus.

*Benevento 35, fols. 197ᵛ–198ʳ (thirteenth of sixteen collected Sanctus now surviving in the MS). Notated with F clef and red line throughout; a D clef is added from [1] . . . *clamare dicentes* until *in nomine domini*. With the trope *Quem cherubim et seraphim non cessant*—for which it is the only known source—and the Hosanna² prosula *Pie Christe descendisti*. The melody for the opening acclamations was recomposed: Thannabaur lists the version as a variant of melody 223 on his p. 190.

(*)Benevento 34, fols. 283ᵛ–284ʳ (the third of eight collected Sanctus—the last of three with tropes, followed by two without tropes and, after Agnus Dei and a MS lacuna, by three more troped Sanctus). Notated with F clef and red line throughout. Without trope but with the Hosanna² prosula **Pie Christe descendisti* (alone transcribed in the main text), which immediately follows *Benedictus qui uenit in nomine domini* with no Hosanna² melisma whatever. From the beginning down through *Benedictus,* the Sanctus melody closely resembles the version of Ben 38 on fol. 167ʳ; the rest varies somewhat from the other versions.

NOTES ON THE MELODY

References: Boe, "Ordinary in English," 2:1073–79 and 3:461–65; Hiley, "The Norman Chant Traditions," p. 29 (table 6b); Hiley, "Ordinary of Mass Chants in English, North French and Sicilian MSS," p. 109; Ireland, 1:116–18 and 2:18–22; MMMA 17, Th 223 (STr 169, HPr 156); and *New Grove* 16:464.

See BTC II/3, pp. 79 and 57 (Thannabaur 213, Var [p. 200]), the phrases of which begin similarly. See References below under *Pie Christe descendisti* for a closely related prosula melody.

The Sanctus melody appears in numerous manuscripts dating from the late tenth century onwards from all regions of western Europe. Thannabaur says it appears 280 times in 255 of the manuscripts he examined. It is thus the third most widely copied melody in his index. (Thannabaur 32 appears 385 times in 321 manuscripts—most of which belong to a later period. Thannabaur 49 appears 478 times in 311 manuscripts.) He lists four tropes and five Hosanna pros(ul)as to which Thannabaur 223 was joined.

As notated in southern Italy, the Sanctus melody touches low B as an unessential lower neighboring note and reaches up to a in the Hosannas. But the melody chiefly hovers between F as dominant and D as final, in the manner of mode 2, protus plagalis. Cadences to the D final are made from below, ED CD D, except in the two identical Hosannas, where the final is approached from above, either EFE(E) D or EF D. The melody can be considered as a precipitate of anaphoral chant. (See BTC II/1, p. xvi. For comparison with the standard formulas of anaphoral chant, this Sanctus should be transposed up a fifth so as to begin GGa a, as in fact notated in Thannabaur's index on p. 143.)

Numerous variants within south Italian sources suggest that the melody was being transcribed or copied from divergent local traditions or from already divergent northern manuscripts. The rubric of Urb 602, *In dominicis diebus*, "on Sundays," perhaps explains why the melody was so often copied. In the version Ben 35[13], the chant phrases for the first two acclamations were thoroughly rewritten so as to seem a different tune, although the body of the melody remains substantially the same.

Three of the Sanctus versions—Urb 602, Ben 35[13], and Ben 34—incorporate the south Italian Hosanna prosula *Pie Christe descendisti*, found nowhere else. The melody for this prosula is derived from that of *Qui uenisti carnem sumens*. (See the discussion of *Pie Christe descendisti*, below, where words and melody are treated together. For the single south Italian connection of this Sanctus melody, Thannabaur 223, with the prosa *Laudes Deo ore pio,* see Sources with Hosanna Pros(ul)a, above.) The melody for *Pie Christe descendisti,* like the melody for Hosanna, tends to emphasize the note a as the dominant, thus implying mode 1 rather than mode 2. In spite of its modal similarity, the Hosanna melody here does not actually employ the prosula melody in the expected melismatic form.

The melody for the trope elements that begin *Mundi fabricator* meanders through standard formulas within the octave A to a , but always so as to end on D . The formulas suggest mode 1, except in [4] *Nobis nunc famulis,* where figures surrounding the two low A's instead suggest mode 2.

On the other hand, the two-element trope *Quem cherubim et seraphim non cessant,* known only from Ben 35, uses mode-2 configurations within the range A to G . The first two *Sanctus* acclamations preceding it were recomposed, but (as mentioned) hardly with the intention of adjusting the Sanctus to the trope melody.

The fact that substantial melodic differences exist in three versions of Thannabaur 223, copied in the same manuscript within a folio or two of each other, raises the question of how Sanctus was sung at Benevento and by whom, the question of what role oral and written tradition played for the scribe, and the question of how musically perceptive this particular scribe was or was not. For if the scribe intended to present three differing versions of the same melody and was conscious of their differences as he copied them, then it must have been the case that Sanctus at Benevento was sung from notes, not from memory, and in all likelihood by a soloist or soloists who sang the trope and pros(ul)a rather than by the entire congregation of canons, monks, or nuns in choir—who generally are thought still to have been joining in the singing of ordinary chants and who, if they sang, would certainly have been singing from memory. The alternative to supposing a rendition by a soloist or soloists is to suppose a scribe or editor so inadvertent as not to have noticed the differences (or for that matter, the similarities) in these versions—a scribe who copied the graphic signals of whatever exemplar lay before him by visual, not aural, imitation, and who was unaware or only dimly aware that he was copying three different versions of the same melody. I have argued that the music scribe of the latter parts of Ben 35 was competent and reasonably intelligent—as opposed to the text scribe. (See the description of the manuscript in BTC I, p. xvi.) I therefore favor the first supposition: namely, that in whichever late eleventh to early twelfth-century establishment Ben 35 was being used, Sanctus and other ordinary melodies were sung by a soloist or soloists from notation. Or some of them were.

Notes on *Mundi fabricator*

References: CT 7, pp. 134–35 (no. 76, where Iversen cites the pentameter *cui puerile decus prompsit Osanna pium* from the Palm Sunday hymn in elegiac distichs *Gloria laus et honor,* by Theodulph of Orleans, as the source for the word *prompsit* in trope Vs [4] *Cuius in laude puerorum turba deuote promsit*); Hiley, "The Norman Chant Traditions," p. 29 (table 6B); Hiley, "Ordinary of Mass Chants in English, North French and Sicilian MSS," p. 109; and Ireland, 1:116–18 and 2:18–22.

For Kyrie verses having accentual meters similar to those of the trope, cf. BTC II/1, pp. 32 and 84 (*Deus excelse pater sempiterne,* Melnicki 76); pp. 41 and 105 (*Hagie atque benigne,* Melnicki 119); pp. 58 and 146 (*Laudes pangamus,* Melnicki 2); and especially pp. 74 and 189 (*Virginis odas Dauidis exorta radix,* Melnicki 224).

For Gloria tropes having similar meters, cf. BTC II/2, pp. 10 and 32 (*Ciues superni . . . Christus surrexit,* Bosse 51 = 2, Var. 1 and 2) and pp. 22 and 110 (*Pax sempiterna,* Bosse 39).

The expression *mundi fabricator* occurs in Ovid, Metamorphoses, i, 57.

Meter: Irregular. Groups of five or six syllables, each having two accents (5p or 6p; sometimes 5pp or 6pp)—

—are joined to form longer lines. The irregular final units (marked § in the first two verses, [1] . . . *et rector* and [2] . . . *dominus*) each lack two syllables. The unintelligible *flamminis* seems to have been substituted in Ben 35 for the correct *flammis* in order to regularize the meter by producing five syllables—*almis flamminis*—for *almis flammis.*

Source of text and translation below: Ben 35, fols. 196ᵛ–197ʳ

Sanctus.

[1] Mundi fabricator et rector. §

Sanctus.

[2] Vnice ipsius patri et equalis dominus. §

Sanctus dominus deus sabaoth.

[3] Mundi qui culpas almis flamminis
     mire detergis.

Pleni sunt celi et terra gloria tua.
Osanna in excelsis.

[4] Nobis nunc famulis miserere tui
     cuius in laude puerorum turba
     deuote promsit.

Benedictus qui uenit in nomine domini.

Osanna in excelsis.

*

Holy,

[1] Designer and Master of the world;

Holy,

[2] His only [Son], and Lord (*domine*)
equal to the Father; (or *Vnicus . . . dominus*.)

Holy Lord God of hosts,

[3] Who dost wonderfully cleanse
the faults of the world
by nourishing flames (CT: *flammis*),

Heaven and earth are full of thy glory.
Hosanna in the highest!

[4] Upon us thy (CT: *tuis*) servants
now have mercy, [thou] in whose praise
the troop of children devoutly sang:

Blessed is he that comes in the name of the Lord.
Hosanna in the highest.

Iversen lists seven manuscripts from northern Italy and two from Norman Sicily that contain this trope. North Italian scriptoria at Bobbio, Mantua, Nonantola, Norcia, and in the Ravenna area supply concordances for other pieces adopted for the ordinary at Benevento. The concordances for *Mundi fabricator* imply that the trope originated in north Italy and was borrowed for Ben 35, the only south Italian source. I cannot explain its presence in two Norman-Sicilian sources when there are no French or English concordances. Hiley thinks that in this case the Normans borrowed from the Italian repertory; one wonders why they took this piece and where they got it.

According to CT, Vs [2] reads *Vnice ipsius patris et equalis dominus* in every north Italian manuscript but one. The exception, To 18, corrects the vocative *unice* to the nominative *unicus* to agree with the surrounding nominatives *Sanctus* and *dominus*. The readings *flammis* and *tuis* are found in all manuscripts except Ben 35.

Notes on *Quem cherubim et seraphim non cessant*

References: CT 7, pp. 21, 41–42, 166–67 (no. 119), and 360; MMMA 17, Th 63 and STr 168. (CT cites Isa. 6:2–3, Exod. 25:18–22, and the trinitarian preface of the Roman mass as sources for Vs [1]. For the relevant preface text from a Beneventan missal, see below.) For other south Italian Sanctus tropes beginning with mention of the angels' praise, see BTC II/3, pp. 98 and 93 (*Quem cherubim atque seraphim*, Thannabaur 63) and pp. 103 and 102 (*Quem cuncti angeli*, Thannabaur 86).

Meter: Vs [2] is almost certainly borrowed from a pre-existing poem or hymn. This element has the structure

$$(4p + 4p) + (4p + 4pp) + (3p + 3pp)$$

and employs the rhymes *auctor, amator* and *consortium, (sanctorum), omnium*. Vs [1] is prose.

Source of text and translation below: Ben 35, fols. 197^v–198^r

Sanctus. Sanctus. Sanctus dominus deus sabaoth.

[1] Quem cherubim et seraphim
non cessant clamare dicentes.

Pleni sunt celi et terra gloria tua.
Osanna in excelsis.

[2] Ipse auctor et amator
donet nobis consortium
sanctorum omnium.

Benedictus qui uenit in nomine domini.

[ᵽs^I] **Pie christe descendisti ad terram
mundum tuam facturam saluas.
inferni portas confringes fortiter.**

[^{II}] **dyra iura ipsa dextra conculcans
sanctos sursum leuans ad etheram.
Vt tibi semper decantent.
Osanna in excelsis.**

*

Holy, Holy, Holy Lord God of hosts,

[1] Whom cherubim and seraphim
never cease proclaiming, as they sing:

Heaven and earth are full of thy glory.
Hosanna in the highest!

[2] May the Creator and the Lover
himself grant us the fellowship
of all the saints.

Blessed is he that comes in the name of the Lord.

[ᵽs^I] **O faithful Christ, thou cam'st down to earth
to save** (602: *saluans*) **the world, thy making;
to break** (*confringens*) **with might
the gates of hell.**

[^{II}] **By thy right hand crushing harsh laws,
lifting thy saints up to the sky
that they may ever sing to thee:**

Hosanna in the highest!

Vs [1] of the trope was adapted from concluding phrases of a preface. As Iversen points out (see References, above), such a preface is found in the Roman missal; this very preface, CP 879, also occurs in a missal from the early or middle twelfth century—Lo 3511 but formerly Ben 29, written for St. Peter's Nunnery *intra muros*, Benevento—as the eighth of twelve proper prefaces, rubricked *Scē trinitatis*. (Fols. 172^v–173^r: see Beneventan Sources, pp. 1–2; Proper Prefaces in the Missal Lo 3511, pp. 26–28; and pp. xxv–xxvii, above. In southern Italy, the feast of the Holy Trinity was not observed on the octave of Pentecost, but the votive mass of the Trinity—assigned to Sunday in the series of votive masses for days of the week commonly ascribed to Alcuin—was regularly used for the mass of the Transfiguration of Christ on 5 or 6 August, and perhaps at other times as well. Here is the proper section of this preface from Lo 3511 (translated on p. xxv above).

> . . . ęternę deus.
>
> Qui cum unigenito filio tuo et spiritu sancto
> unus es deus unus es dominus ;
>
> Non in unius singularitate personę /
> sed in unius trinitate substantie ;
>
> Quid enim de tua gloria reuelante te credimus /
> hoc de filio tuo hoc de spiritu sancto
> sine differentia discretionis sentimus ;
>
> Vt in confessione uere sempiterneque deitatis /
> et in personis proprietas /
> et in essentia unitas /
> et in maiestatę adoretur ęqualitas ;
>
> Quam laudant angeli atque archangeli
> cherubin quoque et seraphim /
> qui non cessant clamare dicentes.

The alternative proper-preface conclusion beginning *Quam laudant angeli*, from which the trope derives, appears in almost the same form as the third ending for proper prefaces in a Cassinese missal, MC 127, dated 1058–87, fol. 157ᵛ = p. 324 (see pp. xxiii and 3 above):

> Quem laudant angeli atque archangeli.
> cherubin quoque et seraphin
> non cessant clamare dicentes. S̄cs.

Vs [2] *Ipse auctor et amator* is unusual both for its content and for its position within the Sanctus. The editor of Ben 35 must have extracted the lines from a devotional poem or hymn, as he is known to have done in other instances. The hope they express for entrance into the company of saints is beautifully shaped but does not suit their place after *Osanna in excelsis* and before *Benedictus qui uenit*.

Notes on *Pie Christe descendisti*

References: AH 47, no. 361; Boe, "Ordinary in English," 2:1085–89; and CT 7, pp. 158 (no. 109), 355, 358, and 360.

Cf. the treatment of the theme of the harrowing of hell in BTC II/1, pp. 10–11 and 6 (*Hodie Christus resurrexit*, Melnicki 209 [=98?], especially [4–5] and [7]), and pp. 76 and 189 (*Virginis odas Dauidis exorta radix*, Melnicki 224, Vs [7]); in BTC II/2, pp. 13–14 and 32 (*Ciues superni . . . Christus surrexit*, Bosse 51=2, Var. 1 and 2, especially [5] and the prosula for [11]); and pp. 21 and 72 (*Rex hodie Christus*, Bosse 13).

For the model *Pie Christe descendisti* is based upon, see BTC II/3, pp. 71, 38, and 42–45 (*Qui uenisti carnem sumens* with *Deus pater ingenitus*, Thannabaur 154 [=152]). See further pp. 68 and 32 (*Deus fortis*, Thannabaur 154 [=152]), where *Qui uenisti carnem sumens* is cued in the version of Urb 602, and pp. 65 and 29 (*Corona iustitiae*, Thannabaur 152 [=154]), for the prosula *Gloria Christe omnes resurgamus*, also based on the melody of *Qui uenisti carnem sumens*. Text and translation from Ben 35 appear above, under *Quem cherubim et seraphim non cessant*.

Meter:	Words	Melody
[I]	11p + 9p + 11pp	a b c (or a a' b)
[II]	11p + 9p (34: ęthra) + (3–11?) 10pp (35: etheram)	a b c' (or a a' b')

The prosula *Pie Christe descendisti* is modeled upon the Italian and probably Cassinese *Qui uenisti carnem sumens* (see References, above, and especially BTC II/3, pp. 60–64). It uses the same number of syllables per line and nearly the same accentuation. *Pie Christe descendisti* is known only from the three sources listed: Urb 602 (very late eleventh century, also containing the model *Qui uenisti carnem sumens*); Ben 35 (early twelfth century); and Ben 34 (middle twelfth century). The melody of *Qui uenisti carnem sumens*, shorn of its proper Hosanna melisma, was changed in three different ways for the new text and changed most in the two Benevento versions. If *Qui uenisti carnem sumens* is indeed Cassinese, as I believe, then the Cassinese version of *Pie Christe descendisti* as found in Urb 602 would naturally be closest to its model. In Urb 602, the adjustments in the melody for the new text have been made with nice regard for the slight differences in accentuation, especially for the opening accented syllables of the first lines of the two tercets. Here are the Urb 602 versions of these first lines.

f. 61ᵛ

[I] Quĭ ue̽- nís- ti cár- nem su- mens ex ma- tre
[II] Ĕt ĕx- aú- di cúnc- tos fa- mu- los tu- os

f. 73ᵛ   x

[I] Pí- e chris- te de- scen- dís- ti ad ter- ram
[II] Dý- ra iu- ra ip- sa déx- tra con- cul- cans

The change shown above at x, from G to F, tends to reinforce the accent on the following syllable descĕn-dísti and perhaps to differentiate this line from the second line of the tercet (shown below), where the G is mostly retained between the two a's:

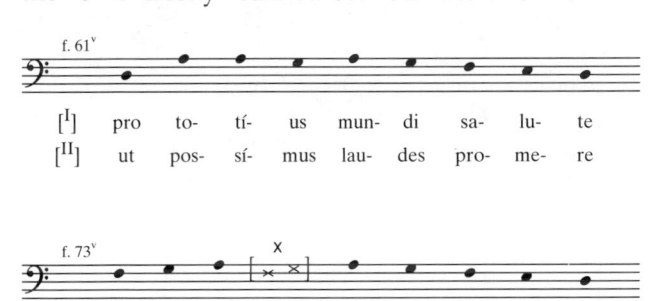

f. 61ᵛ

[I] pro to- tí- us mun- di sa- lu- te
[II] ut pos- sí- mus lau- des pro- me- re

f. 73ᵛ   x

[I] mún- dum tu- a   fac- tu- ra sal- uans.
                   F
[II] sánc- tos sur- sum le- uans in e- thra.
                   G

The end of the last tercet line in [I] was changed in Urb 602 to accommodate the hypermetric (12pp) Cassinese line *Inferni claustra confregisti fortiter*—a correction of the corrupt version recorded in Ben 35: *inferni portas confringes fortiter*. The matching passage in [II] was changed to create a bridge to the final *In excelsis* of the Sanctus melody. The beginning of the line still retains its original shape, with a two-note group on the second syllable, as in *Qui uenisti carnem sumens*:

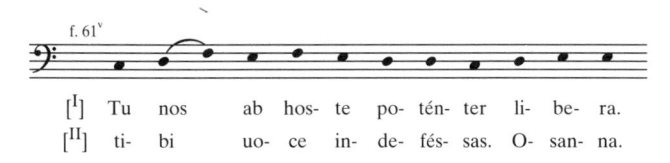

[I] Tu nos ab hos- te po- tén- ter li- be- ra.
[II] ti- bi uo- ce in- de- fés- sas. O- san- na.

The Ben 35 version of the last tercet line derives from [ƌsI].

[I] in- fer- ni por- tas con- frin- ges for- ti- ter.

The number of syllables, 11pp, here follows the pattern of the model, but the future tense *confringes* must be a corruption of the participle *confringens*, which would have been parallel to the other participles *saluans, conculcans,* and *leuans*. By the time Urb 602 was copied, the corrupt *confringes* had been corrected at Montecassino to the hypermetric *confregisti*. For good measure, a Cassinese editor also substituted the elegant *claustra* in place of the everyday word *portas*.

These manuscript clues suggest the following sequence of events. Sometime during the first half of the eleventh century, the model *Qui uenisti carnem sumens* was composed at and for Montecassino or one of its dependent monasteries. Its composer probably came from the North and was well acquainted with prosula technique. The piece, with its Hosanna melisma, spread to Benevento, to Rome, and very likely throughout southern and central Italy.

Sometime during the second half of the eleventh century, again in southern Italy—possibly but not necessarily at one of the dependent Cassinese monasteries—*Pie Christe descendisti* was composed to the same prosula tune, to be sung during Eastertide or on Sundays—the weekly Easters throughout the year.

The new prosula was associated with Sanctus Thannabaur 223 because Thannabaur 223 was often sung on Sundays. Thus the prosula came to be associated with a different Hosanna melisma, though one not entirely dissimilar from its own proper melisma.

At some point, either before or during the copying of Urb 602, the by now corrupted text with *confringes* was corrected at Montecassino and the melody adjusted to accommodate the hypermetric correction, as pointed out above. Further corrections were made to improve the musical accentuation of the new text and to adjust the ending to suit the Hosanna melody of Thannabaur 223.

The Beneventan editor of the ordinary collection in Ben 35 found this piece as copied before the Cassinese textual corrections (described above) had been made—perhaps an outdated and discarded text from Montecassino. He altered the melody. Priding himself on amassing as many different pieces as possible, he may have thought the melody as he found it too similar to that of *Qui uenisti carnem sumens* (if that text was indeed included in his collection); he would certainly have thought it too similar to the new arrangement of that prosula melody for *Gloria Christe omnes resurgamus* with *Corona iustitiae* (see BTC II/3, pp. 65 and 29). He followed the hint of the opening clivis in the first line and introduced some two and three-note groups into the melody, effectively blurring its similarity to the melodies of the other prosulas.

The scribe of Ben 34, who borrowed extensively from the Cassinese repertory, joined the Cassinese reading *confregisti* with the local reading *portas*, (found in Ben 35), and he either altered the neumatic version of the melody in Ben 35 to a different neumatic version or copied some other and to us unknown exemplar. He followed Cassinese usage (as seen in Urb 602) in associating the prosula with Thannabaur 223 without trope, discarding the connection made by the editor of Ben 35 of *Pie Christe descendisti* with *Quem cherubim et seraphim non cessant*.

In Urb 602, the skillfully composed new words of *Pie Christe descendisti* were effectively set to the older prosula tune of *Qui uenisti carnem sumens*. In the two Benevento manuscripts, the tune, deformed, lost its savor.

Omnes tua gratia, [Hosanna]² **Prosa**   *106*
See *Summe Pater de quo*, Thannabaur 56, p. 110

Sanctus 72
Thannabaur 128
Trope: *Pater Deus qui caret initio*

SOURCE

*BAV Urb. lat. 602, fols. 70ʳ–71ᵛ (tenth of twelve collected Sanctus). Notated with accurate diastematy but *in campo aperto* without clefs, as throughout the original MS. The only known source for the piece. Rubric:

In s̄c̄m pentec̄ost.

NOTES ON THE MELODIES

References: MMMA 17, Th 128 (STr 135).

For other pieces having the falling fourth as a prominent interval, see BTC II/1, pp. 71 and 186 (Melnicki 83*, *Rex Deus immense*); pp. 78 and 198 (Melnicki 23*); pp. 79 and 200 (Melnicki 63); pp. 81 and 209 (BTC-Ky 1*); pp. 82 and 211 (BTC-Ky 3); pp. 83 and 212 (BTC-Ky 6*); pp. 83 and 213 (BTC-Ky 8*); and pp. 83 and 214 (BTC-Ky 9*). All the asterisked melodies, most of them unica, are found in Urb 602. Also see BTC II/3, pp. 104 and 104 (Thannabaur 226, *Hosanna² Saluifica tuum plasma*) for a northern melody copied in Urb 602, with many falling fourths.

For tunes employing an initial rising fourth that resemble the melodies for the first three verses of this trope, see BTC II/1, pp. 13 and 24 (Melnicki 31, Var. 1, *Alme Domine rex cunctorum*); pp. 35 and 92 (Melnicki 31, *Deus pater maiestatis*); pp. 59 and 152 (Melnicki 29 = 30, *Magne Michael*); pp. 68 and 176 (*Pater excelse summeque immense*); pp. 78 and 199 (Melnicki 28); pp. 82 and 210 (BTC-Ky 2); and pp. 82–83 and 212 (BTC-Ky 5 and 6). Also cf. BTC II/2, pp. 7 and 15 (Gloria Bosse 21, *Aureas arces*—see especially pp. 20 and 27) and BTC II/3, pp. 74 and 46 (Thannabaur 46, Var. 2, *Immortalis et uerus*).

The melodies for Sanctus and for the lengthy verses of the trope *Pater Deus qui caret initio* share features setting them apart from the native Italian Sanctus tradition on the one hand and from the run of northern trope melodies on the other. I think that the Sanctus melody—a unicum—and the trope melody were composed by one person, and that this person was the editor or scribe of Urb 602, who also seems to have composed verseless Kyries found in this troper—melodies stamped with the trademark of the falling fourth. (See References, above.) Possibly the same man composed the words of the trope as well.

The transcription beginning on F with a final of G chosen for the main text and by Thannabaur is by far the most likely for the melodies, notated *in campo aperto*: an otherwise possible transcription, beginning on c with a final of d, would take the last Hosanna melisma beyond the normal gamut to high b above c. The remaining possibility—to begin on G and end on a (one step higher than in the main text)—is unconvincing, as it would suggest a dominant on G for the temporary D final in the first section of the piece.

The piece as a whole breaks into three sections, sections that hardly seem to belong together musically. The first section consists of three identical Sanctus acclamations, each ending with the interval of a falling fourth and each followed by an exegetical trope verse set neumatically. The three verse melodies make use of patterns found in a common fund of related Italian tunes in mode 8, of which the Kyrie *Pater excelse summeque immense* may serve as an example (see References, above). This Kyrie melody is described as follows in BTC II/1 (where the patterns are notated a fifth higher than in the main-text transcription of *Pater Deus qui caret initio*).

> This plagal G-mode melody . . . shows several south Italian traits . . . an initial rising fourth, G to c; descent to the final, G, from the upper c; and an internal phrase that reaches top e from the major third below: cde d cc.

These same melodic features are present in the first three trope verses of *Pater Deus qui caret initio*. The second half of each verse begins with a rising fourth placed on the first accented syllable: [1] *Ante*, [2] *Qui carnea*, and [3] *Et replesti*. The melody ascends quickly to the sixth above the first note. The rising fourths contrast nicely with the falling fourths that end the three Sanctus acclamations. The opening phrases of the three trope verses fill out that interval expansively, with a lengthy descent from the first note F to the last note C. In the middle of the first and second verses, another rising figure outlines a major triad, which begins on low C: in [1] at *a quo* and in [2] at *qui celitus*. The three Sanctus acclamations and their following trope verses cohere within a transposed mode 8 with C final. (If isolated from the rest of the piece, they would gain from being transposed up a fifth.)

Modality and range change abruptly at *Dominus deus sabaoth*. The purposive melodic design of the first section loosens into mere decoration of the note G. All phrases end on G except for the first *Osanna in excelsis*, which reverts to the original low final of C. The range extends up to c in the melismas for [4] . . . *omnium* and again at *Osanna*. The section is weak, and the composer's apparent attempt to integrate it with the opening section by returning to low C at the end of the first *Osanna in excelsis* remains unconvincing.

A splendid final Hosanna melisma, rising to e and cadencing on G, supplies the third section of the piece. The section is in mode 8, not the transposed mode 8 of the first section but mode 8 with the customary final of G. (If the final section were to be transposed up a fifth to match the upward transposition of the first section proposed earlier, its melody would rise to bb.)

The melisma employs two sets of paired phrases

Osanna (a + a) + (b + b) in excelsis.

that beg to be underlaid with a prosula text. But, so far as we know, no prosula was ever written for them. Falling fourths occur three times at the ends of phrases.

The Cassinese composer imitated certain Frankish melodic techniques. He saved a higher tessitura to effect a climax in the last section and used paired phrase structure in his final melisma. He tried to combine these northern techniques with south Italian mode-8 melodic patterns. Viewed entire, his piece breaks up into two sections in mode 8 pitched a fifth apart and separated by a meandering middle section of indeterminate modality. (Cf. the unsatisfactory juncture of melodies with wide ranges in the neumes sketched for the last Kyrie or Kyries in Urb 602, reproduced in BTC II/1, pp. xlii [pl. 3], 83, and 215.)

NOTES ON *Pater Deus qui caret initio*

References: CT 7, pp. 146–47 (no. 93, with scriptural citations). For a prolix Cassinese Gloria trope in Urb 602, possibly by the same author, see BTC II/2, pp. 5–7 and 3 (*Assit honor*, Bosse 15).

Meter: Lines within the first three verses are made up mostly of two units, each of which has two chief accents. Several lines have eleven syllables, and [3] ends with lines of 11p and 5p. Three musical phrases (whose identity depends on their opening notes, as they vary internally) appear to an extent to regulate the length of the lines of text. The original punctuation, given in the typical text below, reinforces the line divisions—especially the capital letter beginning the line set to musical phrase C. Some syllables rhyme. Vs [1–3] can be regarded either as irregular verse or as rhythmical prose.

	Words			Melody
[1]	4p +	7pp	(=11pp)	A
	5pp +	6	(=11)	B
		7p + 11p		C
[2]	5pp +	4p	(=9p)	A
		10p		B
	6p +	5p	(=11p)	C
[3]	9p +	11pp + 6pp		(A′)
		11p + 5p		C

Vs [4–5] are prose. Vs [6] has marked accentual rhythm, 9 pp + 7pp:

́ ~ ~   ́ ~ ~   ́ ~ ~   +   ~ ~ ́ ~   ́ ~ ~

Similarly, Vs [7] has 12pp:

́ ~ ~ ́ ~   ́ ~ ~ ~ ́ ~ ~

but the rhythms of [6] and [7] may be fortuitous.

Source of text and translation below: Urb 602

Sanctus.

[1] Pater deus   qui caret initio
     a quo omnia   initiata sunt.

     Ante cuius conspectum
       angelica agmina contremiscunt.

Sanctus.

[2] Dei filius   compar patris ⸗
     qui celitus terram descendisti ⸗

     Qui carnea forma   nos redemisti.

Sanctus.

[3] Dei spiritus paraclitus
     qui unus es cum patre ac filio
       essentialiter.

     Et replesti corda discipulorum
       igne diuino.

Dominus deus sabaoth.

[4] Rex regum et dominator omnium rerum.

Pleni sunt cęli et terra gloria tua.

[5] Dum homo factus es
     terra cum cęlo letatur.

Osanna in excelsis.

[6] Salua terrigenos homines
     ut celestes angelos.

Benedictus qui uenit in nomine domini.

[7] Dare celestem gratiam hominibus.

Osanna _____ in excelsis.

*

Holy,

[1] God the Father, who has no beginning,
     by whom all things were begun,
     Before whose face angel-throngs
       do tremble;

Holy,

[2] The Son of God, equal to the Father,
     thou who cam'st down from heaven to earth,
     Who in the substance of flesh
       hast redeemed us;

Holy,

[3] The strengthening Spirit of God,
     thou who art One in Being
     with the Father and the Son,
     And hast filled the disciples' hearts
       with fire divine.

Lord God of hosts,
[4]   King of kings and Ruler of all that is,
Heaven and earth are full of thy glory.
[5]   When thou didst become man,
        earth rejoiced with heaven.
Hosanna in the highest!
[6]   Save men on earth,
        as [thou sav'st] the angels in heaven,
Blessed is he that comes in the name of the Lord,
[7]   To give heavenly grace to men.
Hosanna ———————————— in the highest!

In CT 7, Iversen corrects *caret* to *cares* in [1] to match the second-person verbs in [2] and [3]. But fluctuation between second and third person is characteristic of Sanctus tropes and indeed of the liturgical Sanctus itself: *Sanctus* (not *Sancte*, in spite of the rest of the eucharistic canon addressed directly to God the Father) but *gloria tua*. In Isa. 6:3, the seraphim sing the praises of God's glory to each other: "Holy, holy, holy is the Lord of hosts; the whole earth is full of *his* glory." This being so, it hardly seems worthwhile to correct inconsistencies of person in the trope text: if *caret* to *cares*, why not *filius* to the vocative *fili* in [2] and *paraclitus* to *paraclite* in [3]?

The carefully punctuated and grammatically faultless text *Pater deus qui caret initio* in Urb 602 may be the author's fair copy or a copy made under his supervision. Nothing suggests textual corruption or the mending of textual corruption. The first three verses expound the nature of the Persons of the Trinity and of the relationships between them, in the manner of east Frankish "theological" tropes. That the Beginning is without beginning is striking paradox, one not unexplored by Augustine and the Fathers. (See CT 7, pp. 160–63, nos. 113, 114, and 115, with references.) The shorter verses [4–7] that follow are placed aptly to embroider the base text, although they are in no way original and paraphrase other texts from the liturgy.

Notwithstanding its merits, the text is too long for a Sanctus trope. Another Cassinese text—*Assit honor*, the last of nine Gloria tropes collected in Urb 602—is also excessively long. There (I wrote), "too many trope couplets swamp a plain Gloria melody of no great merit, so that the text of Gloria in excelsis is submerged in the long poem." The same can be said of *Pater Deus qui caret initio*. The Sanctus acclamations are lost in exegesis. Musical techniques that might have restored a more balanced emphasis were unfortunately not put to use. For instance, the acclamations of the base text might have been brought to the fore by a more neumatic or even melismatic style, while the words of the trope might have been delivered quickly in semi-recitative. Instead, the trope verses were given a richly neumatic setting verging on the melismatic, just as in the Gloria trope *Assit honor* (see References, above).

The Sanctus and Gloria tropes may have been written by the same author. The presence of the not-so-common adjective *terrigenus* (in the Sanctus trope, [6] *Salua terrigenos homines*) and of its noun form *terrigena* in the second distich of the Gloria trope (Vs [2] . . . *tartara quemque tremunt terrigeneque simul*) supports this hypothesis.

It is less likely that the author of these words also composed their music, as well as the music of several verseless Kyries in Urb 602. (See Notes on the Melody, above, and the Excursus below.) It is, however, highly likely that the "falling-fourth composer" of this Sanctus and the Kyries was the scribe of Urb 602, as is suggested by the composition sketch or draft for the last Kyrie or Kyries in Urb 602 (BTC-Ky 10 [and 11?]; see BTC II/1, pp. 83 and 215). If poet, composer, and scribe were indeed the same, this person must have been fluent in writing Beneventan script and notation and thoroughly trained in grammar, spelling, and versification. He must have been an admirer and imitator of northern techniques of troping, of prosula construction, and of the structuring of melodies, but he was not skilled in handling the techniques he so admired. On the other hand, Italian melodic patterns—the formula with the initial rising fourth, for instance—came naturally and easily to him. I therefore suppose him to have been native to southern Italy and probably educated at Montecassino or one of its nearby dependent monasteries. He must have been a reformer, in the eleventh-century sense of the word, interested in liturgy and music from the north. The artistic virtues of his products were sometimes marred by the inappropriate length of his tropes: *caruit breuitate*.

EXCURSUS: Aside from Urb 602, only one copy of the works ascribed to the poet-composer-scribe of Urb 602 is known—the copy of the Gloria trope *Assit honor* made for the ordinary collection of Ben 35. (The intonation for its associated Gloria melody, Bosse 15, was never entered in any altar book now surviving.) But both music and words in the copy in Ben 35 diverge from the Urb 602 version. Most of the verbal differences are corruptions of the sorts common in Ben 35, but the MS presents verses [4] and [5] in their right order, whereas the Urb 602 version reverses them. This detail and differences in the melody suggest that the collector-editor of Ben 35 was using an outdated exemplar of the Cassinese trope, an earlier copy than we see in Urb 602, even though the latter part of the MS Ben 35 may have been copied at roughly the same time Urb 602 was written. The differences between the two versions argue that the scribe of Urb 602 was not the author of the Gloria trope *Assit honor* but was copying it from an earlier Cassinese exemplar, where the first word may have read *Adsit* and where verses [4] and [5] appeared in the correct order. The case for the identity of the Urb 602 scribe with the falling-fourth composer is stronger. We can therefore posit two individuals: a scribe-composer and an earlier author-poet.

Sanctus
Thannabaur 60 (? = 66, 67)

Trope: *Pax in caelo*
   (= *Laudatur trina maiestas*)

Sources

*Cologny-Geneva, Bodmer 74, fol. 124[r-v] (eighth of nine collected Sanctus). A tenor on c is used for internal recitatives of the Sanctus text beginning *Dominus deus sabaoth*. All phrases of Sanctus except *Benedictus . . . domini* and the last *in excelsis* end with a melodic refrain, either FGa baaG or Fa baaG. Three quilismas—a neume rarely found in this manuscript—occur for the notes FGa in the melodic refrain, after the first and third *Sanctus* and after *gloria tua*. The last *Osanna* is replaced by the words *O alme* so that the ending reads *O alme in excelsis*. The trope begins with Vs [1] *Pax in celo . . . cum electis suis* after the first Sanctus and its melodic refrain, not with *Laudatur trina maiestas*, which in this manuscript follows the second acclamation as Vs [2].

Benevento 35, fol. 198[r-v] (fourteenth of sixteen collected Sanctus now surviving in the manuscript). A tenor on c is used, as in Bod 74 (see above). The melodic refrain Fab aaG is notated only after the first Sanctus and then at . . . *domini* and the final *in excelsis* melisma—the two places where melodic refrains were not notated in Bod 74. (The refrains were probably meant to be sung at the end of every phrase, according to the habitual abbreviation practiced by this music scribe.) The trope begins with Vs [1] *Pax in celo . . . cum electis suis* as in Bod. 74. Significant differences from Bod 74 are few. (See the main text.)

Notes on the Melody

References: Hiley, *Western Plainchant*, p. 163; Levy, "Byzantine Sanctus," pp. 20–22, exs. 5 and 6; MGG 11, cols. 1348–55 and music exs. 2, 6, and 7 facing col. 1360; and MMMA 17, Th 60 (STr 149b).

For other members of this family of Sanctus melodies, see BTC II/3, pp. 103 and 102 (Thannabaur 86, *Quem cuncti angeli*); Thannabaur 9, notated so as to begin on c; and Thannabaur 64, 66, and 67 (see below). Also see BTC II/3, pp. 96 and 90 (Thannabaur 62, *Quam pulchra est*) for a similar application of patterns to internal Sanctus phrases.

In this family of Sanctus melodies comprising Thannabaur 9, 60, 66, 67, and 86, text and music are joined in an unusual way. The three acclamations use the same anaphoral-chant melisma; the internal phrases are all sung to one recitative formula; and the final Hosanna has yet another melisma. The acclamations in the present melody, Thannabaur 60, are given an expansive stepwise melisma, which extends the Gab kernel up to c and, if the melodic refrain is included, down to F. In the Nonantola version of Thannabaur 60 without trope, the clauses set to recitative following the acclamations have a tenor on b (or on e in Thannabaur 9). In manuscripts from the Ravenna area (Thannabaur 66; see Hiley's transcription in *Western Plainchant*, ex. II.19.1) Norcia (?—Thannabaur 67), and in the troped sources from Rome and Benevento, when the tenor is b, an accented syllable near the end of the clause rises to c, from which note the phrase descends to its final of G through a group of two or three-note neumes. This concluding formula varies from manuscript to manuscript, although it is usually consistent within a given source. The final Hosanna melisma also varies between the different manuscripts.

A standardized melodic tag or refrain of several notes is attached to one or all acclamations and to the ends of the internal recitative phrases. (In the BoU 2824 version from Nonantola, the tag reads GF Gab aaG.) Similar melodic tags—I hesitate to call them melodic tropes—are found with other central Italian ordinary chants. Some of those found in Bod 74 were borrowed for Ben 35.

The various manuscript versions record local crystallizations of an Italian formula for singing Sanctus. The formula was certainly an oral one to begin with, though not necessarily improvisatory. It is hard to say when it began to be written down. No less than seven instances of the tune, all without tropes (see Thannabaur 9 as well as Thannabaur 60), occur in manuscripts from the abbey of Nonantola, northeast of Modena and northwest of Bologna. The Sanctus melody might therefore have been diffused in writing from Nonantola.

The similar versions of Bod 74 and Ben 35 were copied from written exemplars. The Bod 74 version is notated with three quilismas, a neume already going out of fashion in the years before 1071 and otherwise rarely used in Bod 74 (see Sources, above). It would be gratifying to be able to name the exemplar the scribe of Bod 74 was copying from. It must have had a tenor on c and must have had a trope beginning *Pax in caelo*. Unfortunately, in the manuscript RoV C 52 (where the tenor is on c), the trope begins V *Laudatur trina magestas* and displays a very different realization of the melodies. The manuscript used to be assigned to the abbey of Sant'Eutizio near Norcia: it certainly is connected in other respects with the liturgy of Rome. (See Supino Martini, *Roma e l'area grafica romanesca*, p. 335.) Mod 7—the only other manuscript besides Ben 35 to survive with the trope —is for the same reasons an unlikely source for the version of Bod 74.

On the other hand, the source of the version in Ben 35 is not in doubt. It was copied either from Bod 74 itself, or from a copy of Bod 74, or from some other and now lost Roman or possibly other central Italian source. The slight possibility that the direction of influence might in this instance have been reversed—from Benevento to Rome—is ruled out by the dates of the manuscripts. This Sanctus is not found in south Italian manuscripts earlier than Ben 35. I conclude that the piece is one of several ordinary melodies borrowed for Ben 35 from Roman sources.

The trope melody in Bod 74 and Ben 35 is divided into three phrases, which for discussion here are labeled X, B, and C. The second and third—B and C—are identifiable in all trope verses, though freely varied to fit the different texts. Motives B and C employ motivic ideas found in many other G-mode tropes. Phrase B begins on the note b, quickly touches d, and then descends to a stylized cadence on G. Phrase C touches the subfinal F, outlining the subtonic triad before the final is reached. But the initial phrase of the trope, X, is constantly varied so as to mesh with the Sanctus melody, either by imitation or by contrast. Vs [1], Vs [5], and Vs [6] imitate the initial rising-fourth pes that begins the internal Sanctus phrases, whereas Vs [2–4] contrast with the invariant Sanctus phrases by beginning on a low note, D or E. The linked combination of trope melody with Sanctus melody is altogether successful.

The trope is found only with Sanctus that have a c-tenor—namely those in Mod 7, RoV C 52, and Bod 74 together with Ben 35. Although the trope melodies in these manuscripts are similar in overall effect, they differ greatly in detail. Here are the first two trope verses as found in RoV C 52.

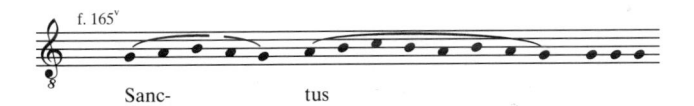

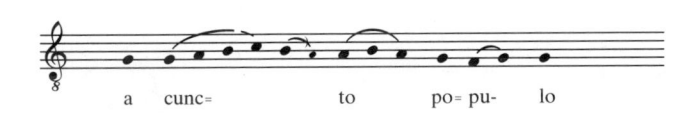

It is evident that the Bod 74 trope melody (see the main text) cannot be derived directly or indirectly from the RoV C 52 version. These versions are independent realizations of the same formula for the same words, producing closely related Sanctus melodies.

NOTES ON *Pax in caelo*
(=*Laudatur trina maiestas*)

References: AH 47, no. 309 (where the text has been manipulated so as to display artificial symmetries that contradict the musical phrases, the wording *O alme in excelsis* at the end having been suppressed); CT 7, pp. 125–26 (no. 66); Leach 1:36 (table 2) and 300–4, 2:97–100; and Luke 19:38, suggested by Leach as having inspired the transfer of the trope from Gloria in excelsis to Sanctus.

See BTC II/2, pp. 31–36 and 149 (*Quem ciues caelestes*, Bosse 43), for a Gloria trope melody similar to that used for *Pax in caelo* in its original guise in North Italy as a Gloria trope.

Meter: The trope in the form interpolating Sanctus is best regarded as prose, but containing passages in quasi-quantitative dactylic meters. In its original form as a Gloria trope (as in Ox 222), the first verse was shaped by the musical phrase—or vice versa—so as to break after *deo*:

Pax in celo permanet semper cum deo
et cum electis eius.

If the break is taken after *semper*, two lines in dactylic tetrameter result, but with a false quantity for the first syllable of *electis*. Vs [3] *Te benedicunt uirtutes cęlorum* forms a dactylic pentameter (in the sense of a hexameter short one foot).

These relics of quantitative meter echo the hexameters and elegiac distichs of the well-known Gloria tropes that probably served as models for *Pax in caelo*. See, for instance, the following internationally distributed Gloria tropes sung in the Breme-Novalesa community in north Italy, where Ox 222 and *Pax in caelo* seem to have originated: BTC II/2, pp. 18–25 and 72 (*Laudat in excelsis*, elegiac distichs), pp. 36–41 and 162 (*Quem patris ad dextram*, hexameters), and pp. 41–44 and 178 (*Qui Deus et rector*, hexameters).

Source of text and translation below: Bod 74

Sanctus

[1]   Pax in cęlo permanet semper
        cum deo et cum electis eius

Sanctus

[2]   V̄   Laudatur trina maiestas
            et colitur a cuncto populo

Sanctus

[3]   V̄   Te benedicunt uirtutes cęlorum
            et tu gubernas cuncta

Dominus deus sabaoth

[4]   Glorificatur persona diuina
        quę in ęternum permanet

Pleni sunt cęli et terra gloria tua

[5]   V̄   Qui sedes in throno diuino
            exaudi preces nostras
            et miserere nobis

Osanna in excelsis

[6]   V̄   O rex qui in cęlis regnas
            cum patre uiuis in unitate
            succurre nobis

Benedictus qui uenit in nomine domini

[7]   O alme___

in excelsis _____

*

Holy . . .

[1]   Peace in heaven abides always
        with God and with his chosen ones.

[2]   The triune Majesty is praised
        and worshiped by all people.

[3]   The powers of heaven bless thee;
        and thou dost govern all things.

[4]   The divine Person is glorified,
        who abides forever.

[5]   Thou who sittest on the throne divine,
        hear our prayers and have mercy on us.

[6]   O King, who rulest in the heavens
        [and] livest with the Father in unity:
                                    help us,

Blessed is he that comes in the name of the Lord,

[7]   O kind One,_____

in the highest!_____

In RoV C 52, the trope is distributed in the Sanctus text (fol. 165ᵛ) as follows:

Sanctus S⟨an⟩c⟨tu⟩s

[2¹]   V   Laudatur trina magestas
            et colitur a cuncto populo

Dominus deus sabaoth

[3²]   Te benedicunt uirtutes celorum
        et tu gurbernas [sic] cuncta

Pleni sunt celi et terra gloria tua

[4³]   V   Glorificamus personam diuinam
            que in eternum permanet

Osanna in excelsis

[5⁴]   V   Qui sedes in throno diuino
            exaudi preces nostras
            et miserre [sic] nobis

Benedictus qui uenit in nomine domini

[6⁵]   V   O rex qui in celis regnas
            cum patre unus (or uiuus?) in unitate
            succurre et miserere nobis

Osanna in excelsis

The text as a Gloria trope (presented below in BTC II/2 format, but based on Leach's transcription from Ox 222, fol. 52ᵛ) seems to have originated in the monastic community at Breme-Novalesa in north Italy. (See References, above.)

Gloria in excelsis deo
Et in terra pax hominibus bone uoluntatis.

[1]   Pax in cęlo permanet semper cum deo
        et cum electis eius

Laudamus te

[2]   Laudatur trina maiestas et colitur
        a cuncto populo

Benedicimus te

[3]   Te benedicunt uirtutes cęlorum
        et tu gubernas cuncta

Adoramus te

[+⁴]   Oramus te domine pater redemptor
        defende nos in proelio

Glorificamus te

[4⁵]   Glorificamus persona diuina
        quę in eternum permanet

Gratias agimus tibi
propter magnam gloriam tuam

[+⁶]   Quod tu regis regnum cęlorum et terram
        mare atque ab eis continentur

Domine deus rex celestis
....

Qui sedes ad dexteram patris
Miserere nobis

[5⁷]   Qui sedes in trhono diuino
        exaudi preces populi tui
        et miserere nobis

Quoniam tu solus sanctus Tu solus dominus
Tu solus altissimus

[6⁸]   O rex qui in cęlis regnas
        cum patre uiuis in unitate
        succurre nobis

Iesu christe
Cum sancto spiritu in gloria dei patris
Amen

The Breme-Novalesa version makes it clear that *Pax in caelo* was composed in the first place to be sung with Gloria in excelsis, not with Sanctus. (It was similarly copied on fol. 41ᵛ and cued on fol. 34ʳ of RoC 3830, a north Italian troper that may also come from Breme-Novalesa, according to Leach. The only manuscript where the text appears both as Gloria trope and as Sanctus trope is Mod 7.) As a Sanctus trope, the piece spread a little in central Italy, thanks perhaps to the close relationship of the music of the trope to the anaphoral-chant Sanctus tune. As a text for Sanctus, the piece is intriguing but unsatisfactory. Most of the verses are inappropriate. Leach suggests that the Lucan version of the acclamations for Christ's entry into Jerusalem—*Benedictus qui uenit rex in nomine Domini: pax in caelo, et gloria in excelsis*—may have provoked the new association; but, as he remarks, the quotation from the scriptural acclamation, [1] *Pax in caelo,* was in fact omitted from the Mod 7 Sanctus version, the sole surviving manuscript to have the trope for both Gloria in excelsis and Sanctus. Only the texts from Bod 74 and Ben 35 have Vs [1], which of course was part of the original Gloria version. One can see why this verse came to be omitted from the Sanctus version: *Sanctus* followed by *Pax in caelo* is a non sequitur; while on the contrary, *Sanctus* [*Sanctus Sanctus*] followed by *Laudatur trina maiestas* makes sense, even if the later verses do not.

Why then is Vs [1] *Pax in cęlo* found in the version of Bod 74? (Ben 35 is a copy from an exemplar very much like Bod 74—see Notes on the Melody, above.) Or, to put the question another way, what intermediary version, now lost, having [1] *Pax in caelo* and using a c-tenor in the Sanctus melody and quilismas in the notation, was copied for Bod 74? If only we could determine this, we should know a good deal more about sources for the non-Roman ordinary chants in Bod 74. At any rate, the place of origin for this piece was northern Italy, not Montecassino or Benevento.

Sanctus 83
Thannabaur 49; Vatican IV

Trope: *Perpetuo numine*
(*Perpetuo lumine*)

Sources

*BAV Urb. lat. 602, fol. 64ʳ⁻ᵛ (fourth of twelve collected Sanctus). With the trope *Perpetuo numine*. Rubric:

In sci mauri. abbatis.

*Montecassino 546, fol. 69ʳ (last of six collected Sanctus). The red and yellow lines were incorrectly entered for . . . *sanna in excelsis* at the end. Without trope.

*Benevento 38, fol. 167ʳ (third of six collected Sanctus copied some time after the original MS was completed). Clefs or lines were never added; the notation remains *in campo aperto*. Without trope. (Thannabaur lists this version as a variation of melody 49, on his p. 141.)

*Benevento 34, fol. 190ʳ⁻ᵛ (in the Pentecost mass, after *V Regna terre cantate deo . . . ad orientem. tibi* of the offertory *Confirma hoc*—incorrectly rubricked *Seq.*—and before *Agnus dei . . . V Quem laudant omnes cęli*). F clef and line and c clef are used throughout, but no trace of a yellow line is now visible in the MS. With the trope *Perpetuo lumine*.

Notes on the Melodies

References: Boe, "Ordinary in English," 2:758–70 and 3:290–92; Hiley, "Ordinary of Mass Chants in English, North French and Sicilian MSS," p. 99; Ireland 1:172 and 2:144–79; Levy, "Byzantine Sanctus," pp. 21–22; MMMA 17, Th 49 (STr 151); *New Grove* 16:464; and Thannabaur, pp. 61–64 (with complete versions of eight MSS showing chief variants of the melody).

Thannabaur 49 (Vatican IV) is one of the two Sanctus most often copied in the middle ages. Thannabaur says that it appears in 478 places in 311 of the manuscripts he examined. (Its rival for popularity, Thannabaur 32, Vatican XVII, is listed in his index as appearing 385 times in 321 manuscripts.) Thannabaur lists 62 French, 3 Norman-Sicilian, 4 English (there are in fact many more: Hiley lists 18), 91 German, 23 east European, 80 Italian, 2 Friulian, and 13 Iberian manuscripts, plus 33 from centralized monastic and preaching orders. Even if less than completely accurate, the numbers vividly demonstrate how often sung and how widely spread this melody was. Its universal distribution is still more striking in view of the fact that only eight of Thannabaur's 230 melodies are found in more than two "national" repertories, namely, 32 (XVII), 41 (XVIII), 49 (IV), 116 (VIII), 177 (XII), 202 (XI), 203 (II), and 223 (XV). Of these, only four—Thannabaur 32, 41, 49, and 223—found their way to south Italy.

At least 55 tropes and 10 Hosanna prosulas are known to have been associated with this melody. (Thannabaur lists 49 tropes, besides the only known vernacular Sanctus trope, *Beaus peres tuoz puissanz,* from early fourteenth-century Fontevrault.) Far more tropes were associated with this Sanctus melody than with any other. Of these, *Perpetuo numine* was the most widely sung (see below).

Many of Thannabaur's earlier eleventh-century sources are Aquitanian, suggesting that the melody may have originated in southern France. If the versions beginning Gb instead of Gc show the way the melody was composed and originally sung, then the likely place of origin would indeed be Aquitaine, where, in the written mass propers, b-tenors survived that elsewhere (for the most part) were notated as c-tenors. (PaN 909, dated before 1031, has the Sanctus with the second note as b, as do two later north Italian manuscripts, Mod 16 and Mza 77; see Thannabaur, pp. 62–64, and the variants to melody 49 at the top of p. 142.) But the more frequent form with c as the second note was the one adopted in southern Italy. By the end of the eleventh century, the melody in this later form had entered the repertories of Montecassino and Benevento, but it did not figure among the ordinary chants of Bod 74 collected at Rome, nor in the large Sanctus collection of Ben 35, for which several pieces seem to have been borrowed from Roman collections. (But Thannabaur 49 might have been copied on one of the now missing folios in Ben 35.)

Why was this melody so successful? Why did it penetrate almost every regional chant repertory of Europe? First, because it employed an up-to-date eleventh-century compositional technique I call the *motive row*. (Some proper chants from the old Beneventan rite used a kind of motive row much earlier.) However, this technique (to be explained shortly) was applied freely in the case of Thannabaur 49, so that cadences of the text would coincide with cadences of the musical phrase. Secondly, it was successful because the motives of this particular row inhabit the tonal field of anaphoral chant. The field was modernized and expanded so as to exploit the full octave, d to D, the plagal final of G being firmly reiterated. In the version having the second note as b, the first and third Sanctus phrases (which to a degree stand outside the row) closely follow the ancient ways of singing Sanctus, as in Mod 16, where the acclamation reads

<pre>
          Gba EFG
          Sanctus
</pre>

to be echoed by the first trope phrase,

<pre>
     Gab b a G aa   GG E   F G G
     Perpetuo numine cuncta regens.
</pre>

No doubt the reference to anaphoral-chant Sanctus made it especially easy to accept the melody in Italy, even though in the south it was received in the form with c as the second note. (See the discussion of anaphoral chant in BTC II/1, p. xvi, and Levy, "Byzantine Sanctus.")

The term *motive row* denotes an arrangement in a fixed order of discrete note groups or motives, an order that is repeated, when the technique is applied rigidly, with little or no regard for the text and its divisions. The modified motive row of Sanctus Thannabaur 49 is shown in the following music example, which uses the version of Urb 602.

*Bracketed passages outside the motive row.

In Thannabaur 49, application of the motive row to the Sanctus text is modified as follows. The identical first and third *Sanctus* acclamations are left outside the row, although in some versions these acclamations are assimilated to the middle motive of the row (Y in the music example above). (2) The final cadencing motive, labeled Z, is made to coincide with the ends of all text divisions: *deus sábaoth, tú-___a, dómini,* and *cél-sis* in some versions. Coincidence is achieved by beginning *Dominus* midway through motive Y and by doubling back or repeating a few notes within a motive, as at *sunt cęli + et terra*. (3) The opening syllable of *Osanna* is expanded by a melisma in most versions (a melisma that sometimes bears a prosula), and the final cadence of *excelsis* is often changed so that the final note is approached from above instead of from below. The reciprocal relation of text and melody in this modified motive-row setting should be compared with that found in the older "set forms"—flexible formulas adaptable to each line of text. The set form carries within each of its patterns the possibility of precise adjustment of music to text segments of differing length and accentuation, so that the musical cadence by definition corresponds with the verbal cadence. (For an example, see Thannabaur 60 [? = 66, 67], the immediately preceding Sanctus in this edition.) Strict motive-row settings ignore such niceties: the regular sequence and musical integrity of the motives is maintained at the cost of the words. Gloria in excelsis Bosse 25, Vatican V, supplies another easily accessible example, though not in BTC II. Apel (*Gregorian Chant*, pp. 411–12) comments in regard to this Gloria:

> Practically the entire melody consists of nothing but a single phrase which is reiterated eleven times, but with a complete disregard of the textual structure. The phrase itself can be divided into three motives (a, b, c) which can best be seen in connection with the verse *Gratias* (a) *agimus tibi* (b) *propter magnam gloriam tuam* (c). Only in this and three other verses of similar length . . . does the musical phrase coincide with a textual one. Usually the repetition of music cuts right across the textual divisions, so that some verses start with motive b, others consist only of a + b, yet others of c + a. Only the initial *Gloria*, the words *bonae voluntatis*, and the closing *-men* stand outside this rigid repeat scheme.

Without question, the set form is a more sensitive way of singing words, but the musically independent motive row contributed to the development of polyphony, as seen in the rigid repetition of an *ordo* of an *ars antiqua* tenor or of a *talea* in an isorhythmic motet.

The trope melody for *Perpetuo numine*, which was probably composed to be sung with the Sanctus version having b as second note, echoes the preceding *Sanctus* phrases (as in the quotation from Mod 16 given above), so that the first three acclamations together with their tropes yield the structure S + S'; X + X'; S + S" (where S is related to Y). The melody for trope element [4] *O deitas clemens* freely combines and enlarges motives X and Y. Vs [4] is intruded into the regular repetition of the motive row in different places in the different manuscripts. Nevertheless, this trope element is found in all known versions of the trope, and its meter and sense suggest that it is original, even though its music interrupts the motive-row rotation of the base text.

NOTES ON *Perpetuo numine*
(*Perpetuo lumine*)

References: AH 47, no. 286; Boe, "Ordinary in English," 3:290–92; CT 7, pp. 156–57 (no. 106, where CT nos. 29, 49, and 110 are cited as also including the word *Sanctus* as part of the verse line); and Ireland 1:172 and 2:144–49.

Meter: The word *Sanctus* is included in the poetic structure of Vs [1], [2], and [3]. Vs [2] and [4] are hexameters, and Vs [1] and [3] are pentameters; that is, the order "hexameter-pentameter" of the elegiac distich is reversed. (The last word of [3], *nūtris*, has a long *vowel* where the verse pattern demands a short syllable. The fault is marked § in the typical text below.)

Source of text and translation below: Urb 602

Sanctus. [1] Perpetuo numine cuncta regens.
Sanctus. [2] Regna patris disponens iure parili.
Sanctus. [3] Consimilis qui bona cuncta nutris.   §

Dominus deus sabaoth.
Pleni sunt cęli et terra gloria tua.
O _____ sanna in excelsis.

[4] O deitas clemens seruorum suscipe laudes.
Benedictus qui uenit in nomine domini.
O _____ sanna in excelsis.

*

Holy, [1] ruling all things by ever divine power;
Holy, [2] governing the Father's kingdoms by just law;
Holy, [3] like to Both, fostering all good things;

Lord God of hosts!
Heaven and earth are full of thy glory.
Hosanna in the highest!

[4] O merciful God, receive [thy] servants' praises.

Blessed is he that comes in the name of the Lord.
Hosanna in the highest!

Perpetuo numine, the most often copied of some 55 Sanctus tropes attached to Thannabaur 49, appears in 34 sources, according to CT 7. AH 47 lists 27 sources, of which 12 are French, 8 German, and 4 Italian. Of these 55 tropes, only *Deus pater cuius praesentia (prouidentia)*, *Fons uiuus uitae*, and *Sancte ingenite genitor*—and of course *Perpetuo numine*—can claim early and general use. The rest were local products or else late compositions like *Diuinum mysterium*.

The words of *Perpetuo numine* must have originated in France—or so at least the distribution and age of the sources imply—but whether in northern or southern France is hard to say. The fact that the trope melody seems more closely related to the form of the

Sanctus melody using b as its second note (rather than c) points to the south of France. But a trope melody to match an Aquitanian version of Sanctus having b instead of c as its second note might nonetheless have been composed in Aquitaine for northern French words. It might then have been recombined in southern Italy with the other Sanctus version; that is, one using c as the second note. However and wherever composed, the trope text is concise, clear, and apt for its purpose.

The Ben 34 variants—*lumine* for *numine* in [1] and *patris* for *clemens* in [4]—are found together in a twelfth-century troper and proser from Gerona in what is now northern Spain, PaN 495, and separately in a few other manuscripts. (See Iversen's notes in CT 7.) It is possible that details like these in Ben 34, differing from Urb 602, were already present in the exemplar the Ben 34 scribe was using: they need not have originated with him. In any event, the scribe of Ben 34 was probably copying an exemplar *not* from Montecassino, since the Cassinese version of Urb 602 reads *Perpetuo numine* (not *lumine*) and in Vs [4] *clemens* (not *patris*).

Pie Christe descendisti, **Hosanna² Prosula**   64
See p. 82, *Mundi fabricator*, Thannabaur 223.

Plasmatum populum, **Hosanna¹ Prosa**   24, 128
See p. 63, *Caelestia sidera*, Thannabaur 197.

Sanctus   90
Thannabaur 62
Trope: *Quam pulchra est*

Sources

*Cologny-Geneva, Bodmer 74, fol. 122ʳ (third of nine collected Sanctus). With three trope elements. Rubric:

In scē MARIE.

*Benevento 35, fol. 198ᵛ (last of sixteen collected Sanctus now surviving in the MS). Incomplete—the piece now breaks off in the middle of trope element [+4ᴮ], just before *Pleni sunt*. The folio with the rest is missing.

Notes on the Melody

References: MMMA 17, Th 62 (STr 167). For other pieces seemingly borrowed for Ben 35 from Roman collections, see BTC II/1, pp. 11–13 and 18 (*Adest reducta dies*, Melnicki 29); pp. 28–32 and 74 (*Deuote canentes*, Melnicki 77); and pp. 74–77 and 189 (*Virginis odas Dauidis exorta radix*, Melnicki 224). Similarly, in BTC II/3, see pp. lxx–lxxi, 90, and 76 (*Pax in caelo* [= *Laudatur trina maiestas*], Thannabaur 60 [? = 66, 67]).

For a list of chants that begin with a rising fourth, see BTC II/3, p. 87 (References for *Pater Deus qui caret initio*, under Notes on the Melodies). For similar applications of formulas like those of Thannabaur 62 to internal lines of Sanctus, see pp. 90 and 76 (Thannabaur 60 [= 66, 67], *Pax in caelo* [= *Laudatur trina maiestas*]).

The portion of Sanctus Thannabaur 62 surviving in Ben 35 mostly resembles the melody of Bod 74. The versions of the opening acclamations—where divergence between sources is the rule—are identical in the two manuscripts. (The Ben 35 scribe regularly abbreviated the notation of repeated melismas throughout this manuscripts, merely cueing repetitions.) On the other hand, the two melodies are unlike at *Dominus deus sabaoth*: evidently, a different exemplar was used for each manuscript, in spite of their similarities.

The two versions show nearly the same melodies for the first three trope verses, except for variants in the final cadences. The now truncated Vs [+4ᴮ] in Ben 35, *Surge propera columba mea*, was probably added at Benevento in order to retain or recall the text of the old Beneventan ingressa for the Assumption (Ben 40, fol. 118ʳ). All in all, the version of the Ben 35 trope is remarkably close to that of Bod 74, aside from the addition of Vs [+4ᴮ]. The scribe must have copied a source like that of Bod 74—a Roman source, for reasons shortly to be presented.

The melody of Sanctus and trope, like many Italian G-mode melodies for the ordinary, moves mostly in stepwise loops of two or three-note neumes, which alternate with syllabic passages and short melismas. In the opening acclamations with their accompanying tropes, the composer assembled the clichés of anaphoral chant in a skillful way so as to structure a long span by means of a carefully placed climax. (Cf. the same material, assembled more casually in a Roman Kyrie, Melnicki 49, *Adest reducta dies*—see References, above—and in a south Italian Kyrie, Melnicki 46, *Omnipotens stelligeri*, BTC II/1, pp. 63 and 162.) The single melody for the acclamations of Thannabaur 62, which in varied form serves for the three tropes that follow them, is confined to the range of a mere fourth, G to c , with two exceptions: the first word of the trope touches low E with an initial liquescent, and the end of the third trope element ascends to d at **uirgo maria**. The note c serves as tenor in several passages, as at *Benedictus qui uenit in nomine domini* and *Osianna*. The last three phrases of Sanctus, *Osanna . . .*, *Benedictus . . .*, and *Osianna . . .*, all begin with a rising fourth, Gc . The last *in excelsis* reaches e , a sixth above the final. The melody for *Osianna in excelsis* thus reproduces all the traits of the Italian rising-fourth tunes. (See References, above.) A melodic tag, GabaG , is attached to the ends of the two phrases beginning *Benedictus qui uenit* and *Osianna*. Such melodic tags or refrains are found in other Roman and central Italian tunes for the ordinary.

If the piece is taken as a whole, the anaphoral-chant basis is expanded into a clear mode 8; but the opening acclamations and tropes mostly employ the anaphoral-chant kernel, organized in patterns often found in Roman ordinary melodies.

Notes on *Quam pulchra est*

References: CT 7, p. 165 (no. 117, where Song of Songs 7:6 is cited for Vs [1], the fragment [+4^B] found in Ben 35 being entirely omitted, as also at p. 361); see Song of Songs 2:13–14 and the old Beneventan Assumption ingressa *Surge propera columba mea* for [+4^B] and the hymn *Aue maris stella* for [3] (cf. the CT 7 commentary at no. 55).

For the use of the prophetic idiom *Adest . . . dies* (as in Vs [2]) in a Roman Kyrie, see BTC II/1, pp. 11–13 and 18 (*Adest reducta dies*, Melnicki 49). Also cf. a Marian Kyrie, pp. 74–77 and 189 (*Virginis odas Dauidis exorta radix*, Melnicki 189, especially Vs [8]).

The trope is prose.

Source of text and translation below: Bod 74

Sanctus

[1]   Quam pulchra est casta
      et inuiolata maria

Sanctus

[2]   Adest preclara inquam dies
      in qua mundo migrasse

Sanctus

[3]   Quem maris stella fulgentem
      uirgo maria

Dominus deus sabaoth

[35: +4^B]   *Surge propera columba mea*
             . . . .

Pleni sunt celi et terra gloria tua
Osanna in excelsis _____

Benedictus qui uenit in nomine domini
Osianna in excelsis _____
              *

[1]   How beautiful she is!
      Mary, chaste and inviolate.

[2]   The splendid day, I say, is here
      for her to leave the world.
      (*migrassit* = *migraret, migrauerit?*)

[3]   What shining star of the sea!
      (*Quam . . . stellam*)
      [It is] the Virgin Mary!

Or:
[2–3]   The splendid day, I say, is here
        for that shining star (*stellam*) of the sea
        to leave the world: O Virgin Mary!

[35: +4^B]   Arise, hasten, my dove
             . . . .

Quam pulchra est was written for the feast of the Assumption of the Virgin. Peculiar features stamp the piece as Roman. The trope verses, dissociated from the Sanctus acclamations, proceed independently. They celebrate Mary's "migration" from earth to heaven in traditional phrases of Marian praise, taken chiefly from the Song of Songs and a famous office hymn. But these praises are placed in the third person, save for the Beneventan addition, Vs [+4^B]. The characteristic dissociation from the base text and third-person description or narration are features of native Roman Kyrie verse. (See BTC II/1, p. xxvi.) In Vs [2] *Adest preclara inquam dies in qua mundo migrasse*, the old-testament prophetic idiom *Adest . . . dies*, which was put to liturgical use in the Roman Kyrie *Adest reducta dies* for St. Lawrence (see References, above), is here intensified by the use of the prophetic *inquam*: "The day, I say, is at hand." The Ben 35 scribe misunderstood the irregular *-am* ending of the first-person singular indicative of this verb. Perhaps writing from dictation, he "corrected" his exemplar to read *in qua dies in qua mundo migrauit*, making bad grammar, worse style, but clumsy sense: "in that day that she left the world."

The matter-of-fact *migrauit* found in Ben 35 may have been in the exemplar used for Bod 74 also. In Bod 74, the original word was erased and corrected to read *migrasse*. *Migrasse* is the normal contracted form of the Latin perfect infinitive *migrauisse*. If *migrasse* is so read, Vs [2] must be taken together with Vs [3]: *Adest preclara dies, in qua, inquam, quem maris stella(m)migrasse: O uirgo maria!* But if Vs [2] and Vs [3] were taken separately—as the cantor(s) who sang them must have done—then *migrasse* would have been understood as a romance-Italian past subjunctive third-person singular: "The splendid day is at hand, I say, on which she should leave the world." The verse must in fact often have been so understood. The first part of Vs [3]—if detached, and again reading *quam* for *quem* and *stellam* for *stella*—can be taken as an accusative of exclamation (as in the first alternative in the translation above). *Virgo maria*, however, remains stubbornly nominative or perhaps vocative. (Iversen corrects the line to read *Quam maris stella fulgens*, implying *Quam fulgens est!* to parallel *Quam pulchra est!* But this correction deprives the music of a necessary syllable.) When separated from [2], Vs [3] may also have been pronounced and understood in a partly vernacular-romance way.

Quem maris stella fulgentem
Che mari-stella fulgente, virgo maria!

What a shining star of the sea is the Virgin Mary!"

The text reflects romance speech habits in the written Latin of the liturgy—another Roman characteristic. (See BTC II/1, pp. xiii and xv.)

When all these features—which are similar to those of other texts considered to be Roman—are weighed together with the strongly Roman cast of the trope melody (see above), it seems evident that the piece was composed at Rome. For its author, I propose a reform-minded Roman cleric, or a northern cleric long resident at Rome, who placed his interpolations as he found them in northern Sanctus tropes—namely, after each of the three acclamations. But he imitated local Roman Kyrie verse by dissociating the sense of trope from Sanctus and by praising Mary in the third person. He also naturally used a Sanctus melody based on anaphoral chant and paraphrased the Sanctus melody in the trope elements.

That this Marian text should have been introduced to the ordinary collection of Ben 35 along with the Marian Kyrie *Virginis odas Dauidis exorta radix* is not surprising. The most likely destination for Ben 35 was the cathedral of Benevento, dedicated to the Mother of God. (See BTC II/1, pp. 76–77.) It is, however, surprising that the piece was not copied in Ben 34, which included the Kyrie *Virginis odas Dauidis exorta radix* and a troped Gloria in excelsis among the propers for the Assumption.

Sanctus 93
Thannabaur 63

Tropes: *Quem cherubim atque seraphim + Cui pueri Hebraeorum*

Hosanna² Prosula: *Hebraeorum pueri ramos*

Sources

*Cologny-Geneva, Bodmer 74, fol. 124ʳ (seventh of nine collected Sanctus). With the trope *Quem cherubim atque seraphim + Cui pueri ębręorum* but without prosula.

Benevento 34, fols. 282ᵛ–283ʳ (first of eight collected Sanctus—three with tropes followed by two without tropes and, after Agnus Dei and a MS lacuna, by three more troped Sanctus). Notated with F clef and red line and c clef throughout. If a yellow line for c was ever present, it is not visible except for possible vestiges on fol. 283ʳ. With the trope *Quem cherubim atque seraphim + Cui pueri ebreorum* and a uniquely expanded version of the Hosanna² prosula *Hebreorum pueros ramos*.

*BAV Urb. lat. 602, fols. 68ᵛ–69ʳ (eighth of twelve collected Sanctus). With the three trope verses beginning *Quem cherubin atque seraphin* only. Rubric:

In S̄ci angli.

*BAV Urb. lat. 602, fols. 64ᵛ–65ᵛ (fifth of twelve collected Sanctus). The three verses beginning *Quem cherubin atque seraphin* are absent; the trope begins *Cui pueri hebreorum*, followed by two more verses (one more than in the first two sources above), which are followed by the Hosanna² prosula *Ebreorum pueri ramos*. Rubric:

Dominica in palmis.

Notes on the Melodies

References: Levy, "Byzantine Sanctus," pp. 21–22 and ex. 6; MMMA 17, Th 63 (STr 168, HPr 87a).

For the source of the melody and words of the extra trope verse [+MC²] *Ebreorum proles ore personuerunt* in Urb 602⁵, see BTC II/3, pp. 55, 12, and especially p. 16 (Thannabaur 92, *Altissime creator* = *Altissimeque rector*, Vs [6ᴹᶜ] *Ebreorum proles*).

Thannabaur's variant for melody 63, supposedly from Ben 34 (which he gives at the bottom of p. 149 of his index), should be deleted. There is no such variant. In the first and second *Sanctus*, Thannabaur misunderstood the large descending liquescent of the first neume and the first neume of *-tus* (which is in fact a scandicus resupinus), interpreting them respectively as a separate scandicus and as a torculus. These neumes are the same in Ben 34 as in Urb 602 (see main text).

The Sanctus melody is found in manuscripts from several northern, central, and southern Italian centers but never outside of Italy. In all sources it is associated with the trope complex *Quem cherubim atque seraphim + Cui pueri Hebraeorum*. It was never joined to any other trope and only twice to a Hosanna prosula, *Hebraeorum pueri ramos*. The Sanctus is never found without trope in the sources listed by Thannabaur.

Of the ten manuscripts Thannabaur and Iversen list as having the melody, three come from Nonantola (BoU 2824, RoC 1741, RoN 1343) and one each from Ravenna-Forlimpopoli (Mod 7); from Pistoia (Pst 121); perhaps from Sant'Eutizio, Val Castoriana near Norcia (RoV C 52: Supino Martini says "maybe Tuscany"); and from "Italy" (BoC 7)—besides the Roman, Cassinese, and Beneventan manuscripts used here. This pattern of concordances is common to other ordinary chants borrowed for Benevento from collections further north. As possible points of origin or centers for distribution of this melody, Montecassino and Benevento are ruled out by the dates of the manuscripts involved and even more cogently by the ways the complex *Quem cherubim atque seraphim + Cui pueri Hebraeorum* with *Hebraeorum pueri ramos* was edited at Montecassino and Benevento.

Where, then, did the Sanctus with its tropes come from? Perhaps from Nonantola, where the piece was copied in three manuscripts that survive. But the survival of three manuscripts from one center may only be fortunate accident. Three variants for the single word *flamini*, two of which spoil the verbal cursus of the line, suggest that the Nonantolan versions were not close to the original. It can only be said that the complex of Sanctus melody and trope (though not the prosula) must come from central or northern Italy.

The Sanctus melody is firmly grounded in anaphoral chant. (See BTC II/1, p. xvi, and Levy, "Byzantine Sanctus," cited in References, above.) Many Italian ordinary melodies based on anaphoral chant are structured loosely, or else they rely on set-form principles. (See, for instance, Thannabaur 60 [?=66, 67], *Pax in caelo* [=*Laudatur trina maiestas*], pp. 90 and 76.) In such melodies, melismas for the Sanctus acclamations and for the Hosannas—melismas varying greatly in different versions of the same tune—are contrasted with stable, quasi-syllabic, set-form recitations. The present Sanctus, Thannabaur 63, is not one of these. Instead, distinct building blocks consisting of contrasted segments of anaphoral chant are deployed in a balanced and integrated manner. I now describe this procedure by means of the following chart, based on the version 602[8] of the main text, leaving discussion of the trope melody until later.

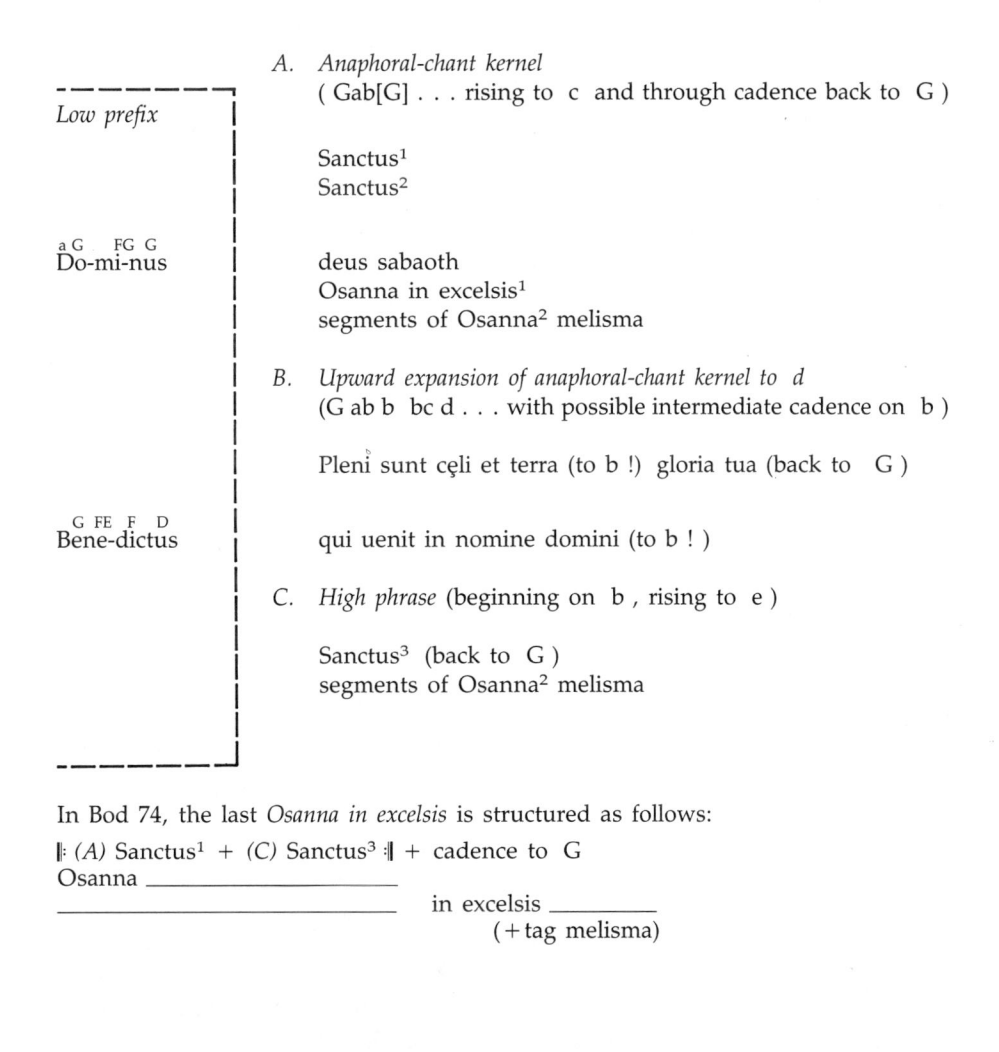

```
                          A.  Anaphoral-chant kernel
--------┐                     ( Gab[G] . . . rising to c and through cadence back to G )
Low prefix  │
            │                 Sanctus¹
            │                 Sanctus²
 a G  FG G  │
 Do-mi-nus  │                 deus sabaoth
            │                 Osanna in excelsis¹
            │                 segments of Osanna² melisma
            │
            │             B.  Upward expansion of anaphoral-chant kernel to d
            │                 (G ab b  bc d . . . with possible intermediate cadence on b )
            │
            │                 Pleni sunt cęli et terra (to b !) gloria tua (back to  G )
            │
 G FE F D   │
 Bene-dictus│                 qui uenit in nomine domini (to b !)
            │
            │             C.  High phrase (beginning on b , rising to e )
            │
            │                 Sanctus³ (back to G )
            │                 segments of Osanna² melisma
            │
--------┘
```

In Bod 74, the last *Osanna in excelsis* is structured as follows:

‖: *(A)* Sanctus¹ + *(C)* Sanctus³ :‖ + cadence to G
Osanna _____
_____ in excelsis _____
(+tag melisma)

Most anaphoral-chant Sanctus have the same melisma for all three opening acclamations. The change made here for the high third *Sanctus* is abrupt, but in the second Hosanna melisma the high segment of the third *Sanctus* returns. Both the third *Sanctus* and the final Hosanna melisma may have been composed later than the rest of the tune.

If so, the melody in its original state would have had the same tune for all three acclamations (as in Urb 608[5]) and the same melody for the last *Osanna in excelsis* as for the first. At any rate, the opening acclamations and final Hosanna melisma are now integrated into the rest of the piece in a highly satisfactory way.

Sanctus Thannabaur 63 is never found without trope. Naturally, therefore, the trope melody is closely related to the Sanctus melody. The trope phrases employ *A* and *B* in an organized way, but *C* not at all. (The labels from the preceding chart are used in the chart below; *A-* describes the anaphoral-chant kernel rising only to b , as in the first half of Vs [1].) The kernel, *A* or *A-*, functions as a conclusion to each verse line. After Vs [1], contrasting material —*B* in [2] and [3]—is used in the first halves of verses; and in [4] and [5], new material—*X* and *Y*—not derived from anaphoral chant and contrasting still more strongly is introduced. (Italic letters in the charts do not stand for precise motives in the context of a motive-row, but rather represent patterns freely applied, using different segments of the tonal field.

Elements of contrast in the combination of Sanctus and trope are supplied by the low prefixes, the *B* phrases, and the *C* phrase of the third *Sanctus* and the final *Osanna*, whereas the *A* phrases integrate Sanctus and trope into a harmonious whole. The non-anaphoral chant material, *X* and *Y*, which touches the F a c side of mode 8, supplies further contrast at the beginning of [4] and [5]. In combined trope and Sanctus, anaphoral-chant patterns are developed, expanded, varied, and contrasted with other material in a controlled, fluid manner. The resulting piece (omitting the trope verse and prosula added in Urb 602) must rank among the greatest Italian melodic achievements for the ordinary chants of the mass, an achievement wrought entirely by means of Italian idioms.

	Low prefix		
[1]	GE Quem	*A–* cherubim . . . seraphim	*A* ↘G incessanter proclamant.
[2]		*B* b Qui senas . . . habent	*A* ↘G cotidie decantant.
[3]	D (or E) Pa-	*B* tri prolique almo	*A–* G G qui est . . . et in éuum.
[4]		*X* Cui pueri ebreorum	*A* G G obuiantes clamábant.
[5]	GD ua-	*Y* Et plebs . . uociferantes	*A* G G ticinantes dicébant.

The editor of Urb 602 chopped off the last five or six notes of the first and second *Sanctus* in both his versions. As mentioned, he made the third *Sanctus* in his Palm Sunday version (602⁵) the same as the first two. Vs [4¹] *Cui pueri hebreorum* (which begins on the note c) immediately follows the third *Sanctus* in this version. Vs [+MC²] in the Palm Sunday version (Urb 602⁵) was borrowed intact, words and music together, from Sanctus *Altissime creator* found on fol. 62ᵛ in Urb 602 (see References, above and below) and included in the Palm Sunday edition in order to augment the two trope verses [4¹] and [5³], which alone remained when Vs [1–3] were removed to the Sanctus rubricked In S⟨an⟩c⟨t⟩i ang⟨e⟩li (that is, Urb 602⁸). This borrowed line in Urb 602⁵, [+MC²] *Ebreorum proles personuerunt*, is described by the technical term *wandering verse* in CT 7, but in this case it wandered only three folios from its original site, from fol. 62ᵛ to fol. 65ʳ. The melody of [+MC²] does not fit its new surroundings: it seems abruptly angular. Indeed, for it is the melody of *Benedictus qui uenit* in a different Sanctus: Thannabaur 92 with *Altissime creator*. (See References, above and below.)

The prosula **Hebraeorum pueri ramos** is known only from Urb 602⁵ and from its clumsy expansion in Ben 34. The prosula words are generally appropriate for interpolation in *Hosanna* ___ *in excelsis*, especially so on Palm Sunday. Unfortunately, the underlay of text to the music of the melisma and the pairing of word accent between versicles was poorly done. Two notes to a single syllable might pass muster in prosula style, but the four notes on the last syllables of *cedebant* and *clamant* exceed the limits of the style and are badly placed. On the last syllable of *gloria*, a nine-note melisma leads into the base text *in excelsis*. The melisma is perhaps effective for the word *gloria* but odd for a prosula.

In fact, the composer paired the wrong melisma segments. In Urb 602⁵, the melisma is structured as follows (cf. the first chart above).

   A–   ‖: C   +   A :‖   (cadence ➘)
   Osanna   [for prosula!]   in excelsis.

However, the prosula was inserted by omitting the word *Osanna* and substituting *Ebreorum pueri ramos*, the tune for which does not closely match the tune for *obuiam parant domino*, as it ought, and the leftover *A* segment of the tune at the end is made into the strange melisma for the word *gloria*.

A-	+ C	
Ebreorum pueri	ramos cedebant teneros	

A	+ C	+ A (left over)
obuiam parant domino	omnesque clamant gloria _____	in excelsis.

This basic error adds to the awkwardness of the setting. A fresh set of words should have been written to suit the paired melismas. The editor of Urb 602—in so many ways an admirable editor—here failed to pair repeated music to suitable words. His Palm Sunday version shows weak Cassinese editing.

NOTES ON *Quem cherubim atque seraphim*
 + *Cui pueri Hebraeorum*

References: CT 7, pp. 21–22, 41–42, 89 (no. 24, where Matt. 21:8–9, Mark 11:9–10, Luke 19:37–38, and John 12:13 are cited for [4], [+MC], and [5], along with antiphons, responds, and hymns for Palm Sunday), 66–67 (no. 118, where Isa. 6:2–3 and Exod. 25:18–22 are cited for Vs [1–3]), 353–55, 358, and 394 (pl. 30, Pst 121); Iversen, "Sur la géographie des tropes du Sanctus," pp. 58–59.

For other south Italian Sanctus tropes beginning with mention of angelic praise, see BTC II/3, pp. 82 and 64 (*Quem cherubim et seraphim non cessant*, Thannabaur 223), and pp. 103 and 102 (*Quem cuncti angeli*, Thannabaur 86). For the immediate source for [+MC²] *Ebreorum proles ore personuerunt* in Urb 602⁵, see pp. 55–56, 12, and 16 (*Altissime creator* = *Altissimeque rector*, Thannabaur 92, Vs [6]); also cf. pp. 65, 67, 29, and 30 (*Corona iustitiae*, Thannabaur 152 [=154], Vs [4]).

Also see the south Italian Palm Sunday Kyrie with the lines [6] *Sanctus sanctus sanctus deus miserere reos* and [9] *Osanna filio dauid benedictus qui es* in BTC II/1, pp. 22–24 and 54.

For Gloria trope verses beginning with the relative *Qui*, as in [1], [2], and [4] of this Sanctus trope, cf. BTC II/2, pp. 15–18 (*Coetus in arce*, especially [7] *Cui . . .*), pp. 36–40 (*Quem patris ad dextram*), and pp. 41–43 (*Qui Deus et rector*).

No south Italian preface text appears to have a wording close to that of [1–2], although the theme of angelic praise is universal.

The tropes are prose. All verses except [2] end with the accentual *cursus planus*: ´ ~ ~ ´ ~. (See pp. xxxiv–xxxvii, above.) Vs [2] could be read . . . *cotídiē dēcāntānt* to conform to that pattern. The first halves of [4] and [5] end with the accentual *cursus uelox*: ´ ~ ~ ~ ~ ´ ~ . These distinctive prose rhythms may simply imitate the style of the mass prefaces, which often employ the cursus. At least, this may be so in Vs [1–2]. Each trope verse except [3] ends with a verb of saying, with the rhythm ~ ´ ~, facilitating formation of the cursus. The cursus is reflected in the musical cadences, although it is not treated so consistently as it would have been in a strict set form. In Vs [1] . . . *incessanter proclamant*, the musical cadence exactly reflects the prose rhythm. Beginning with [3], a different cadence treatment of the cursus appears, with repeated notes G̃ G̃ for the last two syllables. The complete form of this second cadence appears in [4] and [5], and in partial form in [3]:

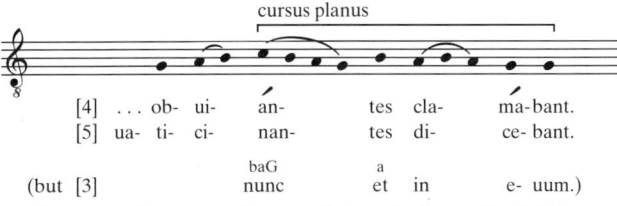

```
                    cursus planus
[4] ... ob-  ui-  an-   tes  cla-  ma- bant.
[5] ua- ti- ci-  nan-   tes  di-   ce- bant.
              baG    a
(but [3]      nunc   et  in       e- uum.)
```

Source of text and translation below: Bod 74

Sanctus
[1] V̄ Quem cherubim atque seraphim
         incessanter proclamant
Sanctus
[2] V̄ Qui senas alas habent
         cotidie decantant   §
Sanctus
Dominus deus sabaoth
[3]   Patri prolique flammineo almo
         qui est ante secula nunc et in euum
Pleni sunt cęli et terra gloria tua
Osanna in excelsis
[4]   Cui pueri ębręorum
         obuiantes clamabant
Benedictus qui uenit in nomine domini
[5]   Et plebs ębrea uociferantes
         uaticinantes dicebant
Osanna _____
in excelsis __

*

Holy
[1]   To whom cherubim and seraphim
         continually do cry:
"Holy!"
[2]   They who have each six wings,
         day after day they sing:
"Holy,
Lord God of hosts!"
[3]   To the Father and the Son,
         to the Spirit kind,
         who is
         before the ages, now and forever.
Heaven and earth are full of thy glory.
Hosanna in the highest!
[4]   To whom the children of the Hebrews,
         as they met him in the way, cried out:
"Blessed is he that comes in the name of the Lord!
Hosanna in the highest!"
[5]   And the shouting Hebrew people,
         prophesying said:
"Hosanna _____ in the highest!"

In the carefully planned and accurately executed troper Urb 602, the editor divided *Quem cherubim atque seraphim* + *Cui pueri Hebraeorum* into two separate pieces: one for St. Michael the Archangel, rubricked *In S⟨an⟩c⟨t⟩i Ang⟨e⟩li*, the eighth Sanctus, and the other for Palm Sunday, the fifth Sanctus. The melodies for both are identical, save that the third *Sanctus* acclamation in the Palm Sunday version has the same melody as the first and second acclamations, as mentioned.

The Cassinese guardians of the trope repertory were concerned to the point of fussiness with liturgical propriety and grammatical correctness in the texts they admitted to Montecassino. Verses [1–3] provide a vivid description of the never-ending heavenly Sanctus of the angels, ending with a trinitarian doxology. In that sense, the Urb 602 editor was justified in separating them from the account in verses [4–5] of the human praise of Christ on his entry into Jerusalem. However, the editor must have felt that two trope verses were not enough for his Palm Sunday piece. He therefore borrowed a verse suited to the day but not to the surrounding music. This verse, [+MC²] *Ebreorum proles ore personuerunt*, had been entered in the same Sanctus collection just two folios earlier (see References, above). In order to make room for the added verse [+MC²], the editor moved [4] *Cui pueri Hebraeorum* to an earlier point in the base text preceding *Dominus deus sabaoth*, thereby substituting the children of the Hebrews for the angels, who were saying, "Lord God of hosts!": *Cui pueri hebreorum obuiantes dixerunt: Dominus deus sabaoth!* There are instances elsewhere of Cassinese straining at a gnat and swallowing a camel: compare the corrections in the Montecassino versions of Gloria tropes *Aureas arces*, Bosse 21 (BTC II/2, pp. 7–10 and 15), and Vs [6] of *Rex hodie Christus*, Bosse 13 (BTC II/2, pp. 18–22 and 72).

This lapse aside, did the editor of Urb 602 do right in separating *Quem cherubin atque seraphin* from *Cui pueri hebreorum*? Did he restore pristine independence to what had been wrongly agglomerated? Hardly. Iversen's concordances in CT 7 show that Urb 602 is the only source to split the texts. (A twelfth-century manuscript from Bobbio, now To 18—the only source joining the text to Thannabaur 74 rather than to Thannabaur 63—omits Vs [3] but still joins [1–2] to [4–5] in one piece. Possibly Vs [3], a doxology, was added later, although not much later: Iversen's list of variants are concentrated on this "soft" verse.) The dual emphasis of the joined text—eternal praise of the Godhead in heaven and historical praise of the Son on earth—reflects dual aspects of the complete liturgical Sanctus text. (See Iversen, "On the Iconography of Praise.") Even the Ben 34 editor, who often followed Cassinese initiatives, presented verses [1–5] as one. He also included the Cassinese prosula, attaching extra lines in the ungrammatical and tasteless Beneventan style. (See main text, pp. 100–101, and below.)

I conclude that Vs [1–2] and [4–5] belong together with their melody and Thannabaur 63, but that Vs [3] may be an early addition. Although the eighth Sanctus in Urb 602, split from the complex and using Vs [1–3], is satisfactory, the fifth Sanctus for Palm Sunday is not.

Notes on Hosanna² Prosula
Hebraeorum pueri ramos

References: CT 7, pp. 120–21 (no. 59, with scriptural and liturgical citations). In regard to the spelling *cedebant*, cf. Matt. 21:8, *caedebant ramos*, and Mark 11:18, *frondes caedebant*—"cut down branches." For Vulgate use of the classical adverbial form *obuiam*, cf. John 12:13, *et processerunt obuiam ei*.

The underlay of text to the preexisting Hosanna² melisma is discussed above, under Notes on the Melodies. This Hosanna prosula was omitted in Thannabaur's index.

Source of text and translation below: Urb 602

Osanna _____
[ᶜPsⁱ]   Ebreorum pueri
                    ramos cedebant teneros
[ⁱⁱ]   obuiam parant domino
                    omnesque clamant gloria
_____

in excelsis.

*

Hosanna _____
[ᶜPsⁱ]   The children of the Hebrews
                    as they were going to meet the Lord,
[ⁱⁱ]   make ready tender branches
                    and all cry out, "Glory
_____

in the highest!"

The Urb 602 editor must have written these *uerbeta* (or must have had them written) for his Palm Sunday version of Sanctus Thannabaur 63, from which he excluded Vs [1–3] (see above). The Hosanna² melisma of this Sanctus, in the forms seen in the main text, can fairly be described as a melisma waiting for a prosula. Unfortunately, the prosula supplied in Urb 602 and Ben 34—its only sources—is unworthy of the melisma. The questionable underlay of text to music is discussed above, under Notes to the Melodies.

The problematical word in the prosula text is *cedebant*. If understood as *caedebant* (the cauda for the *e* is missing) on the model of the Vulgate scripture (see References, above), then *parant* is hard to comprehend. It might be corrected to *parent* ("they appear before the Lord"), or, as Iversen suggests, be regarded as confused with the expression *uiam parant Domino* ("they prepare the way before the Lord").

Perhaps, however, scripture was ignored and *cedebant* was understood as from *cedo,* as in my chiastic translation, above.

> ramos teneros parant (34:*parabant*)
> cedebant obuiam domino

The tasteless additions in Ben 34, [+ III] and [+ IV], deserve neither the corrections loyally supplied by Iversen in CT 7 nor translation here. They compound the faults of underlay from the Urb 602 version with crude mistakes in grammar. It is a pity that so splendid a Sanctus should have been so marred.

Quem cherubim et seraphim non cessant 64
See *Mundi fabricator,* Thannabaur 223, p. 82.

Sanctus 102
Thannabaur 86
Trope: *Quem cuncti angeli*

Source

*Benevento 35, fol. 196[v] (ninth of sixteen collected Sanctus now surviving in the MS). In Vs [4] of the trope, the last word, *gaudent,* was corrected to read *congaudent,* to agree with the liquescent neumes of the notation.

Notes on the Melodies

References: MMMA 17, Th 86 (STr 170). For similar Sanctus melodies, see BTC II/3, pp. 77 and 48 (Thannabaur ?64 [cf. 60, 66, 67], *Inuisibiliter penetrauit rex*) and pp. 90 and 76 (Thannabaur 60 [? = 66, 67], *Pax in caelo* [= *Laudatur trina maiestas*]); also see the variant Thannabaur 9, beginning on c.

For related patterns in internal Sanctus phrases and the same melodic refrain tag, see BTC II/3, pp. 96 and 90 (Thannabaur 62, *Quam pulchra est*). Also see BTC II/3, pp. 55 and 12, for the first acclamation of Thannabaur 92, *Altissime creator* = *Altissimeque rector,* which begins by descending below the final, like the acclamations of the present melody.

Thannabaur 86 employs an anaphoral-chant formula in a version but slightly different from that used for internal phrases of Thannabaur 60 (? = 66, 67), *Pax in caelo* (= *Laudatur trina maiestas.*). (See References, above, and Notes on the Melody in the commentary for Thannabaur 60.) Here is the formula applied to Thannabaur 86.

The melodic tag or refrain (G)abaaG —the same as is found in Thannabaur 62, *Quam pulchra est*—is attached to all the phrases except the first *Osanna in excelsis.* It is also imbedded within the cadences of the trope verses.

The Ben 35 editor probably got his version of the formula directly or indirectly from central Italy, perhaps by way of a Roman collection. On the other hand, the melody for the opening acclamations, where the initial phrase falls to E, was probably composed by the Benevento editor as a link to the first two trope verses and would have replaced a conventional, anaphoral-chant-based opening, Gab. (The Ben 35 scribe notated only the beginning of the melismas for the second and third *Sanctus,* as was his custom for repeated melismas; however, the entire melisma is to be sung.) A model for these low acclamations lay at hand in the first acclamation of Thannabaur 92, *Altissimeque rector,* the last part of which Sanctus appears on the recto of fol. 196, now following a lacuna in Ben 35. The present Sanctus, Thannabaur 86, was entered on the verso of the same folio. Furthermore, the last *Osanna in excelsis* of the present melody—which typically forsakes the formula—uses most of the notes of the first *Osanna* melisma of Thannabaur 92. (In the main text, compare p. 15, line 4, with the last two lines of p. 103.)

The melody for the trope is loosely patterned upon other trope melodies based on anaphoral chant. (In BTC II/3, cf. the melodies for *Inuisibiliter penetrauit rex,* p. 48; *Quam pulchra est,* p. 90; and *Quem cherubim atque seraphim* + *Cui pueri Hebraeorum,* p. 93.) The trope melody drifts through bland neumatic figurations in regions of mode 8. The final note of every phrase of both Sanctus melody and trope is G, the finality of which is reinforced by the melodic refrain tag.

Notes on *Quem cuncti angeli*

References: CT 7, pp. 21–23, 41–42, and 167 (no. 120). For other south Italian Sanctus tropes that mention the angels' praise, see BTC II/3, pp. 82 and 64 (*Quem cherubim et seraphim non cessant*, Thannabaur 223—the probable immediate source for Vs [1]). See the citations in the References for *Quem cherubim et seraphim non cessant*, p. 101, and the Beneventan preface *Sc̄ę trinitatis* from Lo 3511, quoted on p. 85. Also see BTC II/3, pp. 98 and 93 (*Quem cherubim atque seraphim*, Thannabaur 63).

Thannabaur's emendation of the title and first line of the trope to read *Quem cunctis angelis et archangelis* (at his melody 86 and on p. 254) cannot stand: it leaves the predicate *non cessant clamare* without a possible subject, and the conjunction used in the text is *atque*, not *et*. The scribe of Ben 35 sometimes used *cunctis* as a nominative plural; perhaps he confused it with *omnes*. For Vs [1] to make sense, *cunctis* must be corrected to *cuncti*, as in CT 7 and in the translation below.

Meter: In its present form, the text must be regarded as prose. However, Vs [1] has the structure 6pp + 6pp + 6p; Vs [3], 5pp + 7pp; and Vs [4], 5p + 7p.

Source of text and translation below: Ben 35

Sanctus.

[1]   Quem cunctis angeli
atque archangeli
non cessant clamare.

S⟨an⟩c⟨tu⟩s

[2]   Pater et filium
sanctoque spiritui
regnas in euum.

S⟨an⟩c⟨tu⟩s.
Dominus deus sabaoth.

[3]   Parce miseris
indulge peccantibus.

Pleni sunt celi et terra gloria tua.
Osanna in excelsis.

[4]   Duc nos ouanter
ubi iusti congaudent.

Benedictus qui uenit in nomine domini.
Osanna _____ in excelsis.

*

Holy!

[1]   Whom all *(cuncti)* the angels
and the archangels
never cease to acclaim;

Holy,

[2]   The Father and the Son *(filius)*
and the Holy Spirit!
(sanctusque spiritus)
thou reignest forever!

Holy,
Lord God of hosts!

[3]   Be sparing to the wretched;
be gentle to sinners.

Heaven and earth are full of thy glory.
Hosanna in the highest.

[4]   Lead us exulting
where the righteous rejoice.

Blessed is he that comes in the name of the Lord.
Hosanna _____ in the highest.

No doubt the text was compiled by the editor of the Ben 35 Sanctus collection. Vs [1] comes from the Trinity mass preface, perhaps by way of its previous incorporation in the Sanctus trope *Quem cherubim et seraphim non cessant clamare dicentes* (see References, above). But "angels and archangels" have taken the place of the "cherubim and seraphim" named in the preface. In the doxological Vs [2], the persons of the Trinity are placed respectively in the nominative (*pater*), accusative (*filium*), and dative (*sanctoque spiritui*), but as subjects of one verb. Vs [3] and Vs [4] apparently come from a devotional hymn or litany, which I have not been able to trace. Touching as its language is, Vs [3] hardly suits its position in the Sanctus.

S⟨an⟩c⟨tu⟩s. Dominus deus sabaoth.
Parce miseris indulge peccantibus.
Pleni sunt celi et terra gloria tua.

So far as is known, the piece was never copied again.

Qui uenisti carnem sumens,   (32), 38
Hosanna² Prosula
    See p. 71, *Deus pater ingenitus,*
    Thannabaur 154 (=152).

Sanctus   104
Thannabaur 226, Var. (p. 199)

Hosanna² Prosa: *Saluifica tuum plasma*

Sources

*BAV Urb. lat. 602, fols. 72ʳ–73ʳ (eleventh of twelve collected Sanctus). Rubric at the bottom of fol. 71ᵛ:

    In dominicis diebus.

Benevento 34, fol. 285ʳ (sixth of eight collected Sanctus—three with tropes followed by two without tropes and, after Agnus Dei and a MS lacuna, by three more troped Sanctus, of which this is the first). Clefs and colored lines for pitch were never added to last group of three Sanctus, the notation of which remains *in campo aperto*. The piece was deprived of the entire Sanctus melody and the beginning of the prosa when a folio preceding fol. 285 disappeared. The fragment now begins [2 .ᴵ] . . . *summo.* [2 .ᴵᴵ] ***Redimere perditum hominem sanguine proprio*** and continues to the end, almost exactly as in Urb 602, aside from substitutions of equivalent neume forms and omission of some liquescents.

Notes on the Melody

References: MGG 11, ex. 12a, b, c, facing col. 1361; MMMA 17, Th 226, Var. (HPr 196).

For south Italian pieces with prominent falling fourths (those bearing an asterisk below are found in Urb 602), see BTC II/1, pp. 71 and 186 (Melnicki *83, *Rex Deus immense*); pp. 78 and 198 (Melnicki *23); pp. 79 and 200 (Melnicki 63); pp. 81 and 209 (*BTC-Ky 1); pp. 82 and 211 (BTC-Ky 3); pp. 83 and 212 (*BTC-Ky 6); pp. 83 and 213 (*BTC-Ky 8); and pp. 83 and 214 (*BTC-Ky 9). In BTC II/3, see pp. 87 and 72 (Thannabaur *128, *Pater Deus qui caret initio*).

To Thannabaur's sources for melody 226 should be added PaN 495, fols. 44ᵛ–45ᵛ, and PaN 1177, fol. 7ʳ. (Thannabaur lists a single "Sanctus trope" for melody 226, *Voce harmonica*, supposedly found in Vich 105 [=111]. This text is in fact another Hosanna prosa immediately following **Hosanna Saluifica tuum plasma**.)

The presence of the Sanctus melody at Montecassino is surprising, chiefly because it does not form part of the Norman-Sicilian repertory. I summarize the eleventh and twelfth-century concordances given by Thannabaur and Iversen.

Four Aquitanian manuscripts—PaN 495, 778, 1177, 1871 (plus two from Limoges, PaN 1086 and 1139, with the words of the prosa but Sanctus Thannabaur 214); and nine northern Spanish and Catalonian manuscripts—Msrt 73, Vich 105, Vich 106, Tsa 135, Hu 4, MaA 51, Barc 1408/9, and the Compostela Codex from Santiago.

The fragment of the piece that survives in Ben 34 is almost exactly the same as the Urb 602 version. If not copied directly from Urb 602, then it was copied from a Cassinese exemplar just like it.

In all but one of Thannabaur's concordances (and that from the fifteenth century, not listed above), the Sanctus melody has the **Hosanna** prosa **Saluifica tuum plasma** and none other, save in Vich 105 (=111), where in addition to this prosa it has the above-mentioned *Voce armonica*. Moreover, *Saluifica tuum plasma* with its tune is found with only one other Sanctus—Thannabaur 214, a similar E-mode melody known from just two manuscripts, PaN 1086 and PaN 1139, both from Limoges. The melody with its prosa, then, probably came from Aquitaine into southernmost France and thence into what is now Catalonia and northern Spain, where it became greatly popular, finding a place in the patronal festival liturgy of the great pilgrimage church of Santiago de Compostela. (See References, below.) But it never penetrated northern France, northern Italy, or the Norman-Sicilian ordinary repertory from which Montecassino borrowed greatly.

The Sanctus melody is in mode 3, but as copied in Urb 602 (where many E's and b's found in other versions have been raised to F's and c's, respectively), in a form of mode 3, wavering between C major Ionian and true Phrygian. (The same form is used in many east Frankish and some Aquitanian ordinary melodies.) The range of the Sanctus is from C to c. The phrases for the second *Sanctus, Dominus deus, Pleni sunt, gloria tua*, the first *Osanna*, and *Benedictus* begin with the note G. Phrases in the tetrachord C to F are freely echoed a fifth higher, in the tetrachord G to c.

All cadences are on E except at *gloria tua*, on C. Three phrases end with the simple franculus cadence from below, DE E: the first and third *Sanctus* and *in nomine domini*. Two more, *sabaoth* and *in excelsis*, approach the franculus cadence from C below: C DE E. Two phrases employ the falling fourth internally—*sabaoth* and *in excelsis*—besides the medial cadences with falling fourths at the first *Osanna* (G d) and at *uenit* (GD D).

Several melodies for the ordinary found only in Urb 602 are distinguished by an unusual number of falling fourths. I have therefore posited a Cassinese "falling-fourth composer," who I suspect was also the scribe of Urb 602. (See References, above, and the South Italian Sanctus Repertory, p. lxvii.) The present Sanctus, Thannabaur 226, was of course not composed at Montecassino, but it was admired there and (I daresay) imitated by the scribe-composer. This, the eleventh Sanctus in the collection, was copied directly after Thannabaur 128, *Pater Deus qui caret initio*, which is a Cassinese product with many falling fourths.

No melody for the ordinary of the mass could be more foreign to the native Italian style than the Cassinese version of Thannabaur 226. Besides the leaps of a fourth at cadences—which are an idiosyncratic stylistic feature of a single Cassinese composer, not of south Italian style in general—there are still other leaps within the phrase, as at *deus*, and two in succession at the *Osanna* that begins the prosa. Leaps of a third abound: three are used at *c̨eli*, and there is an upward fifth at the end of the same word. To use Stäblein's expression, the melody moves *saltuatim*. In a version like that of Urb 602, where E's and b's are consistently raised, the melody moves more *saltuatim* than presumably might have been the case in earlier versions, if they were like that given in Thannabaur's index from Hu 4, where the first *Sanctus* reads CDED FGaGF DE E. The anaphoral-chant kernel Gab is often found transposed to different hexachords in different versions: CDE (or CDF), FGa, and of course Gab (or Gac). Unfortunately, none of the four Aquitanian and none of the nine Spanish-Catalonian concordances for this Sanctus melody sufficiently resembles Urb 602—a version sui generis, with its E's and b's everywhere raised—to yield a clue as to what kind of source the Cassinese editor might have copied from. (See Notes on **Hosanna Saluifica tuum plasma**, below.)

The Urb 602 Sanctus is constructed of four recurring phrases, which are at the same time motives in the loose sense and, more precisely, contrasting segments of modal range: (1) a low phrase for the first and third *Sanctus* and, more or less the same, for *cęli;* (2) a high phrase for the second *Sanctus, Dominus deus,* and *Osanna;* (3) a scalewise descent from G to C for *Pleni sunt* and *gloria tua;* and (4) an expanded form of the low cadence, C DE E (see above), preceded by notes of approach for *sabaoth* and *in excelsis.*

The melody for the prosa—to be further discussed below, with the words—is related to the Sanctus melody. The low, expanded franculus cadence, C D E E , is used at the ends of tunes [1], [2], and [3]. The falling fourth appears as a medial cadence in [1] (*plasma, gloria*) and as a final cadence at the end of [4] (*saluare, benigne*). The note G is important in the prosa, too, as an initial in [2] and [3]. That Sanctus and prosa were conceived as a unity seems very likely; one sees why they were never separated.

NOTES ON *Hosanna Saluifica plasma tuum*

References: AH 17, pp. 205–6. An edition by Dreves (1893) of texts from the festive mass for the patronal feast of St. James, from the "farsed" mass settings in the Calixtinus Codex of Santiago de Compostela. Unacquainted with prosula technique, Dreves expanded the vowels *A, O,* and *E* for the melisma segment that follows each prosa line in this MS to the word *Amen!* (The vowels in fact match the rhymes of the preceding prosa lines; the melisma segments are rubricked *Chorus* and the lines of the prosa, *Cantores.* See the MGG references below, ex. 12c.)

For the Compostela Codex, also see Dreves's preface in AH 17, pp. 5–16; Manuel C. Diaz y Diaz, *El Codice Calixtino de la Catedral de Santiago,* Estudio Codicologico y de contenido (Santiago de Compostela, 1988); and Peter Wagner, *Die Gesänge der Jacobusliturgie zu Santiago de Compostela aus dem sog. Codex Calixtinus* (Freiburg, 1931).

CT 7, pp. 43, 178–79 (no. 138, with an especially extensive list of variants in the MSS; Iversen identifies references in the prosa text to scripture, patristic commentary, and liturgical items), 355, 358, and 385–86 (pls. 21 and 22, PaN 778 and PaN 495). To the references given in CT 7, another should be added for [1 .II] *Temet laus decet honor et gloria rex ęterne in sęcula,* namely, the ancient *Te decet laus, Te decet hymnus, Tibi gloria Deo Patri et Filio, cum Sancto Spiritu in saecula saeculorum. Amen.* (See AM, pp. 1260–61.) St. Benedict established that *Te decet laus* should be sung in monastic matins on Sundays and festivals, after the gospel lesson (*Rule,* xi, 8–10):

> Post quartum autem responsorium incipiat abbas hymnum Te Deum laudamus. Quo perdicto, legat abbas lectionem de Evangelia, cum honore et timore stantibus omnibus. Qua perlecta, respondeant omnes amen. et subsequatur mox abbas Te decet laus, et data benedictione incipiant matutinos [i.e., lauds].

But the text is older still: the Greek original is quoted in the *Apostolic Constitutions,* vii, 48, 3, and is still used in the orthodox morning office. The scriptural model for the *Te decet . . .* constructions seems to be Ps. 64 (65):1, *Te decet hymnus Deus in Sion,* as in all the early Latin psalters.

The biblical source for the name *Lucifer* in [3 .I] is Isa. 14:12—in the Vulgate, *Quomodo cecidisti de caelo, Lucifer, qui mane oriebaris?* The King James version keeps "Lucifer," but all modern translations render the Hebrew for *lucifer,* "light-bearer," as "day star." For the translation of the Hebrew word *Hosanna* as *Saluifica,* "save [now]," see BTC II/3, p. lxvi; and Iversen's comments, CT 7, p. 43 and at nos. 48 and 111.

Also see MGG 11, ex. 12 a, b, c, and d, facing col. 1361 (with the complete prosa text from PaN 1871); Thannabaur 214.

METER (IN THE CASSINESE VERSION OF URB 602):

	Words			Melodic elements
[Ps 1 .I]	11p (3 + 8p)	+	9pp	(α + a) + (M2 + x)
[1 .II]	11pp (3 + 8pp)	+	8pp	(α + a) + (M2 + x)
[2 .I]	7pp	+	8p (3pp + 5p)	b + (m3 + x)
[2 .II]	7pp	+	9pp (3pp + 6pp)	b + (m3 + x)
[3 .I]	8pp + 9pp	+	9pp	c + a' + (M2 + x)
[3 .II]	8pp + 7pp	+	12pp (7pp + 5pp)	c + a' + (zM2 + x)
[4 .I]		7p		d
[4 .II]		7p		d

The lines in [1] end with the vowel *-a;* in [2], with *-o* (once, *-um*); in [3] and [4], with *-e* (*-er,* once).

Source of text and translation below: Urb 602

Sanctus. Sanctus. Sanctus.
Dominus deus sabaoth.
Pleni sunt cęli et terra gloria tua.
Hosanna in excelsis.

Benedictus qui uenit in nomine domini.

[ℙs1 .I]   Osanna saluifica tuum plasma
           qui creasti simul omnia.
[1 .II]   Temet laus decet honor et gloria
           rex ęterne in sęcula.
[2 .I]   Qui de patris gremio
           genitus aduenisti summo.
[2 .II]   Redimere perditum
           hominem sanguine proprio.
[3 .I]   Quem deceperat lucifer
           fraude nequam callidissime
           serpentino coniugis dente.
[3 .II]   Quem expulerat propere
           hoc in ceno criminę
           paradysi cardine adque limine.   §
[4 .I]   Tu dignare saluare /
[4 .II]   Iesu christe benigne

           In excel_____sis.
                        *

Blessed is he that comes in the name of the Lord.

[ℙs1 .I]   HOSANNA—SAVE thy creation, thou
           who didst make all things together;
[1 .II]   To thee belongs praise, honor, and glory,
           O King eternal, through the ages!
[2 .I]   Who didst come, begotten
           from the Father's bosom on high,
[2 .II]   By thine own blood
           to redeem lost man—
[3 .I]   Whom Lucifer most shrewdly
           through vile deception had entrapped
           by serpent tooth of spouse;
[3 .II]   Whom, for this crime, he had quickly
           driven out into the mire (cęnum)
           from the gate and (atque) threshold
           of Paradise.
[4 .I]   O thou kind Jesus Christ,
[4 .II]   vouchsafe to SAVE

           In the high-_____ est!

The extent of the differences between the music for the prosa in Urb 602 and the Aquitanian versions (with E's and b's that have not been raised to F's and c's as in Urb 602) is evident from a comparison of the main text with the following transcription of PaN 778, fols. 204ᵛ–205ʳ, a twelfth-century troper-proser from Narbonne.

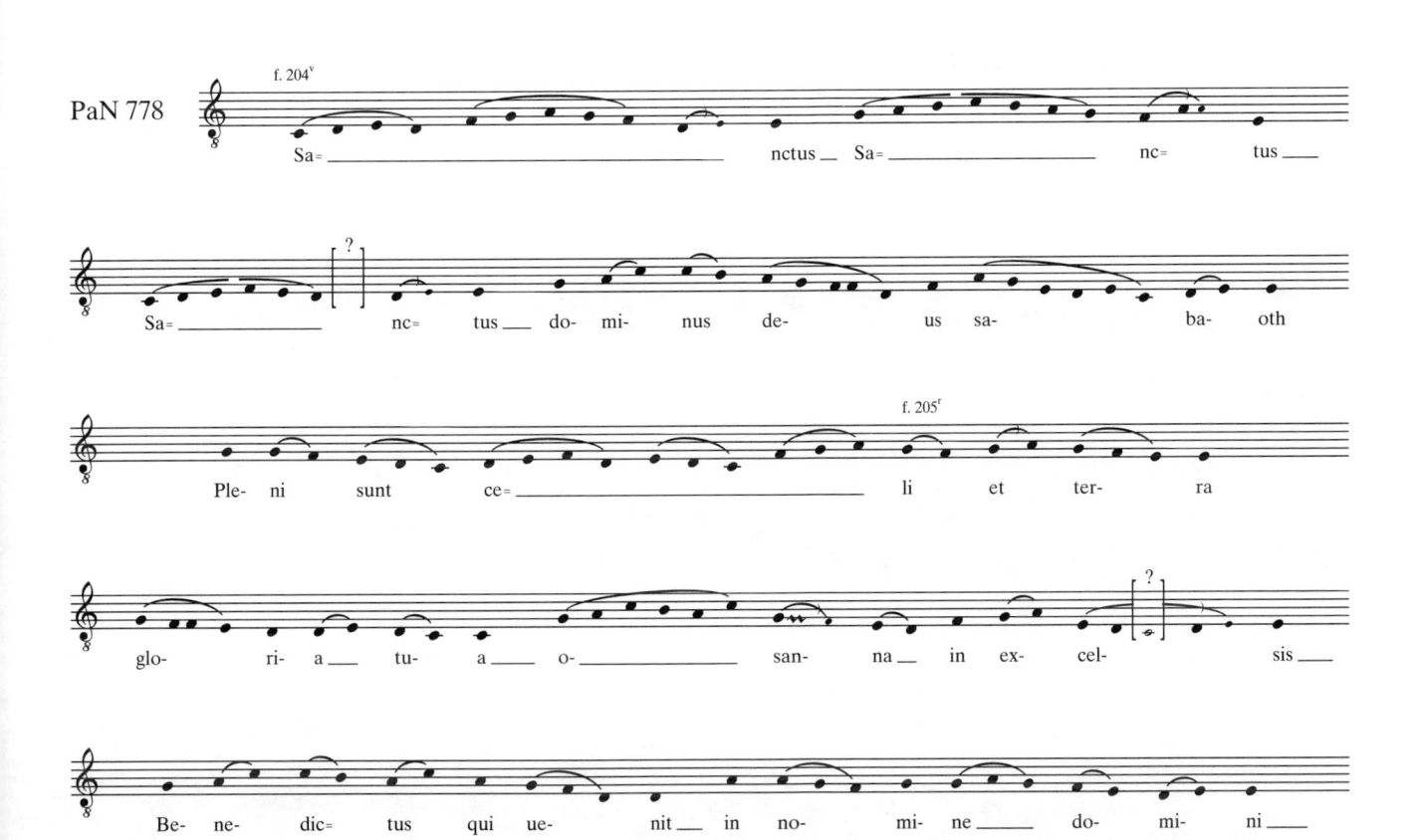

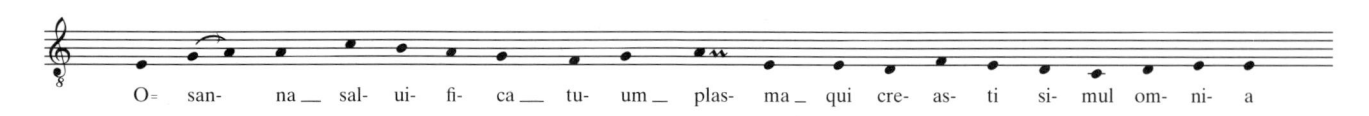

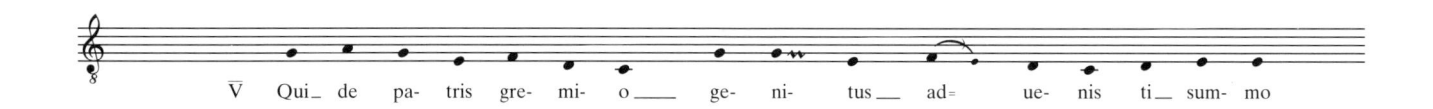

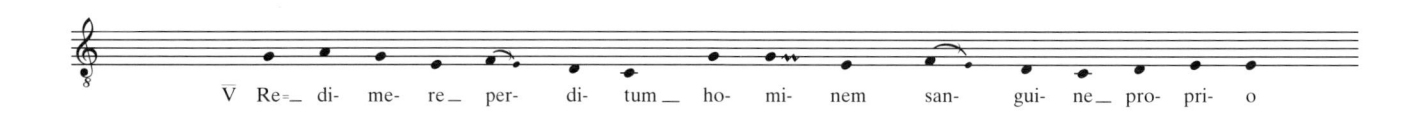

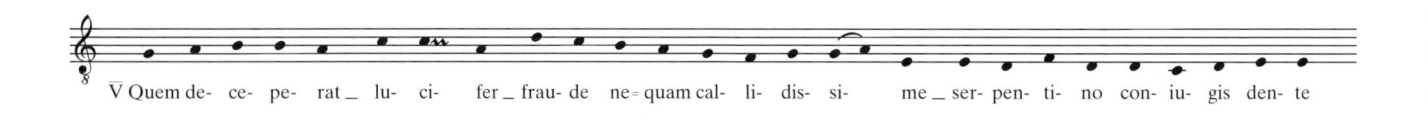

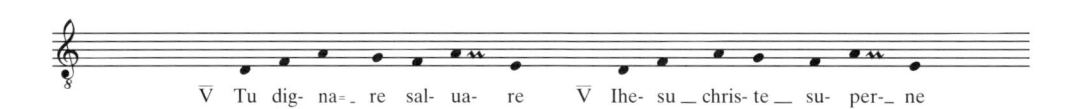

O- san- na — sal- ui- fi- ca — tu- um — plas- ma — qui cre- as- ti si- mul om- ni- a

℣ Ti- bi laus et ho- nor — de- cet et — glo- ri- a — rex e- ter= ne in — se- cu- la

℣ Qui — de pa- tris gre- mi- o — ge- ni- tus ad= ue- nis ti — sum- mo

℣ Re= di- me- re — per- di- tum — ho- mi- nem san- gui- ne pro- pri- o

℣ Quem de- ce- pe- rat — lu- ci- fer — frau- de ne= quam cal- li- dis- si- me — ser- pen- ti- no con- iu- gis den- te

℣ Quem ex- pu- le- rat — pro- pe- re — hoc in= ex- o cri- mi- ne pa- ra- di- si car- di- ne at- que li- mi- te

℣ Tu dig- na= re sal- ua- re ℣ Ihe- su — chris- te — su- per- ne

in ex- ce= l- si- s

f. 204ᵛ (bottom)

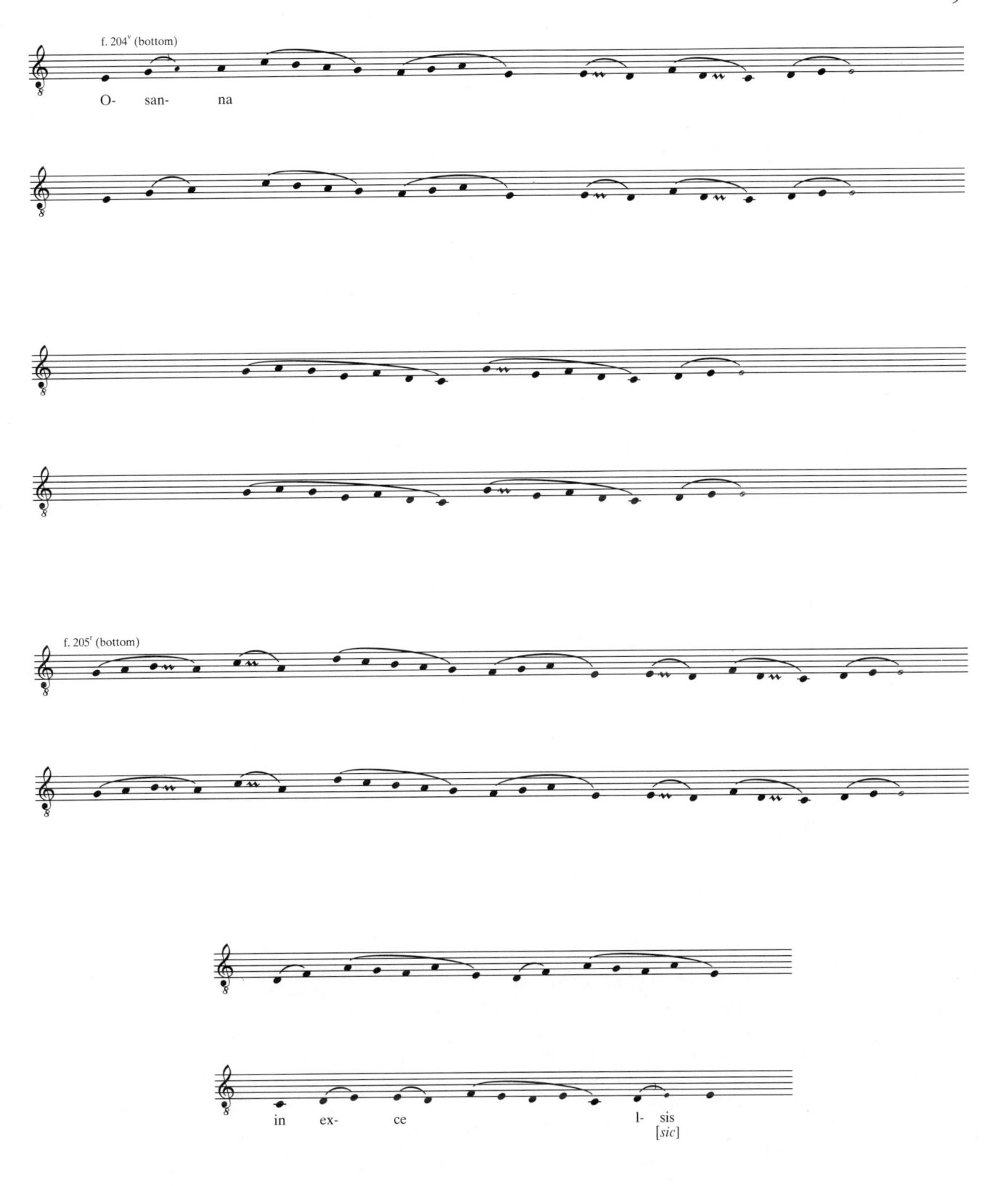

O- san- na

f. 205ʳ (bottom)

in ex- ce l- sis
[sic]

In the version of PaN 778 above, the Hosanna melisma was not incorporated in the Sanctus and prosa text but was notated so as to correspond exactly with the prosa melody, *in campo aperto* across the bottom of fol. 204^v and extending right across the bottom of fol. 205^r. The version is typical of Aquitanian versions of the prosa, although it has the wording [1 .^{II}] *Tibi laus . . .* instead of the standard *Temet laus*. Nevertheless, the music for the prosa varies widely in some of the manuscripts, in spite of the melodic control supposedly exercised by the Hosanna melisma, which is usually present. (Urb 602 omits the Hosanna melisma altogether.) The version of Urb 602 could not have been copied directly from the PaN 778 version or from any other known Aquitanian version. Yet it is possible to imagine the Cassinese version as having finally evolved through intermediate versions from one of these, whereas it is impossible to imagine it as having evolved from any of the Catalonian-Spanish versions, which developed their own very different idiosyncracies. For instance, the Compostela Codex replaces the franculus cadence in [1], for *omnia* and *secula*, with the notes G G FE and C G FE , respectively. The extent of melodic difference and the number and kind of textual variants detailed in CT 7 make it evident that the early transmission of this much sung piece must have involved regional interpretation of adiastematic or imperfectly diastematic neumes, *chacun à son goût*. Thus the piece might have been composed around the year 1000 or a little earlier, before Aquitanian notation had become accurately diastematic.

Hosanna Saluifica tuum plasma fully deserves the term *prosa,* a term often used in Aquitanian manuscripts for the kind of piece usually call *prosula* in BTC. (See Editorial Methods, p. xiii.) It is rubricked *prosa,* without abbreviation, in PaN 1871. The piece is a short sequence, in the east Frankish sense of the word, in Urb 602 having four melodic phrases, each of which is repeated. The length of lines is carefully varied: [1] is fairly long and reaches top c ; [2] is shorter and only reaches a ; [3] is the longest of all (with three internal members instead of two) and reaches d—the only time the note occurs in Sanctus or prosa. Phrase [4] is the shortest, with one member only—its top note, a , capping a d-minor "subtonic" triad outline just before the final on E . As mentioned above, all phrases except [4] end with a franculus cadence approached from the C below.

The number of syllables in each of the members of a versicle (as in the versicle [♂s 1 .^{I}]) is generally the same as in its matching versicle (here, [1 .^{II}]). But sometimes the numbers of syllables in corresponding versicles diverge, as can be seen under Meter, above. Word accent seldom matches exactly. The melody in Urb 602 usually accommodates these irregularities, except for the imbalance in length and line breaks of [3]. Here the music stretches but poorly to accommodate the long versicle [3 .^{II}], with its rhyming triolet *hoc in ceno crimine, paradysi cardine,* and *adque limine.*

The high theme of the text is God's salvation of fallen man.

> Of Man's First Disobedience, and the Fruit
> Of that Forbidden Tree, whose mortal taste
> Brought Death into the World, and all our woe,
> With loss of Eden, till one great Man
> Restore us . . .

The Urb 602 reading in verset [3 .^{II}], *hoc in ceno crimine* (recte *hoc in cenum crimine*), is also found in PaN 495, Vich 105, and the two Limoges manuscripts PaN 1139 and PaN 1086 having Thannabaur 214 for the Sanctus. It is less satisfactory than the reading *hoc innexum crimine* preferred for the CT 7 text. The real problem for the interpretation of [3 .^{II}] is however this: who is the subject of the verb *expulerat?* Who expelled firstman from Eden? Was it the satanic Lucifer, as in the parallel [3 .^{I}] *Quem deceperat lucifer?* In Genesis, the "Lord God" drives man out from the garden of Eden. In Genesis, the serpent, "more subtle than any other wild creature that the Lord God had made," is never identified with Lucifer (see References, above) nor indeed with Satan.

In spite of these ambiguities, the text is among the best Hosanna pros(ul)as. It is to the credit of the editor of Urb 602 that he recognized its worth and included it, presumably introducing it to the Montecassino repertory. That it found some acceptance can be deduced from its having been copied in Ben 34, some fifty years later.

Sanctus 106
Thannabaur 56; Vatican III

Trope: *Summe pater de quo*
[Hosanna]^2 **Prosa:** *Omnes tua gratia*

Source

BAV Urb. lat. 602, fols. 67^r–68^v (seventh of twelve collected Sanctus). Rubric:

Feria iij in alb. Et in dedic eccl.

Notes on the Melody

References: Boe, "Ordinary in English," 2:1013–15 and 3:420–23; Hiley, *Western Plainchant,* pp. 230–31; Hiley, "Ordinary of Mass Chants in English, North French and Sicilian MSS," p. 100; MMMA 17, Th 56 (STr 215, HPr 120); and *New Grove* 16:464.

For a similar melody, see BTC II/1, pp. 49–51 and 116 (Melnicki 48, *Kyrie fons bonitatis* and *Kyrie per quem subsistit*).

The only Italian source for the Sanctus melody is Urb 602. The Cassinese editor got it from the Norman-Sicilian repertory (as will be seen) where it was firmly established with the same trope and Hosanna prosa as in Urb 602. Other concordances for the Sanctus are exclusively French and chiefly northern French, as those from Nevers (PaN 9449, dated 1059–60, and PaN 1235) and St. Evroult (PaN 10508). One of the very few Cluny graduals to survive, PaN 1087 (dated "between 994 and 1048" by Thannabaur and "third quarter 11th c." by Hiley), has the Sanctus without trope or prosa.

The Sanctus melody must therefore have been composed in northern France during the first half of the eleventh century. The acclamations derive from anaphoral chant. The kernel Gab persists in the acclamations in some versions (including that of Urb 602), but in others the b has as often been raised to c as in Vatican Sanctus III, which is the version given by Thannabaur at melody 56. (Also see the variant in the Norman-Sicilian manuscript Ma 19421, transcribed in Hiley's *Western Plainchant*, that Thannabaur gives at the bottom of his p. 143. Thannabaur gives the b-version from the Norman St. Évroult manuscript PaN 10508 as a variant at the bottom of p. 148.) The melody was usually attached to *Summe pater de quo* but to no other Sanctus trope. Often it was joined to the older **Hosanna** prosa *Omnes tua gratia,* either together with *Summe pater de quo* or separately. (The prosa, however, was sung with other Sanctus melodies as well; see below.)

The Urb 602 version must have been copied from an exemplar having the following characteristics: b's not raised to c's in the *Sanctus* acclamations; Vs [4] *Cui pueri laudes* included in the trope *Summe pater de quo*; and the **Hosanna** prosa **Omnes tua gratia** attached. All these features are found in Ma 288, the earliest of the three chief Norman-Sicilian manuscripts, which Hiley dates "ca. 1100." Apart from Urb 602, no other known source combines all these features. (See CT 7, no. 154, for details of the concordances.)

That a Sanctus from the Norman-Sicilian repertory should have been copied into Urb 602 is by no means surprising: several other ordinary chants in that manuscript were borrowed from this repertory. (See BTC II/1, pp. xiii, xxiv–xxv, and xxxii.) The possibility that the Sicilian version of Ma 288 might instead have been copied from Montecassino cannot be entertained in light of the concordances, their dates, and the history of Norman penetration into south Italy.

The E-mode Sanctus melody uses motives or figures, but not a motive row. (See p. 94, above.) Its loose structure joins patterns from mode 4 to those of mode 3 but fails to suggest Ionian C mode, as some E-mode tunes do. In the examples below, the motives or figures are labeled A and B; the two recurring cadential patterns are labeled α and β.

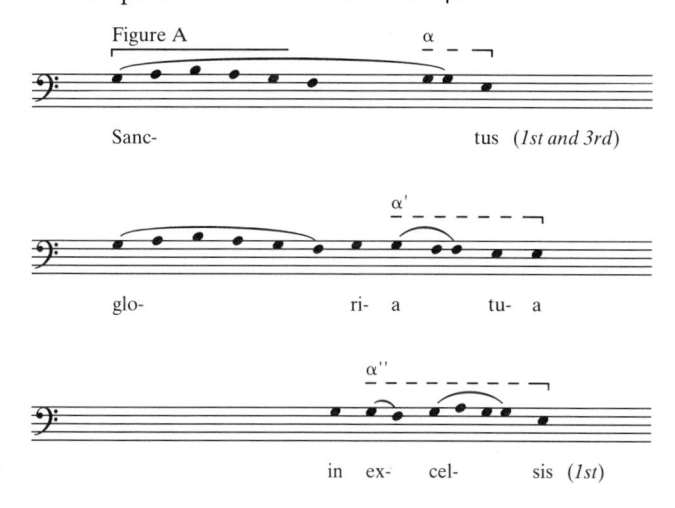

Figure A derives from anaphoral chant. Cadence α emphasizes the fall of a minor third, from G to E, sometimes with intervenient F (that is, GFE). The F is regularly intervenient in certain versions of the melody. Figure B lies low in the range and exposes or implies a D-minor triad outline, as in the second Hosanna.

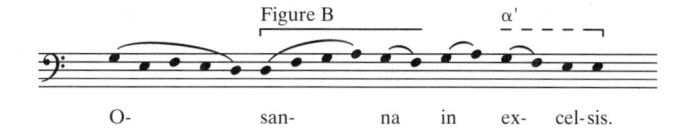

In some versions—the Vatican III Sanctus, for instance—Hosanna and *Deus sabaoth* use figure B, just as above. In Urb 602, however, *deus sabaoth* reads

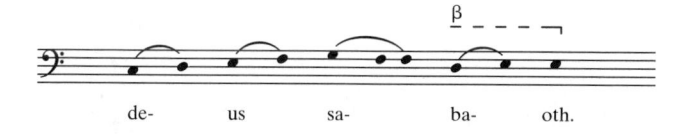

An altered form of figure A with the note b raised to c—transposed down a fifth as in the first example below—is used in the Urb 602 version of the melody to begin phrases.

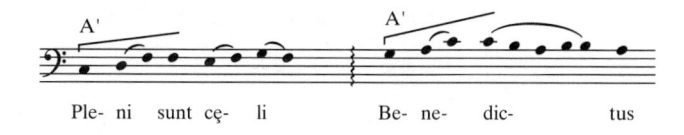

Perhaps the process of raising E's and b's to F's and C's, respectively, began with this figure, labeled A' above.

An alternative cadence, β, approaches the final from below. Cadence β assumes importance in the melodies for the trope and the prosa.

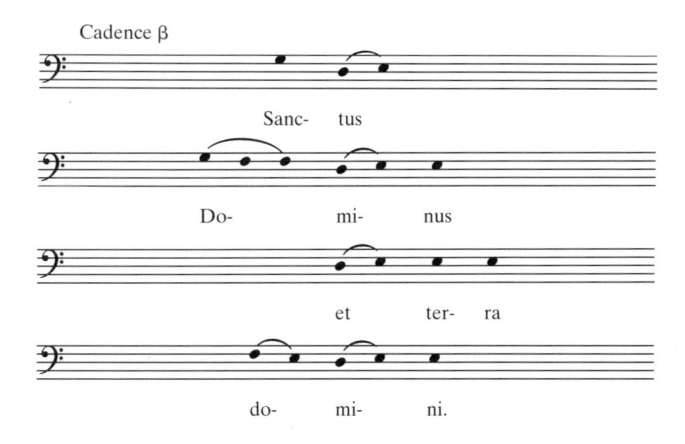

Cadence β

Sanc- tus

Do- mi- nus

et ter- ra

do- mi- ni.

Not only cadence β but most of the other figures and cadences—especially A'—find use in the trope melody, as can be seen in the main text. (The melody for the prosa *[Hosanna] Omnes tua gratia* is discussed below, with the text of the prosa.)

NOTES ON *Summe pater de quo*

References: AH 47, no. 256; CT 7, pp. 38–41, 190–91 (no. 154, citing Rom. 11:36, I Cor. 8:6, and Frankish writers), and 355; Hiley, "The Norman Chant Traditions," p. 29; Hiley, *Western Plainchant*, pp. 230–31; Ireland 1:141 and 2:72–77; and Planchart, 1:278–83 and 2:321–23.

For the text as Agnus Dei trope (in PaN 10508 and PaN 7185), see CT 4, pp. 87ff.

Meter: Hexameters, but flawed (§) in Vs [1] (*principĭa* —short syllable where long is needed; *piē*—where the meter demands the vocative *piĕ*).

Source of text and translation below: Urb 602

Sanctus.

[1] Summe pater de quo mundi principia constant. §

Sanctus.

[2] Filius omnipotens per quem patris est pie uelle. §

Sanctus.

[3] Spiritus in quo par uirtus sine fine refulget.

Dominus deus sabaoth.
Pleni sunt cęli et terra gloria tua.
Osanna in excelsis.

[4] Cui pueri laudes concordi uoce canebant.
Benedictus qui uenit in nomine domini.

[✠Ps 1] Omnes tua gratia
quos a morte redemisti perpetua

[2 .I] Morte tua uim mortis
cum principe proculcans
uite nos reparas.

[2 .II] Deo patri dans carum
te pro nobis pretium
et uiuam hostiam.

[3 .I] Tecum nos resuscita/
Tecum in cęlis colloca
et regni largiaris consortia.

[3 .II] Te ergo deposcimus
ut cum iudex adueneris
cunctorum discernere merita

[4 .I] **Nos cum angelis / et sanctis socies**
[4 .II] **cum quibus tibi canamus**
O _____ sanna in excelsis.
*
Holy,

[1] O highest Father,
from whom the foundations of the world derive;
Holy,

[2] The almighty Son,
through whom the Father works his holy will;
Holy,

[3] The Spirit,
in whom equal virtue shines endlessly:

Lord God of hosts!
Heaven and earth are full of thy glory.
Hosanna in the highest!

[4] To whom children sang praises
with harmonious voice:

Blessed is he that comes in the name of the Lord.

[✠Ps 1] [HOSANNA = SAVE] all by thy grace, those
whom thou hast redeemed from eternal death.

[2 .I] Smiting death's power and [death's] prince
by thy death
thou dost restore us to life,

[2 .II] Giving thyself to God the Father
as the dear price for us
and a living sacrifice.

[3 .I] Raise us up with thee;
place [us] with thee in heaven
and bestow the fellowship of the kingdom.

[3 .II] We therefore pray thee,
that when thou shalt come as Judge
to sift the merits of all:

[4 .I] Thou wilt join us
with the angels and the saints,

[4 .II] with whom let us sing to thee:
Hosanna _____ in the highest!

Some versions include only the three trinitarian interpolations between the *Sanctus* acclamations. It is not entirely clear from the concordances that Vs [4], introducing *Benedictus qui uenit,* is a later addition (see CT 7). The hexameters of the first two verses are slightly marred by incorrect vowel quantities (see Meter, above). As usual, the presence of quantitative meters in the text hardly affects the musical setting.

The trope melody redeploys the figures of the Sanctus (see above) with much more extensive use of the low cadence β, approaching the final, E, from below. As it stands in Urb 602, the trope melody seems to have been meant for a version of Sanctus with b's raised to c's: the figure A' occurs three times, and A never occurs. (Compare [2] . . . *per quem;* [3] *spiritus;* and [4] *Cui pueri.* See Notes on the Melody, above.) Certainly the effect of Sanctus and trope sung together is of an organic and harmonious whole, and one sees why the trope is found only with Thannabaur 56. (In CT 7, Thannabaur 49 is listed on p. 191 as occurring with *Summe pater de quo* as well as Thannabaur 56. Thannabaur does not give *Summe pater de quo* as one of the tropes occurring with melody 49; neither does Thannabaur 49 appear with *Summe pater de quo* anywhere in the "Aperçu des manuscrits" of CT 7 itself for any of the sources given for *Summe pater de quo.* at no. 154.)

Notes on *[Hosanna] Omnes tua gratia*

References: AH 47, no. 339; CT 7, pp. 137–38 (no. 80), 355, 370 (pl. 6, Ox 775), 374 (pl. 10, Ma 19421), and 375 (pl. 11, PaA 1169); Boe, "Ordinary in English," 3:106–07, pl. 11 (facsimile from CC 473); Hiley, *Western Plainchant,* p. 231; Ireland, 2:78–80; Planchart, 1:277–81 and 2:9, 19, and 320.

Meter

	Words	Melodic elements, with first and last notes	
[℞s 1]	7pp + 12pp	x + y	E→E, E→E
[2 .I]	7p + 7p + 6pp	a + b + c	G→G, a→E, E→E
[2 .II]	7p + 7pp + 6pp	a + b + c	G→G, a→E, E→E
[3 .I]	7pp + 8pp + 11pp	d + e + f	F→E, F→D, E→E
[3 .II]	7pp + 8pp + 9pp	d + e + f'	F→E, F→D, ? E
[4 .I]	5pp + 6pp	g + h	F→C, D→E
[4 .II]	8p	g'	F→C→E

Assonance in *-a* predominates. (Text and translation from Urb 602 are given with the trope *Summe pater de quo,* above.)

[Hosanna] Omnes tua gratia is a miniature prosa like ***Hosanna Saluifica tuum plasma*** (see above, pp. 104 and 104) where the number of syllables in paired versicles is usually symmetrical. Only the unequal number of syllables at the ends of [3 .I] and [3 .II] disturbs the symmetry of *[Hosanna] Omnes tua gratia.* Here the asymmetry is even welcome. Phrases [2] and [3] each consist of three members having from six to eight syllables (usually seven), one note to each syllable—with a single exception. Notes are often repeated in pairs at the same pitch: it is this unusual melodic feature, also found in certain sequences, that sets *[Hosanna] Omnes tua gratia* apart. No other Hosanna pros(ul)a sung in south Italy is like it.

The range of the mode-4 melody is narrow, not exceeding the interval of a seventh. Individual phrase members are confined within narrower range segments. Nevertheless, the seven notes are employed in varied patterns, which are better described as intriguing than as "soaring." (See under Meter, above, where the pitches of the first and last notes of members of phrases are given in the right-hand column.)

Word accent is associated with—or is rather dissociated from—the music in a peculiar way, not typical of Italian settings of rhythmical Latin verse or of French "rhythmical-mode-1" settings of accentual Latin poetry. Any modern attempt to impose regular rhythmical patterns on the syllabic melody comes to naught, for no pattern can be maintained. Of course, the last note of each phrase member can and should be lengthened before a breath. Otherwise, the tune must be sung isometrically. The composer-author seems to have been indifferent to Latin word accent.

[Hosanna] Omnes tua gratia is older than Sanctus Thannabaur 56 and older than the trope *Summe pater de quo.* It appears with Thannabaur 154 (following *Deus pater ingenitus*) in both Winchester tropers, in Cai 75 and Apt 17, and in the Nevers manuscripts PaN 9449 and PaN 1235, where the prosa is itself divided up as a Sanctus trope within the base text. It appears with Thannabaur 56 in PaN 778, but without trope, transposed down one step to a D final. It also appears with both Thannabaur 56 and *Summe pater de quo* in the Norman manuscripts Lo 13 and PaN 10508, and in all three chief Norman-Sicilian manuscripts,

Ma 288, Ma 289, and Ma 19421. (Hiley transcribes the Ma 19421 version in *Western Plainchant,* ex. II.23.16.) On the basis of the shared features cited above, I conclude the Urb 602 editor must have found the particular combination of features used there in a Norman-Sicilian manuscript like Ma 288.

Urb 602 also shares the variant [2 .ᴵᴵ] *reparas* (for *reparans*) with the three chief Norman-Sicilian manuscripts. According to CT 7, the only other sources with this variant are PaN 778, PaN 1235, and Apt 17, and none of these can have served as a model for Urb 602. PaN 778 notates the piece with a D final and does not have *Summe pater de quo,* as mentioned; PaN 1235 distributes the prosa as a trope; and PaN 1235 and Apt 17 have Thannabaur 154, not Thannabaur 56, as the Sanctus melody. Among the manuscripts surveyed, only a Norman-Sicilian version can be regarded as a possible source for the version of Urb 602.

Iversen points out that the redistribution of text in certain manuscripts must have come about through failure to understand the meaning of *Hosanna* as "save now." In the present piece, *Osanna* functions as a verbal imperative whose object is the accusative *omnes:* "Save all by thy grace!": *Omnes tua gratia* is correctly placed immediately after *Osanna* of the base text in PaN 778, for instance. But when the word *Osanna* was separated or even omitted—as unfortunately in Urb 602—the isolated opening line of the prosa makes no sense, regardless of whether *Omnes* is taken as accusative or nominative. To remedy this apparent fault, some editors inserted the borrowed trope line *Collaudemus dominum eia* before **Omnes tua gratia** to supply a verb for *Omnes,* understood as nominative. The prosa **Omnes tua gratia** was then sometimes moved back in the base text to be closer to *Collaudemus dominum eia.* (See the notes in CT 7.) The word *Osanna* should certainly be restored before the prosa in a performance of the Urb 602 version. The music for the restored *Osanna* could best be borrowed from the first *Osanna in excelsis* of the Sanctus melody, leaving the second *Osanna in excelsis* intact, as in the manuscript.

Sanctus Chants Lacking Tropes or Prosulas in South Italian Sources

Chants with Thannabaur Numbers

Thannabaur 32; Vatican XVII   111

SOURCES: *Montecassino 546, fols. 68ᵛ–69ʳ (fifth of six collected Sanctus). The highest note in the melody is e.

*Benevento 38, fol. 167ʳ (fourth of six collected Sanctus entered after the completion of the original MS). Copied *in campo aperto* with accurately diastematic notation no earlier than the third quarter of the eleventh century. The highest note is e.

*Benevento 34, fol. 284ʳ (fourth of eight collected Sanctus—the first of two without tropes, which are preceded by three Sanctus with tropes and followed, after Agnus Dei and a MS lacuna, by three more troped Sanctus). Notated with F clef and red line and c clef throughout. A yellow line may have been used for c, but if once present, it is now entirely faded. The melody rises to f at *sabaoth* and at *osanna*.

REFERENCES: Boe, "Ordinary in English," 2:870–84 and 3:353–57; Hiley, "Ordinary of Mass Chants in English, North French and Sicilian MSS," p. 97; MGG 11, col. 1351; MMMA 17, Th 32; Thannabaur, pp. 58 and 77 (with analysis).

See BTC II/1, pp. 80 and 203 (Melnicki 95, Variation).

NOTES: The melody is one of the two most copied Sanctus: Thannabaur found it in 385 places in 321 of the manuscripts he examined. (He says its rival for popularity, Thannabaur 49, Vatican IV, appears in 478 places in 311 manuscripts.) Of the sources he gives, 51 are French, 88 German, 21 east European, 1 Friulian, and 14 Iberian, plus 61 from centralized monastic and preaching orders, in addition to 3 Norman-Sicilian and 3 English manuscripts. (There are more; Hiley lists 6 Norman-Sicilian and 16 English manuscripts that contain Thannabaur 32.) Whatever their accuracy, the numbers certainly show how often and how widely this melody was sung. Thannabaur's earliest northern French source is Cai 75 (according to Planchart, from "Arras, St. Vaast, middle 11th century or slightly earlier"). The first German manuscripts listed by Thannabaur are from the twelfth century; the earliest central and northern Italian sources, from the late eleventh century. At least seventeen tropes and eight Hosanna pros(ul)as are known to have been associated with this Sanctus.

Thannabaur 32 belongs to a group of tunes built upon the major "tonic" triad and using the authentic ambitus of the major scale, a group widely sung in the later middle ages. (Cf. Vatican Kyrie and Gloria VIII and Sanctus and Agnus Dei IX.) The three late south Italian forms of the melody given in the main text diverge a good deal from one another. Both MC 546 and Ben 38 have e as the top note; Ben 34 has a version that rises to f, as in Vatican Sanctus XVII.

The melody uses modified motive-row technique, like its rival, Thannabaur 49. (See above, pp. 94–95.) The opening *Sanctus* and *Dominus deus* use one row with only two motives, the first of which (*a* in the example below) is a simplified inversion of the second (*b*). In the second row—which is structurally primary and should first be viewed as it begins at *Benedictus qui uenit* and continues through the second *Osanna in excelsis*—motive 1 is doubled back by repetition at *in nomine domini* (the syllable *do-* taking the notes de). On its second occurrence, motive *b* (*-minus deus*) leads directly into motive 2 of row II, functioning as a simplified replacement for motive 1 of row II and thus as a common-motive pivot between rows. This motive *b*, the slightly decorated upward major triad outline, is of course preceded by its inverted form, the descending major triad, of motive *a*. A link of four notes is added at *Pleni sunt*, between motives 2 and 3. The rotation of row II therefore reads:

	1'	2	3
Cycle 1:	(Do-)minus deus	sabaoth (Pleni sunt)	cęli et terra
	1		
Cycle 2:	gloria tua.	O- san-	na in excelsis.
Cycle 3:	Benedictus qui uenit in nomine domini.	O- san-	na in excelsis.

The motive rows are given below according to the version of the melody in MC 546.

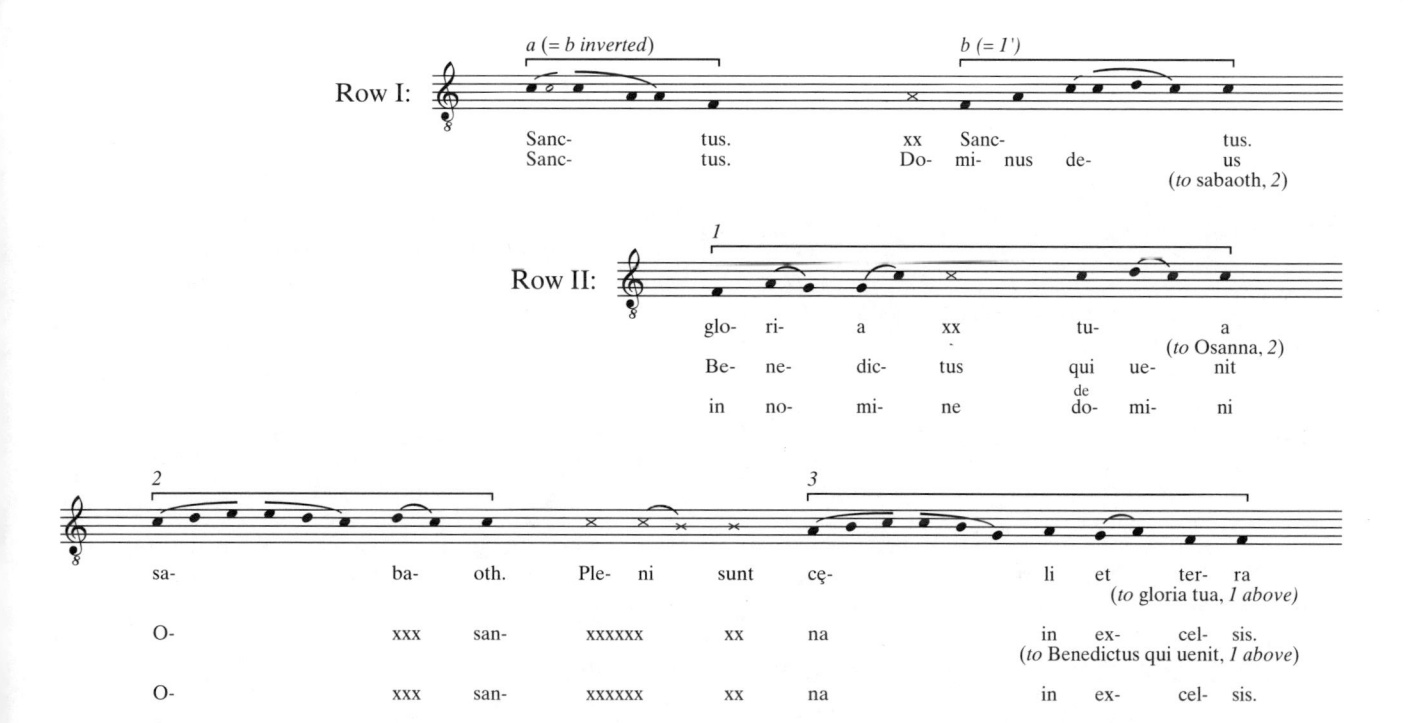

Thannabaur 41, Var. (p. 133) 114
Vatican XVIII

SOURCES: *Benevento 38, fol. 167[r–v] (last of six collected Sanctus entered after the completion of the original MS). Copied *in campo aperto* with accurately diastematic notation no earlier than the third quarter of the eleventh century.

*Rome, Bibl. Casanatense 1574, p. 36, as numbered at the top of the leaves (after Sursum corda and the common preface—the ending is given in letter notation below—and before the conclusion for proper prefaces *ET IDEO CVM ANGELIS ET ARCHANGELIS ⁖ CVM TRONIS ET DOMINATIONIBVS. CVMQVE OMNI MILITIA CĘLESTIS EXERCITVS YMNVM GLORIĘ TVAE CANIMVS SINE FINE DICENTES ⁖).* RoC 1574 is a monastic compendium from p. 76 onwards, containing among other things an office antiphoner written in ordinary minuscule and very small Beneventan notation that begins on p. 188. The first part of the MS includes the priest's prayers for the ordinary of the mass. The beginning of the canon has been torn out, after the proper-preface conclusion, but the canon continues on p. 40. Sanctus and the proper-preface conclusion are written in mixed capitals; common preface, Sanctus, and proper-preface conclusion have Beneventan notation *in campo aperto*. The acuasta is employed as a liquescent note, without regard for its traditional use to indicate low or unaccented syllables or notes. The MS comes from a monastery on the fringes of the Beneventan zone, perhaps Sant'Angelo di Gaeta, where it belonged in the seventeenth century. (See above, under Border-Area Sources, pp. 6 and 38.) The common preface, here pitched to correspond with the notation in the F hexachord of the Sanctus as found in the main text of the edition, ends as follows:

    F   Ga♭♭aGa♭a
   cum quibus et nostras uoces

   G a♭ ♭♭ ♭♭ ♭a Ga♭ a
   ut admitti iubeas deprecamur ⁖

  a♭ aa Ga ♭ aGaF FG a Ga G
  supplici confessi-o- ne dicentes ⁖

*Rome, Bibl. Vallicelliana B 23, fol. 143[v] (immediately before a private prayer for the celebrant, *Aperi domine os meum ad benedicendum nomen sanctum tuum,* and immediately after the conclusion for proper prefaces, *Et ideo . . . dicentes,* given in letter notation below, which is in turn preceded by a notated Sursum corda and entire common preface and a single unnotated proper preface, *Eterne deus. Qui corporali ieiunio uitia comprimis. mentem eleuas. uirtutem largiris et premia, Per christum dominum.,* for Lent). Preface, preface conclusion, and Sanctus were noted *in campo aperto* with clearly heightened neumes blending central Italian and Beneventan features, probably soon after the verbal text was completed. A c clef (or C clef?) and yellow line and, perhaps still later, an intermittent red line for f (or F?) were added, beginning at *Dominus uobiscum* and continuing throughout. Thus *dicentes* of the proper-preface conclusion ends e de d (or E DE D). The Sanctus is heightened so as graphically to begin e ee d (or possibly E EE D) in relation to the proper-preface conclusion but was supplied with low F clef and red line, so as in fact to read a aa G. (See pl. 2.)

The early twelfth-century monastic full missal, written in ordinary minuscule throughout, has been variously assigned to the abbeys of Sant'Eutizio, Val Castoriana (near Norcia), San Bartolomeo di Trisulti (southwest of Subiaco in the Ernici range), or to "the region of Macerata" (by Kelly). However, the monastery of San Bartolomeo di Norcia seems now to be a more likely source. (See above, under Border-Area Sources, pp. 6 and 47.) This version from central Italy is included as an early witness for Thannabaur 41, one that was not included in Thannabaur's index.

The conclusion for proper prefaces, which leads directly into the Sanctus as given in the main text, as corrected reads

  de feed cded cd dd d f f f fe e de e e
  ET i d e o cum angelis et archangelis

  ℓ
  e df ee e e dc cd e de d d
 *cum thronis et d o m i n a t i o n i b u s

  ce dc d . . . . fe de e e
  Cumque omni militia** celestis exercitus

  efg ee df ff f fe d e e
  ymnum glorię tuę canimus

  e e dc cd e de dd
  sine fine dicentes

*The position of the c clef, one step too high, in the MS has been corrected by a dot.
**e erased.

Benevento 34, fol. 266[r] (in the right-hand margin, adjacent to the off *Domine iesu christe rex glorię* of the mass *Requiem eternam:* preceded in the margin by the incipit *Kyrie leyson* for the melody Melnicki 101—the same as the modern Kyrie in the mass for the dead, Vatican edition—and followed in the margin by the incipit *Agnus dei qui tollis* for the melody Schildbach 101, Vatican XVIII—also the same as the modern Agnus Dei for the dead). All three chants are written in a crude fourteenth-century Gothic script and square notation on three or four lines. All pieces are incorrectly cleffed: the Sanctus begins on F. The binder's knife has cut off the continuation of the incipits.

ALTAR BOOK INCIPITS: Montecassino 339, fol. 64[v] = p. 132 (first of two Sanctus incipits, each pendant to an original Sursum corda and preface notated *in campo aperto*.). The Sacramentary of Desiderius, abbot of Montecassino, 1058–87. The Sanctus incipit is attached to the ending of the common preface for Sundays and feasts, the first of a series and the only one for which the original notation remains unerased—although what must have been an illuminated leaf with gold ground for the words *VERE DIGNVM ET IVSTVM EST* has been torn out between the present fols. 63 and 64, that is, between pp. 130 and 131. The Sanctus incipit is immediately followed by the fixed conclusion for proper prefaces, *Et ideo . . . sine fine dicentes.,* in turn followed by a slightly later corrected and more elaborately neumatic version of the same. (A very much later corrected version of the dialogue and common preface follows, which replaces the original everyday setting as described in the entry immediately below. Also see Cassinese Sources, pp. 12 and 23 above.) If transcribed at the F pitch of the Sanctus versions in the main text, the common preface for Sundays and feasts with its Sanctus incipit concludes thus:

ℓ ℓ ⤻
F a G a ♭ G G F a GF Ga G ♭ a a a a Ga a
Cum quibus et nostras uoces ut admitti iubeas deprecamur

ℓ ℓ   →
♭ a G a ♭ a GF FG a aa G
supplici c o n f e s s i o n e dicentes.

F GaG aG   F GaG aG   F GaG aG
S ⟨a n⟩ c ⟨t u⟩ s. S ⟨a n⟩ c ⟨t u⟩ s. S ⟨a n⟩ c⟨t u⟩ s.

Rubric on p. 130 for this first Sursum corda, preface, and Sanctus incipit: *In dominicis seu festis diebus.*

Montecassino 339, fol. 65ᵛ = p. 134 (second of two Sanctus incipits, each pendant to a Sursum corda and preface originally notated *in campo aperto*). The incipit is attached to the ending of the now but partly legible original everyday common preface, the notes for which were erased and replaced by a version like the modern Vatican-edition ferial preface. The replacement was written in Metz notation of the late thirteenth or early fourteenth century on three lines, the topmost of which is red. The original everyday common preface and Sanctus incipit were immediately followed by the fixed conclusion *Et ideo . . . dicentes.,* of which only the first notes can now be read. This notation was likewise replaced by notes in the same Metz style.

A similarly corrected version of the Sunday and festal Sursum corda and common preface follows, intended to replace the unerased original notation of the MC 339 first setting described above (which was probably left untouched to avoid damaging the illumination and gold ground of a now missing folio). What the original and now erased third version in this sacramentary might have been can only be guessed. (See Cassinese Sources, pp. 2 and 11, above.)

If transcribed at the F pitch of the Sanctus versions in the main text, the still legible ending of the original version of the everyday common preface reads thus:

ℓ   ℓ
F G a ♭ ♭ a Ga a G a ♭ ♭ a a ♭ a Ga a
Cum quibus et nostras uoces ut admitti iubeas deprecamur

    ℓ   ⤻
♭ a a G a♭ a G F G Ga G
supplici c o n f e s s i o n e dicentes.

a G aG a G aG a G aG
S ⟨ a n⟩ c⟨t u⟩ s. S⟨ a n⟩ c ⟨t u⟩ s. S⟨ a n⟩ c⟨t u⟩ s.

Rubric on p. 133 for the second Sursum corda, preface, and Sanctus incipit: *In cotidianis diebus.*

BAV Vat. lat. 6082, fol. 145ᵛ (a Sanctus incipit attached to the second of two common-preface chants in the *ordo missae* in the Easter vigil mass and directly followed by the proper-preface conclusion *Et ideo . . . dicentes. S̄cs. S̄cs. S̄cs.*—where the incipit is not notated—and then by the rest of the canon of the mass). Precisely heightened notation *in campo aperto,* in a twelfth-century full missal from the environs of Montecassino. The second common-preface chant for the most part is identical with the version *In dominicis seu festis diebus* of MC 339; the Sanctus incipit, precisely so. (See the source listing for MC 339, fol. 64ᵛ = p. 132, immediately above; also see Cassinese Sources, pp. 3–4.)

Zagreb, MR 166, p. 205 (a Sanctus incipit attached to the last of five common-preface chants—the fourth and fifth of which follow a group of unnotated proper prefaces inserted after the third common preface—and followed by a rubric introducing the unnotated Latin and Greek trisagion; a private prayer for the celebrant, *Aperi os meum*; a series of insertions *infra āc⟨tionem⟩* for the great festivals, beginning with Christmas; and, finally, the rest of the canon). Notated *in campo aperto* with accurately diastematic neumes similar to those of Urb 602 or of the second music scribe of Ben 35. (The first three common prefaces were notated by a slightly different, less skilled hand; see the more extended discussion of the MS and its prefaces under Cassinese Sources, p. 4 above.) The fifth common preface is a uniquely elaborated *tonus sollemnior,* based on Cassinese versions found in the other four prefaces. If transcribed at the F pitch used in the main text for versions of Thannabaur 41, the end of the preface and the Sanctus incipit read thus:

⤻ ℓ   ℓ   ⤻ ℓ
FGa GFG ♭ G a GG F a GF G [illegible . . . .] a Ga a
Cum quibus et nostras uoces ut admitti iubeas deprecamur

 Ga♭ a a G a♭ a GF FG a Ga G
 supplici c o n f e s s i o n e dicentes.

ℓ   ℓ   ℓ
a aG a aG a aG
S⟨anctus⟩. S⟨anctus⟩. S⟨anctus⟩.

Rubric introducing the fifth common preface:

Item ī festiuitatibus s̄corum.

BAV Ottob. lat. 576, fol. 226ʳ (the second of three Sanctus incipits respectively following two common prefaces and the proper-preface conclusion *Et ideo . . . dicentes,* of which incipits only the second and third have notation). Late Beneventan neumes *in campo aperto.* (See p. 5 above. The missal segment from the thirteenth century with the prefaces and Sanctus incipits is the latest of such sources.) If transcribed at the F pitch used in the main text for Thannabaur 41, the end of the preface and Sanctus incipit read

      ⤻ ⤻
F a G a ♭ G G F a GF Ga G ♭ a a ♭ a Ga a
Cum quibus et nostras uoces ut admitti iubeas deprecamur

ℓ   ℓ   ⤻
♭ a G a ♭ a GF FG a Ga G
supplici c o n f e s s i o n e dicentes.
FGa GF FGa GF ℓ
       a G
S⟨an⟩c⟨tu⟩s. S⟨an⟩c⟨tu⟩s. S⟨an⟩c⟨tu⟩s.

Rubric introducing the second common preface:

In dominicis et in sollemnitatibus.

REFERENCES: Apel, *Gregorian Chant,* pp. 415–16; Boe, "Ordinary in English," 2:1063–69 and 3:456–58; Maria Clara Di Franco and Viviana Jemolo, "Nuove testimonanze di scrittura beneventana," *Studi medievali,* serie terza, 8 (1967): 864–66; Hiley, *Western Plainchant,* p. 161; Levy, "Byzantine Sanctus," pp. 27–28; and MGG 11, cols. 1350–51 with ex.1, facing col. 1360.

In BTC II/1, see the excursus on anaphoral chant, p. xvi. For festal versions of the formula, see BTC II/3, pp. 120 and 120 (Thannabaur 109) and pp. 122 and 124 (BTC-Scs 1). Also see pp. 122 and 126 (BTC-Scs 2), where the similarity of *Benedictus qui uenit in nomine domini* shows the connection between the old Beneventan melody and Thannabaur 41. For sacramentaries and missals having the melody or its incipits, see note 2 under The South Italian Sanctus Repertory, p. lxxv above.

NOTES: The derivation of this Sanctus melody from anaphoral chant and its relation to the preface chants (especially to the modern Roman ferial version), to the Lord's Prayer, and to parts of Te Deum laudamus have been frequently commented upon. (See References, above, where only a selection of the literature devoted to the melody is cited.) Thannabaur's cautious remarks (p. 66) reflect the scarcity of written sources for the melody available to him that were earlier than the thirteenth century:

> Melody no. 41 . . . offers a special case of a peculiar kind: this melody is generally regarded as the oldest Sanctus of all. We must leave undecided whether this assumption—which appeals to the simplicity of the melody and its resemblance to the preface (see Wagner III, p. 456)—will hold water without qualification.

Thannabaur then refers to the instance of the melody in Ben 38 as from the "eleventh century" and as the earliest known to him, but without noticing that the six Sanctus (of which this is the last) were later additions to Ben 38, copied no earlier than the third quarter of the eleventh century. He then cites twelfth and thirteenth-century examples (Pia 65, PaN 1414, and PaN 1107) and continues (p. 72):

> These transformations are related to each other in about the same way as the ferial preface [Thannabaur is referring to the modern versions of the Vatican edition] is related to the festal version. The examples make clear that here we are not dealing with rigid formulas.

Some time ago I suggested that Thannabaur 41 was chiefly used by the celebrant alone when singing "private" votive masses. When, at least from the tenth century onwards, mass began to be celebrated often or even daily by every priest, the "private" service was at first nonetheless *sung*—rather than merely said *sotto voce* by the single celebrating priest, as became customary somewhat later. North of the Alps, full missals were compiled with increasing frequency from the contents of the sacramentary, gradual, and lectionaries to provide all the texts and music necessary for a single liturgist—the celebrant—in one book. (Such missals had already been in common use in Italy much longer, and there for solemn public masses as well.)

My hypothesis attempted (1) to relate the late and relatively infrequent appearance north of the Alps of manuscripts containing Thannabaur 41 to the late and infrequent appearance of manuscripts containing notation for the chants of the preface and Pater noster there; (2) to relate the relatively frequent appearance of this melody or its incipits in south Italy to the early systematic notation surviving there for Sursum corda, prefaces, and Pater noster—usually in full missals, and (3) to relate the appearance of this Sanctus melody in early Carthusian, Cistercian, and Dominican manuscripts to the chants for Sursum corda, prefaces, Lord's Prayer, and lections in these same manuscripts, where (north of the Alps) they seem first to have been written down, stabilized, and reformed. According to the hypothesis, the striking divergences among early forms of Thannabaur 41 would have reflected the fact that uniformity in a chant sung by a solo voice (here the celebrant's) was unnecessary; while the preponderant association of Thannabaur 41 with the mass for the dead (when in fourteenth-century manuscripts it was regularly copied) would have been due to the fact that requiems were the most frequent of such "private" masses. (Cf. the late marginal entries in Ben 34, the last item under Sources, above.) When "private" votive masses, including requiems, came ever more often to be celebrated silently or at least without singing, and when masses for the dead grew ever more penitential in character as emphasis upon the doctrine of purgatory increased (the earlier Alleluia verses being suppressed and *Dies irae* introduced) it was natural that the barren ferial or penitential forms of Thannabaur 41 from "private" masses for the dead should have been substituted for the more melismatic festal south Italian forms of Thannabaur 41 or other more jubilant Sanctus acclamations that had formerly been used when a choir assisted at public masses for the dead. (For example, Sarum use down to the sixteenth century assigned Thannabaur 223, Vatican Sanctus XV, to solemn requiems.)

I now regard the foregoing hypothesis as useful for explaining the reduction of the melody to its medieval ferial forms and its virtual restriction, after 1400 or so, to masses for the dead. But when I wrote, I was not aware of the several instances in eleventh-century Italian altar books where Thannabaur 41 or one of its incipits occurs as the sole Sanctus melody following a preface for Sundays and feasts, much less of the venerable popularity these instances imply for the melody. These heretofore uncited instances—including the remarkable case in Za MR 166 where the Thannabaur 41 incipit was appended to an elaborate preface chant rubricked for use *In festiuitatibus scorum*—justify the reinstatement of the formula underlying the protean versions of Thannabaur 41 as one of the earliest Sanctus formulas distilled into settled form from anaphoral chant—indeed, perhaps the earliest. As Thannabaur cautioned, the written codification of the formula as a complete Sanctus melody is no earlier than that of others found in south Italy, some of which were imported from the north or imitated on the basis of northern style. But these other melodies (with the exception of Thannabaur 154—it too expanded from anaphoral chant) do not appear in Italian altar books attached to prefaces as quasi-canonical elements of the great eucharistic prayer.

The three versions of Thannabaur 41 printed in the BTC II/3 main text provide clues for recognizing Sanctus incipits in the altar books as variants of the Thannabaur 41 formula. In these three versions, *Benedictus qui uenit in nomine domini* is nearly identical: the anaphoral-chant kernel F G a (using the pitch of the F hexachord employed in RoV B 23) rises to b [flat] for the accented syllable of *nómine*. In Ben 38, *Pleni sunt* likewise begins with the notes F G a—as do all the internal phrases in Ben 38—whereas in the missals, *Pleni sunt* and other internal phrases mostly begin directly on the tenor, a. But owing to the melodic identity of *Benedictus qui uenit in nomine domini* in all versions, the different segments of anaphoral chant found in the opening Sanctus acclamations—a aG, or FGa aG—can be recognized as initial variants of the same formula or as combinations thereof. In turn, the first Sanctus incipit in Desiderius' sacramentary, MC 339, p. 132, can be seen to resemble the beginning of Thannabaur 41 in RoC 1574, with the addition of one lower neighboring liquescent note between the syllables of *Sanctus*. The second Sanctus incipit of MC 339, as originally notated on p. 134, resembles the incipit of RoV B 23 or the first *Sanctus* in Ben 38, again with the addition of the intervening lower liquescent between the syllables.

Desiderius' sacramentary was probably written just before or shortly after 1071, when the new basilica at Montecassino was consecrated. The choice of festal and ferial forms of Thannabaur 41 for inclusion as the typical Sanctus after festal and ferial prefaces in this sumptuous sacramentary, prepared especially for the most distinguished abbot of Italy, shows how important this anaphoral-chant formula was.

Thannabaur 49; Vatican IV   83
See *Perpetuo numine*, p. 93.

Thannabaur ?64 (cf. 60, 66, 67)   48
See *Inuisibiliter penetrauit rex*, p. 77.
Also see Easter Verses *Hodie Dominus Iesus Christus resurrexit a mortuis*, pp. 124 and 131.

Thannabaur 80   117

SOURCES: *Benevento 38, fol. 167^r (second of six collected Sanctus entered after the completion of the original MS). Copied *in campo aperto*, with only approximately accurate diastematy, no earlier than the third quarter of the eleventh century.

Benevento 34, fol. 284^r (fifth of eight collected Sanctus—the second of two without tropes, which are preceded by three with tropes and followed, after Agnus Dei and a MS lacuna, by three more troped Sanctus). Notated with F clef and red line and c clef throughout. The yellow line for c, if ever present, has faded to invisibility. The notes for the first *Sanctus* read exactly as in Ben 38, including the D for the last note of the phrase, which is illegible in the facsimile and was omitted from Thannabaur's incipit. Except for the phrases below, the melody is exactly the same as in Ben 38.

$$\begin{array}{llllll} a & aG & acbab & aG & abc & acbac \\ \text{in} & \text{excel} & \text{sis} & \text{nomine} & \text{in} & \text{excel sis} \end{array}$$

REFERENCES: Levy, "Byzantine Sanctus," p. 24 and note 2 on that page; MMMA 17, Th 80. For related G-mode melodies using an initial rising fourth and e as top note, see BTC II/1, pp. 68 and 176 (Melnicki 27, *Pater excelse summeque immense*), and citations there of related melodies.

NOTES: The music for *Sanctus dominus deus* is like that for *gloria tua, in excelsis,* and *in nomine domini*; the music for *Pleni sunt celi et terra*, like that for *Benedictus qui uenit*. All these phrases employ the axial G to c relationship of the south Italian rising-fourth family of melodies. (See References, above.) The initial *Sanctus* and *Osanna* extend the formula to low D, employing the full plagal range of mode 8. The characteristics of the phrases, the way they are repeated, and the restricted sources known for the melody (only the two listed here) all suggest a south Italian and probably local Benevento origin for the melody in the mid-eleventh century. The piece is not among the many Sanctus now found in the Ben 35 collection but may perhaps have been included on one of the now missing folios.

Thannabaur 81   118

SOURCES: *BAV Vat. lat. 5319, fol. 83^r (after *Alleluia [V] Confitemini domino quoniam bonus . . . misericordia eius* and *Laudate dominum*—the latter cued to Ember Saturday in Lent, fol. 48, without notation—and before *Agnus dei* of the Easter vigil mass). The notes were entered over an erased melody, BTC-Scs 1, q. v. Notated with an F clef and red line. The neume sequences of the recopied melody resemble those of the SP B 79 Sanctus described below.

*BAV Archivio San Pietro B 79, fol. 196ᵛ (a single Sanctus following three Kyries and an untroped Gloria in excelsis, and preceding a single Agnus Dei, all appended to a thirteenth-century Roman office antiphoner from St. Peter's). Notated with c clef without line and red F line without clef, a fourth higher than in Vat. lat. 5319. The sequences of neumes are similar to those of Vat. lat. 5319, although pitches are realized differently. The bizarre tonal field produced by the cleffing, with a final of b-natural, yields a very different modality from that of Vat. lat. 5319. Perhaps b-flat should be sung throughout, although the resulting tritone outline of the two *Sanctus* would then be harsh. The MS gives two *Sanctus* acclamations only. Evidently the piece was copied carelessly; the term *corrupt* is fairly applied. (See the variant to melody 81, Thannabaur, p. 113.)

REFERENCES: Boe, "Gloria A," pp. 19, 22–25; MMMA 2:523–24; and MMMA 17, Th 81. See BTC II/3, pp. 122 and 124 (BTC-Scs 1) for the legible remains of the original Sanctus in Vat. lat. 5319, erased and replaced by Thannabaur 81.

NOTES: The only Sanctus melody now present in Vat 5319, entered in the Easter vigil mass over erased notes, turns up in a somewhat more elaborate version as the only Sanctus in SP B 79. (The Roman gradual Bod 74 provides neither Sanctus nor Agnus Dei for the Easter vigil mass, nor is this melody found in the extensive Sanctus collection towards the end of that manuscript.) The replacement melody found in Vat 5319 is not derived from anaphoral chant and has not been found elsewhere; I have no idea why it should have been substituted for the original Sanctus. The substitute Agnus Dei that follows it in this manuscript (see BTC II/4, Schildbach 98) is indeed a version of a melody well known in Italy, whereas the substitute Sanctus seems to have been assembled by a local scribe who modeled his distribution of notes to text syllables—at least for the three *Sanctus* acclamations—on that of the old erased melody.

Thannabaur 109   120

SOURCE: *Benevento 35, fol. 195ᵛ (third of sixteen collected Sanctus now surviving in the MS).

ALTAR BOOK INCIPITS: Montecassino 127, p. 323 = fol. 157ʳ (first of two notated Sanctus incipits, following the conclusion for proper prefaces of certain feasts, *Quem laudant . . . non cessant clamare dicentes.* [given below in letter notation], and preceding an erased Sursum corda and preface rubricked *Cotidiana* that was replaced by a version of the modern ferial preface tone, ending with the partly erased and garbled incipit of Thannabaur 41). For a description of the MS, see Cassinese Sources, p. 3 above.) The festival conclusion for certain proper prefaces and its Sanctus incipit (if transcribed at the F pitch of the Ben 35 version) read as follows:

```
        ℓ  ℓ          ⋏              ⋎
        ♭  ♭ a Ga a a ♭ a a Ga a a
       Quem laudant angeli atque archangeli.

         G a  ℓ     ♭    a Ga a    a
               ♭        a
       cherubin quoque et seraphin

        ℓ                        ⋏
        G a♭ a     a GGF FG a Ga G
       non cessant clama re dicentes.

                    ⌢
                  FGaGa  FGaG
                  S⟨an⟩c⟨tu⟩s.
```

Zagreb, MR 166, p. 191 (the first Sanctus incipit of three appended to the first, fourth, and fifth preface chants in a Cassinese-derived missal, this incipit being attached to the conclusion for proper prefaces *Et ideo . . . sine fine dicentes* rubricked *Item que subiungere debes p̄c̄i* [preci] q̄n̄ [quando] *uolueris* following the second common preface—although the conclusion itself matches the chant version of the *first* common preface rubricked *Item pp̄h̄*—the Sanctus incipit being in turn followed by the unnotated alternative conclusion for certain proper prefaces, *Quem laudant angeli . . . non cessant clamare dicentes. S̄.*, and a third common-preface version, incorrectly rubricked *In cotidianis diebus*, which rubric ought correctly to have introduced the second common-preface version). The Cassinese Sunday and festival conclusion for proper prefaces and its Sanctus incipit (if transcribed at the F pitch of the Ben 35 version) read thus:

```
          ℓ                          ⋏
       F G a♭ ♭  ♭ a a  ♭a Ga a a
       Et ideo cum angelis et archangelis

          ?     a♭ a   a   a GF FG a Ga a  a
       cum thronis et domi natio nibus.

        ℓ    ℓ               ⋏
        F    G a  ♭ ♭ ♭aa a ♭a a Ga a a
       Cumque omni militia cęlestis exercitus

        ℓ  ℓ
        G  a    ♭  aa♭a Ga a  a
       ymnum glorię tuę canimus

                              ⋏
              a  a GF FG a Ga G
              sine fi ne dicentes.

                    ⌢
                  FGaGa  FGaG
                  S a n c t u s .
```

Rubric in the MS introducing the second common-preface version, to which the above proper-preface conclusion is attached:

Item ī minimis festis s̄corum.

REFERENCES: Kelly, *The Beneventan Chant*, pp. 130–31 (with transcription); MMMA 17, Th 109. See BTC II/3, pp. 116 and 114 (Thannabaur 41, Var., and the altar-book sources and references given there); pp. 122 and 124 (BTC-Scs 1), and pp. 122 and 126 (BTC-Scs 2). Also see Cassinese Sources, pp. 38 and 4–5 above.

NOTES: The Sanctus melody appears to be a more elaborate and festive version of Thannabaur 41 for use with the preface tone for Sundays and feasts, in the same way that the simpler or "standard" versions of Thannabaur 41 in general belonged with the *cotidiana* preface versions. Thannabaur 109 is rooted in the anaphoral-chant tradition (see BTC II/1, p. xvi).

The incipit of this melody, corresponding in every detail to the Ben 35 version, is found in the Cassinese full missal MC 127, "tempore Desiderii descriptus," and in the twelfth-century votive missal ZaMR 166, the first part of which was taken from the Cassinese region to Dalmatia not long after it was written. The easiest explanation for its appearance in Ben 35—a manuscript from the late eleventh or early twelfth century, written a generation or more after Desiderius' death—is that the editor of Ben 35 borrowed it from Montecassino for inclusion in his Sanctus compendium. The alternative explanation—that a version of this Sanctus in use in mid-eleventh century Benevento should have found its way to Montecassino among the books Desiderius (a native of Benevento and quondam monk at Santa Sofia there) brought with him when he entered the Cassinese abbey—seems perhaps less likely in view of the ordering of Gloria in excelsis intonations in MC 127, a specifically Cassinese ordering not found at Benevento, although the ordering of these intonations in the later missal ZaMR 166 would allow for an ultimate origin at Benevento. (See BTC II/2, pp. xvi–xix.)

In the context of the preceding preface chant, where the equivalent of b-flat was certainly sung, b-flats would probably also have been sung in the Sanctus (transcribed at the pitch of Ben 35). But not necessarily in every instance: the b's do not occur at the beginning of the Sanctus in close conjunction with the preface, and when they do occur, they usually introduce or refer to c and might thus have been sung as b-naturals.

Thannabaur 111, Var. (p. 163) 121

SOURCE: Benevento 35, fol. 195^{r-v} (second of sixteen collected Sanctus now surviving in the MS).

REFERENCES: MMMA 17, Th 111. See two Nonantolan variants, the one at Thannabaur p. 129 (where the first two acclamations begin and end on a and where *Sanctus dominus* begins G d b) and the other at p. 149 (where the first acclamation reads GabaF Ga G but is otherwise pitched as in Ben 35). Also see an Aquitanian variant in Thannabaur, p. 210 (where the first acclamation reads CDEDC DE D and *Sanctus dominus* begins C E G).

Cf. BTC II/3, pp. 123 and 128 (BTC-Scs 3, with an idiosyncratic version of **Osanna plasmatum populum** and **Osanna dulcis est cantica** found in Ben 40). Cf. especially the phrase *Sanctus dominus deus sabaoth.*

NOTES: Nonantola supplies the only Italian concordances for the Ben 35 melody, but Thannabaur lists seventeen instances where it occurs in eight Aquitanian sources, as well as more instances in manuscripts from Apt, Arras, and the Mans region. How it entered the Norman-Sicilian repertory, where it was troped with *Admirabilis splendor* (see BTC II/3, pp. 53 and 3), is uncertain. Its origins appear to have been Aquitanian. In view of other concordances between Ben 35 and the Nonantolan trope repertory for ordinary chants, it seems likely that the melody came to Ben 35 from the abbey of Nonantola, although not exactly in the form of either of the two Nonantolan variants given by Thannabaur.

As Thannabaur remarks, the melody was sometimes notated with a final of D , so that the major triad outline at *Sanctus dominus* read C E G . This transposition implies that at least some of the b's in the Ben 35 version could or should be flattened to correspond with F in the version having the D final. The doubled b's lying between two a's at *sunt* and *domini* should certainly be sung as b-flat and probably some of the others (e.g., that on *Ple-ni*) as well.

With or without b-flat, the melody in its Ben 35 form combines anaphoral-chant elements with more recent melodic idioms extending the range to a tenth. Modal patterns shift ambiguously between those belonging to protus on G and tetrardus on G . In spite of repetition of motivic elements, the melody is diffuse.

Thannabaur 213, Var. (p. 200) 57

See *Laudes Deo ore pio,* p. 79.

Thannabaur 216, Var. (p. 177) 122

SOURCE: Benevento 35, fol. 195^v (fifth of sixteen collected Sanctus now surviving in the MS). At the second *Osanna in ex-,* the red line for F was drawn a third too low; the custodes, however, are correct. The first note of the piece—actually a single liquescent virga E—was erroneously transcribed as two notes, ED , in Thannabaur's index.

REFERENCES: Hiley, *Western Plainchant,* pp. 164–65; MMMA 17, Th 216. Cf. the first acclamation in the Ben 35 version of this melody with Thannabaur 154 (= 152), BTC II/3, pp. 71 and 38. The trope *Deus pater ingenitus,* usually found with Thannabaur 154, is also associated with this melody in five of the French sources listed by Thannabaur.

NOTES: Benevento 35 is the only known south Italian source, but Thannabaur lists central and northern Italian manuscripts from Nonantola, Bobbio, Vercelli, and Mantua as having the melody. In addition to Norman-Sicilian sources, there are many from Aquitaine and northern France. (See Hiley's transcription of the version of PaN 10508 in *Western Plainchant,* ex. II. 19. 3.) Thannabaur lists a single German manuscript, Ba 5—a tonary, troper, and proser from Reichenau, dated 1001. The French and Aquitanian concordances partly resemble the more restricted concordances for the preceding Sanctus, Thannabaur 111.

The melody is expanded from anaphoral chant in the same general way as the more widely known Thannabaur 154, q. v. (See References above.) But Thannabaur 154 ends on E and is thus assigned to mode 4, while this Sanctus, on the contrary, ends on D and belongs more or less to mode 2.

The structure of the melody is clear if artificial. *Pleni sunt celi* uses the same music as *Benedictus qui uenit*, the rising-fifth scale of which is anticipated by the second *Sanctus,* but one step lower. The upward scale is reduced in range to a fourth for *deus* and *in no[mine]*, and to a third for *gloria*. The phrase endings *sabaoth, [glo]ria tua,* and *domini* cadence in the same way, with D as the last note. The two *Osanna in excelsis,* which vary slightly in the Ben 35 version, were intended to match. They exploit the low range of mode 2. Only the brief phrases for the opening acclamations, directly derived from anaphoral chant, end on notes other than D : in Ben 35, the *Sanctus* acclamations end on C , E , and G , respectively.

Thannabaur 223; Vatican XV   **64**
See *Mundi fabricator*
   Quem cherubim et seraphim non cessant, p. 82.

Chants without Thannabaur Numbers
(Assigned BTC-Scs Numbers)

BTC-Scs 1   124

SOURCE: *BAV Vat. lat. 5319, fol. 83ʳ (after *Alleluia [V] Confitemini domino quoniam bonus . . . misericordia eius* and *Laudate dominum*—the latter cued to Ember Saturday in Lent, fol. 48, without notation—and before *Agnus dei* of the Easter vigil mass). BTC-Scs 1 prints the legible portions of the original, now erased melody for which Thannabaur 81 was substituted, q. v. The original verbal text (which now serves the replacement melody) was spaced to accommodate the neumes of the original.

REFERENCES: Boe, "Gloria A," pp. 19 and 22–25; MMMA 2, p. 697. For the Sanctus melody that replaced this in Vat 5319, see BTC II/3, pp. 119 and 118 (Thannabaur 81). Also see Thannabaur 41, p. 114, and its commentary, pp. 116–19 above.

NOTES: At least half the neumes of the lower palimpsest Sanctus in the Vat 5319 Easter vigil can be recovered with the help of ultraviolet light. Illegible areas of erasure are circled above the transcription in the main text. This melody, insofar as it can be read, is not to be found in exactly this form among the eight troped and one untroped Sanctus chants collected at the end of Bod 74, the St. Cecilia gradual, nor is Sanctus mentioned in rubrics or text of the Easter vigil in that manuscript.

Probably b should be sung as b-flat throughout. B-naturals would produce persistent and unvocal tritones, as at the first *Osanna in excelsis*. The tonal field of anaphoral chant is notated here at the F G a b-flat level rather than at the G a b c level. This correspondence can be seen most clearly by comparing the entirely legible phrase *Benedictus qui uenit in nomine domini*, with its typically Roman ornamentation of the reciting note, to the bare anaphoral-chant skeleton seen in Thannabaur 41 (BTC II/3, p. 114) or to the chaste decoration of the same phrase in the old Beneventan Sanctus (BTC-Scs 2, p. 126, immediately following).

The old Beneventan Sanctus affords the closest match for the old Roman version of the formula. (The two melodies are printed together for comparison in the article "Gloria A," cited in References, above.) Though accessible only in eleventh-century notation, these two melodies together strongly imply peninsular use of the properly anaphoral formula for Sanctus, as Levy postulated in the article "Byzantine Sanctus" (see BTC II/1, p. xvi). The Beneventan version may have been derived from Milanese custom brought south after the Lombard invasion or from south Italian pre-Lombardic use surviving in the church of Benevento.

The decipherable fragments of the original melody in Vat 5319 bring us as close as we shall ever come to *the* old Roman Sanctus. The melody would probably have fallen eventual victim to the general purge of Roman chant under Innocent III, 1277–80; but I am at loss to explain why it should have been replaced by an indifferent and almost unique substitute melody many years before that purge, in a manuscript patently devoted to the maintenance of native urban tradition.

BTC-Scs 2   126

SOURCE: Benevento 35, fol. 202ʳ (after $\overline{of}$ *Hodie Christus natus est. . . . uoluntatis alleluia alleluia.* and before *Agnus dei* of the Christmas mass in a fragment from an old Beneventan gradual or ingressarium, now preserved as the end guard-leaf of Ben 35). Notated *in campo aperto* with accurate diastematy. If read as beginning on a—that is, with the alternative tenor clef of the main-text transcription—all or some of the b's might be flattened, but it would also be possible to sing b-natural, at least in the two phrases *Osanna in excelsis*. The intervals resulting from reading the first note as b—that is, with the G-clef of the main-text transcription—or a fifth lower, with a first note of E (or, of course, as beginning on a but with all the b's flattened) correspond with other versions of the Thannabaur 41 formula. (See References, below, and especially the RoC 1574 source for Thannabaur 41.)

REFERENCES: Boe, "Gloria A," pp. 22–25 (this Sanctus compared with the old Roman BTC-Scs 1); Kelly, *The Beneventan Chant*, pp. 42, 91–92, 130 (with transcription), 250, 301, and pl. 13 (facsimile of the Ben 35 guard-leaf, fol. 202ʳ). See BTC II/3, pp. 116 and 114 (Thannabaur 41, Var.); pp. 120 and 120 (Thannabaur 109); and pp. 122 and 124 (BTC-Scs 1).

NOTES: A complete Sanctus fortunately survives among the fragmentary propers for Christmas from the old Beneventan rite. (See Source and References, above.) We may never know whether this particular Beneventan version of the universal ancient formula for the music of the anaphora stems from northern Lombard-Milanese usage or from pre-conquest south-peninsular usage kept alive by Catholic clergy in the Lombard duchy of Benevento.

Appendix I

Sanctus   128
BTC-Scs 3

(?Thannabaur 111, Var., pp. 129 and 149)

Hosanna¹: Plasmatum Populum
Hosanna²: Dulcis est cantica

SOURCE

*Benevento 40, fol. 104ʳ⁻ᵛ (in the second set of propers for the Milanese saints Nazarius and Celsus, after *of Anima nostra* and before c̄o *Iustorum anime*—both entries cued only, without notation). This mass contains two Ambrosian pieces: the ingressa *Reddit iustis deus mercedem laborum ipsorum* and the Milanese version of Gloria in excelsis A, Bosse 39. The Sanctus is notated *in campo aperto* with only approximate diastematic accuracy: cleffed Beneventan MSS with the prosas provide secure pitches for transcription (see pp. 63 and 24). The Sanctus melody in this form is however unique.

NOTES

References: AH 47, p. 343; Atkinson, "Text, Music," especially pp. 104–06; CT 5, pp. 257–58, 373–74, and pls. 2 and 3; CT 7, pp. 109–11 (no. 48), 159–60 (no. 111), and 362; Kelly, "Beneventan and Milanese Chant," pp. 176–77; and Kelly, *The Beneventan Chant*, pp. 183, 199–203.

In BTC II/2, see pp. 22 and 110 (Bosse 39, Gloria A) and especially pp. 48 and 208. In BTC II/3, see pp. 63 and 24 (the prosas *Hosanna Plasmatum populum* and *Hosanna Dulcis est cantica* with Thannabaur 197 and the trope *Caelestia sidera*) and the extensive references here and in CT 7 for the melody and words. Cf. the typical text and translation from Ben 35 on p. 64. Also cf. the phrase *Sanctus dominus deus sabaoth* of this melody with that of Thannabaur 111, Var. (p. 163), BTC II/3, pp. 121 and 121.

The Sanctus melody is not known elsewhere in just this form. Certain phrases of Thannabaur 80, 197, and 226 are similar to it. The triadic outline beginning on C for the phrase *Sanctus dominus deus sabaoth* is reminiscent especially of the Nonantolan variants of Thannabaur 111 listed above. In a general way, BTC-Scs 3 resembles other D-mode Sanctus.

The Sanctus suits the prosa melody and may have been arranged at Benevento to supply a vehicle for a prosa that arrived without accompanying Sanctus—or conceivably arrived equipped with a version of Thannabaur 111 (from the region of Apt, via northern Italy?—see Atkinson's article cited in References, above). Or perhaps the scribe combined the prosa with what the scribe thought was a Milanese source: the introit-ingressa and the Gloria in excelsis in this mass for the Milanese saints Nazarius and Celsus are certifiably Ambrosian. It is true that prosas and verbal tropes were not used in the Ambrosian rite. Nevertheless, the scribe of Ben 40 may have borrowed a popular Aquitanian prosa combined with a Sanctus melody he at least wanted people to think was Ambrosian.

The prosa *Osanna plasmatum populum* begins with a different version of its melody than is found in Ben 34 and Ben 35. Segments of what would have been the Hosanna¹ melisma, if it had been completed, were divided in Ben 40 and placed after each texted section, corresponding to the melody of the preceding text segment. But in the last line of [♃s 1 .¹] (as enumerated in the typical text on p. 64)—which rounds out the small prosa form abb'—the b' section is simply omitted, and the O melisma is repeated, but without *in excelsis*. The second prosa *Osanna dulcis est cantica* likewise appears in truncated form, with not-quite-matching melisma segments attached to each prosa phrase, following *benedictus qui uenit in nomine domini*. This version of the prosa, however, ends ū *Dicant nunc* [*osanna in excelsis*], so as to lead into the last phrase of Sanctus.

The scribe then recopied *Pleni sunt cęli et terra gloria tua* with almost the same melody as before, but he added the heretofore missing first *osanna in excelsis*, complete—presumably in order to supply the missing *in excelsis* of the first *osanna*. By skipping to and fro, it would be possible to sing the complete text of Sanctus, omitting the prosa texts.

Both melody and words of the prosa are garbled. Either the scribe was copying a corrupt exemplar or he did not understand how to distribute the text he was copying. (Cf. the inconsistent treatment of the Kyrie verse *Christe cui* [*cliuis*] *decus in aeuo* copied in Ben 40, BTC II/1, pp. 54–58 and 132. But see the correct treatment of the Hosanna[2] prosula *Qui uenisti carnem sumens* in Ben 40, BTC II/3, pp. 71 and 38.) The stronger wording *Te qui uerum* is used instead of the Beneventan *Et qui uerum*. Yet the words *In hac aula* are clumsily repeated.

Appendix II

Easter Verses: *Hodie Dominus Iesus Christus resurrexit a mortuis* 131

Sources

*Benevento 38, fol. 64ᵛ (after *Co. Mitte manum tuam . . . alleluia* of Low Sunday and before *Ā ad proces̄. Venite adoremus*). Notated *in campo aperto* by the original scribe of the MS, with accurate diastematy. The red F line added later to many pieces in this MS is missing here. Rubric:

Item uersi.

Benevento 40, fol. 41ʳ⁻ᵛ (after *cō Mitte manum . . . alleluia* at the end of the Low Sunday mass and before the rubric *dom̄. i. post oct̄ pasche* and the introit *Misericordia domini*). Notated *in campo aperto* with greater than usual diastematic accuracy, with almost the same neumes as in Ben 38, except for the single virga on the second syllable of
G ♭ aG G
eriperet and the Beneventan episema added to the last note of all tristrophas except in Vs [6] and [7]. The verbal text is also identical with Ben 38, except for two verses:

[3] Hora quam . . .   [6] protoplastum . . . cediderat.

The reading *inciderat* for *cediderat* is found only in Ben 38. The versions may have been copied one from the other or both from an immediate common source. Rubric:

Item ū.

Benevento 39, fols. 49ᵛ–50ʳ (after *cō Mitte manum . . . alleluia* at the end of the Low Sunday mass, which is followed in turn by the inaccurate rubric *dom̄ ij post oct̄ pasche* [recte *dom̄ i post oct̄ pasche*], and directly before *Intrō Misericordias domini* of the second Sunday after Easter). See BTC I, Appendix 3, p. 88. Notated with c clef throughout and with F clef for a brief passage. All neumes written as quilismas in the versions of Ben 38 and Ben 40 appear here as scandicus neumes. Most of the oriscus neumes of those two versions have the shapes of a plain virga or punctum. The scribe used a slightly different melodic cadence than is found in Ben 38 and 40 to accommodate the irregular
             a baa G   a b aa G
paroxytones, [4] . . . *surrexerunt* and [5] . . . *prophetatum*.
                                  ac d a G b aGG
The first verse ends irregularly: [1] . . . *resurrexit a mortuis*.

The verbal text is exactly the same as in Ben 38 except for Vs [6] . . . *qui morte morsu ceciderat*. All verses except the first are labeled ū.

The assignment of the verses (which are in the purest south Italian mode 8) to the introit *Misericordias* in mode 4 seems to have been prompted by the scribe's wish to attach them in the guise of a trope to the nearest available Gregorian item and thus to preserve them. (See *Ad monumentum Domini* with *Maria uidit angelum* in the same MS, BTC II/1, pp. 7 and 6 and pp. 84 and 216.) Rubric:

ū. de intrō.

Benevento 35, fol. 72ʳ (after *V̄ Confregit . . . a montibus eternis āl* of the *Of Terra tremuit* and before *Emitte domine spiritum* of the Easter Day mass). Notated with c and F clefs and red F line at the same pitch as Bod 74. Every quilisma of the Ben 38 and Ben 40 versions appears here as a scandicus. The oriscus neume usually appears as a plain punctum or virga. There are no episemas. The melody is identical in substance with that of Ben 38 throughout, except that the end of Vs [1] is regularized to read . . . *resurrexit*, with two notes on the accented syllable instead of a single d . The verbal text is also the same as Ben 38, except for the following scribal errors (see BTC II/1, p. xv):

[2]   . . . eripere.
[3]   . . . quam dominus expirabit.
[6]   . . . protoplasto . . . mors succiderat.

A fourfold Alleluia, given below in letter notation, concludes the verses. It may have been part of the original hymn and is also found in nearly the same form at the end of the Cassinese version of Urb 602:

G GGG Gab a   G   a G F   a   c cd c Gab aG aG G
Alleluia   alleluia   alleluia   alleluia.

*Cologny-Geneva, Bodmer 74, fols. 122ᵛ–123ʳ (appended to the fourth of nine collected Sanctus). The Sanctus is without trope or prosula. See BTC II/3, pp. 77 and 48, for the Sanctus melody, Thannabaur ?64 (cf. 60, 66, 67). Remarkably like the Beneventan versions except for the very end of Vs [8] and the attached melisma in Roman style. Rubric before the Sanctus:

IN RESV̄R.

BAV Vat. lat. 602, fols. 83ʳ–84ᵛ (after *Victime paschali . . . Tu nobis rex christe deus miserere. Amen.* and before *Mane prima sabbati surgens*—rubricked for singing during general communion, like four other pieces, of which three are sequences). Notated *in campo aperto* with precisely accurate diastematy. Every quilisma of the Ben 38 and Ben 40 versions appears as a scandicus. Oriscus neumes appearing in those versions at the summit of a phrase are replaced by virgas, but some modified oriscus have been introduced for repeated notes, and the notation of liquescence is more thorough than in Ben 38 and 40. The end of Vs [1] reads as in Ben 35 (see above). Vs [4] and Vs [5] treat the paroxytone cadences slightly differently from other versions, and the Cassinese editor has added the word *sunt* to [4]:

[4] Monumenta aperta sunt
     et qui dormierant surrexerunt.

[5] . . . prophetatum.

Six additional verses were inserted after [5] and before [6] (see below). Vs [6] reads . . . *protoplaustum* . . . *ceciderat.* Vs [7] is followed by a fourfold Alleluia, almost as in Ben 35:

Alleluia alleluia alleluia?alleluia;

Rubric at the bottom of fol. 82ᵛ:

In pascha quando communicant.

NOTES

References: AH 47, no. 365 (the text corrected by Blume to achieve prosa-like parallelism); Boe, "Hymns and Poems at Mass in 11th-c. Southern Italy," pp. 516–17 and 524–25; Boe, "The 'Lost' Palimpsest Kyries in the Vatican MS Urbinas latinus 602," p. 2; Brunner, "Catalogo delle sequenze," pp. 192–287 and especially p. 236; Brunner, "A Perspective on the Southern Italian Sequence," pp. 117–54 and especially p. 131; CT 7, pp. 33–34, 121–22 (no. 60), and 352; and Levy, "Lux de luce," p. 51 (with transcription of Vs [1–3] of the Urb 602 version).

In BTC I, see Appendix 3, p. 88; in BTC II/3, see pp. 77 and 48 (Thannabaur ?64 [cf. 60, 66, 67]).

Meter: (based on the text of Ben 38)

[1]	10 p	+	8 pp
[2]	9 p	+	13 pp
			(=9pp + 4pp)
			9pp 4pp
[3]	10 p	+	8 pp
[4]	7 p	+	10 pp
[5]	10 p	+	9 p
[6]	9 p	+	9 pp
[7]	9 p	+	8 pp
[8]	9 p	+	10 pp

The verses added in the Cassinese version of Urb 602 (see below) have the following meter:

[+⁶]	9 p	+	10 pp
			(but "p" cadence in music)
[+⁷]	9 p	+	10 p
[+⁸]	9 p	+	10 p
[+⁹]	10 p	+	10 p
	(1st half Scriptural quotation)		
[+¹⁰]	8 p	+	11 p
[+¹¹]	8 p	+	9 p

Source of text and translation below: Bod 74

Sanctus Sanctus Sanctus dominus deus sabaoth
       Pleni sunt cęli et terra gloria tua
              Osanna in excelsis
       Benedictus qui uenit in nomine domini
              Osanna in excelsis

[1] V̄ Hodie dominus iesus christus
     resurrexit a mortuis

[2] V̄ Pro nobis pependit in ligno
     ut nos de iugo diaboli eriperet

[3] V̄ Hora qua dominus expirauit
     totus mundus contremuit

[4] V̄ Monumenta aperta
     et qui dormierunt surrexerunt

[5] V̄ Descendit dominus ad infernum
     sicut fuerat prophetatum

[6] V̄ Inde excussit protoplasto
     qui morte morsu ceciderat

[7]   Electos quos ibi inuenit
     suo morsu extracti sunt

[8]   A fauce inferni abstracti
     cum eo surrexerunt hodie

                    *

[1] Today the Lord Jesus Christ
    rose from the dead.

[2] For us he hung on the cross,
    to free us from the devil's yoke.

[3] In the hour the Lord breathed his last
    the whole world shuddered.

[4] The graves were opened
    and those who had slept (40, 39: *dormierant*)
    arose.

[5] The Lord went down to hell,
    as had been prophesied.

[6] He wrested first-man thence (40: *protoplastum*),
    who by a bite had fallen into death (38: *mortem*).
    (*Or:* who, through the sting of death (*mortis*),
      had fallen.)

[7] The chosen (AH: *Electi*) ones he found there
    were released from his bite;
       (*Or:* from the bite [of death];)

[8] Dragged out from the jaws of hell,
    they rose with him today!

The following six additional verses appear in Urb 602 between [5] and [6].

[+⁶]	Hominem quem fecerat ipse ad cęlos uocare dignatus est.
[+⁷]	Prophetę audientes ipsum in gaudio magno exultabant.
[+⁸]	Quale signum dedit latroni qui cum ipso fuerat in cruce.
[+⁹]	Quia surrexit dominus uere et apparuit symoni petro.
[+¹⁰]	Cherubin in paradyso congaudent latronem ad se perductum.
[+¹¹]	Vectes ferreos confregit et multas animas liberauit.
[6¹²]	Inde excussit . . .
[7¹³]	Electos quos ibi inuenit . . .
[8¹⁴]	A fauce inferni . . .
	Alleluia alleluia, alleluia alleluia ;

*

[+⁶]	[The] Man, whom he had made, he deigned to summon to heaven.
[+⁷]	The prophets hearing him rejoiced with great joy.
[+⁸]	Such a pledge he gave the thief who was with him on the cross.
[+⁹]	For the Lord is risen indeed and has appeared to Simon Peter.
[+¹⁰]	The cherubim in paradise rejoice because the thief was brought to them.
[+¹¹]	He broke the iron bars and freed many souls.

Hodie Dominus Iesus Christus resurrexit a mortuis was copied in four of the five surviving Benevento graduals. (It is missing only in the latest, Ben 34.) These four versions, plus that of the Roman manuscript Bod 74, all have eight verses in the same order. A final verse appears only in Ben 35 and Urb 602, consisting of four Alleluias sung jointly to the same melody as the preceding verses. The text recounts Christ's death, his harrowing of hell, and his rising together with his ransomed elect. The verses are not "didactic" (as Blume complained) but celebratory.

On the other hand, the six additional verses found in the Cassinese manuscript Urb 602, rubricked to be sung along with the others *In pascha quando communicant*, contemplate the resurrection at a reflective distance from the narrative account. Vs [+⁶] of the Cassinese versions refers indirectly to the first and second Adam of St. Paul (I Cor. 5:46–47); Vs [+⁷], to the Old Testament prophets; and Vs [+⁸], to the penitent thief on the cross. Vs [+⁹] jumps ahead to the post-Emmaus recollection of Christ's resurrection appearance to Peter and quotes Luke 24:34 directly. In Vs [+¹⁰], the cherubim guarding primeval paradise (Gen. 3:24) rejoice at the entrance of the penitent thief (Luke 23:43) where the first man was expelled, and in Vs [+¹¹], the Old Testament image of the breaking of the iron bars (Isa. 45:2) pictures the harrowing of hell.

The final cadence of these added verses is paroxytonic—like Vs [4] and Vs [5] that immediately precede them and may have served as their model (see under Meter, above). (Vs [+⁶], however, is incorrectly set to the paroxytonic musical cadence.) Content and form suggest that the Cassinese editor expanded the south Italian original by adding six verses within the original eight, probably in order to occupy more time during the general communion of Easter, as many of the added verses being sung as needed.

The incipit of the piece (without notation) is included in the list of sequences in the second tonary of the Montecassino manuscript Codex 318, as Brunner notes. (See References, above.) Yet the text is *not* a sequence in the usual sense: why then was it included in the tonary list of sequences? Because in Urb 602—or in some other Cassinese collection—it was surrounded by true sequences for use during general communion: the compiler of the tonary, recognizing several items as well-known sequences, included this piece too.

Hodie Dominus Iesus Christus resurrexit a mortuis in the Roman gradual Bod 74 does not use the expanded Cassinese text. It resembles the versions of Ben 35 and Ben 39, though with very slight melodic variants and the addition of a concluding melisma in Roman style—a fact that would seem to suggest that in this instance Rome borrowed from Benevento rather than from Montecassino. However, Bod 74 was finished in 1071 and Urb 602 cannot be earlier than slightly before 1100, so that the extra verses in Urb 602 might have been added at Montecassino after the text had been borrowed from the abbey—or elsewhere—for use at Rome.

The melody, the same for all verses with slight adjustments to accommodate the varying number of syllables and changing accentuation, consists of two halves. The first half ends on F , always followed by an initial a that leads to a short tenor recitation on c in the second half of the verse, which in turn descends to the final, G . A strongly accented syllable in the first half-verse is reinforced by a rising three-note group, Gab ; in the second half-verse, an accented syllable is reinforced by the accent-podatus cd (or the single note d) rising above the tenor c .

The cadence on F at the end of the first half-verse is paroxytonic (except in the corrected Cassinese version of [4] . . . *apérta sùnt*). The cadence on G at the end of the second half-verse, which was designed for proparoxytones, is modified for paroxytones variously in Vs [4] and [5] and is doubled to accommodate extra syllables in Vs [2].

Certain hymn-like texts, cast in strophes with more or less regular syllable count and rhythmical or metrical structure, were associated with the Roman mass rite and with relics of old Beneventan propers in southern Italy. (See Boe, "Hymns and Poems at Mass in 11th-c. Southern Italy," cited in References, above.) Most of these texts must have existed independently as hymns or poems before being assigned diverse liturgical functions in the eleventh and early twelfth-century manuscripts where they are found. Some may have persisted from a time when nonscriptural songs were being introduced at mass, as Walafrid, writing in 841 about Paulinus of Aquileia, stated:

> porro ymni metrici et rithmici in Ambrosianis officiis dicuntur; quos etiam in missarum sollemniis propter compunctionis gratiam, quae ex dulcedine concinna augetur, interdum assumere consuerunt. Traditur siquidem Paulinum Foroiulensem patriarchiam saepius et maxime in privatis missis circa immolationem sacramentorum ymnos vel ab aliis vel a se compositos celebrasse. Ego vero crediderim tantum tantaeque scientiae virum hoc nec sine auctoritate nec sine rationis ponderatione fecisse.

Besides, metrical and rhythmical hymns are sung in the Ambrosian services, which hymns they were accustomed sometimes to adopt at the celebration of mass (*in missarum sollemniis*) for compunction's sake, which is increased by elegant sweetness [of style]. In any event it is reported that the patriarch Paulinus often, and mostly in private masses, performed (*celebrasse*) sacramental hymns at the time of offering (*circa immolationem*) composed either by others or by himself. I should not have believed such a man with such knowledge would have done this without authority or without deliberate consideration. (MGH, Cap. II,3, p. 506)

The rhythmical strophes beginning *Hodie Dominus Iesus Christus resurrexit a mortuis* in their various liturgical assignments illuminate typical eleventh-century attempts to preserve local material, much of it having strophic character, while conforming local usage to a rite and chant perceived as more universal.

Acknowledgments

My colleagues Charles Atkinson, Terence Bailey, Virginia Brown, Joseph Dyer, Richard Gyug, David Hiley, Thomas Kelly, and Kenneth Levy variously criticized segments of typescript, responded with useful suggestions, kindly supplied microfilms, xeroxes, and manuscript readings, and otherwise advanced the preparation and long-delayed publication of this volume of Preface and Sanctus chants.

Beneventanum Troporum Corpus II was made possible first of all by a fellowship in 1977–78 and a grant-in-aid in 1981 for research in Italian libraries from the American Council of Learned Societies. The University of Arizona Humanities Grants Committee and Committee for Foreign Travel furnished additional funds in 1981, 1985, and 1989. The Council for the International Exchange of Scholars and the Commission for Educational Exchange between the United States and Sweden awarded a senior Fulbright research grant in 1985–86 to enable me to consult the editors of Corpus Troporum at the University of Stockholm on the translation of the Latin texts and their presentation in the commentaries. I am greatly in debt to Gunilla Iversen for her expert and thoughtful advice while I was in Sweden, and in previous correspondence, and for allowing me to use a draft copy of CT 7, *Tropes du Sanctus,* while I was resident at the Bellagio Study and Conference Center of the Rockefeller Foundation in 1989.

I wish to thank the American Academy in Rome for welcoming me as a visiting scholar on several occasions and to thank John D'Arms, then director of the Academy, for his valued assistance to my family and me during 1977–78. Directors James Melchert and Joseph Connors again extended the Academy's hospitality in 1987 and 1991. Among the ever helpful staff, I particularly want to thank the librarian of the Academy, Lucilla Marino (now *emerita*) and her assistant, Antonella Bucci.

Libraries in Rome, Benevento, Montecassino, and Geneva patiently allowed me to consult their manuscripts for extended periods of time. I wish to thank Don Faustino Avagliano, O.S.B., *archivista* and more recently prior at Montecassino; Dr. Hans Braun, director of the Foundation Martin Bodmer, and his staff at the Bibliotheca Bodmeriana in Cologny-Geneva; and Don Lauro Maio, custodian of the Chapter Library and sometime rector of the diocesan seminary in Benevento, and his predecessor as Librarian, the well-remembered Vicar-General of Benevento, the late Don Angelo Ferrara. Their unfailing interest and patience on my several visits greatly expedited my work, as did the vast resources and efficient staff of the Vatican Library. I gratefully acknowledge permission from these institutions to transcribe and publish sections from the manuscripts they hold.

The staff of A-R Editions, Inc., made every effort during the years following the start of the project in 1981 to meet the special challenges presented by BTC. Lila Aamodt, then in charge of music production, supervised the adaptation of computer music-typesetting to the special needs of chant transcriptions in the music text. Before her retirement from full-time work at A-R, she oversaw the first proofs of the BTC II/3 main text and wrote the grant proposal to the National Endowment for the Humanities to support its publication. I am grateful to Didi King for her careful expertise in typesetting the music of the main text. Charles Atkinson (in his capacity as series editor for Recent Researches in the Music of the Middle Ages and Early Renaissance) expedited publication of BTC II/3.

I thank Dom Jean Mallet, O.S.B., for notice given of the edition in *Les Manuscrits en écriture bénéventaine de la Bibliothèque Capitulaire de Bénévent,* for the many citations and references he supplied, and in particular for film strips of Ben 19 and 20.

Most of all I want first to thank my coeditor Alejandro Planchart, who at the inception of the edition checked the entire main text of BTC II against his own microfilms, supplied other microfilms and concordances, and furnished counsel on many occasions. Secondly, I want to thank my colleague Steven Whiting, who at the time of his move to Ann Arbor nevertheless unstintingly read all the preliminary essays and individual Sanctus commentaries and by his informed criticism and apt suggestions greatly improved their arrangement and wording.

John Boe

Index of Chants by Thannabaur Numbers

Sanctus melodies in BTC II/3 that were included in Thannabaur's catalogue (*Das einstimmige Sanctus der römischen Messe in der handschriftlichen Überlieferung des 11. bis 16. Jahrhunderts* [Munich, 1962]) are listed below in order of their index numbers, together with the text incipits of their tropes and pros(ul)as, if any. Smaller page numbers to the left of the commas refer to individual commentaries; larger page numbers, to the right, refer to the main text. (See the Contents list at the beginning of the volume for references to three additional melodies not included in Thannabaur's index.)

T. 32		114,	111
T. 41, Variation		116,	114
T. 45	Antra modicis deserti	61,	22
T. 46, Var. 2	Immortalis et uerus	74,	46
T. 49	Perpetuo numine (lumine)	93,	83
T. 56	Summe pater de quo		
	[Hosanna] Omnes tua gratia	110,	106
T. 60 (? = 66, 67)	Pax in caelo		
	(= Laudatur trina maiestas)	90,	76
T. 62	Quam pulchra est	96,	90
T. 63	Quem cherubim atque seraphim		
	+Cui pueri Hebraeorum		
	Hebraeorum pueri ramos	98,	93
T. ?64 (cf. 60, 66, 67)	V̄ Hodie Dominus Iesus Christus resurrexit a mortuis		
	Inuisibiliter penetrauit rex		
	Hosanna cuncta procedens	77,	48
(T. 66, 67: see T. 64)			
T. 74	Admirabilis splendor		
	Indefessas uoces	53,	3
T. 80		119,	117
T. 81		119,	118
T. 86	Quem cuncti angeli	103,	102
T. 92	Altissime creator = Altissimeque rector		
	Conditor alme Domine	55,	12
T. 109		120,	120
T. 111, Variation		121,	121
T. 128	Pater Deus qui caret initio	87,	72
T. 152 (= 154)	Corona iustitiae		
	Gloria Christe omnes resurgamus	65,	29
T. 154 (= 152)	Deus fortis (cue: **Qui uenisti**)	68,	32
	Deus pater ingenitus		
	Qui uenisti carnem sumens	71,	38
T. 178	*Ante thronum Domini*	60,	20

T. 197	*Caelestia sidera*		
	Hosanna[1] Plasmatum populum		
	Hosanna[2] Dulcis est cantica	63,	24
T. 213, Variation	**Laudes Deo ore pio**	79,	57
T. 216, Variation		121,	122
T. 223	*Mundi fabricator*		
	Quem cherubim et seraphim non cessant		
	Pie Christe descendisti	82,	64
T. 226, Variation	**Saluifica tuum plasma, Hosanna**	104,	104